STUDY AND SOLUTIONS GUIDE

FOR

Precalculus: Functions and Graphs
A Graphing Approach

AND

Precalculus With Limits:
A Graphing Approach

Larson/Hostetler/Edwards

Bruce H. Edwards

University of Florida
Gainesville, Florida

Dianna L. Zook

Indiana University
Purdue University at Fort Wayne, Indiana

D. C. Heath and Company

Lexington, Massachusetts   Toronto

International Standard Book Number: 0–669–35209–8

10   9   8   7   6   5   4   3

TO THE STUDENT

The *Study and Solutions Guide for Precalculus: Functions and Graphs A Graphing Approach* is a supplement to the text by Roland E. Larson, Robert P. Hostetler, and Bruce H. Edwards.

As mathematics instructors, we often have students come to us with questions about the assigned homework. When we ask to see their work, the reply often is "I didn't know where to start." The purpose of the *Study Guide* is to provide brief summaries of the topics covered in the textbook and enough detailed solutions to problems so that you will be able to work the remaining exercises.

This *Study Guide* is the result of the efforts of Dan Bruce, Debra Rieger, Jennifer O'Neil, Laurie Sontheimer, Lena Tanner and Michele Bliss. Thanks to Lisa Edwards for her help in preparing this project, and to Edward Schlindwein.

If you have any corrections or suggestions for improving this *Study Guide*, we would appreciate hearing from you.

Good luck with your study of precalculus.

Bruce H. Edwards
University of Florida
Gainesville, Florida 32611
(be@ math.ufl.edu)

Dianna L. Zook
Indiana University,
Purdue University
at Fort Wayne, Indiana 46805

CONTENTS

STUDY STRATEGIES

- Attend all classes and come prepared. Have your homework completed. Bring the text, paper, pen or pencil, and a graphing calculator to each class.

- Read the section in the text that is to be covered before class. As you read, use your graphing calculator to verify results and reproduce graphs in the text. Make notes about any questions that you have and, if they are not answered during the lecture, ask them at the appropriate time.

- Participate in class. As mentioned above, ask questions. Also, do not be afraid to answer questions.

- Take notes on all definitions, concepts, rules, formulas and examples. After class, read your notes and fill in any gaps, or make notations of any questions that you have. Make a habit of using your calculator often.

- DO THE HOMEWORK!!! You learn mathematics by doing it yourself. Mathematics is not a spectator sport! Allow **at least** two hours outside of each class for homework. Do not fall behind.

- Seek help when needed. Visit your instructor during office hours and come prepared with specific questions; check with your school's tutoring service; find a study partner in class; check additional books in the library for more examples—just do something before the problem becomes insurmountable.

- Do not cram for exams. Each chapter in the text contains a set of chapter review exercises. Work these problems a few days before the exam and review any areas of weakness.

CHAPTER P

Prerequisites: A Review of Basic Algebra

Section P.1   The Real Number System

■ You should know the following sets.

(a) The set of real numbers includes the rational numbers and the irrational numbers.

(b) The set of rational numbers includes all real numbers that can be written as the ratio p/q of two integers, where $q \neq 0$.

(c) The set of irrational numbers consists of all real numbers which are not rational.

(d) The set of integers: $\{\ldots, -3, -2, -1, 0, 1, 2, 3, \ldots\}$

(e) The set of whole numbers: $\{0, 1, 2, 3, 4, \ldots\}$

(f) The set of natural numbers: $\{1, 2, 3, 4, \ldots\}$

■ The real number line is used to represent the real numbers.

■ Know the inequality symbols.

(a) $a < b$ means a is less than b.

(b) $a \leq b$ means a is less than or equal to b.

(c) $a > b$ means a is greater than b.

(d) $a \geq b$ means a is greater than or equal to b.

■ You should know the bounded and unbounded intervals on the real line.

■ You should know that

$$|a| = \begin{cases} a, & \text{if } a \geq 0 \\ -a, & \text{if } a < 0. \end{cases}$$

■ Know the properties of absolute value.

(a) $|a| \geq 0$ (b) $|-a| = |a|$ (c) $|ab| = |a|\,|b|$ (d) $\left|\dfrac{a}{b}\right| = \dfrac{|a|}{|b|}$

■ The distance between a and b on the real line is $|b - a| = |a - b|$.

1. (a) Natural numbers: $\{5,\ 1\}$

   (b) Integers: $\{-9,\ 5,\ 0,\ 1\}$

   (c) Rational numbers:
   $\{-9,\ -\frac{7}{2},\ 5,\ \frac{2}{3},\ 0,\ 1\}$

   (d) Irrational numbers: $\{\sqrt{2}\,\}$

3. Note that $\sqrt{4} = 2$.

   (a) Natural numbers: $\{12,\ 1,\ \sqrt{4}\,\}$

   (b) Integers: $\{12,\ -13,\ 1,\ \sqrt{4}\,\}$

   (c) Rational numbers:
   $\{12,\ -13,\ 1,\ \sqrt{4},\ \frac{3}{2}\,\}$

   (d) Irrational numbers: $\{\sqrt{6}\,\}$

5. (a) Natural numbers: $\left\{\frac{6}{3}\right\}$

(b) Integers: $\left\{\frac{6}{3}\right\}$

(c) Rational numbers: $\left\{-\frac{1}{3}, \frac{6}{3}, -7.5\right\}$

(d) Irrational numbers: $\left\{-\pi, \frac{1}{2}\sqrt{2}\right\}$

7. 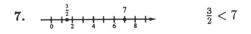 $\frac{3}{2} < 7$

9.  $-4 > -8$

11. 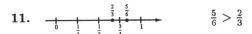 $\frac{5}{6} > \frac{2}{3}$

13. The interval $[-1, 3]$ denotes all real numbers greater than or equal to -1 and less than or equal to 3. That is, $-1 \le x \le 3$, which is bounded.

15. The interval $(10, \infty)$ denotes all real numbers greater than 10. That is, $x > 10$, which is unbounded.

17. The inequality $x \le 5$ denotes all real numbers less than or equal to 5. That is, $(-\infty, 5]$.

19. The inequality $x < 0$ denotes all real numbers that are less than zero. That is, $(-\infty, 0)$.

21. The inequality $x \ge 4$ denotes all real numbers greater than or equal to 4. That is, $[4, \infty)$.

23. The inequality $-2 < x < 2$ denotes all real numbers between -2 and 2, not including -2 or 2. That is, $(-2, 2)$.

25. The inequality $-1 \le x < 0$ denotes all real numbers between -1 and 0, including -1 but not including 0. That is, $[-1, 0)$.

27. $x < 0$, $(-\infty, 0)$

29. $y \le 25$, $(-\infty, 25]$

31. $A \ge 30$, $[30, \infty)$

33. $3.5\% \le r \le 6\%$, $[0.035, 0.06]$

35. $\dfrac{-5}{|-5|} = \dfrac{-5}{-(-5)} = \dfrac{-5}{5} = -1$

37. $-3|-3| = -3(3) = -9$

39. $-|16.25| + 20 = -16.25 + 20 = 3.75$

41. Since $|-3| = 3$ and $-|-3| = -3$, we have $|-3| \boxed{>} -|-3|$.

43. Since $-|5| = -5$, we have $-5 \boxed{=} -|5|$.

45. Since $-|-2| = -2$ and $-|2| = -2$, we have $-|-2| \boxed{=} -|2|$.

47. $d\left(-\frac{5}{2}, 0\right) = \left|0 - \left(-\frac{5}{2}\right)\right| = \left|\frac{5}{2}\right| = \frac{5}{2}$

49. $d(126, 75) = |75 - 126| = 51$

51. $d(9.34, -5.65) = |9.34 - (-5.65)|$
$$= |9.34 + 5.65|$$
$$= |14.99| = 14.99$$

53. Since $d(x, 5) = |x - 5|$ and $d(x, 5) \le 3$, we have $|x - 5| \le 3$.

55. Since $d\left(z, \frac{3}{2}\right) = \left|z - \frac{3}{2}\right|$ and $d\left(z, \frac{3}{2}\right) > 1$, we have $\left|z - \frac{3}{2}\right| > 1$.

57. Since $d(y, 0) = |y - 0| = |y|$ and $d(y, 0) \ge 6$, we have $|y| \ge 6$.

59. $\frac{7071}{5000} = 1.4142$
$\frac{584}{413} \approx 1.414043584$
$\sqrt{2} \approx 1.42\overline{42}$
$\frac{47}{33} = 1.42\overline{42}$
$\frac{127}{90} = 1.41\overline{1}$
$\frac{127}{90} < \frac{584}{413} < \frac{7071}{5000} < \sqrt{2} < \frac{47}{33}$

61. $\frac{5}{8} = 0.625$

63. $\frac{41}{333} = 0.123123\ldots$

65. False. The reciprocal of 2 is $\frac{1}{2}$ which is not an integer.

67. True. If the real number can be written as the quotient of two integers, p/q, it is rational. Otherwise, the real number is irrational.

Section P.2   Properties of Real Numbers and the Basic Rules of Algebra

■ You should be able to identify the terms in an algebraic expression.

■ You should know and be able to use the basic rules of algebra.

■ Commutative Property
  (a) Addition: $a + b = b + a$ (b) Multiplication: $a \cdot b = b \cdot a$

■ Associative Property
  (a) Addition: $(a + b) + c = a + (b + c)$ (b) Multiplication: $(ab)c = a(bc)$

■ Identity Property
  (a) Addition: 0 is the identity; $a + 0 = 0 + a = a$.
  (b) Multiplication: 1 is the identity; $a \cdot 1 = 1 \cdot a = a$.

■ Inverse Property
  (a) Addition: $-a$ is the inverse of a; $a + (-a) = -a + a = 0$.
  (b) Multiplication: $1/a$ is the inverse of a, $a \neq 0$; $a(1/a) = (1/a)a = 1$.

■ Distributive Property
  (a) Left: $a(b + c) = ab + ac$ (b) Right: $(a + b)c = ac + bc$

■ Properties of Negatives
  (a) $(-1)a = -a$ (b) $-(-a) = a$
  (c) $(-a)b = a(-b) = -ab$ (d) $(-a)(-b) = ab$
  (e) $-(a + b) = (-a) + (-b) = -a - b$

■ Properties of Zero
  (a) $a \pm 0 = a$ (b) $a \cdot 0 = 0$
  (c) $0 \div a = 0/a = 0$, $a \neq 0$ (d) If $ab = 0$, then $a = 0$ or $b = 0$.
  (e) $a/0$ is undefined.

■ Properties of Fractions ($b \neq 0$, $d \neq 0$)

(a) Equivalent Fractions: $a/b = c/d$ if and only if $ad = bc$.

(b) Rule of Signs: $-a/b = a/-b = -(a/b)$ and $-a/-b = a/b$

(c) Equivalent Fractions: $a/b = ac/bc$, $c \neq 0$

(d) Addition and Subtraction

    1. Like Denominators: $(a/b) \pm (c/b) = (a \pm c)/b$

    2. Unlike Denominators: $(a/b) \pm (c/d) = (ad \pm bc)/bd$

(e) Multiplication: $(a/b) \cdot (c/d) = ac/bd$

(f) Division: $(a/b) \div (c/d) = (a/b) \cdot (d/c) = ad/bc$ if $c \neq 0$.

■ Properties of Equality

(a) Reflexive: $a = a$

(b) Symmetric: If $a = b$, then $b = a$.

(c) Transitive: If $a = b$ and $b = c$, then $a = c$.

(d) Substitution: If $a = b$, then a can be replaced by b in any statement involving a or b.

    1. If $a = b$, then $a + c = b + c$.

    2. If $a = b$, then $ac = bc$.

■ Cancellation Laws

(a) If $a + c = b + c$, then $a = b$.   (b) If $ac = bc$ and $c = 0$, then $a = b$.

■ You should know the properties of exponents.

(a) $a^1 = a$ (b) $a^0 = 1$, $a \neq 0$

(c) $a^m a^n = a^{m+n}$ (d) $a^m/a^n = a^{m-n}$, $a \neq 0$

(e) $a^{-n} = 1/a^n$, $a \neq 0$ (f) $(a^m)^n = a^{mn}$

(g) $(ab)^n = a^n b^n$ (h) $(a/b)^n = a^n/b^n$, $b \neq 0$

(i) $(a/b)^{-n} = (b/a)^n$, $a \neq 0$, $b \neq 0$ (j) $|a^2| = |a|^2 = a^2$

■ You should be able to write numbers in scientific notation, $c \times 10^n$, where $1 \leq c < 10$ and n is an integer.

■ You should be able to use your calculator to evaluate expressions involving exponents.

1. Terms: $7x$, 4

3. $x^2 - 4x + 8 = x^2 + (-4x) + 8$
Terms: x^2, $-4x$, 8

5. $4x^3 + x - 5 = 4x^3 + x + (-5)$
Terms: $4x^3$, x, -5

7. (a) $4(-1) - 6 = -4 - 6 = -10$
(b) $4(0) - 6 = 0 - 6 = -6$

9. (a) $(-2)^2 - 3(-2) + 4 = 4 + 6 + 4 = 14$
(b) $(2)^2 - 3(2) + 4 = 4 - 6 + 4 = 2$

11. (a) $\dfrac{1+1}{1-1} = \dfrac{2}{0}$ which is undefined.
You cannot divide by zero.
(b) $\dfrac{-1+1}{-1-1} = \dfrac{0}{-2} = 0$

13. $x + 9 = 9 + x$,
Commutative Property of Addition

15. $\dfrac{1}{(h+6)}(h+6) = 1$, $h \neq -6$
Inverse Property of Multiplication

17. $2(x+3) = 2 \cdot x + 2 \cdot 3 = 2x + 6$
Distributive Property

19. $1 \cdot (1+x) = 1 + x$,
Identity Property of Multiplication

21. $x(3y) = (x \cdot 3)y$ by the Associative Property of Multiplication
$\qquad = (3x)y$ by the Commutative Property of Multiplication

23. $\dfrac{81 - (90 - 9)}{5} = \dfrac{81 - 81}{5} = \dfrac{0}{5} = 0$

25. $\dfrac{8-8}{-9+(6+3)} = \dfrac{8-8}{-9+9} = \dfrac{0}{0}$,
which is undefined since the denominator is zero.

27. $10 - 6 - 2 = 4 - 2 = 2$

29. $(4-7)(-2) = (-3)(-2)$
$\qquad = 6$

31. $\dfrac{3}{16} + \dfrac{5}{16} = \dfrac{3+5}{16}$
$\qquad = \dfrac{8}{16} = \dfrac{1}{2}$

33. $\dfrac{5}{8} - \dfrac{5}{12} + \dfrac{1}{6} = \dfrac{5 \cdot 3}{8 \cdot 3} - \dfrac{5 \cdot 2}{12 \cdot 2} + \dfrac{1 \cdot 4}{6 \cdot 4}$
$\qquad = \dfrac{15 - 10 + 4}{24} = \dfrac{9}{24} = \dfrac{3}{8}$

35. $\frac{4}{5} \cdot \frac{1}{2} \cdot \frac{3}{4} = \frac{1}{5} \cdot \frac{1}{2} \cdot \frac{3}{1} = \frac{3}{10}$

37. $\frac{2}{3} \div 8 = \frac{2}{3} \times \frac{1}{8} = \frac{1}{12}$

39. $12 \div \frac{1}{4} = 12 \times \frac{4}{1} = 12 \times 4 = 48$

41. $-3 + \dfrac{3}{7} = \dfrac{-18}{7} \approx -2.57$

43. $\dfrac{11.46 - 5.37}{3.91} = \dfrac{6.09}{3.91} \approx 1.56$

45. $5^{-1} + 2^{-3} = \dfrac{1}{5} + \dfrac{1}{2^3} = \dfrac{1}{5} + \dfrac{1}{8}$

$= \dfrac{8+5}{40} = \dfrac{13}{40} \approx 0.33$

47. $\dfrac{7^4 + 32}{7^4 - 200} = \dfrac{2401 + 32}{2401 - 200} = \dfrac{2433}{2201} \approx 1.11$

49. $\dfrac{5^5}{5^2} = 5^{5-2} = 5^3 = 125$

51. $(3^3)^2 = 3^6 = 729$

53. $(2^3 \cdot 3^2)^2 = (8 \cdot 9)^2 = 72^2 = 5184$

55. $\dfrac{4 \cdot 3^{-2}}{2^{-2} \cdot 3^{-1}} = \dfrac{4 \cdot 2^2 \cdot 3^1}{3^2} = \dfrac{4 \cdot 4}{3} = \dfrac{16}{3}$

57. $-3(2)^3 = -3(8) = -24$

59. $6(10)^0 - (6 \cdot 10)^0 = 6 \cdot 1 - (60)^0$

$= 6 - 1 = 5$

61. $(-5z)^3 = (-1)^3(5)^3(z^3) = -125z^3$

63. $6y^2(2y^4)^2 = 6y^2(2)^2(y^4)^2$

$= 6y^2(4)(y^8) = 24y^{10}$

65. $\dfrac{3x^5}{x^3} = 3x^{5-3} = 3x^2$

67. $\dfrac{7x^2}{x^3} = 7x^{2-3} = 7x^{-1} = \dfrac{7}{x}$

69. $\dfrac{12(x+y)^3}{9(x+y)} = \dfrac{3 \cdot 4(x+y)^{3-1}}{3 \cdot 3}$

$= \dfrac{4(x+y)^2}{3}$

71. $(x+5)^0 = 1, \ x \neq -5$

73. $(-2x^2)^3(4x^3)^{-1} = \dfrac{(-2x^2)^3}{4x^3}$

$= \dfrac{-8x^6}{4x^3} = -2x^3$

75. $\left(\dfrac{x}{10}\right)^{-1} = \dfrac{10}{x}$

77. $3^n \cdot 3^{2n} = 3^{n+2n} = 3^{3n}$

79. $57{,}500{,}000 = 5.75 \times 10^7$

81. $0.0000899 = 8.99 \times 10^{-5}$

83. $5.24 \times 10^8 = 524{,}000{,}000$

85. $4.8 \times 10^{-10} = 0.00000000048$

87. (a) $750\left(1 + \dfrac{0.11}{365}\right)^{800} \approx 954.448$

$750 \ \boxed{\times} \ \boxed{(} \ 1 \ \boxed{+} \ 0.11 \ \boxed{\div} \ 365 \ \boxed{)} \ \boxed{y^x} \ 800 \ \boxed{=}$

(b) $\dfrac{67{,}000{,}000 + 93{,}000{,}000}{0.0052} \approx 3.077 \times 10^{10}$

$\boxed{(} \ 67000000 \ \boxed{+} \ 93000000 \ \boxed{)} \ \boxed{\div} \ 0.0052 \ \boxed{=}$

Section P.3 Radicals and Rational Exponents

■ You should know the properties of radicals.

(a) $\sqrt[n]{a^m} = (\sqrt[n]{a})^m$

(b) $\sqrt[n]{a} \cdot \sqrt[n]{b} = \sqrt[n]{ab}$

(c) $\dfrac{\sqrt[n]{a}}{\sqrt[n]{b}} = \sqrt[n]{\dfrac{a}{b}}, \quad b \neq 0$

(d) $\sqrt[m]{\sqrt[n]{a}} = \sqrt[mn]{a}$

(e) $(\sqrt[n]{a})^n = a$

(f) For n even, $\sqrt[n]{a^n} = |a|$
For n odd, $\sqrt[n]{a^n} = a$

(g) $a^{1/n} = \sqrt[n]{a}$

(h) $a^{m/n} = (\sqrt[n]{a})^m = \sqrt[n]{a^m}$

■ You should be able to simplify radicals.

(a) All possible factors have been removed from the radical sign.
(b) All fractions have radical-free denominators.
(c) The index for the radical has been reduced as far as possible.

■ You should be able to use your calculator to evaluate radicals.

1. Radical form: $\sqrt{9} = 3$
Rational exponent form: $9^{1/2} = 3$

3. Radical form: $\sqrt{196} = 14$
Rational exponent form: $196^{1/2} = 14$

5. Radical form: $\sqrt[3]{-216} = -6$
Rational exponent form: $(-216)^{1/3} = -6$

7. Radical form: $\sqrt[3]{27^2} = 9$
Rational exponent form:
$(27^2)^{1/3} = 27^{2/3} = 9$

9. Radical form: $\sqrt[4]{81^3} = 27$
Rational exponent form:
$(81^3)^{1/4} = 81^{3/4} = 27$

11. $\sqrt{9} = 3$

13. $\sqrt[3]{8} = \sqrt[3]{2^3} = 2$

15. $\sqrt{36} = \sqrt{6^2} = 6$

17. $-\sqrt[3]{-27} = -\sqrt[3]{(-3)^3}$
$= -(-3) = 3$

19. $\dfrac{4}{\sqrt{64}} = \dfrac{4}{8} = \dfrac{1}{2}$

21. $(\sqrt[3]{-125})^3 = -125$

23. $16^{1/2} = \sqrt{16} = 4$

25. $(32)^{-3/5} = (\sqrt[5]{32})^{-3}$

$\qquad = 2^{-3}$

$\qquad = \dfrac{1}{2^3}$

$\qquad = \dfrac{1}{8}$

27. $\left(\dfrac{16}{81}\right)^{-3/4} = \left(\dfrac{81}{16}\right)^{3/4}$

$\qquad = \left(\sqrt[4]{\dfrac{81}{16}}\right)^3$

$\qquad = \left(\dfrac{3}{2}\right)^3$

$\qquad = \dfrac{27}{8}$

29. $\left(-\dfrac{1}{64}\right)^{-1/3} = (-64)^{1/3}$

$\qquad = \sqrt[3]{-1}\sqrt[3]{64}$

$\qquad = -\sqrt[3]{4^3}$

$\qquad = -4$

31. $\sqrt{8} = \sqrt{4 \cdot 2}$

$\qquad = \sqrt{4}\sqrt{2}$

$\qquad = 2\sqrt{2}$

33. $\sqrt{9 \times 10^{-4}} = \sqrt{9}\sqrt{(10^{-2})^2}$

$\qquad = 3(10^{-2})$

$\qquad = 3 \times 10^{-2}$

$\qquad = \dfrac{3}{100}$

35. $\sqrt{72x^3} = \sqrt{36 \cdot 2 \cdot x^2 \cdot x}$

$\qquad = 6x\sqrt{2x}$

37. $\sqrt[3]{16x^5} = \sqrt[3]{8 \cdot 2 \cdot x^3 \cdot x^2}$

$\qquad = 2x\sqrt[3]{2x^2}$

39. $\sqrt{75x^2y^{-4}} = \sqrt{\dfrac{75x^2}{y^4}}$

$\qquad = \sqrt{\dfrac{25 \cdot 3x^2}{y^4}}$

$\qquad = \dfrac{5|x|\sqrt{3}}{y^2}$

41. $\dfrac{1}{\sqrt{3}} = \dfrac{1}{\sqrt{3}} \cdot \dfrac{\sqrt{3}}{\sqrt{3}}$

$\qquad = \dfrac{\sqrt{3}}{3}$

43. $\dfrac{8}{\sqrt[3]{2}} = \dfrac{8}{\sqrt[3]{2}} \cdot \dfrac{\sqrt[3]{2^2}}{\sqrt[3]{2^2}}$

$\qquad = \dfrac{8\sqrt[3]{2^2}}{\sqrt[3]{2^3}}$

$\qquad = \dfrac{8\sqrt[3]{4}}{2}$

$\qquad = 4\sqrt[3]{4}$

45. $\dfrac{2x}{5-\sqrt{3}} = \dfrac{2x}{5-\sqrt{3}} \cdot \dfrac{5+\sqrt{3}}{5+\sqrt{3}}$

$\qquad = \dfrac{2x(5+\sqrt{3})}{25-3}$

$\qquad = \dfrac{2x(5+\sqrt{3})}{22}$

$\qquad = \dfrac{x(5+\sqrt{3})}{11}$

47. $\dfrac{3}{\sqrt{5}+\sqrt{6}} = \dfrac{3}{\sqrt{5}+\sqrt{6}} \cdot \dfrac{\sqrt{5}-\sqrt{6}}{\sqrt{5}-\sqrt{6}}$

$= \dfrac{3(\sqrt{5}-\sqrt{6})}{5-6}$

$= -3(\sqrt{5}-\sqrt{6})$

$= 3(\sqrt{6}-\sqrt{5})$

49. $\dfrac{\sqrt{8}}{2} = \dfrac{\sqrt{8}}{2} \cdot \dfrac{\sqrt{8}}{\sqrt{8}}$

$= \dfrac{8}{2\sqrt{8}} = \dfrac{4}{\sqrt{8}}$

$= \dfrac{4}{\sqrt{4 \cdot 2}} = \dfrac{4}{2\sqrt{2}} = \dfrac{2}{\sqrt{2}}$

51. $\dfrac{\sqrt{5}+\sqrt{3}}{3} = \dfrac{\sqrt{5}+\sqrt{3}}{3} \cdot \dfrac{\sqrt{5}-\sqrt{3}}{\sqrt{5}-\sqrt{3}}$

$= \dfrac{5-3}{3(\sqrt{5}-\sqrt{3})}$

$= \dfrac{2}{3(\sqrt{5}-\sqrt{3})}$

53. $\dfrac{\sqrt{7}-3}{4} = \dfrac{\sqrt{7}-3}{4} \cdot \dfrac{\sqrt{7}+3}{\sqrt{7}+3}$

$= \dfrac{7-9}{4(\sqrt{7}+3)}$

$= \dfrac{-2}{4(\sqrt{7}+3)}$

$= \dfrac{-1}{2(\sqrt{7}+3)}$

55. $\sqrt[4]{3^2} = 3^{2/4}$

$= 3^{1/2}$

$= \sqrt{3}$

57. $\sqrt[6]{(x+1)^4} = (x+1)^{4/6}$

$= (x+1)^{2/3}$

$= \sqrt[3]{(x+1)^2}$

59. $\sqrt{\sqrt{32}} = (32^{1/2})^{1/2}$

$= 32^{1/4}$

$= \sqrt[4]{32}$

$= 2\sqrt[4]{2}$

61. $\sqrt{\sqrt[4]{2x}} = \left((2x)^{1/4}\right)^{1/2} = (2x)^{1/8} = \sqrt[8]{2x}$

63. $5\sqrt{x} - 3\sqrt{x} = (5-3)\sqrt{x} = 2\sqrt{x}$

65. $2\sqrt{50} + 12\sqrt{8} = 2\sqrt{25 \cdot 2} + 12\sqrt{4 \cdot 2}$

$= 2(5)\sqrt{2} + 12(2)\sqrt{2}$

$= 10\sqrt{2} + 24\sqrt{2} = 34\sqrt{2}$

67. $-2\sqrt{9y} + 10\sqrt{y} = -2 \cdot 3\sqrt{y} + 10\sqrt{y}$

$= -6\sqrt{y} + 10\sqrt{y}$

$= 4\sqrt{y}$

69. $\dfrac{x^{-3}x^{1/2}}{x^{3/2}x^{-1}} = \dfrac{x^{1/2}x^1}{x^3x^{3/2}} = \dfrac{x^{3/2}}{x^{9/2}}$

$= \dfrac{1}{x^{(9/2)-(3/2)}} = \dfrac{1}{x^{6/2}} = \dfrac{1}{x^3}$

71. $(3x^{-1/3}y^{3/4})^2 = \left(\dfrac{3y^{3/4}}{x^{1/3}}\right)^2 = \dfrac{9y^{3/2}}{x^{2/3}}$

73. $\dfrac{18y^{4/3}z^{-1/3}}{24y^{-2/3}z} = \dfrac{3y^{6/3}}{4z^{4/3}} = \dfrac{3y^2}{4z^{4/3}}$

75. $\left(\dfrac{x^{1/4}}{x^{1/6}}\right)^3 = (x^{1/12})^3 = x^{1/4}$

77. $(c^{3/2})^{1/3} = c^{1/2} = \sqrt{c}$

79. $\sqrt{57} \approx 7.550$

57 $\boxed{\sqrt{}}$ $\boxed{=}$

81. $\sqrt[6]{125} \approx 2.236$

125 $\boxed{y^x}$ $\boxed{(}$ 1 $\boxed{\div}$ 6 $\boxed{)}$ $\boxed{=}$

83. $\sqrt{75 + 3\sqrt{8}} \approx 9.137$

$\boxed{(}$ 75 $\boxed{+}$ $\boxed{(}$ 3 $\boxed{\times}$ 8 $\boxed{\sqrt{}}$ $\boxed{)}$ $\boxed{)}$ $\boxed{\sqrt{}}$

85. $\sqrt{5} + \sqrt{3} \approx 3.968$

$\sqrt{5+3} = \sqrt{8} \approx 2.828$

Therefore,

$\sqrt{5} + \sqrt{3} > \sqrt{5+3}.$

87. $\sqrt{3^2 + 2^2} = \sqrt{9 + 4}$

$= \sqrt{13}$

≈ 3.6056

Therefore,

$5 > \sqrt{3^2 + 2^2}.$

89. $\sqrt{3} \cdot \sqrt[4]{3} \approx 2.280$

$\sqrt[8]{3} \approx 1.147$

Therefore,

$\sqrt{3} \cdot \sqrt[4]{3} > \sqrt[8]{3}.$

91. Repeatedly taking the square root of a positive real number, the display appears to be approaching 1. For example,

$$\sqrt{10} = 3.16227766$$

$$\sqrt{3.16227766} = 1.77827941$$

$$\sqrt{1.77827941} = 1.333521432$$

$$\sqrt{1.333521432} = 1.154781985$$

and so on.

Section P.4   Polynomials and Special Products

- Given a polynomial in x, $a_n x^n + a_{n-1} x^{n-1} + \cdots + a_1 x + a_0$, where $a_n \neq 0$, you should be able to identify the following.
  - (a) Degree: n
  - (b) Terms: $a_n x^n$, $a_{n-1} x^{n-1}$, ..., $a_1 x$, a_0
  - (c) Coefficients: a_n, a_{n-1}, ..., a_1, a_0
  - (d) Leading coefficient: a_n
  - (e) Constant term: a_0

- You should be able to add and subtract polynomials.

- You should be able to multiply polynomials by either
  - (a) The Distributive Law or
  - (b) The Vertical Method.

- You should know the special binomial products.
  - (a) $(ax + b)(cx + d) = acx^2 + adx + bcx + bd$ FOIL

    $$= acx^2 + (ad + bc)x + bd$$
  - (b) $(u \pm v)^2 = u^2 \pm 2uv + v^2$
  - (c) $(u + v)(u - v) = u^2 - v^2$
  - (d) $(u \pm v)^3 = u^3 \pm 3u^2 v + 3uv^2 \pm v^3$

---

1. Standard form:
$2x^2 - x + 1$
Degree: 2
Leading coefficient: 2

3. Standard form: $x^5 - 1$
Degree: 5
Leading coefficient: 1

5. Standard form:
$4x^5 + 6x^4 - x - 1$
Degree: 5
Leading coefficient: 4

7. $2x - 3x^3 + 8$
This is a polynomial.
Standard form:
$-3x^3 + 2x + 8$

9. $\dfrac{3x + 4}{x} = \dfrac{3x}{x} + \dfrac{4}{x}$

$$= 3 + 4x^{-1}$$

This is not a polynomial
because of the negative
exponent.

11. $y^2 - y^4 + y^3$
This is a polynomial.
Standard form:
$-y^4 + y^3 + y^2$

13. $(6x + 5) - (8x + 15) = 6x + 5 - 8x - 15 = (6x - 8x) + (5 - 15) = -2x - 10$

15. $-(x^3 - 2) + (4x^3 - 2x) = -x^3 + 2 + 4x^3 - 2x = (4x^3 - x^3) - 2x + 2 = 3x^3 - 2x + 2$

17. $(15x^2 - 6) - (-8x^3 - 14x^2 - 17) = 15x^2 - 6 + 8x^3 + 14x^2 + 17$

$$= 8x^3 + (15x^2 + 14x^2) + (-6 + 17) = 8x^3 + 29x^2 + 11$$

19. $5z - [3z - (10z + 8)] = 5z - (3z - 10z - 8)$

$$= 5z - 3z + 10z + 8 = (5z - 3z + 10z) + 8 = 12z + 8$$

21. $3x(x^2 - 2x + 1) = 3x(x^2) + 3x(-2x) + 3x(1) = 3x^3 - 6x^2 + 3x$

23. $-5z(3z - 1) = -5z(3z) + (-5z)(-1)$

$$= -15z^2 + 5z$$

25. $(-2x)(-3x)(5x + 2) = 6x^2(5x + 2)$

$$= 6x^2(5x) + 6x^2(2)$$

$$= 30x^3 + 12x^2$$

27. $(x + 3)(x + 4) = x^2 + 4x + 3x + 12$

$$= x^2 + 7x + 12$$

29. $(3x - 5)(2x + 1) = 6x^2 + 3x - 10x - 5$

$$= 6x^2 - 7x - 5$$

31. $(x + 6)^2 = x^2 + 2(x)(6) + 6^2$

$$= x^2 + 12x + 36$$

33. $(2x - 5y)^2 = (2x)^2 - 2(2x)(5y) + (5y)^2$

$$= 4x^2 - 20xy + 25y^2$$

35. $[(x - 3) + y]^2 = (x - 3)^2 + 2(x - 3)y + y^2$

$$= x^2 - 6x + 9 + 2xy - 6y + y^2 = x^2 + 2xy + y^2 - 6x - 6y + 9$$

37. $(x + 10)(x - 10) = x^2 - 100$

39. $(x + 2y)(x - 2y) = x^2 - 4y^2$

41. $(m - 3 + n)(m - 3 - n) = [(m - 3) + n][(m - 3) - n]$

$$= (m - 3)^2 - n^2 = m^2 - 6m + 9 - n^2 = m^2 - n^2 - 6m + 9$$

43. $(2r^2 - 5)(2r^2 + 5) = 4r^4 - 25$

45. $(x + 1)^3 = x^3 + 3x^2(1) + 3x(1^2) + 1^3$

$$= x^3 + 3x^2 + 3x + 1$$

47. $(2x - y)^3 = (2x)^3 - 3(2x)^2 y + 3(2x)y^2 - y^3 = 8x^3 - 12x^2 y + 6xy^2 - y^3$

49. $(\sqrt{x} + \sqrt{y})(\sqrt{x} - \sqrt{y}) = (\sqrt{x})^2 - (\sqrt{y})^2$

$$= x - y$$

51. $(4x^3 - 3)^2 = (4x^3)^2 - 2(4x^3)(3) + (3)^2$

$$= 16x^6 - 24x^3 + 9$$

53. $(x^2 + 9)(x^2 - x - 4) = (x^2 + 9)x^2 - (x^2 + 9)(x) - (x^2 + 9)(4)$

$$= x^4 + 9x^2 - x^3 - 9x - 4x^2 - 36$$

$$= x^4 - x^3 + 5x^2 - 9x - 36$$

55. By the Vertical Method we have:

$$
\begin{array}{l}
x^2 - x + 1 \\
\underline{x^2 + x + 1} \\
x^4 - x^3 + x^2 \\
 x^3 - x^2 + x \\
 \underline{x^2 - x + 1} \\
x^4 + 0x^3 + x^2 + 0x + 1
\end{array}
$$

which equals $x^4 + x^2 + 1$.

57. $5x(x+1) - 3x(x+1) = 5x^2 + 5x - 3x^2 - 3x = 2x^2 + 2x$

59. $(x + \sqrt{5})(x - \sqrt{5})(x + 4) = (x^2 - 5)(x + 4) = x^3 + 4x^2 - 5x - 20$

61. We form the product of two polynomials of degrees m and n, as follows.

$$
(a_m x^m + a_{m-1} x^{m-1} + \cdots + a_0)(b_n x^n + b_{n-1} x^{n-1} + \cdots + b_0)
$$

$$
= a_m x^m (b_n x^n + \cdots + b_0) + \cdots + a_0 (b_n x^n + \cdots + b_0)
$$

$$
= a_m b_n x^{m+n} + \cdots + a_0 b_0
$$

Thus, the degree of the product is $m + n$.

Section P.5   Factoring

- You should be able to factor out all common factors, the first step in factoring.
- You should be able to factor the following special polynomial forms.
  - (a) $u^2 - v^2 = (u + v)(u - v)$
  - (b) $u^2 \pm 2uv + v^2 = (u \pm v)^2$
  - (c) $mx^2 + nx + r = (ax + b)(cx + d)$, where $m = ac$, $r = bd$, $n = ad + bc$
    Note: Not all trinomials can be factored (using real coefficients).
  - (d) $u^3 \pm v^3 = (u \pm v)(u^2 \mp uv + v^2)$
- You should be able to factor by grouping.

1. $3x + 6 = 3(x + 2)$

3. $2x^3 - 6x = 2x(x^2 - 3)$

5. $(x - 1)^2 + 6(x - 1) = (x - 1)(x - 1 + 6)$
$$= (x - 1)(x + 5)$$

7. $x^2 - 36 = x^2 - 6^2 = (x + 6)(x - 6)$

9. $16y^2 - 9 = (4y)^2 - (3)^2 = (4y + 3)(4y - 3)$

11. $(x - 1)^2 - 4 = (x - 1)^2 - (2)^2$
$$= [(x - 1) + 2][(x - 1) - 2]$$
$$= (x + 1)(x - 3)$$

13. $x^2 - 4x + 4 = x^2 - 2(2)(x) + 2^2$
$$= (x - 2)^2$$

15. $4t^2 + 4t + 1 = (2t)^2 + 2(2t)(1) + (1)^2$
$$= (2t + 1)^2$$

17. $25y^2 - 10y + 1 = (5y)^2 - 2(5y)(1) + 1^2$
$$= (5y - 1)^2$$

19. $x^2 + x - 2 = (x + 2)(x - 1)$ since $(2)(-1) = -2$ and $(2) + (-1) = 1$.

21. $s^2 - 5s + 6 = (s - 2)(s - 3)$ since $(-2)(-3) = 6$ and $(-2) + (-3) = -5$.

23. $y^2 + y - 20 = (y + 5)(y - 4)$ since $(5)(-4) = -20$ and $(5) + (-4) = 1$.

25. $x^2 - 30x + 200 = (x - 10)(x - 20)$ since $(-10)(-20) = 200$ and $(-10) + (-20) = -30$.

27. $3x^2 - 5x + 2 = (3x - 2)(x - 1)$ since $(-2)(-1) = 2$ and $(-3) + (-2) = -5$.

29. $9z^2 - 3z - 2 = (3z + 1)(3z - 2)$ since $(1)(-2) = -2$ and $(-6) + (3) = -3$.

31. $5x^2 + 26x + 5 = (5x + 1)(x + 5)$ since $(1)(5) = 5$ and $(25) + (1) = 26$.

33. $x^3 - 8 = x^3 - 2^3 = (x - 2)(x^2 + 2x + 4)$

35. $y^3 + 64 = y^3 + 4^3 = (y + 4)(y^2 - 4y + 16)$

37. $8t^3 - 1 = (2t)^3 - 1^3 = (2t - 1)(4t^2 + 2t + 1)$

39. $\begin{aligned} x^3 - x^2 + 2x - 2 &= (x^3 - x^2) + (2x - 2) \\ &= x^2(x - 1) + 2(x - 1) \\ &= (x - 1)(x^2 + 2) \end{aligned}$

41. $\begin{aligned} 2x^3 - x^2 - 6x + 3 &= (2x^3 - x^2) + (-6x + 3) \\ &= x^2(2x - 1) - 3(2x - 1) \\ &= (2x - 1)(x^2 - 3) \end{aligned}$

43. $\begin{aligned} 6 + 2x - 3x^3 - x^4 &= (6 + 2x) + (-3x^3 - x^4) \\ &= 2(3 + x) - x^3(3 + x) \\ &= (3 + x)(2 - x^3) \end{aligned}$

45. $\begin{aligned} 3x^2 + 10x + 8 &= 3x^2 + 6x + 4x + 8 \\ &= (3x^2 + 6x) + (4x + 8) \\ &= 3x(x + 2) + 4(x + 2) \\ &= (x + 2)(3x + 4) \end{aligned}$

47. $\begin{aligned} 6x^2 + x - 2 &= 6x^2 + 4x - 3x - 2 \\ &= (6x^2 - 3x) + (4x - 2) \\ &= 3x(2x - 1) + 2(2x - 1) \\ &= (2x - 1)(3x + 2) \end{aligned}$

49. $\begin{aligned} 15x^2 - 11x + 2 &= 15x^2 - 6x - 5x + 2 \\ &= (15x^2 - 6x) - (5x - 2) = 3x(5x - 2) - (5x - 2) = (5x - 2)(3x - 1) \end{aligned}$

51. $3x^2 + 7x + 2 = (3x + 1)(x + 2)$

53. $2x^2 + 7x + 3 = (2x + 1)(x + 3)$

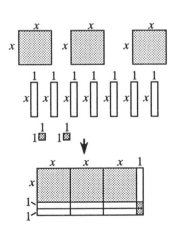

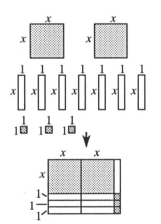

55. $x^3 - 9x = x(x^2 - 9)$
$$= x(x - 3)(x + 3)$$

57. $x^3 - 4x^2 = x^2(x - 4)$

59. $x^2 - 2x + 1 = (x - 1)^2$

61. $1 - 4x + 4x^2 = (1 - 2x)^2$

63. $-2x^2 - 4x + 2x^3 = 2x^3 - 2x^2 - 4x$
$$= 2x(x^2 - x - 2)$$
$$= 2x(x - 2)(x + 1)$$

65. $9x^2 + 10x + 1 = (9x + 1)(x + 1)$

67. $3x^3 + x^2 + 15x + 5 = x^2(3x + 1) + 5(3x + 1) = (3x + 1)(x^2 + 5)$

69. $x^4 - 4x^3 + x^2 - 4x = x(x^3 - 4x^2 + x - 4) = x[x^2(x - 4) + (x - 4)] = x(x - 4)(x^2 + 1)$

71. $25 - (x + 5)^2 = [5 - (x + 5)][5 + (x + 5)] = -x(x + 10)$

73. $(x^2 + 1)^2 - 4x^2 = [(x^2 + 1) + 2x][(x^2 + 1) - 2x]$
$$= (x^2 + 2x + 1)(x^2 - 2x + 1) = (x + 1)^2(x - 1)^2$$

75. $2t^3 - 16 = 2(t^3 - 8) = 2(t - 2)(t^2 + 2t + 4)$

77. $4x(2x - 1) + (2x - 1)^2 = (2x - 1)(4x + (2x - 1)) = (2x - 1)(6x - 1)$

79. $2(x + 1)(x - 3)^2 - 3(x + 1)^2(x - 3) = (x + 1)(x - 3)[2(x - 3) - 3(x + 1)]$
$$= (x + 1)(x - 3)[2x - 6 - 3x - 3]$$
$$= (x + 1)(x - 3)(-x - 9)$$
$$= -(x + 1)(x - 3)(x + 9)$$

Section P.6   Fractional Expressions

■ You should know how to find the domain of an algebraic expression.

■ You should know that a rational expression is the quotient of two polynomials.

■ You should be able to simplify rational expressions by reducing them to lowest terms. This may involve factoring both the numerator and the denominator.

■ You should be able to add, subtract, multiply, and divide rational expressions.

■ You should be able to simplify compound fractions.

---

1. The domain of the polynomial $3x^2 - 4x + 7$ is the set of all real numbers.

3. The domain of the polynomial $4x^3 + 5x + 3$, $x \geq 0$ is the set of nonnegative real numbers, since the polynomial is restricted to that set.

5. The domain of $\dfrac{1}{x - 2}$ is the set of all real numbers except $x = 2$, which would produce an undefined division by zero.

7. The domain of $\dfrac{x - 1}{x(x - 4)}$ is the set of all real numbers except $x = 0$ and $x = 4$, which would produce an undefined division by zero.

9. The domain of $\sqrt{x + 1}$ is the set of real numbers greater than or equal to -1 since $x + 1 \geq 0$ when $x \geq -1$.

11. $\dfrac{5}{2x} = \dfrac{5(3x)}{(2x)(3x)} = \dfrac{15x}{6x^2}$

13. $\dfrac{x + 1}{x} = \dfrac{x + 1}{x} \cdot \dfrac{x - 2}{x - 2}$

$\qquad = \dfrac{(x + 1)(x - 2)}{x(x - 2)}, \quad x \neq 2$

15. $\dfrac{3x}{x - 3} = \dfrac{3x(x + 2)}{(x - 3)(x + 2)}$

$\qquad = \dfrac{3x(x + 2)}{x^2 - x - 6}, \quad x \neq -2$

17. $\dfrac{15x^2}{10x} = \dfrac{5x(3x)}{5x(2)} = \dfrac{3x}{2}, \quad x \neq 0$

19. $\dfrac{3xy}{xy + x} = \dfrac{3xy}{x(y+1)} = \dfrac{3y}{y+1}, \quad x \neq 0$

21. $\dfrac{x-5}{10-2x} = \dfrac{x-5}{-2(x-5)} = -\dfrac{1}{2}, \quad x \neq 5$

23. $\dfrac{x^3 + 5x^2 + 6x}{x^2 - 4} = \dfrac{x(x+2)(x+3)}{(x+2)(x-2)}$

$\qquad = \dfrac{x(x+3)}{x-2}, \quad x \neq -2$

25. $\dfrac{y^2 - 7y + 12}{y^2 + 3y - 18} = \dfrac{(y-3)(y-4)}{(y+6)(y-3)}$

$\qquad = \dfrac{y-4}{y+6}, \quad y \neq 3$

27. $\dfrac{2 - x + 2x^2 - x^3}{x-2} = \dfrac{(2-x) + x^2(2-x)}{x-2}$

$\qquad = \dfrac{(2-x)(1+x^2)}{x-2} = \dfrac{-(x-2)(x^2+1)}{x-2} = -(x^2+1), \quad x \neq 2$

29. $\dfrac{z^3 - 8}{z^2 + 2z + 4} = \dfrac{(z-2)(z^2 + 2z + 4)}{z^2 + 2z + 4} = z - 2$

31. $\dfrac{5}{x-1} \cdot \dfrac{x-1}{25(x-2)} = \dfrac{1}{5(x-2)}, \quad x \neq 1$

33. $\dfrac{r}{r-1} \cdot \dfrac{r^2 - 1}{r^2} = \dfrac{r}{r-1} \cdot \dfrac{(r+1)(r-1)}{r^2} = \dfrac{r+1}{r}, \quad r \neq 1$

35. $\dfrac{y^3 - 8}{2y^3} \cdot \dfrac{4y}{y^2 - 5y + 6} = \dfrac{(y-2)(y^2 + 2y + 4)}{2y^3} \cdot \dfrac{4y}{(y-3)(y-2)} = \dfrac{2(y^2 + 2y + 4)}{y^2(y-3)}, \quad y \neq 2$

37. $\dfrac{3(x+y)}{4} \div \dfrac{x+y}{2} = \dfrac{3(x+y)}{4} \cdot \dfrac{2}{x+y} = \dfrac{3}{2}, \quad x \neq -y$

39. $\dfrac{\left(\dfrac{x^2}{(x+1)^2}\right)}{\left(\dfrac{x}{(x+1)^3}\right)} = \dfrac{x^2}{(x+1)^2} \div \dfrac{x}{(x+1)^3} = \dfrac{x^2}{(x+1)^2} \cdot \dfrac{(x+1)^3}{x} = x(x+1), \quad x \neq 0, -1$

41. $\dfrac{5}{x-1} + \dfrac{x}{x-1} = \dfrac{5+x}{x-1} = \dfrac{x+5}{x-1}$

43. $6 - \dfrac{5}{x+3} = \dfrac{6(x+3)}{(x+3)} - \dfrac{5}{x+3}$

$\qquad = \dfrac{6(x+3) - 5}{x+3} = \dfrac{6x + 13}{x+3}$

45. $\dfrac{3}{x-2} + \dfrac{5}{2-x} = \dfrac{3}{x-2} - \dfrac{5}{x-2} = \dfrac{3-5}{x-2} = -\dfrac{2}{x-2}$

47. $\dfrac{2}{x^2 - 4} - \dfrac{1}{x^2 - 3x + 2} = \dfrac{2}{(x + 2)(x - 2)} - \dfrac{1}{(x - 1)(x - 2)}$

$$= \dfrac{2(x - 1)}{(x + 2)(x - 2)(x - 1)} - \dfrac{x + 2}{(x + 2)(x - 2)(x - 1)}$$

$$= \dfrac{2(x - 1) - (x + 2)}{(x + 2)(x - 2)(x - 1)} = \dfrac{x - 4}{(x + 2)(x - 2)(x - 1)}$$

49. $-\dfrac{1}{x} + \dfrac{2}{x^2 + 1} + \dfrac{1}{x^3 + x} = -\dfrac{1}{x} + \dfrac{2}{x^2 + 1} + \dfrac{1}{x(x^2 + 1)}$

$$= \dfrac{-(x^2 + 1)}{x(x^2 + 1)} + \dfrac{2x}{x(x^2 + 1)} + \dfrac{1}{x(x^2 + 1)} = \dfrac{-x^2 - 1 + 2x + 1}{x(x^2 + 1)}$$

$$= \dfrac{-x^2 + 2x}{x(x^2 + 1)} = \dfrac{-x(x - 2)}{x(x^2 + 1)} = -\dfrac{x - 2}{x^2 + 1} = \dfrac{2 - x}{x^2 + 1}, \quad x \neq 0$$

51. $x^2(x^2 - 1)^{-1/2} + (x^2 - 1)^{1/2} = (x^2 - 1)^{-1/2}(x^2 + (x^2 - 1)) = \dfrac{2x^2 - 1}{(x^2 - 1)^{1/2}}$

53. $3(x - 2)^{-1/3} - x(x - 2)^{-4/3} = (x - 2)^{-4/3}(3(x - 2) - x) = \dfrac{2x - 6}{(x - 2)^{4/3}} = \dfrac{2(x - 3)}{(x - 2)^{4/3}}$

55. $\dfrac{\left(\dfrac{x}{2} - 1\right)}{(x - 2)} = \dfrac{\left(\dfrac{x}{2} - 1\right)}{(x - 2)} \cdot \dfrac{2}{2}$

$$= \dfrac{(x - 2)}{2(x - 2)} = \dfrac{1}{2}, \quad x \neq 2$$

57. $\dfrac{\left(\dfrac{1}{x} - \dfrac{1}{x + 1}\right)}{\left(\dfrac{1}{x + 1}\right)} = \dfrac{\dfrac{(x + 1) - x}{x(x + 1)}}{\dfrac{1}{x + 1}}$

$$= \dfrac{1}{x(x + 1)} \cdot \dfrac{x + 1}{1}$$

$$= \dfrac{1}{x}, \quad x \neq -1$$

59. $\dfrac{\left(\dfrac{1}{(x + h)^2} - \dfrac{1}{x^2}\right)}{h} = \dfrac{\left(\dfrac{1}{(x + h)^2} - \dfrac{1}{x^2}\right)}{h} \cdot \dfrac{x^2(x + h)^2}{x^2(x + h)^2} = \dfrac{x^2 - (x + h)^2}{hx^2(x + h)^2}$

$$= \dfrac{[x + (x + h)][x - (x + h)]}{hx^2(x + h)^2} = \dfrac{(2x + h)(-h)}{hx^2(x + h)^2} = -\dfrac{2x + h}{x^2(x + h)^2}, \quad h \neq 0$$

61. $\dfrac{2a^{-1} + b^{-1}}{ab} = \dfrac{2a^{-1}}{ab} + \dfrac{b^{-1}}{ab}$

$$= \dfrac{2}{a^2 b} + \dfrac{1}{ab^2}$$

$$= \dfrac{2b + a}{a^2 b^2}$$

63. $\dfrac{\left(\sqrt{x} - \dfrac{1}{2\sqrt{x}}\right)}{\sqrt{x}} = \dfrac{\left(\sqrt{x} - \dfrac{1}{2\sqrt{x}}\right)}{\sqrt{x}} \cdot \dfrac{2\sqrt{x}}{2\sqrt{x}}$

$$= \dfrac{2x - 1}{2x}, \quad x > 0$$

65. $\dfrac{\dfrac{t^2}{\sqrt{t^2+1}} - \sqrt{t^2+1}}{t^2} = \dfrac{\dfrac{t^2}{\sqrt{t^2+1}} - \sqrt{t^2+1}}{t^2} \cdot \dfrac{\sqrt{t^2+1}}{\sqrt{t^2+1}} = \dfrac{t^2 - (t^2+1)}{t^2\sqrt{t^2+1}} = -\dfrac{1}{t^2\sqrt{t^2+1}}$

67. $\dfrac{\sqrt{x+2} - \sqrt{x}}{2} = \dfrac{\sqrt{x+2} - \sqrt{x}}{2} \cdot \dfrac{\sqrt{x+2} + \sqrt{x}}{\sqrt{x+2} + \sqrt{x}}$

$$= \dfrac{(x+2) - x}{2(\sqrt{x+2} + \sqrt{x})} = \dfrac{2}{2(\sqrt{x+2} + \sqrt{x})} = \dfrac{1}{\sqrt{x+2} + \sqrt{x}}$$

Section P.7   The Cartesian Plane

■ You should be able to plot points.

■ You should know that the distance between $(x_1,\ y_1)$ and $(x_2,\ y_2)$ in the plane is
$$d = \sqrt{(x_2 - x_1)^2 + (y_2 - y_1)^2}.$$

■ You should know that the midpoint of the line segment joining $(x_1,\ y_1)$ and $(x_2,\ y_2)$ is
$$\left(\frac{x_1 + x_2}{2},\ \frac{y_1 + y_2}{2} \right).$$

■ You should know the equation of a circle:
$$(x - h)^2 + (y - k)^2 = r^2.$$

1.

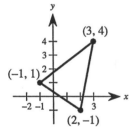

3.

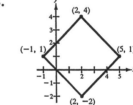

5. Since the points $(6,\ -3)$ and $(6,\ 5)$ lie on the same horizontal line, the distance between the points is given by the absolute value of the difference of their y-coordinates.
$$d = |5 - (-3)| = |5 + 3| = |8| = 8$$

7. Since the points $(-3,\ -1)$ and $(2,\ -1)$ lie on the same vertical line, the distance between the points is given by the absolute value of the difference of their x-coordinates.
$$d = |-3 - 2| = 5$$

9. (a) $a = |4 - 0| = 4$
$$b = |3 - 0| = 3$$
$$c = \sqrt{4^2 + 3^2} = \sqrt{25} = 5$$
   (b) $d = \sqrt{(4 - 0)^2 + (3 - 0)^2}$
$$= \sqrt{16 + 9} = \sqrt{25} = 5$$

11. (a) $a = |-3 - 7| = 10$
$$b = |4 - 1| = 3$$
$$c = \sqrt{10^2 + 3^2} = \sqrt{109}$$
   (b) $c = \sqrt{(7 - (-3))^2 + (4 - 1)^2}$
$$= \sqrt{10^2 + 3^2} = \sqrt{109}$$

13. (a)

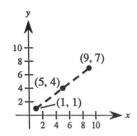

(b) $d = \sqrt{(9-1)^2 + (7-1)^2}$

$\quad = \sqrt{8^2 + 6^2}$

$\quad = \sqrt{100} = 10$

(c) $m = \left(\dfrac{1+9}{2}, \ \dfrac{1+7}{2} \right) = (5, \ 4)$

15. (a)

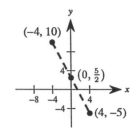

(b) $d = \sqrt{(-4-4)^2 + (10-(-5))^2}$

$\quad = \sqrt{(-8)^2 + (15)^2}$

$\quad = \sqrt{289} = 17$

(c) $m = \left(\dfrac{-4+4}{2}, \ \dfrac{10+(-5)}{2} \right) = \left(0, \ \dfrac{5}{2} \right)$

17. (a)

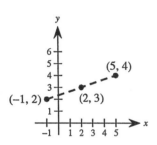

(b) $d = \sqrt{(5+1)^2 + (4-2)^2}$

$\quad = \sqrt{36+4} = 2\sqrt{10}$

(c) $m = \left(\dfrac{-1+5}{2}, \ \dfrac{2+4}{2} \right) = (2, \ 3)$

19. (a)

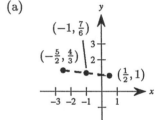

(b) $d = \sqrt{\left(\dfrac{1}{2} + \dfrac{5}{2} \right)^2 + \left(1 - \dfrac{4}{3} \right)^2}$

$\quad = \sqrt{9 + \dfrac{1}{9}} = \dfrac{\sqrt{82}}{3}$

(c) $m = \left(\dfrac{-\frac{5}{2} + \frac{1}{2}}{2}, \ \dfrac{\frac{4}{3} + 1}{2} \right) = \left(-1, \ \dfrac{7}{6} \right)$

21. (a)

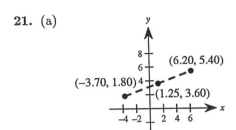

(b) $d = \sqrt{(6.2 - (-3.7))^2 + (5.4 - 1.8)^2}$

$= \sqrt{(9.9)^2 + (3.6)^2}$

$= \sqrt{110.97}$

(c) $m = \left(\dfrac{6.2 + (-3.7)}{2}, \dfrac{5.4 + 1.8}{2} \right)$

$= (1.25, \ 3.6)$

23. (a)

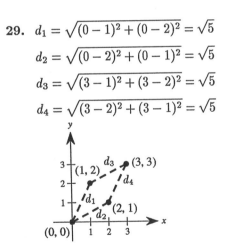

(b) $d = \sqrt{(48 + 36)^2 + (-72 + 18)^2}$

$= \sqrt{7056 + 2916}$

$= \sqrt{9972} = 6\sqrt{277}$

(c) $m = \left(\dfrac{-36 + 48}{2}, \dfrac{-18 - 72}{2} \right)$

$= (6, \ -45)$

25. $\dfrac{520,000 + 740,000}{2} = 630,000$

The estimated sales for 1991 is \$630,000.

27. $d_1 = \sqrt{(-1 - 2)^2 + (-5 - 1)^2} = \sqrt{45}$

$d_2 = \sqrt{(2 - 4)^2 + (1 - 0)^2} = \sqrt{5}$

$d_3 = \sqrt{(4 - (-1))^2 + (0 - (-5))^2} = \sqrt{50}$

Since $d_1{}^2 + d_2{}^2 = d_3{}^2$, we can conclude by the Pythagorean Theorem that the triangle is a right triangle.

29. $d_1 = \sqrt{(0 - 1)^2 + (0 - 2)^2} = \sqrt{5}$

$d_2 = \sqrt{(0 - 2)^2 + (0 - 1)^2} = \sqrt{5}$

$d_3 = \sqrt{(3 - 1)^2 + (3 - 2)^2} = \sqrt{5}$

$d_4 = \sqrt{(3 - 2)^2 + (3 - 1)^2} = \sqrt{5}$

Since $d_1 = d_2 = d_3 = d_4$, we can conclude that the points form the vertices of a rhombus.

31.
$$\sqrt{(x-1)^2 + (-10-2)^2} = 13$$
$$\sqrt{x^2 - 2x + 1 + 144} = 13$$
$$x^2 - 2x + 145 = 169$$
$$x^2 - 2x - 24 = 0$$
$$(x+4)(x-6) = 0$$
$$x = -4 \quad \text{or} \quad x = 6$$

33.
$$\sqrt{(8-0)^2 + (y-0)^2} = 17$$
$$\sqrt{64 + y^2} = 17$$
$$64 + y^2 = 289$$
$$y^2 = 225$$
$$y = \pm 15$$

35. The distance between $(4, -1)$ and (x, y) is equal to the distance between $(-2, 3)$ and (x, y).
$$\sqrt{(x-4)^2 + (y+1)^2} = \sqrt{(x+2)^2 + (y-3)^2}$$
$$(x-4)^2 + (y+1)^2 = (x+2)^2 + (y-3)^2$$
$$x^2 - 8x + 16 + y^2 + 2y + 1 = x^2 + 4x + 4 + y^2 - 6y + 9$$
$$-12x + 8y + 4 = 0$$
$$3x - 2y - 1 = 0$$

37. $x > 0 \Rightarrow x$ lies in Quadrant I or in Quadrant IV.

$y < 0 \Rightarrow y$ lies in Quadrant III or in Quadrant IV.

$x > 0$ and $y < 0 \Rightarrow (x, y)$ lies in Quadrant IV.

39. $x > 0 \Rightarrow x$ lies in Quadrant I or in Quadrant IV.

$y > 0 \Rightarrow y$ lies in Quadrant I or in Quadrant II.

$x > 0$ and $y > 0 \Rightarrow (x, y)$ lies in Quadrant I.

41. $x = -4 \Rightarrow x$ is negative $\Rightarrow x$ lies in Quadrant II or Quadrant III.

$y > 0 \Rightarrow y$ lies in Quadrant I or Quadrant II.

$x = -4$ and $y > 0 \Rightarrow (x, y)$ lies in Quadrant II.

43. $y < -5 \Rightarrow y$ is negative $\Rightarrow y$ lies in either Quadrant III or Quadrant IV.

45. If $xy > 0$, then either x and y are both positive, or both negative. Hence, (x, y) lies in either Quadrant I or Quadrant III.

47. Since $(x, -y)$ is in Quadrant II, we know that

$x < 0$ and $-y > 0$. If $-y > 0$, then $y < 0$.

$x < 0 \Rightarrow x$ lies in Quadrant II or in Quadrant III.

$y < 0 \Rightarrow y$ lies in Quadrant III or in Quadrant IV.

$x < 0$ and $y < 0 \Rightarrow (x, y)$ lies in Quadrant III.

49.

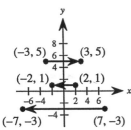

The points are reflected through the y-axis.

51. $(x-0)^2 + (y-0)^2 = 3^2$
$x^2 + y^2 = 9$

53. $(x-2)^2 + (y+1)^2 = 4^2$
$(x-2)^2 + (y+1)^2 = 16$

55. $(x+1)^2 + (y-2)^2 = r^2$
$(0+1)^2 + (0-2)^2 = r^2 \Rightarrow r^2 = 5$
$(x+1)^2 + (y-2)^2 = 5$

57. $r = \dfrac{1}{2}\sqrt{(6-0)^2 + (8-0)^2} = \dfrac{1}{2}\sqrt{100} = 5$
$\text{Center} = \left(\dfrac{0+6}{2},\ \dfrac{0+8}{2}\right) = (3,\ 4)$
$(x-3)^2 + (y-4)^2 = 25$

Section P.8   Exploring Data: Representing Data Graphically

1. By scanning the data, we see that the largest number is 24 and the smallest number is 10. We construct the line plot on the interval [10, 24] as follows:

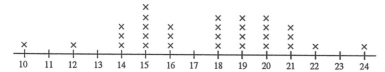

The score of 15 occurred with the greatest frequency (5).

3. By scanning the data, we see that the largest number is 100 and the smallest number is 70. We construct the line plot on the interval [70, 100] as follows:

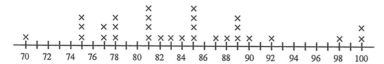

The scores of 81 and 85 occurred with the greatest frequency (4).

5. Since the scores range from 70 to 100, the stems are 7, 8, 9 and 10:

Stems	Leaves
7	0 5 5 5 7 7 8 8 8
8	1 1 1 1 2 3 4 5 5 5 5 7 8 9 9 9
9	0 2 8
10	0 0

7. Since the expenditures range from 618 to 1626, the stems are $6, 7, \ldots, 16$:

Stems	*Leaves*
6	18 68 71 94
7	16 19 25 25 42 57 58 76 84 88
8	13 28 35 41 46 59 61 62 66 81 83 89 91 92 92
9	05 06 15 18 25 25 26 28 41 44 83 90 92
10	04 10 62 95
11	51 78 86
12	23
13	
14	
15	
16	26

9.

11.

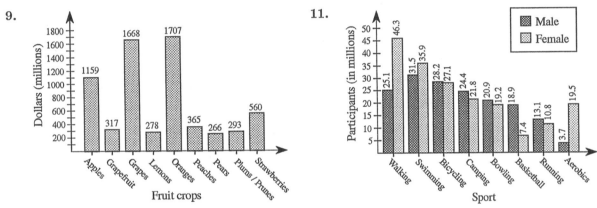

13. Let the vertical axis represent the number of barrels of oil (in millions) and the horizontal axis the year. Plot the 9 points and connect them with line segments as follows:

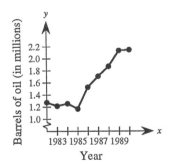

CHAPTER 1

Functions and Graphs

Section 1.1   Graphs and Graphing Utilities

- ■ You should be able to graph an equation by the point-plotting method.
- ■ You should be able to find the intercepts of a graph of an equation.
- ■ You should be able to graph an equation using a graphing utility.
- ■ You should be able to determine an appropriate viewing rectangle to show all the important features of a graph.
- ■ You should be able to use the zoom and trace features of a graphing utility.

1. (a) $\sqrt{0+4} = 2$, yes
   (b) $\sqrt{5+4} = 3$, yes

3. (a) $2(1) - 2 - 3 = -3 \neq 0$, no
   (b) $2(1) - (-1) - 3 = 0$, yes

5. (a) $1^2\left(\frac{1}{5}\right) - 1^2 + 4\left(\frac{1}{5}\right) = 0$
   yes
   (b) $2^2\left(\frac{1}{2}\right) - 2^2 + 4\left(\frac{1}{2}\right) = 0$
   yes

7. $y = x^2 + C$
$$6 = (2)^2 + C$$
$$6 = 4 + C$$
$$C = 2$$

9. $y = C\sqrt{x+1}$
$$8 = C\sqrt{3+1}$$
$$2C = 8$$
$$C = 4$$

11. $2x + y = 3$
$$y = -2x + 3$$

x	-4	-2	0	2	4
y	11	7	3	-1	-5
$(x,\ y)$	$(-4,\ 11)$	$(-2,\ 7)$	$(0,\ 3)$	$(2,\ -1)$	$(4,\ -5)$

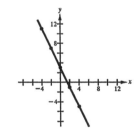

13. $y = 4 - x$

x-intercept: $(4, \ 0)$

y-intercept: $(0, \ 4)$

Matches graph (c)

```
RANGE
Xmin=-2
Xmax=6
Xscl=1
Ymin=-1
Ymax=5
Yscl=1
```

15. $y = \sqrt{4 - x^2}$

x-intercepts:

$(2, \ 0), \ (-2, \ 0)$

y-intercept: $(0, \ 2)$

Matches graph (d)

```
RANGE
Xmin=-3
Xmax=3
Xscl=1
Ymin=-1
Ymax=3
Yscl=1
```

17. $y = x^3 - x$

x-intercepts:

$(-1, \ 0), \ (0, \ 0), \ (1, \ 0)$

y-intercept: $(0, \ 0)$

Matches graph (e)

```
RANGE
Xmin=-2
Xmax=2
Xscl=1
Ymin=-2
Ymax=2
Yscl=1
```

19. $y = -3x + 2$

Intercepts: $(0, \ 2), \ \left(\frac{2}{3}, \ 0\right)$

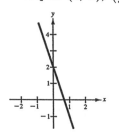

21. $y = 1 - x^2$

Intercepts:

$(-1, \ 0), \ (0, \ 1), \ (1, \ 0)$

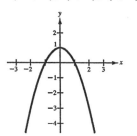

23. $y = x^3 + 2$

Intercepts:

$(-\sqrt[3]{2}, \ 0), \ (0, \ 2)$

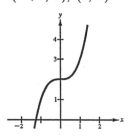

25. $y = (x - 3)(x + 2)$

Intercepts:

$(3, \ 0), \ (-2, \ 0), \ (0, \ -6)$

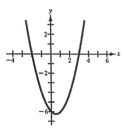

27. $y = \sqrt{x - 3}$

Intercept: $(3, \ 0)$

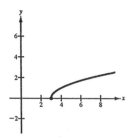

29. $y = |x - 2|$

Intercepts: $(0, \ 2), \ (2, \ 0)$

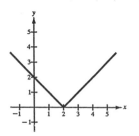

31. $y = x^2 - 4x + 3$

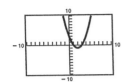

The graph intersects the x-axis twice and the y-axis once.

33. $y = 3x^4 - 6x^2$

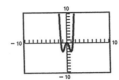

The graph intersects the x-axis three times and the y-axis once.

35. $y = x\sqrt{4 - x}$

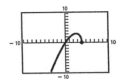

The graph intersects the x-axis twice and the y-axis once.

37. $y = \dfrac{10x}{x^2 + 1}$

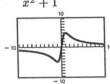

The graph intersects the x-axis once and the y-axis once.

39. $y = x^4 - 4x^3 + 16x$

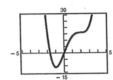

The graph intersects the x-axis twice and the y-axis once.

41. $y = 100x\sqrt{25 - x}$

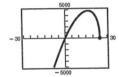

The graph intersects the x-axis twice and the y-axis once.

43. $x^2 - 100y - 1000 = 0 \Rightarrow 100y = x^2 - 1000$
$$\Rightarrow y = \tfrac{1}{100}x^2 - 10$$

The graph intersects the x-axis twice and the y-axis once.

45. $x^2 + y^2 = 64 \Rightarrow y^2 = 64 - x^2$
$$\Rightarrow y = \pm\sqrt{64 - x^2}$$
$$y_1 = \sqrt{64 - x^2}, \quad y_2 = -\sqrt{64 - x^2}$$

47. $6x^2 + y^2 = 72 \Rightarrow y^2 = 72 - 6x^2$

$$\Rightarrow y = \pm\sqrt{72 - 6x^2}$$

$y_1 = \sqrt{72 - 6x^2}, \quad y_2 = -\sqrt{72 - 6x^2}$

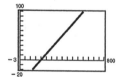

49. $9x + 27y - 1000 = 0 \Rightarrow 27y = -9x + 1000$

$$\Rightarrow y = -\tfrac{1}{3}x + \tfrac{1000}{27}$$

Since the y-intercept is $\frac{1000}{27} \approx 37.04$, we can use:

Xmin=−1   Ymin=−1
Xmax=100   Ymax=40
Xscl=5   Yscl=2

(Answer is not unique.)

51. $y = -(x - 5)^2(x - 15)$

Since the x-intercepts are 5 and 15, we can use:

Xmin=−1   Ymin=−25
Xmax=20   Ymax=150
Xscl=1   Yscl=10

(Answer is not unique.)

53. $y = 0.25x - 50$

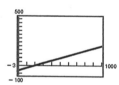

The first viewing rectangle is preferred because it shows a greater rate of increase.

55. $y = \sqrt[3]{x}$

(a)

x	-1	0	1
y	-1	0	1

(b)

x	-1	$-\frac{3}{4}$	$-\frac{1}{2}$	$-\frac{1}{4}$	0	$\frac{1}{4}$	$\frac{1}{2}$	$\frac{3}{4}$	1
y	-1	-0.91	-0.79	-0.63	0	0.63	0.79	0.91	-1

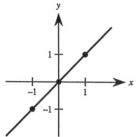

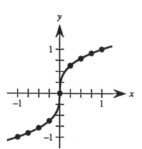

(c)

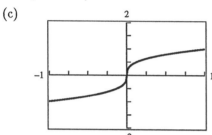

57. $y = \sqrt{5 - x}$

(a) $(2, y)$, $y = 1.73$

(b) $(x, 3)$, $x = -4.00$

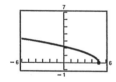

59. $y = x^5 - 5x$

(a) $(-0.5, y)$, $y = 2.47$

(b) $(x, -4)$, $x = 1, -1.65$

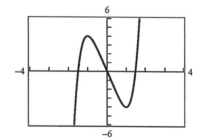

61. $y = 225{,}000 - 20{,}000x$, $0 \le x \le 8$

(a)

```
RANGE
Xmin=0
Xmax=8
Xscl=1
Ymin=0
Ymax=250000
Yscl=50000
```

(b)

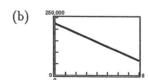

63. $y = 0.40x^3 - 9.42x^2 + 1053.24$

(a)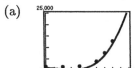

(b) Using the zoom and trace features,
   we have $y = 16889.72$ when $x = 44$
   (year 1994).

65. $y = 1.097x + 0.15, \quad 0 \le x \le 6$

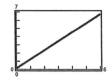

67. If the x-intercept of the graph of $y = \sqrt{ax + b}$ is $(5, \ 0)$, then $0 = \sqrt{5a + b}$ or $5a + b = 0$.
Hence, there are many correct answers. For instance, $a = 1, \ b = -5$.

Section 1.2   Lines in the Plane

You should know the following important facts about lines.

■ The slope of the line through (x_1, y_1) and (x_2, y_2) is
$$m = \frac{y_2 - y_1}{x_2 - x_1}.$$

■ (a) If $m > 0$, the line rises from left to right.
(b) If $m = 0$, the line is horizontal.
(c) If $m < 0$, the line falls from left to right.
(d) If m is undefined, the line is vertical.

■ Equations of Lines
(a) Point-Slope: $y - y_1 = m(x - x_1)$
(b) Two-Point: $y - y_1 = \dfrac{y_2 - y_1}{x_2 - x_1}(x - x_1)$
(c) Slope-Intercept: $y = mx + b$
(d) General: $Ax + By + C = 0$
(e) Vertical: $x = a$
(f) Horizontal: $y = b$

■ You should be able to graph a line using a graphing utility. This graph may not appear to have the slope indicated by its equation unless you are using the "square" viewing rectangle.

■ Given two distinct nonvertical lines
$$L_1 : y = m_1 x + b_1 \quad \text{and} \quad L_2 : y = m_2 x + b_2$$

(a) L_1 is parallel to L_2 if and only if $m_1 = m_2$ and $b_1 \neq b_2$.
(b) L_1 is perpendicular to L_2 if and only if $m_1 = -1/m_2$.

1. Slope $= \dfrac{\text{rise}}{\text{run}} = \dfrac{6}{5}$

3. Since the line is horizontal, it has a slope of zero.

5. Slope $= \dfrac{\text{rise}}{\text{run}} = \dfrac{-3}{1} = -3$

7.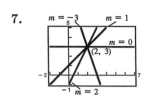

9. $m = \dfrac{6-(-2)}{1-(-3)} = \dfrac{8}{4} = 2$

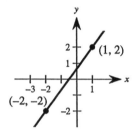

11. $m = \dfrac{4-(-1)}{-6-(-6)} = \dfrac{5}{0}$

The slope is undefined.

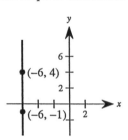

13. Slope $= \dfrac{2+2}{1+2} = \dfrac{4}{3}$

15. Since $m = 0$, the line is horizontal, and since the line passes through $(2, 1)$, all other points on the line will be of the form $(x, 1)$. Three additional points are $(0, 1)$, $(3, 1)$, and $(-1, 1)$.

17. Since $m = 1$, y increases by 1 for every one unit increase in x. Three points are $(6, -5)$, $(7, -4)$, and $(8, -3)$.

19. The slope of L_1 is
$$m_1 = \frac{9-(-1)}{5-0} = \frac{10}{5} = 2.$$
The slope of L_2 is
$$m_2 = \frac{1-3}{4-0} = -\frac{2}{4} = -\frac{1}{2}.$$
Since m_1 and m_2 are negative reciprocals of each other, the lines are perpendicular.

21. The slope of L_1 is
$$m_1 = \frac{6-0}{3-(-6)} = \frac{6}{9} = \frac{2}{3}.$$
The slope of L_2 is
$$m_2 = \frac{\frac{7}{3}-(-1)}{5-0} = \frac{\frac{10}{3}}{5} = \frac{2}{3}.$$
Since $m_1 = m_2$, the lines are parallel.

23. The slope between the first two points is
$$\frac{0-(-4)}{2-0} = 2$$ and the slope between the
second and third points is $\frac{2-0}{3-2} = 2.$
Hence, the three points are collinear.

25. Since the slope is $-12/100$ and you have
descended 2000 feet, $-12/100 = -2000/x$,
which gives $x = 16{,}666.67$ feet
horizontally.

27. $5x - y + 3 = 0$
$$-y = -5x - 3$$
$$y = 5x + 3$$
Slope: $m = 5$
y-intercept: $(0, 3)$

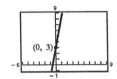

29. $5x - 2 = 0$
$$5x = 2$$
$$x = \tfrac{2}{5} \quad \text{Vertical line}$$
Slope: Undefined
y-intercept: None

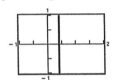

31. $m = \dfrac{5-(-1)}{-5-5} = \dfrac{6}{-10} = -\dfrac{3}{5}$
$$y + 1 = -\frac{3}{5}(x - 5)$$
$$5y + 5 = -3(x - 5)$$
$$5y + 5 = -3x + 15$$
$$3x + 5y - 10 = 0$$

33. $m = \dfrac{\frac{5}{4}-\frac{1}{2}}{\frac{1}{2}-2} = \dfrac{\frac{3}{4}}{-\frac{3}{2}} = -\dfrac{1}{2}$
$$y - \frac{1}{2} = -\frac{1}{2}(x - 2)$$
$$2y - 1 = -(x - 2)$$
$$2y - 1 = -x + 2$$
$$x + 2y - 3 = 0$$

35. $m = \dfrac{7-1}{-8-(-8)} = \dfrac{6}{0}$
Undefined
$$x = -8$$
$$x + 8 = 0$$

37. $y + 2 = 3(x - 0)$
$$y + 2 = 3x$$
$$3x - y - 2 = 0$$

39. $y - \frac{5}{2} = -\frac{4}{3}(x - 4)$
$$y - \frac{5}{2} = -\frac{4}{3}x + \frac{16}{3}$$
$$y = -\frac{4}{3}x + \frac{47}{6}$$
$$6y + 8x - 47 = 0$$

41. Since the slope is undefined, the line is
vertical, and since the line passes through
$(6, -1)$, its equation is $x = 6$ or $x - 6 = 0$.

43. $y = 0.5x - 3$

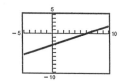

45.

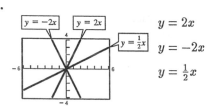

$y = 2x$

$y = -2x$

$y = \frac{1}{2}x$

47.

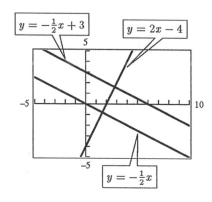

$y = -\frac{1}{2}x$

$y = -\frac{1}{2}x + 3$

$y = 2x - 4$

49. $\dfrac{x}{5} + \dfrac{y}{-3} = 1 \Rightarrow \dfrac{y}{-3} = \dfrac{-x}{5} + 1 \Rightarrow y = \dfrac{3}{5}x - 3$

51. $\dfrac{x}{2} + \dfrac{y}{3} = 1$

$3x + 2y = 6$

$3x + 2y - 6 = 0$

$a = 5$ is the x-intercept and $b = -3$ is the y-intercept.

53. $4x - 2y = 3$

$$-2y = -4x + 3$$

$$y = 2x - \frac{3}{2}$$

The slope of the given line is $m_1 = 2$.

(a) The slope of the parallel line is $m_2 = m_1 = 2$.

$$y - 1 = 2(x - 2)$$

$$y - 1 = 2x - 4$$

$$2x - y - 3 = 0$$

(b) The slope of the perpendicular line is $m_2 = -1/m_1 = -1/2$.

$$y - 1 = -\frac{1}{2}(x - 2)$$

$$2y - 2 = -(x - 2)$$

$$2y - 2 = -x + 2$$

$$x + 2y - 4 = 0$$

55. $y = -3$

The slope of the given line is $m_1 = 0$.

(a) The slope of the parallel line is $m_2 = m_1 = 0$.

$$y - 0 = 0(x + 1)$$

$$y = 0$$

(b) The slope of the perpendicular line is $m_2 = -1/m$, undefined.

$$x = -1$$

$$x + 1 = 0$$

57. Value = \$2540 + (\$125)(the number of years t after 1990)

$$V = 125t + 2540, \quad 0 \le t \le 5$$

59. Value = \$20,400 + (\$2000)(the number of years t after 1990)

$$V = 2000t + 20,400, \quad 0 \le t \le 5$$

61. A person is paying $10 per week to a friend to repay a $100 loan, $y = 100 - 10x$. Matches graph (b). The slope is $m = -10$. This represents the decrease in the amount of the loan each week.

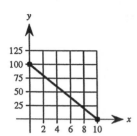

63. A sales representative receives $20 per day for food plus $0.25 for each mile traveled, $y = 20 + 0.25x$. Matches graph (a). The slope is 0.25 and the y-intercept is 20.

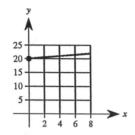

65. Using the points $(0, 32)$ and $(100, 212)$, we have

$$m = \frac{212 - 32}{100 - 0} = \frac{180}{100} = \frac{9}{5}$$

$$F - 32 = \frac{9}{5}(C - 0)$$

$$F = \frac{9}{5}C + 32.$$

67. Let $t = 0$ represent 1990.

$$(0, \ 28{,}500), \ (2, \ 32{,}900)$$

$$m = \frac{32{,}900 - 28{,}500}{2 - 0} = \frac{4400}{2} = 2200$$

$$S - 28{,}500 = 2200(t - 0)$$

$$S = 2200t + 28{,}500$$

When $t = 5$,

$$S = 2200(5) + 28{,}500 = \$39{,}500.$$

69. (a) Using the points $(0, \ 875)$ and $(5, \ 0)$ where the first coordinate represents the year x and the second coordinate represents the value y, we have:

$$m = \frac{0 - 875}{5 - 0} = -175$$

$$y - 875 = -175(x - 0)$$

$$y = -175x + 875, \quad 0 \leq x \leq 5$$

(c) When $x = 2$, $y = 525.00$ dollars.

(d) When $y = 200$, $x = 3.86$ years.

(b)

71. Monthly wage = Monthly salary + 7% of sales

$$W = 2500 + 0.07S$$

73. (a) $C = 5.25t + 11.50t + 36,500$

$C = 16.75t + 36,500$

(b) $R = 37t$

(c) The break-even point is $t = 1802$ hours, the t-value of the point where the two lines intersect.

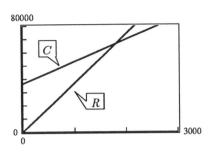

75. (Many answers possible) The cost of producing each toy is \$25, and the fixed costs are \$450. Find the cost function for producing x toys.

77. Since the triangles are similar, the result immediately follows.

$$\frac{y_2{}^* - y_1{}^*}{x_2{}^* - x_1{}^*} = \frac{y_2 - y_1}{x_2 - x_1}$$

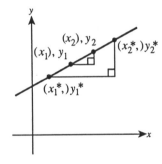

Section 1.3   Functions

- You should know the definition of a function, domain, and range.

- Given a set or an equation, you should be able to determine if it represents a function.

- You should understand function notation.

- Given a function, you should be able to do the following.
  (a) Find the domain.
  (b) Evaluate the function at specific values.

- You should be able to use the function keys on your calculator.

---

1. (a) Each element of A is matched with exactly one element of B, so it does represent a function.
   (b) The element 1 in A is matched with two elements, -2 and 1 of B, so it does not represent a function.
   (c) Each element of A is matched with exactly one element of B, so it does represent a function.
   (d) The element 2 in A is not matched with an element of B, so it does not represent a function.

3. y is not a function of x since some values of x give two values for y. For example, if $x = 0$, then $y = \pm 2$.

5. $x^2 + y = 4$

$$y = -x^2 + 4$$

y is a function of x. No value of x yields more than one value of y.

7. $x^2 y - x^2 + 4y = 0$

$$(x^2 - 4)y = x^2$$

$$y = \frac{x^2}{x^2 - 4}$$

y is a function of x. No value of x yields more than one value of y.

9. y is not a function of x since some values of x give two values for y. For example, if $x = 3$, then $y = \pm\sqrt{8}$.

11. (a) $f(3) = 6 - 4(3) = -6$
(b) $f(-7) = 6 - 4(-7) = 34$
(c) $f(t) = 6 - 4(t) = 6 - 4t$
(d) $f(c + 1) = 6 - 4(c + 1)$
$\qquad = 2 - 4c$
$\qquad = 2(1 - 2c)$

13. (a) $f(4) = \dfrac{1}{(4) + 1} = \dfrac{1}{5}$
(b) $f(0) = \dfrac{1}{(0) + 1} = 1$
(c) $f(4x) = \dfrac{1}{(4x) + 1} = \dfrac{1}{4x + 1}$
(d) $f(x + h) = \dfrac{1}{(x + h) + 1} = \dfrac{1}{x + h + 1}$

15. (a) $f(1) = 2(1) - 3 = -1$
(b) $f(-3) = 2(-3) - 3 = -9$
(c) $f(x - 1) = 2(x - 1) - 3 = 2x - 5$
(d) $f\left(\frac{1}{4}\right) = 2\left(\frac{1}{4}\right) - 3 = -\frac{5}{2}$

17. (a) $h(2) = 2^2 - 2(2) = 0$
(b) $h(-1) = (-1)^2 - 2(-1) = 3$
(c) $h(x + 2) = (x + 2)^2 - 2(x + 2) = x^2 + 2x$
(d) $h(1.5) = (1.5)^2 - 2(1.5) = -0.75$

19. (a) $f(2) = \dfrac{|2|}{2} = 1$
(b) $f(-2) = \dfrac{|-2|}{-2} = -1$
(c) $f(x^2) = \dfrac{|x^2|}{x^2} = 1$
(d) $f(x - 1) = \dfrac{|x - 1|}{x - 1}$

21. (a) $f(-1) = 2(-1) + 1$
$\qquad = -1$
(b) $f(0) = 2(0) + 2 = 2$
(c) $f(1) = 2(1) + 2 = 4$
(d) $f(2) = 2(2) + 2 = 6$

23. All real numbers x

25. $y - 10 \geq 0$
$\qquad y \geq 10$
Therefore, the domain is
$y \geq 10$.

27. All real numbers except
$t = 0$

29. $x \neq 0, x + 2 \neq 0 \Rightarrow x \neq -2$
Therefore, the domain is
all real numbers except
$x = 0, -2$.

31. $\{(-2, f(-2)), (-1, f(-1)), (0, f(0)), (1, f(1)), 2, f(2))\}$
$\{(-2, 4), (-1, 1), (0, 0), (1, 1), (2, 4)\}$

33. $\{(-2, f(-2)), (-1, f(-1)), (0, f(0)), (1, f(1)), (2, f(2))\}$
$\{(-2, 0), (-1, 1), (0, \sqrt{2}), (1, \sqrt{3}), (2, 2)\}$

35. (a) $(32.5)^2 = 1056.250$
(b) $(4.3)^5 = 1470.084$

37. (a) $\dfrac{1}{8.5} = 0.118$
(b) $\dfrac{1}{0.047} = 21.277$

39. The data fits the
quadratic model $y = cx^2$
with $c = -2$.

41. Since y is undefined for $x = 0$, the data fits the model $y = c/x$ with $c = 32$.

43.
$$f(x) = 2x$$
$$f(x + h) = 2(x + h) = 2x + 2h$$
$$f(x + h) - f(x) = 2h$$
$$\frac{f(x + h) - f(x)}{h} = 2, \quad h \neq 0$$

45.
$$f(x) = x^3$$
$$f(x + h) = (x + h)^3 = x^3 + 3x(h)^2 + 3x^2h + (h)^3$$
$$f(x + h) - f(x) = 3x(h)^2 + 3x^2h + (h)^3$$
$$\frac{f(x + h) - f(x)}{h} = 3xh + 3x^2 + (h)^2, \quad h \neq 0$$

47. $A = \pi r^2, \quad C = 2\pi r$

$$r = \frac{C}{2\pi}$$

$$A = \pi \left(\frac{C}{2\pi}\right)^2 = \frac{C^2}{4\pi}$$

49. $A = \frac{1}{2}bh = \frac{1}{2}xy$

Since $(0, y)$, $(1, 2)$ and $(x, 0)$ all lie on the same line, the slopes between any pair are equal.

$$\frac{2 - y}{1 - 0} = \frac{0 - 2}{x - 1}$$

$$2 - y = -\frac{2}{x - 1}$$

$$y = \frac{2}{x - 1} + 2 = \frac{2x}{x - 1}$$

Therefore, $A = \frac{1}{2}x\left(\frac{2x}{x - 1}\right) = \frac{x^2}{x - 1}$.

Since $\frac{x^2}{x - 1} > 0$, $x > 1$.

Therefore, the domain is $x > 1$.

51. $y + 4x = 108$

$$y = 108 - 4x$$

$$V = x(x)y = x^2(108 - 4x)$$

$$= 108x^2 - 4x^3$$

$$= 4x^2(27 - x)$$

$x > 0$ and $108 - 4x > 0$

$$-4x > -108$$

$$x < 27$$

Therefore, the domain is $0 < x < 27$.

55. (a) Cost = Variable costs + Fixed costs

$$C = 12.30x + 98,000$$

(b) Revenue = Price per unit $\times$ Number of units

$$R = 17.98x$$

(c) Profit = Revenue $-$ Cost

$$P = 17.98x - (12.30x + 98,000)$$

$$P = 5.68x - 98,000$$

53. By the Pythagorean Theorem we have:

$$h^2 + 2000^2 = d^2$$

$$h^2 = d^2 - 2000^2$$

$$h = \sqrt{d^2 - 2000^2}$$

Since $d^2 - 2000^2 \geq 0$ and $d \geq 0$, we have a domain of $d \geq 2000$ feet.

Section 1.4   Graphs of Functions

- ■ You should be able to determine the domain and range of a function from its graph.
- ■ You should be able to use the vertical line test for functions.
- ■ You should be able to graph functions using your graphing utility.
- ■ You should know that the graph of $f(x) = c$ is a horizontal line through $(0, c)$.
- ■ You should be able to determine when a function is constant, increasing, or decreasing.
- ■ You should be able to approximate relative minimum and maximum values of a function using your graphing utility.
- ■ You should know the definition and graph of the greatest integer function.
- ■ You should know that f is
  - (a) Odd if $f(-x) = -f(x)$.
  - (b) Even if $f(-x) = f(x)$.

1. From the graph we see that the x-values are greater than or equal to 1. Therefore, the domain is $[1, \infty)$. Similarly, the y-values are greater than or equal to 0. Therefore, the range is $[0, \infty)$.

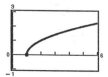

3. From the graph we see that the x-values are less than or equal to -2 and greater than or equal to 2. Therefore, the domain is $(-\infty, -2]$, $[2, \infty)$. Similarly, the y-values are greater than or equal to 0. Therefore, the range is $[0, \infty)$.

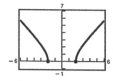

5. From the graph we see that the x-values are between -5 and 5 including -5 and 5. Therefore, the domain is $[-5, 5]$. Similarly, the y-values are between 0 and 5 including 0 and 5. Therefore, the range is $[0, 5]$.

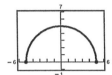

7. Since no vertical line would ever cross the graph more than one time, y *is* a function of x. You could use the following viewing window to produce the given graph.

```
RANGE
Xmin=-3
Xmax=3
Xscl=1
Ymin=-1
Ymax=4
Yscl=1
```

9. Some vertical lines cross the graph more than once. For example, the vertical line $x = 4$ crosses the graph at $(4, \ 2)$ and $(4, \ -2)$. Therefore, y is not a function of x. You could use the following viewing window and the equations $y_1 = \sqrt{x}$ and $y_2 = -\sqrt{x}$ to produce the given graph.

```
RANGE
Xmin=-1
Xmax=5
Xscl=1
Ymin=-3
Ymax=3
Yscl=1
```

11. Since no vertical line would ever cross the graph more than one time, y *is* a function of x. You could use the following viewing window and the equation

$$y = \frac{x^2 + 1}{x}$$

to produce the given graph.

```
RANGE
Xmin=-5
Xmax=5
Xscl=1
Ymin=-4
Ymax=4
Yscl=1
```

13. $f(x) = -0.2x^2 + 3x + 32$
    (b) shows the most complete graph.

15. $f(x) = 4x^3 - x^4$
    (a) shows the most complete graph.

17. By its graph we see that f is increasing on $(-\infty, \infty)$.

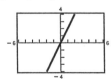

19. By its graph we see that f is increasing on $(-\infty, 0)$ and $(2, \infty)$ and is decreasing on $(0, 2)$.

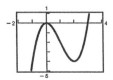

21. By its graph we see that f is increasing on $(-1, 0)$ and $(1, \infty)$ and is decreasing on $(-\infty, -1)$ and $(0, 1)$.

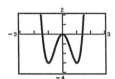

23. By its graph we see that f is increasing on $(-2, \infty)$ and decreasing on $(-3, -2)$.

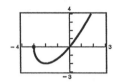

25. Using the zoom and trace features, we find that $(3.00, -9.00)$ is a relative minimum of $f(x) = x^2 - 6x$.

27. Using the zoom and trace features, we find that $(-2.00, 20.00)$ is a relative maximum, and $(1.00, -7.00)$ is a relative minimum.

29. Using the zoom and trace features, we find that $(0.33, -0.38)$ is a relative minimum.

31. (a) Since the perimeter is 100 feet and x is the length of one side of the rectangle, the width is $50 - x$. The area is the length times the width, $A = x(50 - x)$.

(b)
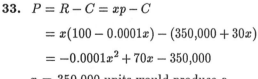

(c) Using the zoom and trace features, the maximum of the area function is 625.00. This occurs when $x = 25.00$, and hence, the dimensions of the rectangle which yields the maximum area are 25×25 (a square!).

33. $P = R - C = xp - C$

$$= x(100 - 0.0001x) - (350{,}000 + 30x)$$

$$= -0.0001x^2 + 70x - 350{,}000$$

$x = 350{,}000$ units would produce a maximum profit.

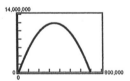

35. $f(x) = \begin{cases} 2x + 3, & x < 0 \\ 3 - x, & x \geq 0 \end{cases}$

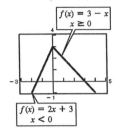

37. $f(x) = \begin{cases} x^2 + 5, & x \leq 1 \\ -x^2 + 4x + 3, & x > 1 \end{cases}$

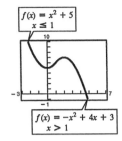

39. $s(x) = 2[\![x - 1]\!]$

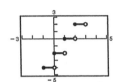

(*Hint:* use dot mode, not connected.)
Domain: all x
Range: $\{\ldots, -4, -2, 0, 2, 4, \ldots\}$

41. (a) $C = 0.65 + 0.42[\![t]\!]$

(b)

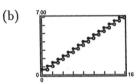

(c) Less than 13 minutes

43. (a) $(-5, 6)$
(b) $(-5, -6)$

45. (a) $\left(\frac{3}{2}, -2\right)$
(b) $\left(\frac{3}{2}, 2\right)$

47. $f(x) = 3$

$f(-x) = 3 = f(x)$

f is even. The graph is symmetric with respect to the y-axis.

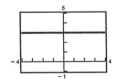

49. $f(x) = 5 - 3x$

$f(-x) = 5 - 3(-x)$

$= 5 + 3x$

$\neq f(x) \neq -f(x)$

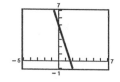

f is neither odd nor even. The graph is not symmetric with respect to the origin nor the y-axis.

51. $g(s) = \dfrac{s^3}{4}$

$g(-s) = \dfrac{(-s)^3}{4}$

$= -\dfrac{s^3}{4} = -g(s)$

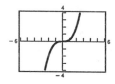

g is odd. The graph is symmetric with respect to the origin.

53. $f(x) = \sqrt{1 - x}$

$f(-x) = \sqrt{1 - (-x)}$

$= \sqrt{1 + x}$

$\neq f(x) \neq -f(x)$

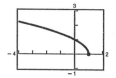

f is neither odd nor even. The graph is not symmetric with respect to the origin nor the y-axis.

55. $g(x) = \dfrac{5x}{x^2 + 1}$

$g(-x) = \dfrac{5(-x)}{(-x)^2 + 1}$

$= \dfrac{-5x}{x^2 + 1}$

$= -g(x)$

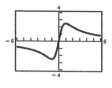

g is odd. The graph is symmetric with respect to the origin.

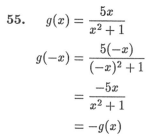

57. $f(x) = \dfrac{x^6}{3} - 2x^2$

$f(-x) = \dfrac{(-x)^6}{3} - 2(-x)^2$

$ = \dfrac{x^6}{3} - 2x^2$

$ = f(x)$

f is even.

59. $g(x) = x^3 - 5x$

$g(-x) = (-x)^3 - 5(-x)$

$ = -x^3 + 5x$

$ = -(x^3 - 5x)$

$ = -g(x)$

g is odd.

61.

$f(t) = t^2 + 2t - 3$

$f(-t) = (-t)^2 + 2(-t) - 3$

$ = t^2 - 2t - 3$

$ \neq f(t) \neq -f(t)$

f is neither even nor odd.

63. $f(x) \geq 0$

$4 - x \geq 0$

$x \leq 4$

$f(x) \geq 0$ on the interval $(-\infty, 4]$.

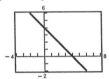

65. $f(x) \geq 0$

$1 - x^4 \geq 0$

$x^4 \leq 1$

$|x| \leq 1$

$-1 \leq x \leq 1$

$f(x) \geq 0$ on the interval $[-1, 1]$.

67. $f(x) \geq 0$

$5 \geq 0$

$f(x) > 0$ for all x.

69. $h = $ top $-$ bottom

$h = (4x - x^2) - 3$

71. $h = $ top $-$ bottom

$h = (4x - x^2) - x^2$

$h = 4x - 2x^2$

73. $L = $ right $-$ left

$L = (4 - y^2) - (y + 2)$

$L = -y^2 - y + 2$

75.

Interval	Intake Pipe	Drain Pipe 1	Drain Pipe 2
[0, 5]	Open	Closed	Closed
[5, 10]	Open	Open	Closed
[10, 20]	Closed	Closed	Closed
[20, 30]	Closed	Closed	Open
[30, 40]	Open	Open	Open
[40, 45]	Open	Closed	Open
[45, 50]	Open	Open	Open
[50, 60]	Open	Open	Closed

77. $f(x) = a_{2n}x^{2n} + a_{2n-2}x^{2n-2} + \cdots + a_2 x^2 + a_0$

$f(-x) = a_{2n}(-x)^{2n} + a_{2n-2}(-x)^{2n-2} + \cdots + a_2(-x)^2 + a_0$

$\qquad = a_{2n}x^{2n} + a_{2n-2}x^{2n-2} + \cdots + a_2 x^2 + a_0 = f(x)$

Section 1.5   Shifting, Reflecting, and Stretching Graphs

■ You should know the graphs of the most commonly used functions in algebra, and be able to reproduce them on your graphing utility.

(a) Constant function: $f(x) = c$

(b) Identity function: $f(x) = x$

(c) Absolute value function: $f(x) = |x|$

(d) Square root function: $f(x) = \sqrt{x}$

(e) Squaring function: $f(x) = x^2$

(f) Cubing function: $f(x) = x^3$

■ You should know how the graph of a function is changed by vertical and horizontal shifts.

■ You should know how the graph of a function is changed by a reflection.

■ You should know how the graph of a function is changed by nonrigid transformations, like stretches and shrinks.

■ You should know how the graph of a function is changed by a sequence of transformations.

1.

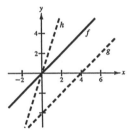

3.

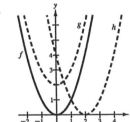

5.

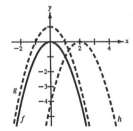

7.

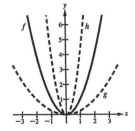

9. Since the vertex of g is at $(1,\ 1)$, $g(x) = (x-1)^2 + 1$. Since the vertex of h is at $(2,\ 4)$ and h opens downward, $h(x) = -(x-2)^2 + 4$.

11. Since the vertex of g is at $(3,\ -2)$, $g(x) = (x-3)^2 - 2$. Since the vertex of h is at $(0,\ 3)$ and h opens downward, $h(x) = -x^2 + 3$.

13. $f(x) = x^3 - 3x^2$

$g(x) = f(x+2) = (x+2)^3 - 3(x+2)^2$ horizontal shift 2 units to the left

$h(x) = f\left(\tfrac{1}{2}x\right) = \left(\tfrac{1}{2}x\right)^3 - 3\left(\tfrac{1}{2}x\right)^2$ stretched horizontally by factor of 2

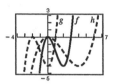

15. $f(x) = x^3 - 3x^2$

$g(x) = -\tfrac{1}{3}f(x) = -\tfrac{1}{3}(x^3 - 3x^2)$ reflection in the x-axis and vertical shrink

$h(x) = f(-x) = (-x)^3 - 3(-x)^2$ reflection in the y-axis

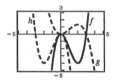

17. The graph of g is obtained from that of f by first negating f, and then shifting vertically one unit upward: $g(x) = -x^3 + 3x^2 + 1$.

19. $y = \sqrt{x} + 2$ is $f(x)$ shifted up two units.

21. $y = \sqrt{x-2}$ is $f(x)$ shifted right two units.

23. $y = \sqrt{2x}$ is a vertical stretch of $f(x)$ by $\sqrt{2}$.

25. $y = \sqrt[3]{x} - 1$ is $f(x)$ shifted down one unit.

27. $y = \sqrt[3]{x-1}$ is $f(x)$ shifted right one unit.

29. $y = \sqrt[3]{-x} = -\sqrt[3]{x}$ is $f(x)$ reflected in the y-axis.

31. $f(x-4)$

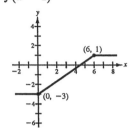

33. $f(x)+4$

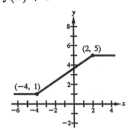

35. $2f(x)$

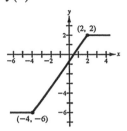

37. $g(x) = 4 - x^3$ is obtained from $f(x)$ by a reflection in the x-axis followed by a vertical shift upward of four units.

39. $h(x) = \frac{1}{4}(x+2)^3$ is obtained from $f(x)$ by a left shift of two units and a vertical shrink by a factor of $\frac{1}{4}$.

41. $p(x) = \left(\frac{1}{3}x\right)^3 + 2$ is obtained from $f(x)$ by a horizontal stretch, followed by a vertical shift of two units upward.

43. (a) $P(x) = 80 + 20x - 0.5x^2, \quad 0 \le x \le 20$

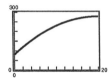

(b) $P(x)$ is shifted downward by a vertical shift of -2500.

$$P(x) = -2420 + 20x - 0.5x^2$$
$$0 \le x \le 20$$

(c) $P(x)$ is changed by a *horizontal stretch*.

$$P(x) = 80 + 20\left(\frac{x}{100}\right) - 0.5\left(\frac{x}{100}\right)^2$$
$$= 80 + 0.2x - 0.00005x^2$$

45. These three even functions are nonnegative. As the exponent increases, the graphs become flatter in the interval $(-1,\ 1)$ while they grow more rapidly as x tends to infinity.

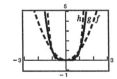

47.

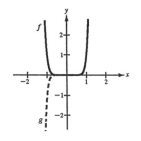

49. $f(x) = x^2(x - 6)^2$

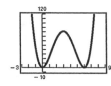

51. $f(x) = x^2(x - 6)^3$

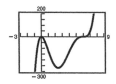

Section 1.6   Combinations of Functions

■ Given two functions, f and g, you should be able to form the following functions, (if defined).

1. Sum: $(f+g)(x) = f(x) + g(x)$
2. Difference: $(f-g)(x) = f(x) - g(x)$
3. Product: $(fg)(x) = f(x)g(x)$
4. Quotient: $(f/g)(x) = f(x)/g(x)$, $g(x) \neq 0$
5. Composition of f with g: $(f \circ g)(x) = f(g(x))$
6. Composition of g with f: $(g \circ f)(x) = g(f(x))$

---

1. (a) $(f+g)(x) = f(x) + g(x)$

$$= (x+1) + (x-1) = 2x$$

(b) $(f-g)(x) = f(x) - g(x)$

$$= (x+1) - (x-1) = 2$$

(c) $(fg)(x) = f(x) \cdot g(x)$

$$= (x+1)(x-1) = x^2 - 1$$

(d) $\left(\dfrac{f}{g}\right)(x) = \dfrac{f(x)}{g(x)} = \dfrac{x+1}{x-1}, \quad x \neq 1$

The domain of f/g is $(-\infty, 1)$, $(1, \infty)$.

3. (a) $(f+g)(x) = f(x) + g(x)$

$$= (x^2 + 5) + \sqrt{1-x}$$

(b) $(f-g)(x) = f(x) - g(x)$

$$= (x^2 + 5) - \sqrt{1-x}$$

(c) $(fg)(x) = f(x) \cdot g(x)$

$$= (x^2 + 5)\sqrt{1-x}$$

(d) $\left(\dfrac{f}{g}\right)(x) = \dfrac{f(x)}{g(x)} = \dfrac{x^2 + 5}{\sqrt{1-x}}, \quad x < 1$

The domain of f/g is $(-\infty, 1)$.

5. (a) $(f+g)(x) = f(x) + g(x) = \dfrac{1}{x} + \dfrac{1}{x^2} = \dfrac{x+1}{x^2}$

(b) $(f-g)(x) = f(x) - g(x) = \dfrac{1}{x} - \dfrac{1}{x^2} = \dfrac{x-1}{x^2}$

(c) $(fg)(x) = f(x) \cdot g(x) = \dfrac{1}{x}\left(\dfrac{1}{x^2}\right) = \dfrac{1}{x^3}$

(d) $\left(\dfrac{f}{g}\right)(x) = \dfrac{f(x)}{g(x)} = \dfrac{1/x}{1/x^2} = \dfrac{x^2}{x} = x, \quad x \neq 0$

The domain of f/g is $(-\infty, 0)$, $(0, \infty)$.

7. $(f+g)(3)$
$$= f(3) + g(3)$$
$$= [(3)^2 + 1] + (3 - 4)$$
$$= 10 - 1$$
$$= 9$$

9. $(f-g)(2t)$
$$= f(2t) - g(2t)$$
$$= [(2t)^2 + 1] - [(2t) - 4]$$
$$= 4t^2 + 1 - 2t + 4$$
$$= 4t^2 - 2t + 5$$

11. $(fg)(4) = f(4)g(4)$
$$= [4^2 + 1][4 - 4]$$
$$= 0$$

13. $\left(\dfrac{f}{g}\right)(5) = \dfrac{f(5)}{g(5)}$
$$= \dfrac{5^2 + 1}{5 - 4}$$
$$= 26$$

15. $\left(\dfrac{f}{g}\right)(-1) - g(3) = \dfrac{f(-1)}{g(-1)} - g(3)$
$$= \dfrac{(-1)^2 + 1}{-1 - 4} - (3 - 4)$$
$$= -\dfrac{2}{5} + 1 = \dfrac{3}{5}$$

17.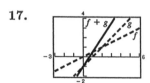

19.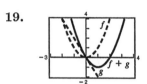

21. When $0 \le x \le 2$, f contributes the most. When $x > 5$, g contributes the most.

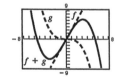

23. $R(x) = \frac{3}{4}x$, $B(x) = \frac{1}{15}x^2$,
$$T = R(x) + B(x) = \frac{3}{4}x + \frac{1}{15}x^2$$

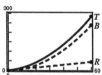

25. (a) $(f \circ g)(x) = f(g(x)) = f(x - 1) = (x - 1)^2 = x^2 - 2x + 1$
(b) $(g \circ f)(x) = g(f(x)) = g(x^2) = x^2 - 1$
(c) $(f \circ f)(x) = f(f(x)) = f(x^2) = (x^2)^2 = x^4$

27. (a) $(f \circ g)(x) = f(g(x)) = f(5 - x) = 3(5 - x) + 5 = 20 - 3x$
(b) $(g \circ f)(x) = g(f(x)) = g(3x + 5) = 5 - (3x + 5) = -3x$
(c) $(f \circ f)(x) = f(f(x)) = f(3x + 5) = 3(3x + 5) + 5 = 9x + 20$

29. (a) $f \circ g = f\left(g(x)\right) = f(x^2) = \sqrt{x^2 + 4}$

(b) $g \circ f = g\left(f(x)\right) = g(\sqrt{x + 4}) = (\sqrt{x + 4})^2 = x + 4$

31. (a) $f \circ g = f(g(x)) = f(3x + 1) = \frac{1}{3}(3x + 1) - 3 = x + \frac{1}{3} - 3 = x - \frac{8}{3}$

(b) $g \circ f = g(f(x)) = g\left(\frac{1}{3}x - 3\right) = 3\left(\frac{1}{3}x - 3\right) + 1 = x - 9 + 1 = x - 8$

33. (a) $f \circ g = f\left(g(x)\right) = f(x + 6) = |x + 6|$

(b) $g \circ f = g\left(f(x)\right) = g(|x|) = |x| + 6$

35. (a) $(f + g)(3) = f(3) + g(3) = 2 + 1 = 3$

(b) $\left(\dfrac{f}{g}\right)(2) = \dfrac{f(2)}{g(2)} = \dfrac{0}{2} = 0$

37. (a) $(f \circ g)(2) = f(g(2)) = f(2) = 0$

(b) $(g \circ f)(2) = g(f(2)) = g(0) = 4$

39. Let $f(x) = x^2$ and $g(x) = 2x + 1$, then

$$(f \circ g)(x) = f(2x + 1)$$
$$= (2x + 1)^2 = h(x).$$

41. Let $f(x) = \sqrt[3]{x}$ and $g(x) = x^2 - 4$, then

$$(f \circ g)(x) = f(x^2 - 4)$$
$$= \sqrt[3]{x^2 - 4} = h(x).$$

43. Let $f(x) = 1/x$ and $g(x) = x + 2$, then

$$(f \circ g)(x) = f(x + 2)$$
$$= \frac{1}{x + 2} = h(x).$$

45. Let $f(x) = x^2 + 2x$ and $g(x) = x + 4$, then

$$(f \circ g)(x) = f(x + 4) = (x + 4)^2 + 2(x + 4) = h(x).$$

47. (a) The domain of $f(x) = \sqrt{x}$ is $x \geq 0$.

(b) The domain of $g(x) = x^2 + 1$ is all real numbers.

(c) $f \circ g = f(g(x)) = f(x^2 + 1) = \sqrt{x^2 + 1}$; The domain of $f \circ g = \sqrt{x^2 + 1}$ is all real numbers.

49. (a) The domain of $f(x) = 3/(x^2 - 1)$ is all real numbers except $x = \pm 1$.

(b) The domain of $g(x) = x + 1$ is all real numbers.

(c) $f \circ g = f\left(g(x)\right) = f(x + 1) = \dfrac{3}{(x + 1)^2 - 1} = \dfrac{3}{x^2 + 2x} = \dfrac{3}{x(x + 2)}$

The domain of $f \circ g$ is all real numbers except $x = 0$ and $x = -2$.

51. (a) $(A \circ r)(t)$ gives the area of the circle as a function of time.

$$(A \circ r)(t) = A(r(t))$$
$$= A(0.6t)$$
$$= \pi(0.6t)^2 = 0.36\pi t^2$$

(b) $A = 20$ square feet when $t = 4.21$.

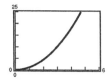

53. (a) $(C \circ x)(t) = C(x(t))$
$$= C(50t)$$
$$= 60(50t) + 750$$
$$= 3000t + 750$$

$C \circ x$ represents the cost after t production hours.

(b) When $C = 15,000$, $t = 4.75$ hours.

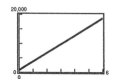

55. The rebate discount is given by $R(x) = x - 1200$. The 15% discount is given by $D(x) = x - 0.15x = 0.85x$. Taking the rebate first, we have $(D \circ R)(x) = D(x - 1200) = 0.85(x - 1200)$. For $x = 18,400$, $(D \circ R)(18,400) = 0.85(18,400 - 1200) = \$14,620$. Taking the 15% discount first, we have $(R \circ D)(x) = R(0.85x) = 0.85x - 1200$. For $x = 18,400$, $(R \circ D)(18,400) = 0.85(18,400) - 1200 = \$14,440$. The sale price obtained by taking the 15% discount first is lower.

57. As an example, note that the product of the odd function $f(x) = x^3$ and the even function $g(x) = x^2$ is $h(x) = x^3 \cdot x^2 = x^5$, which is odd. In general, let $f(x)$ be an odd function, $g(x)$ be an even function, and define $h(x) = f(x)g(x)$. Then

$$h(-x) = f(-x)g(-x) = [-f(x)]g(x) = -f(x)g(x) = -h(x).$$

Thus, h is odd.

59. Given any function $f(x)$, write

$$f(x) = \tfrac{1}{2}[f(x) + f(-x)] + \tfrac{1}{2}[f(x) - f(-x)]$$

which is the sum of an even function, $\tfrac{1}{2}[f(x) + f(-x)]$, and an odd function, $\tfrac{1}{2}[f(x) - f(-x)]$.

Section 1.7   Inverse Functions

- You should know the definition of the inverse of a function.
- Two functions f and g are inverses of each other if $f(g(x)) = x$ for every x in the domain of g and $g(f(x)) = x$ for every x in the domain of f.
- A function f has an inverse if and only if f is one-to-one.
- You should be able to find the inverse of a function, if it exists.
- You should be able to use your graphing utility to graphically verify if two functions are inverses of each other.

---

1. To "undo" 8 times x, let f^{-1} divide x by 8.

$$f^{-1}(x) = \frac{x}{8}$$

Now, we have

$$f(f^{-1}(x)) = f\left(\frac{x}{8}\right) = 8\left(\frac{x}{8}\right) = x$$

and

$$f^{-1}(f(x)) = f^{-1}(8x) = \frac{8x}{8} = x.$$

3. To "undo" x plus 10, let f^{-1} equal x minus 10.

$$f^{-1}(x) = x - 10$$

Now, we have

$$f(f^{-1}(x)) = f(x - 10)$$
$$= x - 10 + 10 = x$$

and

$$f^{-1}(f(x)) = f^{-1}(x + 10)$$
$$= x + 10 - 10 = x.$$

5. To "undo" the cubed root of x, let f^{-1} equal x cubed.

$$f^{-1}(x) = x^3$$

Now, we have

$$f(f^{-1}(x)) = f(x^3) = \sqrt[3]{x^3} = x$$

and

$$f^{-1}(f(x)) = f^{-1}\left(\sqrt[3]{x}\right) = \left(\sqrt[3]{x}\right)^3 = x.$$

7. (a) $f(g(x)) = f\left(\frac{x}{2}\right) = 2\left(\frac{x}{2}\right) = x$

$$g(f(x)) = g(2x) = \frac{(2x)}{2} = x$$

(b)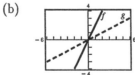

The graphs of f and g are reflections in the line $y = x$.

9. (a) $f(g(x)) = f\left(\dfrac{x-1}{5}\right)$

$= 5\left(\dfrac{x-1}{5}\right) + 1 = x$

$g(f(x)) = g(5x+1)$

$= \dfrac{(5x+1)-1}{5} = x$

(b)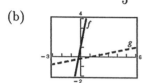

The graphs of f and g are reflections in the line $y = x$.

11. (a) $f(g(x)) = f(\sqrt[3]{x}) = (\sqrt[3]{x})^3 = x$

$g(f(x)) = g(x^3) = \sqrt[3]{x^3} = x$

(b)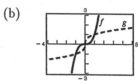

The graphs of f and g are reflections in the line $y = x$.

13. (a) $f(g(x)) = f(x^2+4)$, $x \geq 0$

$= \sqrt{(x^2+4)-4} = x$

$g(f(x)) = g(\sqrt{x-4})$

$= (\sqrt{x-4})^2 + 4 = x$

(b)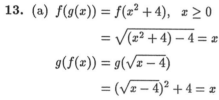

The graphs of f and g are reflections in the line $y = x$.

15. (a) $f(g(x)) = f(\sqrt{9-x})$, $x \leq 9$

$= 9 - (\sqrt{9-x})^2 = x$

$g(f(x)) = g(9-x^2)$, $x \geq 0$

$= \sqrt{9-(9-x^2)} = x$

(b)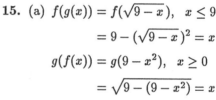

The graphs of f and g are reflections in the line $y = x$.

17. $g(x) = \dfrac{4 - x}{6}$

By the horizontal line test, g is one-to-one.

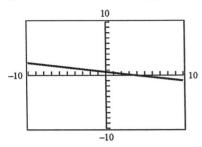

19. $h(x) = |x + 4| - |x - 4|$

By the horizontal line test, h is not one-to-one.

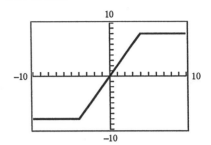

21. $f(x) = -2x\sqrt{16 - x^2}$

By the horizontal line test, f is not one-to-one.

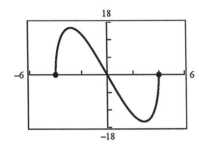

23. $f(x) = 2x - 3$

$$y = 2x - 3$$

$$x = 2y - 3$$

$$2y = x + 3$$

$$y = \frac{x + 3}{2}$$

$$f^{-1}(x) = \frac{x + 3}{2}$$

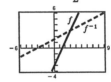

25. $f(x) = x^5$

$y = x^5$

$x = y^5$

$y = \sqrt[5]{x}$

$f^{-1}(x) = \sqrt[5]{x}$

27. $f(x) = \sqrt{x}$

$y = \sqrt{x}$

$x = \sqrt{y}$

$y = x^2$

$f^{-1}(x) = x^2, \ x \geq 0$

29. $f(x) = \sqrt{4 - x^2}, \ 0 \leq x \leq 2$

$y = \sqrt{4 - x^2}$

$x = \sqrt{4 - y^2}$

$4 - y^2 = x^2$

$y^2 = 4 - x^2$

$y = \sqrt{4 - x^2}$

$f^{-1}(x) = \sqrt{4 - x^2}, \ 0 \leq x \leq 2$

31. $f(x) = \sqrt[3]{x - 1}$

$y = \sqrt[3]{x - 1}$

$x = \sqrt[3]{y - 1}$

$y - 1 = x^3$

$y = x^3 + 1$

$f^{-1}(x) = x^3 + 1$

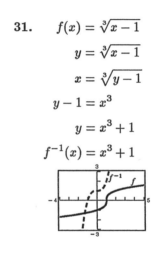

33. Since $f(1) = 1$ and $f(-1) = 1$, f is not one-to-one and does not have an inverse. Or, notice that the graph of f fails the horizontal line test.

35. $g(a) = g(b)$

$$\frac{a}{8} = \frac{b}{8}$$

$$a = b$$

Therefore, g is one-to-one.

$$g(x) = \frac{x}{8}$$

$$y = \frac{x}{8}$$

$$x = \frac{y}{8}$$

$$8x = y$$

$$g^{-1}(x) = 8x$$

39. $h(a) = h(b)$

$$\frac{1}{a} = \frac{1}{b}$$

$$a = b$$

Therefore, h is one-to-one.

$$h(x) = \frac{1}{x}$$

$$y = \frac{1}{x}$$

$$x = \frac{1}{y}$$

$$xy = 1$$

$$y = \frac{1}{x}$$

$$f^{-1}(x) = \frac{1}{x}$$

37. $f(a) = f(b)$

$$(a+3)^2 = (b+3)^2$$

$$a + 3 = b + 3, \quad \text{since } a, \ b \geq -3$$

$$a = b$$

Therefore, f is one-to-one.

$$f(x) = (x+3)^2, \quad x \geq -3$$

$$y = (x+3)^2$$

$$x = (y+3)^2$$

$$y + 3 = \sqrt{x}$$

$$y = \sqrt{x} - 3$$

$$f^{-1}(x) = \sqrt{x} - 3, \quad x \geq 0$$

41. $f(a) = f(b)$

$$\sqrt{2a+3} = \sqrt{2b+3}$$

$$2a + 3 = 2b + 3$$

$$2a = 2b$$

$$a = b$$

Therefore, f is one-to-one.

$$f(x) = \sqrt{2x+3}$$

$$y = \sqrt{2x+3}$$

$$x = \sqrt{2y+3}$$

$$2y + 3 = x^2$$

$$2y = x^2 - 3$$

$$y = \frac{x^2 - 3}{2}$$

$$f^{-1}(x) = \frac{x^2 - 3}{2}, \quad x \geq 0$$

43. Since $g(0) = 0$ and $g(1) = 0$, g is not one-to-one and does not have an inverse. Or, notice that the graph of g fails the horizontal line test.

45. $f(a) = f(b)$

$25 - a^2 = 25 - b^2$

$a^2 = b^2$

$a = b,$ since $a, b \leq 0$

Therefore, f is one-to-one.

$f(x) = 25 - x^2, \quad x \leq 0$

$y = 25 - x^2$

$x = 25 - y^2$

$y^2 = 25 - x$

$y = -\sqrt{25 - x}$

$f^{-1}(x) = -\sqrt{25 - x}$

47. Delete the part corresponding to $x < 3$.

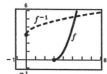

$f(x) = (x - 3)^2, \quad x \geq 3$

$y = (x - 3)^2$

$x = (y - 3)^2$

$y - 3 = \sqrt{x}$

$y = \sqrt{x} + 3$

$f^{-1}(x) = \sqrt{x} + 3, \quad x \geq 0$

49. Delete the part corresponding to $x < -3$.

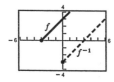

$f(x) = |x + 3|, \quad x \geq -3$

$f(x) = x + 3$

$y = x + 3$

$x = y + 3$

$y = x - 3$

$f^{-1}(x) = x - 3, \quad x \geq 0$

51.

x	0	1	2	3	4
$f^{-1}(x)$	-2	0	1	2	4

In Exercises 53 and 55, $f(x) = \frac{1}{8}x - 3$, $f^{-1}(x) = 8(x + 3)$, $g(x) = x^3$, $g^{-1}(x) = \sqrt[3]{x}$.

53. $(f^{-1} \circ g^{-1})(1) = f^{-1}(g^{-1}(1))$

$= f^{-1}(\sqrt[3]{1})$

$= 8(1 + 3)$

$= 32$

55. $(f^{-1} \circ f^{-1})(6) = f^{-1}(f^{-1}(6))$

$= f^{-1}(8[6 + 3])$

$= 8[8(6 + 3) + 3]$

$= 600$

In Exercises 57 and 59, $f(x) = x + 4$, $f^{-1}(x) = x - 4$, $g(x) = 2x - 5$, $g^{-1}(x) = \frac{1}{2}(x + 5)$.

57. $(g^{-1} \circ f^{-1})(x) = g^{-1}(x - 4) = \frac{1}{2}(x - 4 + 5) = \frac{1}{2}(x + 1)$

59. $(f \circ g)(x) = f(2x - 5) = (2x - 5) + 4 = 2x - 1$

Hence, $(f \circ g)^{-1}(x) = \frac{1}{2}(x + 1)$. Alternatively, observe that $(f \circ g)^{-1}(x) = (g^{-1} \circ f^{-1})(x)$, as in Exercise 57.

61. (a) $y = 0.03x^2 + 254.50,\ \ 0 < x < 100$ **(b)**

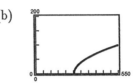

$$x = 0.03y^2 + 254.50$$

$$0.03y^2 = x - 254.50$$

$$y^2 = \frac{100}{3}x - \frac{25{,}450}{3}$$

$$y = \sqrt{\frac{50}{3}(2x - 509)}$$

$$y = \frac{5\sqrt{2}}{\sqrt{3}}\sqrt{2x - 509}$$

$$y = \frac{5\sqrt{6}}{3}\sqrt{2x - 509}$$

y represents the percentage load and x represents the exhaust temperature.

63. If f is an even function, then $f(-x) = f(x)$. This implies that f is not one-to-one. Thus f^{-1} does not exist. The statement is false. For example, $f(x) = x^2$ is even and is not one-to-one.

65. $f(x) = x^n$,   where n is odd

$$f(a) = f(b)$$

$$a^n = b^n$$

$$a = b$$

Therefore, f is one-to-one and its inverse exists. The statement is true.

Chapter 1   Review Exercises

1. $y - 2x - 3 = 0$

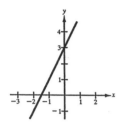

3. $x - 5 = 0$

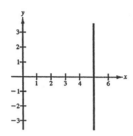

5. $y = \sqrt{5 - x}$

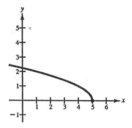

7. $y + 2x^2 = 0$

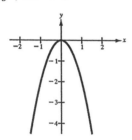

9. $y = \sqrt{25 - x^2}$

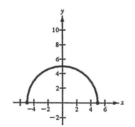

11. $y = \frac{1}{4}(x + 1)^3$ intersects the x-axis once and the y-axis once.

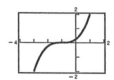

13. $y = \frac{1}{4}x^4 - 2x^2$ intersects the x-axis three times and the y-axis once.

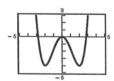

15. $y = x\sqrt{9 - x^2}$ intersects the x-axis three times and the y-axis once.

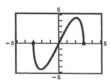

17. $y = |x - 4| - 4$ intersects the x-axis twice and the y-axis once.

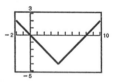

19. $2y^2 = x^3$

$$y = \pm\sqrt{x^3/2}$$

$$y_1 = \sqrt{x^3/2}$$

$$y_2 = -\sqrt{x^3/2}$$

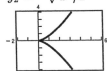

21. The line through $(-2,\ 5)$ and $(1,\ 1)$ is:

$$y - 5 = \frac{1 - 5}{1 + 2}(x + 2)$$

$$y - 5 = -\frac{4}{3}(x + 2)$$

$$3y - 15 = -4x - 8$$

$$4x + 3y = 7$$

For $(0,\ t)$ to be on this line also, it must satisfy the equation $4x + 3y = 7$.

$$4(0) + 3(t) = 7$$

Thus, $t = \frac{7}{3}$.

23. The line through $(1,\ -4)$ and $(5,\ 10)$ is:

$$y + 4 = \frac{10 + 4}{5 - 1}(x - 1)$$

$$y + 4 = \frac{7}{2}(x - 1)$$

$$2y + 8 = 7(x - 1)$$

$$2y + 8 = 7x - 7$$

$$7x - 2y = 15$$

For $(t,\ 3)$ to be on this line also, it must satisfy the equation $7x - 2y = 15$.

$$7(t) - 2(3) = 15$$

$$7t = 21$$

Thus, $t = 3$.

25. Since the points lie on a vertical line, $x = 0$.

27. $y - 1 = \dfrac{6 - 1}{14 - 2}(x - 2) = \dfrac{5}{12}(x - 2) \Rightarrow y = \dfrac{5}{12}x + \dfrac{1}{6}$ or $5x - 12y + 2 = 0$

29. $y - 0 = \dfrac{2 - 0}{6 + 1}(x + 1) = \dfrac{2}{7}(x + 1) \Rightarrow y = \dfrac{2}{7}x + \dfrac{2}{7}$ or $2x - 7y + 2 = 0$

31.
$$y + 5 = \tfrac{3}{2}(x - 0)$$
$$2y + 10 = 3x$$
$$3x - 2y - 10 = 0$$

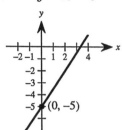

33.
$$y - 0 = -\tfrac{2}{3}(x - 3)$$
$$3y = -2(x - 3)$$
$$3y = -2x + 6$$
$$2x + 3y - 6 = 0$$

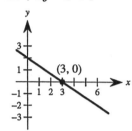

35. $5x - 4y = 8$
$$-4y = -5x + 8$$
$$y = \tfrac{5}{4}x - 2 \quad \Rightarrow \quad m_1 = \tfrac{5}{4}$$
(a) Parallel slope $m_2 = \tfrac{5}{4}$
$$y - (-2) = \tfrac{5}{4}(x - 3)$$
$$y + 2 = \tfrac{5}{4}x - \tfrac{15}{4}$$
$$4y + 8 = 5x - 15$$
$$5x - 4y - 23 = 0$$
(b) Perpendicular slope $m_2 = -\tfrac{4}{5}$
$$y - (-2) = -\tfrac{4}{5}(x - 3)$$
$$y + 2 = -\tfrac{4}{5}x + \tfrac{12}{5}$$
$$5y + 10 = -4x + 12$$
$$4x + 5y - 2 = 0$$

37. $(2,\ 160{,}000),\quad (3,\ 185{,}000)$
$$m = \frac{185{,}000 - 160{,}000}{3 - 2} = 25{,}000$$
$$S - 160{,}000 = 25{,}000(t - 2)$$
$$S = 25{,}000t + 110{,}000$$

For the fourth quarter let $t = 4$. Then we have
$$S = 25{,}000(4) + 110{,}000 = \$210{,}000.$$

39. $f(x) = x^2 + 1$
(a) $f(2) = 2^2 + 1 = 5$
(b) $f(-4) = (-4)^2 + 1 = 17$
(c) $f(t^2) = (t^2)^2 + 1 = t^4 + 1$
(d) $-f(x) = -(x^2 + 1) = -x^2 - 1$

41. $h(x) = 6 - 5x^2$

(a) $h(2) = 6 - 5(2)^2 = -14$

(b) $h(x + 3) = 6 - 5(x + 3)^2 = -5x^2 - 30x - 39$

(c) $\dfrac{h(4) - h(2)}{4 - 2} = \dfrac{-74 + 14}{4 - 2} = -30$

(d) $\dfrac{h(x + t) - h(x)}{t} = \dfrac{6 - 5(x + t)^2 - 6 + 5x^2}{t}$

$$= \dfrac{-5(x^2 + 2xt + (t)^2 - x^2)}{t}$$

$$= \dfrac{-5t(2x + t)}{t} = -5(2x + t) = -10x - 5t, \quad t \neq 0$$

43. (a) $f(x) = \frac{1}{2}x + c$

    $c = -2$: $f(x) = \frac{1}{2}x - 2$

    $c = 0$: $f(x) = \frac{1}{2}x$

    $c = 2$: $f(x) = \frac{1}{2}x + 2$

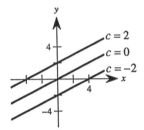

(b) $f(x) = \frac{1}{2}(x - c)$

    $c = -2$: $f(x) = \frac{1}{2}(x + 2)$

                  $= \frac{1}{2}x + 1$

    $c = 0$: $f(x) = \frac{1}{2}x$

    $c = 2$: $f(x) = \frac{1}{2}(x - 2)$

                  $= \frac{1}{2}x - 1$

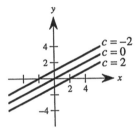

(c) $f(x) = \frac{1}{2}(cx)$

    $c = -2$: $f(x) = \frac{1}{2}(-2x)$

               $= -x$

    $c = 0$: $f(x) = \frac{1}{2}(0x)$

               $= 0$

    $c = 2$: $f(x) = \frac{1}{2}(2x)$

               $= x$

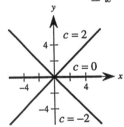

45. $25 - x^2 \geq 0$

       $x^2 \leq 25$

  $-5 \leq x \leq 5$

The domain is $[-5, 5]$.

47. $3s - 9 \neq 0$

      $3s \neq 9$

       $s \neq 3$

The domain is all real numbers except $s = 3$.

49. $x^2 - x - 6 \neq 0$

  $(x - 3)(x + 2) \neq 0$

          $x \neq -2, \, 3$

The domain is all real numbers except $x = -2, \, 3$.

51. $v(t) = -32t + 48$

(a) $v(1) = -32(1) + 48 = 16$ ft/sec

(c) $v(2) = -32(2) + 48 = -16$ ft/sec

(b) $v(t) = 0$

$$-32t + 48 = 0$$

$$-32t = -48$$

$$t = 1.5 \text{ seconds}$$

53. If x and y are the two sides, then the perimeter P is given by $P = 2x + 2y = 24.$ Hence,

$$x + y = 12$$

$$y = 12 - x.$$

$$A = xy = x(12 - x)$$

$$A = 12x - x^2$$

Since $A > 0$ and x is the shortest side, the domain is $(0, \ 6)$.

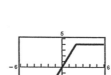

55. (a) Constant on $(-\infty, \ -2)$ and $(2, \ \infty)$

Increasing on $(-2, \ 2)$

(b) Minimum is -4 on $(-\infty, \ -2)$.

Maximum is 4 on $(2, \ \infty)$.

(c) Since

$$g(-x) = |-x + 2| - |-x - 2|$$

$$= |x - 2| - |x + 2|$$

$$= -g(x),$$

the function is odd.

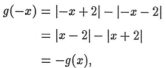

57. (a) Increasing on $(-\infty, \ 0)$ and $(0, \ 3)$

Decreasing on $(3, \ \infty)$

(b) Relative maximum at $(3, \ 27)$

(c) Since

$$h(-x) = 4(-x)^3 - (-x)^4$$

$$= -4x^3 + x^4,$$

h is neither even nor odd.

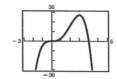

59. (a) At time t, ship A is $100 - 12t$
miles east of $(0, 0)$, whereas, ship
B is $-10t$ south of $(0, 0)$. Hence,
by the Pythagorean Theorem,
the distance between the ships is
$d = \sqrt{(100 - 12t)^2 + (-10t)^2}$.

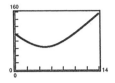

(b) Using the zoom and trace features,
we see that the minimum distance of
$d = 64.02$ miles occurs at $t = 4.92$
hours.

61. $f(x) = \frac{1}{2}x - 3$

(a) $f^{-1}(x) = 2x + 6$

(b)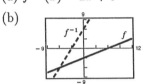

63. $f(x) = \sqrt{x + 1}$

(a) $f^{-1}(x) = x^2 - 1, \quad x \geq 0$

(b)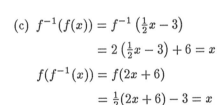

(c) $f^{-1}(f(x)) = f^{-1}\left(\frac{1}{2}x - 3\right)$

$\qquad = 2\left(\frac{1}{2}x - 3\right) + 6 = x$

$f(f^{-1}(x)) = f(2x + 6)$

$\qquad = \frac{1}{2}(2x + 6) - 3 = x$

(c) $f^{-1}(f(x)) = f^{-1}(\sqrt{x + 1})$

$\qquad = (x + 1) - 1 = x$

$f(f^{-1}(x)) = f(x^2 - 1), \quad x \geq 0$

$\qquad = \sqrt{x^2 - 1 + 1} = x$

65. $f(x) = x^2 - 5, \quad x \geq 0$

(a) $f^{-1}(x) = \sqrt{x + 5}, \quad x \geq -5$

(b)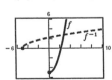

(c) $f^{-1}(f(x)) = f^{-1}(x^2 - 5), \quad x \geq 0$

$\qquad = \sqrt{x^2 - 5 + 5}$

$\qquad = x$

$f(f^{-1}(x)) = f(\sqrt{x + 5})$

$\qquad = (x + 5) - 5$

$\qquad = x$

67. $f(x) = 2(x - 4)^2$ is increasing on the interval $[4, \infty)$.

$$f(x) = 2(x - 4)^2, \quad x \geq 4$$
$$y = 2(x - 4)^2, \quad x \geq 4$$
$$x = 2(y - 4)^2$$
$$\sqrt{x} = \sqrt{2}(y - 4)$$
$$\frac{\sqrt{x}}{\sqrt{2}} + 4 = y$$
$$f^{-1}(x) = \sqrt{\frac{x}{2}} + 4, \quad x \geq 0$$

69. $f(x) = \sqrt{x^2 - 4}$ is increasing on the interval $[2, \infty)$.

$$f(x) = \sqrt{x^2 - 4}, \quad x \geq 2$$
$$y = \sqrt{x^2 - 4}, \quad x \geq 2$$
$$x = \sqrt{y^2 - 4}$$
$$y^2 - 4 = x^2$$
$$y^2 = x^2 + 4$$
$$y = \sqrt{x^2 + 4}$$
$$f^{-1}(x) = \sqrt{x^2 + 4}, \quad x \geq 0$$

71. $(f - g)(4) = f(4) - g(4)$
$$= (3 - 2 \cdot 4) - \sqrt{4}$$
$$= -7$$

73. $(fh)(1) = f(1) \cdot h(1)$
$$= (3 - 2 \cdot 1)(3 \cdot 1^2 + 2)$$
$$= 5$$

75. $(h \circ g)(7) = h(g(7))$
$$= h(\sqrt{7})$$
$$= 3(\sqrt{7})^2 + 2$$
$$= 23$$

77. $g^{-1}(x) = x^2, \quad x \geq 0$
$$g^{-1}(3) = 3^2 = 9$$

CHAPTER 2

Intercepts, Zeros, and Solutions

Section 2.1   Linear Equations and Modeling

■ You should know how to solve linear equations: $ax + b = 0$

■ An identity is an equation whose solution consists of every real number in its domain.

■ To solve an equation you can:

(a) Add or subtract the same quantity from both sides.
(b) Multiply or divide both sides by the same nonzero quantity.

■ To solve an equation that can be simplified to a linear equation:

(a) Remove all symbols of grouping and all fractions.
(b) Combine like terms.
(c) Solve by algebra.
(d) Check the answer algebraically and graphically.

■ A "solution" that does not satisfy the original equation is called an extraneous solution.

---

1. $2(x - 1) = 2x - 2$

$2x - 2 = 2x - 2$

Identity

3. $-2(x - 3) + 5 = -2x + 10$

$-2x + 6 + 5 = -2x + 10$

$-2x + 11 = -2x + 10$

$11 \neq 10$

No solution; conditional

5. $4(x + 1) - 2x = 2(x + 2)$

$4x + 4 - 2x = 2x + 4$

$2x + 4 = 2x + 4$

Identity

7. $x^2 - 8x + 5 = (x - 4)^2 - 11$

$= x^2 - 8x + 16 - 11$

$= x^2 - 8x + 5$

Identity

9. $3 + \dfrac{1}{x + 1} = \dfrac{4x}{x + 1}$

$\dfrac{3x + 4}{x + 1} = \dfrac{4x}{x + 1}$

$3x + 4 = 4x$

$x = 4$

Conditional

11. $5x - 3 = 3x + 5$

(a) $5(0) - 3 \overset{?}{=} 3(0) + 5$

$\quad -3 \neq 5$

$\quad x = 0$ *is not* a solution.

(c) $5(4) - 3 \overset{?}{=} 3(4) + 5$

$\quad 17 = 17$

$\quad x = 4$ *is* a solution.

(b) $5(-5) - 3 \overset{?}{=} 3(-5) + 5$

$\quad -28 \neq -10$

$\quad x = -5$ *is not* a solution.

(d) $5(10) - 3 \overset{?}{=} 3(10) + 5$

$\quad 47 \neq 35$

$\quad x = 10$ *is not* a solution.

13. $(x + 5)(x - 3) = 20$

(a) $(3 + 5)(3 - 3) \overset{?}{=} 20$

$\quad\quad 0 \neq 20$

$\quad x = 3$ *is not* a solution.

(c) $(5 + 5)(5 - 3) \overset{?}{=} 20$

$\quad\quad 20 = 20$

$\quad x = 5$ *is* a solution.

(b) $(-5 + 5)(-5 - 3) \overset{?}{=} 20$

$\quad\quad 0 \neq 20$

$\quad x = -5$ *is not* a solution.

(d) $(-7 + 5)(-7 - 3) \overset{?}{=} 20$

$\quad\quad 20 = 20$

$\quad x = -7$ *is* a solution.

15. $x + 10 = 15$

$\quad x = 5$

17. $7 - 2x = 15$

$\quad -2x = 8$

$\quad x = -4$

19. $8x - 5 = 3x + 10$

$\quad 5x = 15$

$\quad x = 3$

21. $2(x + 5) - 7 = 3(x - 2)$

$\quad 2x + 10 - 7 = 3x - 6$

$\quad 2x + 3 = 3x - 6$

$\quad -x = -9$

$\quad x = 9$

23. $6[x - (2x + 3)] = 8 - 5x$

$\quad 6[-x - 3] = 8 - 5x$

$\quad -6x - 18 = 8 - 5x$

$\quad -x = 26$

$\quad x = -26$

25.
$$\frac{5x}{4} + \frac{1}{2} = x - \frac{1}{2}$$
$$4\left(\frac{5x}{4}\right) + 4\left(\frac{1}{2}\right) = 4(x) + 4\left(-\frac{1}{2}\right)$$
$$5x + 2 = 4x - 2$$
$$x = -4$$

27.
$$\tfrac{3}{2}(z + 5) - \tfrac{1}{4}(z + 24) = 0$$
$$4\left(\tfrac{3}{2}\right)(z + 5) - 4\left(\tfrac{1}{4}\right)(z + 24) = 4(0)$$
$$6(z + 5) - (z + 24) = 0$$
$$6z + 30 - z - 24 = 0$$
$$5z = -6$$
$$z = -\tfrac{6}{5}$$

29. $x + 8 = 2(x - 2) - x$

$x + 8 = 2x - 4 - x$

$x + 8 = x - 4$

$8 = -4$

Not possible; no solution

31. $$\frac{100 - 4u}{3} = \frac{5u + 6}{4} + 6$$

$$12\left(\frac{100 - 4u}{3}\right) = 12\left(\frac{5u + 6}{4}\right) + 12(6)$$

$$4(100 - 4u) = 3(5u + 6) + 72$$

$$400 - 16u = 15u + 18 + 72$$

$$-31u = -310$$

$$u = 10$$

33. $$\frac{5x - 4}{5x + 4} = \frac{2}{3}$$

$3(5x - 4) = 2(5x + 4)$

$15x - 12 = 10x + 8$

$5x = 20$

$x = 4$

35. $$10 - \frac{13}{x} = 4 + \frac{5}{x}$$

$$(x)10 - (x)\frac{13}{x} = (x)4 + (x)\frac{5}{x}$$

$$10x - 13 = 4x + 5$$

$$6x = 18$$

$$x = 3$$

37. $$\frac{1}{x - 3} + \frac{1}{x + 3} = \frac{10}{x^2 - 9}$$

$$\frac{1}{x - 3}(x + 3)(x - 3) + \frac{1}{x + 3}(x + 3)(x - 3) = \frac{10}{x^2 - 9}(x + 3)(x - 3)$$

$$x + 3 + x - 3 = 10$$

$$2x = 10$$

$$x = 5$$

39. $$\frac{x}{x + 4} + \frac{4}{x + 4} + 2 = 0$$

$$\frac{x}{x + 4}(x + 4) + \frac{4}{x + 4}(x + 4) + 2(x + 4) = 0$$

$$x + 4 + 2x + 8 = 0$$

$$3x = -12$$

$$x = -4$$

A check reveals that $x = -4$ is an extraneous solution, so there is no solution. Or, notice that the graph of

$$y = \frac{x}{x + 4} + \frac{4}{x + 4} + 2$$

lies entirely above the x-axis.

41.
$$\frac{7}{2x+1} - \frac{8x}{2x-1} = -4$$

$$\frac{7}{2x+1}(2x+1)(2x-1) - \frac{8x}{2x-1}(2x+1)(2x-1) = -4(2x+1)(2x-1)$$

$$7(2x-1) - 8x(2x+1) = -4(4x^2-1)$$

$$14x - 7 - 16x^2 - 8x = -16x^2 + 4$$

$$6x = 11$$

$$x = \frac{11}{6}$$

43.
$$\frac{1}{x} + \frac{2}{x-5} = 0$$

$$\frac{1}{x}(x)(x-5) + \frac{2}{x-5}(x)(x-5) = 0(x)(x-5)$$

$$x - 5 + 2x = 0$$

$$3x = 5$$

$$x = \frac{5}{3}$$

45.
$$\frac{3}{x(x-3)} + \frac{4}{x} = \frac{1}{x-3}$$

$$\frac{3}{x(x-3)}(x)(x-3) + \frac{4}{x}(x)(x-3) = \frac{1}{x-3}(x)(x-3)$$

$$3 + 4(x-3) = x$$

$$3 + 4x - 12 = x$$

$$3x = 9$$

$$x = 3$$

A check reveals that $x = 3$ is an extraneous solution, so there is no solution.

47. $(x+2)^2 - x^2 = 4(x+1)$

$x^2 + 4x + 4 - x^2 = 4x + 4$

$4 = 4$

The equation is an identity; every real number is a solution.

49. $4(x+1) - ax = x + 5$

$4x + 4 - ax = x + 5$

$3x - ax = 1$

$x(3-a) = 1$

$x = \dfrac{1}{3-a}, \ a \neq 3$

If $a = 3$, there is no solution.

51. $4 - 2(x - 2b) = ax + 3$

$4 - 2x + 4b = ax + 3$

$4b + 1 = ax + 2x$

$4b + 1 = x(a + 2)$

$$x = \frac{4b + 1}{a + 2}, \quad a \neq -2$$

If $a = -2$, there are two possibilities.
If $b = -\frac{1}{4}$, every x is a solution, and if
$b \neq -\frac{1}{4}$, there is no solution.

53. $0.275x + 0.725(500 - x) = 300$

$0.275x + 362.5 - 0.725x = 300$

$-0.45x = -62.5$

$x \approx 138.889$

Or, using a graphing utility, you can
show that the x-intercept of the function
$y = 0.275x + 0.725(500 - x) - 300$ is
$x = 138.89$.

55.
$$\frac{x}{0.6321} + \frac{x}{0.0692} = 1000$$

$$\frac{x}{0.6321}(0.6321)(0.0692) + \frac{x}{0.0692}(0.6321)(0.0692) = 1000(0.6321)(0.0692)$$

$$0.0692x + 0.6321x = 1000(0.6321)(0.0692)$$

$$(0.0692 + 0.6321)x = 1000(0.6321)(0.0692)$$

$$x = \frac{1000(0.6321)(0.0692)}{(0.0692 + 0.6321)}$$

$$x \approx 62.372$$

Or, using a graphing utility, you can show that the x-intercept of the function

$$y = \frac{x}{0.6321} + \frac{x}{0.0692} - 1000$$

is $x = 62.37$.

57. $ax + b = cx$

$ax - cx = -b$

$x(a - c) = -b$

$$x = \frac{-b}{a - c}$$

Since $x = 2$, we have $2 = -b/(a - c)$. Choose any combination of a, b and c that satisfies this
equation. One possibility is $a = 1$, $b = 4$, and $c = 3$. The equation is $x + 4 = 3x$.

59. *Verbal Model* Perimeter $= 2 \cdot$ Width $+ 2 \cdot$ Length

Labels Perimeter $= 75$ feet
Width (in feet) $= x$
Length (in feet) $= 1.5 \cdot$ Width $= 1.5x$

Algebraic Equation $75 = 2x + 2(1.5x)$

$$75 = 5x$$

$$x = 15$$

Width $= x = 15$ feet, length $= 1.5x = 22.5$ feet

61. $(\text{Time}) = \dfrac{(\text{Distance})}{(\text{Rate})}$

$(\text{Rate}) = \dfrac{25 \text{ miles}}{30 \text{ minutes}}$

$= \dfrac{25 \text{ miles}}{\frac{1}{2} \text{ hour}}$

$= 50 \dfrac{\text{miles}}{\text{hour}}$

$t = \dfrac{150}{50} = 3$ hours

63. Distance $=$ Rate $\cdot$ Time

$d_1 = 40$ miles per hour $\cdot t$

$d_2 = 55$ miles per hour $\cdot t$

Distance between cars $=$ Second distance $-$ First distance

$$5 = d_2 - d_1$$

$$5 = 55t - 40t = 15t$$

$$t = \tfrac{1}{3} \text{ hour}$$

65. (a) Time for the first family: $t_1 = \dfrac{d}{r_1} = \dfrac{160}{42} \approx 3.8$ hours

Time for the other family: $t_2 = \dfrac{d}{r_2} = \dfrac{160}{50} = 3.2$ hours

(b) $t = \dfrac{d}{r} = \dfrac{100}{42 + 50} = \dfrac{100}{92} \approx 1.1$ hours

(c) $d = rt = 42 \left(\dfrac{160}{42} - \dfrac{160}{50} \right) = 25.6$ miles

67.   Total speed = (Air speed) + (Wind speed)

$$s_1 = 600 \text{ mph} + x \qquad \text{(trip out)}$$

$$s_2 = 600 \text{ mph} + (-x) \quad \text{(return trip)}$$

(Time out) = (Return time)

$$\frac{1500 \text{ miles}}{s_1} = \frac{1500 \text{ miles} - 300 \text{ miles to go}}{s_2}$$

$$\frac{1500}{600 + x} = \frac{1200}{600 - x}$$

$$1500(600 - x) = 1200(600 + x)$$

$$2700x = 180,000$$

$$x = \frac{200}{3} \approx 66.7 \text{ mph}$$

69. By similar triangles,

$$\frac{\text{Height of building}}{\text{Building's shadow}} = \frac{\text{Height of stake}}{\text{Stake's shadow}}$$

$$\frac{x}{50} = \frac{4}{3.5}$$

$$x = 50 \left(\frac{4}{3.5} \right)$$

$$\approx 57.1 \text{ feet}$$

71. $$\frac{\text{Height of pole}}{\text{Pole's shadow}} = \frac{\text{Height of person}}{\text{Person's shadow}}$$

$$\frac{x}{30 + 5} = \frac{6}{5}$$

$$x = 35 \left(\frac{6}{5} \right) = 42 \text{ feet}$$

73. *Verbal Model*

$$\frac{\text{Sum of scores}}{\text{Sum of possible points}} = \text{Average}$$

Labels

Sum of scores $= 87 + 92 + 84 + x$
Sum of possible points $= 400$
Average $= 0.9$

Algebraic Equation

$$\frac{87 + 92 + 84 + x}{400} = 0.9$$

$$\frac{263 + x}{400} = 0.9$$

$$263 + x = 360$$

$$x = 97 \text{ (or greater)}$$

75. Interest $=$ Interest rate $\times$ Principal

$$i_1 = 10.5\% \times \$x$$

$$i_2 = 13\% \times \$(12{,}000 - x)$$

Total interest $=$ (Interest in first account) $+$ (Interest in second account)

$$\$1447.50 = i_1 + i_2$$

$$1447.50 = 0.105x + 0.13(12000 - x)$$

$$x = \frac{112.5}{0.025} = 4500$$

You have \$4500 in the 10.5% fund and \$7500 in the 13% fund.

77. Interest $=$ Interest rate $\times$ Principal

$$i_1 = 9.5\% \times \$12{,}000$$

$$i_2 = r \times \$8000$$

Total interest $=$ (Interest in first account) $+$ (Interest in second account)

$$\$2054.40 = i_1 + i_2$$

$$2054.40 = 0.095(12000) + 8000r$$

$$r = \frac{914.40}{8000} = 0.1143 = 11.43\%$$

79. (Final concentration)(Amount) $=$ (Solution 1 concentration)(Amount)

$$+ \text{(Solution 2 concentration)(Amount)}$$

$$(75\%)(55 \text{ gal}) = (40\%)(55 - x) + (100\%)x$$

$$41.25 = 0.60x + 22$$

$$x \approx 32.1 \text{ gallons}$$

81. Cost = (Fixed costs) + (Variable cost)(Number of units)

$85,000 = $10,000 + $8.50x$

$$x = \frac{75,000}{8.5} \approx 8823.5$$

At most, the company can manufacture 8823 units.

83. $A = \frac{1}{2}bh$

$2A = bh$

$\frac{2A}{b} = h$

85. $I = Prt$

$r = \frac{I}{Pt}$

87. $A = \frac{1}{2}(a+b)h$

$\frac{2A}{h} = a + b$

$\frac{2A - ah}{h} = b$

89. $V = \frac{1}{3}\pi h^2(3r - h)$

$\frac{3V}{\pi h^2} = 3r - h$

$\frac{3V + \pi h^3}{\pi h^2} = 3r$

$\frac{3V + \pi h^3}{3\pi h^2} = r$

91. $F = \alpha\frac{m_1 m_2}{r^2}$

$Fr^2 = \alpha m_1 m_2$

$\frac{Fr^2}{\alpha m_1} = m_2$

93. $S = \frac{rL - a}{r - 1}$

$S(r - 1) = rL - a$

$Sr - S = rL - a$

$Sr - rL = S - a$

$r(S - L) = S - a$

$r = \frac{S - a}{S - L}$

95. $W_1 x = W_2(L - x)$

$50x = 75(10 - x)$

$50x = 750 - 75x$

$125x = 750$

$x = 6$ ft from the 50-lb child

Section 2.2   Solving Equations Graphically

> ■ You should be able to find the intercepts of the graph of an equation.
>
> ■ You should be able to find the zeros of a function $y = f(x)$ by solving the equation $f(x) = 0$.
>
> ■ You should be able to find the solutions of an equation graphically using a graphing utility.
>
> ■ You should be able to use the zoom and trace features to find solutions to any desired accuracy.
>
> ■ You should be able to find the points of intersection of two graphs.

1. $y = x - 5$

Let $y = 0$: $0 = x - 5 \Rightarrow x = 5 \Rightarrow (5, \ 0)$ x-intercept
Let $x = 0$: $y = 0 - 5 \Rightarrow y = -5 \Rightarrow (0, \ -5)$ y-intercept

3. $y = x^2 + x - 2$

Let $y = 0$: $(x^2 + x - 2) = (x + 2)(x - 1) = 0 \Rightarrow x = -2, \ 1 \Rightarrow (-2, \ 0), \ (1, \ 0)$ x-intercepts
Let $x = 0$: $y = 0^2 + 0 - 2 = -2 \Rightarrow (0, \ -2)$ y-intercept

5. $y = x\sqrt{x + 2}$

Let $y = 0$: $0 = x\sqrt{x + 2} \Rightarrow x = 0, \ -2 \Rightarrow (0, \ 0), \ (-2, \ 0)$ x-intercepts
Let $x = 0$: $y = 0\sqrt{0 + 2} = 0 \Rightarrow (0, \ 0)$ y-intercept

7. $xy - 2y - x + 1 = 0$

Let $y = 0$: $-x + 1 = 0 \Rightarrow x = 1 \Rightarrow (1, \ 0)$ x-intercept
Let $x = 0$: $-2y + 1 = 0 \Rightarrow y = \frac{1}{2} \Rightarrow \left(0, \ \frac{1}{2}\right)$ y-intercept

9. $f(x) = 12 - 4x$

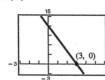

11. $f(x) = x^2 - 2.5x - 6$

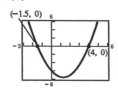

13. $f(x) = \dfrac{x+2}{3} - \dfrac{x-1}{5} - 1$

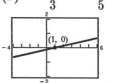

15. $25(x - 3) = 12(x + 2) - 10$

$25x - 75 = 12x + 24 - 10$

$13x - 89 = 0$

17. $\dfrac{2x}{3} = 10 - \dfrac{1}{x}$

$\dfrac{2x}{3} + \dfrac{1}{x} - 10 = 0$

19. $\dfrac{3}{x+2} - \dfrac{4}{x-2} = 5$

$\dfrac{3}{x+2} - \dfrac{4}{x-2} - 5 = 0$

21. $27 - 4x = 12$

$-4x = -15$

$x = \dfrac{15}{4}$

$27 - 4x - 12 = 0$

$f(x) = 15 - 4x = 0$

$x = 3.75$

23. $\dfrac{3x}{2} + \dfrac{1}{4}(x - 2) = 10$

$\dfrac{6x}{4} + \dfrac{x}{4} = 10 + \dfrac{1}{2}$

$\dfrac{7x}{4} = \dfrac{21}{2}$

$x = 6$

$f(x) = \dfrac{3x}{2} + \dfrac{1}{4}(x - 2) - 10 = 0$

$x = 6.0$

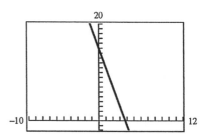

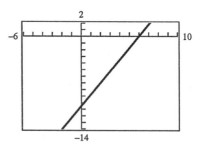

25. $3(x + 3) = 5(1 - x) - 1$

$$3x + 9 = 5 - 5x - 1$$

$$8x = -5$$

$$x = -\frac{5}{8}$$

$$f(x) = 3(x + 3) - 5(1 - x) + 1 = 0$$

$$x = -0.625$$

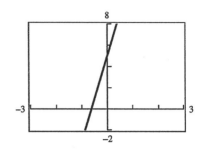

27. $\frac{1}{4}(x^2 - 10x + 17) = 0$

$x = 2.172, \ 7.828$

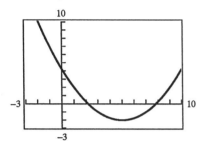

29. $x^3 + x + 4 = 0$

$x = -1.379$

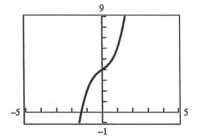

31. $2x^3 - x^2 - 18x + 9 = 0$

$x = -3.0, \ 0.5, \ 3.0$

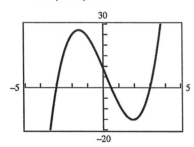

33. $\qquad x^4 = 2x^3 + 1$

$$x^4 - 2x^3 - 1 = 0$$

$$x = -0.717, \ 2.107$$

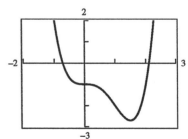

35. $\dfrac{2}{z+2} = 3$

$\dfrac{2}{z+2} - 3 = 0$

$z = -1.333$

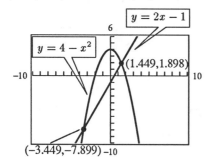

37. $y = 2 - x$

$y = 2x - 1$

$(x,\ y) = (1,\ 1)$

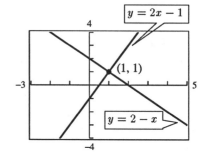

39. $y = 4 - x^2$

$y = 2x - 1$

$(x,\ y) = (1.449,\ 1.898),\ (-3.449,\ -7.898)$

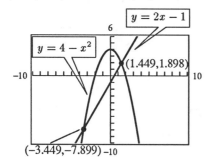

41. $y = 8$

$y = 3x^2 + 2x$

$(x,\ y) = (-2,\ 8),\ (1.333,\ 8)$

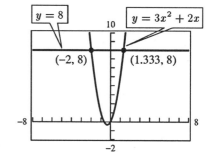

43. $y = 3(x + 1)$

$y = x^2 + 2x + 1$

$(x, y) = (-1, 0), (2, 9)$

```
┌─────────────────┐      ┌─────────────┐
│ y = x² + 2x + 1 │      │ y = 3(x+1)  │
└─────────────────┘      └─────────────┘
              12
                        •(2, 9)

        (-1, 0)

 -5 ────────────────────── 7
              -2
```

45. $y = 2x^2$

$y = x^4 - 2x^2$

$(x, y) = (0, 0), (2, 8), (-2, 8)$

```
         ┌────────┐      ┌──────────────┐
         │ y = 2x²│      │ y = x⁴ - 2x²  │
         └────────┘      └──────────────┘
                    14
   (-2, 8)•                  •(2, 8)

 -4 ────────────────────────── 4
                  (0, 0)
                   -6
```

47. (a) $\dfrac{1 + 0.73205}{1 - 0.73205} = \dfrac{1.73205}{0.26795}$

$= 6.464079 = 6.46$

(b) $\dfrac{1 + 0.73205}{1 - 0.73205} = \dfrac{1.73205}{0.26795}$

$= \dfrac{1.73}{0.27}$

$= 6.407407 = 6.41$

The second method decreases accuracy.

49. (a) $\dfrac{3.33 + (1.98/0.74)}{4 + (6.25/3.15)} = \dfrac{6.005675676}{5.984126984}$

$= 1.00360098$

$= 1.00$

(b) $\dfrac{3.33 + (1.98/0.74)}{4 + (6.25/3.15)} = \dfrac{6.01}{5.98}$

$= 1.005016722$

$= 1.01$

The second method decreases accuracy.

51. (a) $T = \dfrac{x}{63} + \dfrac{(280 - x)}{54}$

(b) Domain: $0 \le x \le 280$

(c) If the time was 4 hours and 45 minutes, then $T = 4\frac{3}{4}$ and $x \approx 164.5$ miles.

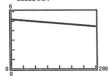

53. (a) $C = x + 0.33(55 - x)$

(b) Domain: $0 \le x \le 55$

(c) If the final mixture is 60% concentrate, then $C = 0.6(55) = 33$ and $x = 22.2$.

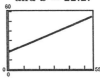

55. $S = I + G$

$S = x + 8000 - \frac{1}{2}x$

$= \frac{1}{2}x + 8000, \quad 0 \le x \le 16{,}000$

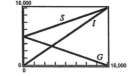

(a) The government payment decreases.

(b) The spendable income increases.

57. If $S = 11{,}800$, then:

$11{,}800 = \frac{1}{2}x + 8000$

$x = 7600$

Section 2.3   Complex Numbers

- You should know how to work with complex numbers, $a + bi$, where $i = \sqrt{-1}$.
- Operations on Complex Numbers
  - (a) Addition: $(a + bi) + (c + di) = (a + c) + (b + d)i$
  - (b) Subtraction: $(a + bi) - (c + di) = (a - c) + (b - d)i$
  - (c) Multiplication: $(a + bi)(c + di) = (ac - bd) + (ad + bc)i$
  - (d) Division: $\dfrac{a + bi}{c + di} = \dfrac{a + bi}{c + di} \cdot \dfrac{c - di}{c - di} = \dfrac{ac + bd}{c^2 + d^2} + \dfrac{bc - ad}{c^2 + d^2}i$

- The complex conjugate of $a + bi$ is $a - bi$: $(a + bi)(a - bi) = a^2 + b^2$
- The additive inverse of $a + bi$ is $-a - bi$.
- The multiplicative inverse of $a + bi$ is $\dfrac{a - bi}{a^2 + b^2}$.
- $\sqrt{-a} = \sqrt{a}\, i$ for $a > 0$.
- You should be able to find the complex solutions to a quadratic equation.
- You should be able to plot complex numbers in the complex plane.

---

1. $i = \quad i \qquad i^5 = \quad i \qquad i^9 = \quad i \qquad i^{13} = \quad i$

   $i^2 = -1 \qquad i^6 = -1 \qquad i^{10} = -1 \qquad i^{14} = -1$

   $i^3 = -i \qquad i^7 = -i \qquad i^{11} = -i \qquad i^{15} = -i$

   $i^4 = \quad 1 \qquad i^8 = \quad 1 \qquad i^{12} = \quad 1 \qquad i^{16} = \quad 1$

3. $a + bi = -10 + 6i$

   $a = -10$

   $b = 6$

5. $(a - 1) + (b + 3)i = 5 + 8i$

   $a - 1 = 5 \;\Rightarrow\; a = 6$

   $b + 3 = 8 \;\Rightarrow\; b = 5$

7. $4 + \sqrt{-9} = 4 + \sqrt{9}\, i$

   $= 4 + 3i$

9. $2 - \sqrt{-27} = 2 - \sqrt{27}\, i$

   $= 2 - 3\sqrt{3}\, i$

11. $\sqrt{-75} = \sqrt{75}\, i$

   $= 5\sqrt{3}\, i$

13. $-6i + i^2 = -6i + (-1)$

   $= -1 - 6i$

15. $-5i^5 = -5(i^4)i = -5i$

17. 8 is in standard form.
The imaginary part is 0.

19. $(5 + i) + (6 - 2i) = 5 + i + 6 - 2i$
$$= (5 + 6) + (1 - 2)i$$
$$= 11 - i$$

21. $(8 - i) - (4 - i) = 8 - i - 4 + 1$
$$= (8 - 4) + (-1 + 1)i$$
$$= 4 + 0i$$
$$= 4$$

23. $(-2 + \sqrt{-8}) + (5 - \sqrt{-50}) = -2 + 2\sqrt{2}\,i + 5 - 5\sqrt{2}\,i = (-2 + 5) + \sqrt{2}(2 - 5)i = 3 - 3\sqrt{2}\,i$

25. $-\left(\frac{3}{2} + \frac{5}{2}i\right) + \left(\frac{5}{3} + \frac{11}{3}i\right) = -\frac{3}{2} - \frac{5}{2}i + \frac{5}{3} + \frac{11}{3}i = \left(-\frac{3}{2} + \frac{5}{3}\right) + \left(-\frac{5}{2} + \frac{11}{3}\right)i = \frac{1}{6} + \frac{7}{6}i$

27. The complex conjugate of $5 + 3i$ is $5 - 3i$.
$$(5 + 3i)(5 - 3i) = 5^2 - (3i)^2 = 25 - 9i^2 = 25 + 9 = 34$$

29. The complex conjugate of $-2 - \sqrt{5}\,i$ is $-2 + \sqrt{5}\,i$.
$$(-2 - \sqrt{5}\,i)(-2 + \sqrt{5}\,i) = (-2)^2 - (\sqrt{5}\,i)^2$$
$$= 4 - 5i^2$$
$$= 4 + 5$$
$$= 9$$

31. $\sqrt{-6} \cdot \sqrt{-2} = (\sqrt{6}\,i)(\sqrt{2}\,i)$
$$= \sqrt{12}\,i^2$$
$$= -2\sqrt{3}$$
(Note that it is incorrect to write
$\sqrt{-6} \cdot \sqrt{-2} = \sqrt{(-6)(-2)} = \sqrt{12} = 2\sqrt{3}$.)

33. $(\sqrt{-10})^2 = (\sqrt{10}\,i)^2$
$$= (\sqrt{10})^2(i^2)$$
$$= -10$$

35. $(1 + i)(3 - 2i) = 3 - 2i + 3i - 2i^2$
$$= 3 + i + 2$$
$$= 5 + i$$

37. $6i(5 - 2i) = 30i - 12i^2 = 12 + 30i$

39. $(\sqrt{14} + \sqrt{10}\,i)(\sqrt{14} - \sqrt{10}\,i) = 14 - 10i^2$
$$= 14 + 10$$
$$= 24$$

41. $(4 + 5i)^2 = 16 + 40i + 25i^2$
$$= 16 + 40i - 25$$
$$= -9 + 40i$$

43. $(2 + 3i)^2 + (2 - 3i)^2 = (4 + 12i + 9i^2) + (4 - 12i + 9i^2)$

$$= 8 + 18i^2$$

$$= 8 - 18$$

$$= -10$$

45. $\dfrac{4}{4 - 5i} = \dfrac{4}{4 - 5i} \cdot \dfrac{4 + 5i}{4 + 5i}$

$$= \dfrac{16 + 20i}{16 + 25}$$

$$= \dfrac{16}{41} + \dfrac{20}{41}i$$

47. $\dfrac{2 + i}{2 - i} = \dfrac{2 + i}{2 - i} \cdot \dfrac{2 + i}{2 + i}$

$$= \dfrac{4 + 4i + i^2}{4 + 1}$$

$$= \dfrac{3 + 4i}{5}$$

$$= \dfrac{3}{5} + \dfrac{4}{5}i$$

49. $\dfrac{6 - 7i}{i} = \dfrac{6 - 7i}{i} \cdot \dfrac{-i}{-i}$

$$= \dfrac{-6i + 7i^2}{1}$$

$$= -7 - 6i$$

51. First, note that

$$(1 + i)^3 = (1 + i)(1 + i)^2$$

$$= (1 + i)(2i) = -2 + 2i.$$

Then

$$\dfrac{5}{(1 + i)^3} = \dfrac{5}{-2 + 2i} \cdot \dfrac{-2 - 2i}{-2 - 2i}$$

$$= \dfrac{-10 - 10i}{8} = \dfrac{-5}{4} - \dfrac{5}{4}i.$$

53. $\dfrac{(21 - 7i)(4 + 3i)}{(2 - 5i)} = \dfrac{105 + 35i}{2 - 5i} \cdot \dfrac{2 + 5i}{2 + 5i}$

$$= \dfrac{(210 - 175) + (70 + 525)i}{4 + 25} = \dfrac{35 + 595i}{29} = \dfrac{35}{29} + \dfrac{595}{29}i$$

55.

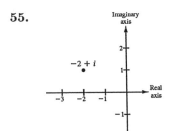

57.

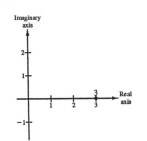

59.

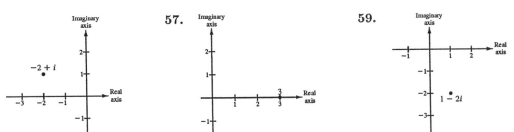

61. The complex number 0 is in the Mandelbrot Set since for $c = 0$, the corresponding Mandelbrot sequence is 0, 0, 0, 0, 0, 0, ... which is bounded.

63. The complex number $\frac{1}{2}i$ is in the Mandelbrot Set since for $c = \frac{1}{2}i$, the corresponding Mandelbrot sequence is

$$\frac{1}{2}i, \quad -\frac{1}{4} + \frac{1}{2}i, \quad -\frac{3}{16} + \frac{1}{4}i, \quad -\frac{7}{256} + \frac{13}{32}i, \quad \frac{-10,767}{65,536} + \frac{1957}{4096}i, \quad -\frac{864,513,055}{4,294,967,296} + \frac{46,037,845}{134,217,728}i$$

which is bounded. Or in decimal form

$$0.5i, \quad -0.25 + 0.5i, \quad -0.1875 + 0.25i, \quad -0.02734 + 0.40625i,$$
$$-0.164291 + 0.477783i, \quad -0.201285 + 0.343009i.$$

65. The complex number 1 is not in the Mandelbrot Set since for $c = 1$, the corresponding Mandelbrot sequence is 1, 2, 5, 26, 677, 458,330 which is unbounded.

67. $2^3 = 8$

$$(-1 + \sqrt{3}\,i)^3 = (-1)^3 + 3(-1)^2(\sqrt{3}\,i) + 3(-1)(\sqrt{3}\,i)^2 + (\sqrt{3}\,i)^3$$
$$= -1 + 3\sqrt{3}\,i + 9 - 3\sqrt{3}\,i = 8$$
$$(-1 - \sqrt{3}\,i)^3 = (-1)^3 - 3(-1)^2(\sqrt{3}\,i) + 3(-1)(\sqrt{3}\,i)^2 - (\sqrt{3}\,i)^3$$
$$= -1 - 3\sqrt{3}\,i + 9 + 3\sqrt{3}\,i = 8$$

All three numbers are cube roots of 8.

69. $(a + bi) + (a - bi) = (a + a) + (b - b)i$
$$= 2a + 0i$$
$$= 2a$$

which is a real number.

71. $(a + bi)(a - bi) = a^2 - abi + abi - (bi)^2$
$$= a^2 - b^2i^2$$
$$= a^2 + b^2$$

which is a real number.

Section 2.4   Solving Equations Algebraically

- A quadratic equation is of the form $ax^2 + bx + c = 0$, $a \neq 0$.
- You should be able to factor a quadratic.
- You should be able to solve a quadratic by extracting square roots.
- You should be able to complete the square on any quadratic.

---

1. $6x^2 + 3x = 0$

$3x(2x + 1) = 0$

$3x = 0 \ \Rightarrow \ x = 0$

$2x + 1 = 0 \ \Rightarrow \ x = -\frac{1}{2}$

3. $x^2 - 2x - 8 = 0$

$(x + 2)(x - 4) = 0$

$x + 2 = 0 \ \Rightarrow \ x = -2$

$x - 4 = 0 \ \Rightarrow \ x = \ \ 4$

5. $x^2 + 10x + 25 = 0$

$(x + 5)^2 = 0$

$x + 5 = 0 \ \Rightarrow \ x = -5$

7. $3 + 5x - 2x^2 = 0$

$(3 - x)(1 + 2x) = 0$

$3 - x = 0 \ \Rightarrow \ x = 3$

$1 + 2x = 0 \ \Rightarrow \ x = -\frac{1}{2}$

9. $2x^2 + 8x - 6 = x^2 + 4x + 6$

$x^2 + 4x = 12$

$x^2 + 4x - 12 = 0$

$(x + 6)(x - 2) = 0$

$x + 6 = 0 \ \Rightarrow \ x = -6$

$x - 2 = 0 \ \Rightarrow \ x = 2$

11. $x^2 + 2ax + a^2 = 0$

$(x + a)^2 = 0$

$x + a = 0$

$x = -a$

13. $3x^2 = 36$

$x^2 = 12$

$x = \pm\sqrt{12}$

$x = \pm 2\sqrt{3} \approx \pm 3.46$

15. $(x - 12)^2 = 18$

$x - 12 = \pm 3\sqrt{2}$

$x = 12 \pm 3\sqrt{2}$

$x \approx 16.24 \text{ or } x \approx 7.76$

17. $(x+2)^2 = 12$

$\qquad x+2 = \pm\sqrt{12}$

$\qquad\quad x = -2 \pm 2\sqrt{3}$

$\qquad\qquad x \approx 1.46 \text{ or } x \approx -5.46$

19. $(x-7)^2 = (x+3)^2$

$\qquad x-7 = \pm(x+3)$

$\qquad$ For $x-7 = +(x+3)$

$\qquad\qquad -7 = +3, \text{ No solution}$

$\qquad$ For $x-7 = -(x+3)$

$\qquad\qquad x-7 = -x-3$

$\qquad\qquad\quad 2x = 4$

$\qquad\qquad\quad x = 2$

21. $x^2 + 6x + 2 = 0$

$\qquad\quad x^2 + 6x = -2$

$\qquad x^2 + 6x + 3^2 = -2 + 3^2$

$\qquad\quad (x+3)^2 = 7$

$\qquad\quad x+3 = \pm\sqrt{7}$

$\qquad\qquad x = -3 \pm \sqrt{7}$

23. $9x^2 - 18x + 3 = 0$

$\qquad\quad x^2 - 2x + \frac{1}{3} = 0$

$\qquad\qquad x^2 - 2x = -\frac{1}{3}$

$\qquad x^2 - 2x + 1^2 = -\frac{1}{3} + 1^2$

$\qquad\qquad (x-1)^2 = \frac{2}{3}$

$\qquad\qquad x-1 = \pm\sqrt{\frac{2}{3}}$

$\qquad\qquad\quad x = 1 \pm \sqrt{\frac{2}{3}}$

$\qquad\qquad\quad x = 1 \pm \frac{\sqrt{6}}{3}$

25. $8 + 4x - x^2 = 0$

$\qquad\quad x^2 - 4x - 8 = 0$

$\qquad\qquad x^2 - 4x = 8$

$\qquad x^2 - 4x + 2^2 = 8 + 2^2$

$\qquad\qquad (x-2)^2 = 12$

$\qquad\qquad x-2 = \pm\sqrt{12}$

$\qquad\qquad\quad x = 2 \pm 2\sqrt{3}$

27. $2x^2 + x - 1 = 0$

$\qquad a = 2, \ b = 1, \ c = -1$

$\qquad x = \dfrac{-1 \pm \sqrt{1^2 - 4(2)(-1)}}{2(2)}$

$\qquad\quad = \dfrac{-1 \pm \sqrt{9}}{4} = \dfrac{-1 \pm 3}{4}$

$\qquad x = \dfrac{-1+3}{4} = \dfrac{1}{2} \text{ or}$

$\qquad x = \dfrac{-1-3}{4} = -1$

29. $16x^2 + 8x - 3 = 0$

$a = 16, \; b = 8, \; c = -3$

$$x = \frac{-8 \pm \sqrt{8^2 - 4(16)(-3)}}{2(16)}$$

$$= \frac{-8 \pm \sqrt{256}}{32} = \frac{-8 \pm 16}{32}$$

$$x = \frac{-8 + 16}{32} = \frac{1}{4} \text{ or}$$

$$x = \frac{-8 - 16}{32} = -\frac{3}{4}$$

31. $2 + 2x - x^2 = 0$

$x^2 - 2x - 2 = 0$

$a = 1, \; b = -2, \; c = -2$

$$x = \frac{-(-2) \pm \sqrt{(-2)^2 - 4(1)(-2)}}{2(1)}$$

$$= \frac{2 \pm \sqrt{12}}{2} = \frac{2 \pm 2\sqrt{3}}{2}$$

$$x = 1 \pm \sqrt{3}$$

33. $x^2 + 14x + 44 = 0$

$a = 1, \; b = 14, \; c = 44$

$$x = \frac{-14 \pm \sqrt{14^2 - 4(1)(44)}}{2(1)}$$

$$= \frac{-14 \pm \sqrt{20}}{2} = \frac{-14 \pm 2\sqrt{5}}{2}$$

$$x = -7 \pm \sqrt{5}$$

35. $x^2 + 8x - 4 = 0; \; a = 1, \; b = 8, \; c = -4$

$$x = \frac{-8 \pm \sqrt{8^2 - 4(1)(-4)}}{2(1)}$$

$$= \frac{-8 \pm \sqrt{80}}{2} = \frac{-8 \pm 4\sqrt{5}}{2}$$

$$x = -4 \pm 2\sqrt{5}$$

37. $12x - 9x^2 = -3$

$9x^2 - 12x - 3 = 0$

$3x^2 - 4x - 1 = 0$

$a = 3, \; b = -4, \; c = -1$

$$x = \frac{-(-4) \pm \sqrt{(-4)^2 - 4(3)(-1)}}{2(3)}$$

$$= \frac{4 \pm \sqrt{28}}{6} = \frac{4 \pm 2\sqrt{7}}{6}$$

$$x = \frac{2}{3} \pm \frac{\sqrt{7}}{3}$$

39. $36x^2 + 24x - 7 = 0$

$a = 36, \; b = 24, \; c = -7$

$$x = \frac{-24 \pm \sqrt{24^2 - 4(36)(-7)}}{2(36)}$$

$$= \frac{-24 \pm \sqrt{1584}}{72} = \frac{-24 \pm 12\sqrt{11}}{72}$$

$$x = \frac{-2 \pm \sqrt{11}}{6} = -\frac{1}{3} \pm \frac{\sqrt{11}}{6}$$

41. $4x^2 + 4x = 7$

$4x^2 + 4x - 7 = 0;\ a = 4,\ b = 4,\ c = -7$

$$x = \frac{-4 \pm \sqrt{4^2 - 4(4)(-7)}}{2(4)}$$

$$= \frac{-4 \pm \sqrt{128}}{8} = \frac{-4 \pm 8\sqrt{2}}{8}$$

$$x = -\frac{1}{2} \pm \sqrt{2}$$

43. $28x - 49x^2 = 4$

$49x^2 - 28x + 4 = 0$

$a = 49,\ b = -28,\ c = 4$

$$x = \frac{-(-28) \pm \sqrt{(-28)^2 - 4(49)(4)}}{2(49)}$$

$$= \frac{28 \pm \sqrt{0}}{98} = \frac{2}{7}$$

45. $25h^2 + 80h + 61 = 0$

$a = 25,\ b = 80,\ c = 61$

$$h = \frac{-80 \pm \sqrt{(80)^2 - 4(25)(61)}}{2(25)}$$

$$= \frac{-80 \pm \sqrt{300}}{50} = \frac{-80 \pm 10\sqrt{3}}{50}$$

$$h = \frac{-8 \pm \sqrt{3}}{5} = -\frac{8}{5} \pm \frac{\sqrt{3}}{5}$$

47. $(y - 5)^2 = 2y$

$y^2 - 10y + 25 = 2y$

$y^2 - 12y + 25 = 0$

$a = 1,\ b = -12,\ c = 25$

$$x = \frac{-(-12) \pm \sqrt{(-12)^2 - 4(1)(25)}}{2(1)}$$

$$= \frac{12 \pm \sqrt{44}}{2} = \frac{12 \pm 2\sqrt{11}}{2}$$

$$x = 6 \pm \sqrt{11}$$

49. $x^3 - 2x^2 - 3x = 0$

$x(x^2 - 2x - 3) = 0$

$x(x - 3)(x + 1) = 0$

$x = 0$

$x - 3 = 0 \ \Rightarrow \ x = 3$

$x + 1 = 0 \ \Rightarrow \ x = -1$

51. $5x^3 + 30x^2 + 45x = 0$

$5x(x^2 + 6x + 9) = 0$

$5x(x + 3)^2 = 0$

$5x = 0 \ \Rightarrow \ x = 0$

$x + 3 = 0 \ \Rightarrow \ x = -3$

53. $x^3 - 3x^2 - x + 3 = 0$

$x^2(x - 3) - (x - 3) = 0$

$(x - 3)(x^2 - 1) = 0$

$(x - 3)(x + 1)(x - 1) = 0$

$x - 3 = 0 \ \Rightarrow \ x = 3$

$x + 1 = 0 \ \Rightarrow \ x = -1$

$x - 1 = 0 \ \Rightarrow \ x = 1$

55. $x^4 - 10x^2 + 9 = 0$

$(x^2 - 1)(x^2 - 9) = 0$

$(x + 1)(x - 1)(x + 3)(x - 3) = 0$

$x + 1 = 0 \ \Rightarrow \ x = -1$

$x - 1 = 0 \ \Rightarrow \ x = 1$

$x + 3 = 0 \ \Rightarrow \ x = -3$

$x - 3 = 0 \ \Rightarrow \ x = 3$

57. $\dfrac{1}{t^2} + \dfrac{8}{t} + 15 = 0$

$1 + 8t + 15t^2 = 0$

$(1 + 3t)(1 + 5t) = 0$

$1 + 3t = 0 \;\Rightarrow\; t = -\dfrac{1}{3}$

$1 + 5t = 0 \;\Rightarrow\; t = -\dfrac{1}{5}$

59. $5 - 3x^{1/3} - 2x^{2/3} = 0$

$(5 + 2x^{1/3})(1 - x^{1/3}) = 0$

$x^{1/3} = -\dfrac{5}{2} \;\Rightarrow\; x = -\dfrac{125}{8}$

$x^{1/3} = 1 \;\Rightarrow\; x = 1$

61. $\sqrt{2x} - 10 = 0$

$\sqrt{2x} = 10$

$2x = 100$

$x = 50$

63. $\sqrt[3]{2x + 5} + 3 = 0$

$\sqrt[3]{2x + 5} = -3$

$2x + 5 = -27$

$2x = -32$

$x = -16$

65. $\sqrt{x + 1} - 3x = 1$

$\sqrt{x + 1} = 3x + 1$

$(\sqrt{x + 1})^2 = (3x + 1)^2$

$x + 1 = 9x^2 + 6x + 1$

$0 = 9x^2 + 5x = x(9x + 5)$

$x = 0$

$9x + 5 = 0 \;\Rightarrow\; x = -\dfrac{5}{9}, \quad \text{extraneous}$

67. $\sqrt{x} + \sqrt{x - 20} = 10$

$\sqrt{x} = 10 - \sqrt{x - 20}$

$(\sqrt{x})^2 = (10 - \sqrt{x - 20})^2$

$x = 100 - 20\sqrt{x - 20} + x - 20$

$-80 = -20\sqrt{x - 20}$

$4 = \sqrt{x - 20}$

$16 = x - 20$

$36 = x$

69. $\sqrt{x + 5} + \sqrt{x - 5} = 10$

$\sqrt{x + 5} = 10 - \sqrt{x - 5}$

$(\sqrt{x + 5})^2 = (10 - \sqrt{x - 5})^2$

$x + 5 = 100 - 20\sqrt{x - 5} + x - 5$

$20\sqrt{x - 5} = 90$

$\sqrt{x - 5} = \dfrac{9}{2}$

$x - 5 = \dfrac{81}{4}$

$x = \dfrac{101}{4}$

71. $\dfrac{20 - x}{x} = x$

$20 - x = x^2$

$x^2 + x - 20 = 0$

$(x + 5)(x - 4) = 0$

$x + 5 = 0 \;\Rightarrow\; x = -5$

$x - 4 = 0 \;\Rightarrow\; x = 4$

73.

$$\frac{1}{x} - \frac{1}{x+1} = 3$$

$$x(x+1)\frac{1}{x} - x(x+1)\frac{1}{x+1} = x(x+1)(3)$$

$$x+1-x = 3x(x+1)$$

$$1 = 3x^2 + 3x$$

$$0 = 3x^2 + 3x - 1$$

$a = 3, \ b = 3, \ c = -1$

$$x = \frac{-3 \pm \sqrt{(3)^2 - 4(3)(-1)}}{2(3)} = \frac{-3 \pm \sqrt{21}}{6} = -\frac{1}{2} \pm \frac{\sqrt{21}}{6}$$

Or, using a graphing utility to graph

$$y = \frac{1}{x} - \frac{1}{x+1} - 3,$$

we see that there are two x-intercepts: $x = -1.264$ and $x = 0.264$.

75.

$$\frac{4}{x+1} - \frac{3}{x+2} = 1$$

$$(x+1)(x+2)\frac{4}{x+1} - (x+1)(x+2)\frac{3}{x+2} = (x+1)(x+2)(1)$$

$$4(x+2) - 3(x+1) = (x+1)(x+2)$$

$$4x+8-3x-3 = x^2 + 3x + 2$$

$$0 = x^2 + 2x - 3$$

$$0 = (x+3)(x-1)$$

$$x+3 = 0 \ \Rightarrow \ x = -3$$

$$x-1 = 0 \ \Rightarrow \ x = 1$$

77. $|2x - 1| = 5$

$$2x - 1 = 5 \ \Rightarrow \ x = 3$$

$$-(2x - 1) = 5 \ \Rightarrow \ x = -2$$

79. $|x| = x^2 + x - 3$

$$x = x^2 + x - 3 \qquad\qquad -x = x^2 + x - 3$$
$$x^2 - 3 = 0 \qquad\qquad x^2 + 2x - 3 = 0$$
$$x = \pm\sqrt{3} \qquad\qquad (x - 1)(x + 3) = 0$$
$$x - 1 = 0 \;\Rightarrow\; x = 1$$
$$x + 3 = 0 \;\Rightarrow\; x = -3$$

Only $x = \sqrt{3}$ and $x = -3$ are solutions. Or, using a graphing utility we see that $y = |x| - x^2 - x + 3$ has two x-intercepts: $x = -3$ and $x = 1.732$.

81. $x^4 - x^3 + x - 1 = 0$

Using the zoom and trace features, we find that $x = 1, -1$.

83. $x^4 + 5x^2 - 36 = 0$

Using the zoom and trace features, we find that $x = 2, -2$.

85. $2x + 9\sqrt{x} - 5 = 0$

Using the zoom and trace features, we find that $x = 0.25$.

87. $-\sqrt{26 - 11x} + 4 = x$

Using the zoom and trace features, we find that $x = 2, -5$.

89. $\sqrt{7x + 36} - \sqrt{5x + 16} = 2$

Using the zoom and trace features, we find that $x = 0, 4$.

91. $x = \dfrac{3}{x} + \dfrac{1}{2}$

Using the zoom and trace features, we find that $x = 2, -1.5$.

93. $\dfrac{1}{x} = \dfrac{4}{x - 1} + 1$

Using the zoom and trace features, we find that $x = -1$.

95. $|x - 10| = x^2 - 10x$

Using the zoom and trace features, we find that $x = -1, 10$.

97. $3.2x^4 - 1.5x^2 - 2.1 = 0$

Using the zoom and trace features, we find that $x = \pm 1.04$.

99. $1.8x - 6\sqrt{x} - 5.6 = 0$

Using the zoom and trace features, we find that $x = 16.76$.

101. $0 = -16t^2 + 1821$

$16t^2 = 1821$

$t^2 = \frac{1821}{16}$

$t = \pm\sqrt{\frac{1821}{16}}$

$t \approx \pm 10.67$

Since $t > 0$, it will take ≈ 10.67 seconds for the object to hit the ground.

103. Total fencing $= 4x + 3y = 200$ feet
Enclosed area $= 2xy = 1400$ feet
Since $y = (200 - 4x)/3$,

$$2x\left(\frac{200 - 4x}{3}\right) = 1400$$

$$400x - 8x^2 = 4200$$

$8x^2 - 400x + 4200 = 0.$

Thus, $a = 8$, $b = -400$, $c = 4200$.

$$x = \frac{-(-400) \pm \sqrt{400^2 - 4(8)(4200)}}{2(8)}$$

$$= \frac{400 \pm 160}{16}$$

$x = 35$ or $x = 15$

$x = 35$ ft yields $y = \dfrac{200 - 4(35)}{3} = 20$ ft.

$x = 15$ ft yields $y = \dfrac{200 - 4(15)}{3} = \dfrac{140}{3}$ ft.

105. (a) $C = 0.45x^2 - 1.65x + 50.75$, $10 \le x \le 25$

(b) If $C = 150$, then $x = 16.797$ degrees.

(c) If the temperature is increased from $10°$ to $20°$, then C increases from 79.25 to 197.75, a factor of 2.5.

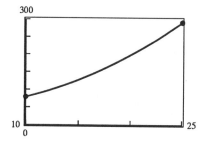

107. Let x = average speed of the plane, then we have a travel time of $t = 720/x$. If the average speed is increased by 40 mph,

$$t - \frac{12}{60} = \frac{720}{x+40}$$

$$t = \frac{720}{x+40} + \frac{1}{5}.$$

Equate these two equations and solve for x.

$$\frac{720}{x} = \frac{720}{x+40} + \frac{1}{5}$$

$$720(5)(x+40) = 720(5)x + x(x+40)$$

$$3600x + 144{,}000 = 3600x + x^2 + 40x$$

$$0 = x^2 + 40x - 144{,}000$$

$$0 = (x+400)(x-360)$$

Using the positive value for x we have $x = 360$ mph and $x + 40 = 400$ mph. The airspeed required to obtain the decrease in travel time is 400 miles per hour.

109. (a) $T = 75.82 - 2.11x + 43.51\sqrt{x}$

$5 \le x \le 40$

(b) When $x = 14.696$, the model predicts $T = 211.609$, which is very accurate.

(c) If $T = 240$, then $x = 24.725$.

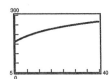

111. $37.55 = 40 - \sqrt{0.01x + 1}$

$$\sqrt{0.01x + 1} = 2.45$$

$$0.01x + 1 = 6.0025$$

$$0.01x = 5.0025$$

$$x = 500.25$$

Rounding x to the nearest whole unit yields $x \approx 500$ units.

Section 2.5   Solving Inequalities Algebraically and Graphically

- You should know the properties of inequalities.
  - (a) Transitive: $a < b$ and $b < c$ implies $a < c$.
  - (b) Addition: $a < b$ and $c < d$ implies $a + c < b + d$.
  - (c) Adding or Subtracting a Constant: $a \pm c < b \pm c$ if $a < b$.
  - (d) Multiplying or Dividing by a Constant: For $a < b$,
    - 1. If $c > 0$, then $ac < bc$ and $\dfrac{a}{c} < \dfrac{b}{c}$.

    - 2. If $c < 0$, then $ac > bc$ and $\dfrac{a}{c} > \dfrac{b}{c}$.

- You should be able to solve inequalities algebraically and graphically.

- You should know that

$$|x| = \begin{cases} x & \text{if } x \geq 0 \\ -x & \text{if } x < 0. \end{cases}$$

- You should be able to solve inequalities involving absolute value.
  - (a) $|x| < a$ if and only if $-a < x < a$.
  - (b) $|x| > a$ if and only if $x < -a$ or $x > a$.

---

1. $x < 4$ indicates all points to the left of $x = 4$; graph (c).

3. $-2 < x \leq 5$ indicates all points from $x = -2$ up to and including $x = 5$; graph (f).

5. $|x| < 4$ indicates all points less than 4 units from $x = 0$; graph (g).

7. $|x - 5| > 2$

$$x - 5 < -2 \quad \text{or} \quad x - 5 > 2$$

$$x < 3 \qquad \qquad x > 7$$

Graph (b)

9. $4x < 12$

$x < 3$

11. $-10x < 40$

$x > -4$

13. $x - 5 \geq 7$

$\qquad x \geq 12$

15. $4(x + 1) < 2x + 3$

$\qquad 4x + 4 < 2x + 3$

$\qquad 2x < -1$

$\qquad x < -\dfrac{1}{2}$

17. $1 < 2x + 3 < 9$

$\quad -2 < \quad 2x \quad < 6$

$\quad -1 < \quad x \quad < 3$

19. $-4 < \dfrac{2x - 3}{3} < 4$

$\quad -12 < 2x - 3 < 12$

$\quad -9 < \quad 2x \quad < 15$

$\quad -\dfrac{9}{2} < \quad x \quad < \dfrac{15}{2}$

21. $\dfrac{3}{4} > x + 1 > \dfrac{1}{4}$

$\quad -\dfrac{1}{4} > \quad x \quad > -\dfrac{3}{4}$

23. $|x| < 5$

$\qquad -5 < x < 5$

25. $\left| \dfrac{x}{2} \right| > 3$

$\quad \dfrac{x}{2} < -3 \quad$ or $\quad \dfrac{x}{2} > 3$

$\quad x < -6 \qquad x > 6$

27. $|x - 20| \leq 4$

$\quad -4 \leq x - 20 \leq 4$

$\quad 16 \leq \quad x \quad \leq 24$

29. $|x - 20| \geq 4$

    $x - 20 \leq -4$ or $x - 20 \geq 4$

        $x \leq 16$ $x \geq 24$

31. $|9 - 2x| - 2 < -1$

        $|9 - 2x| < 1$

    $-1 < 9 - 2x < 1$

   $-10 < -2x < -8$

     $5 > \quad x \quad > 4$

33. $|x - 5| < 0$

No solution

35. Graphing $y_1 = 4 - 2x - 3 = 1 - 2x$ on $[-2, 2] \times [-2, 2]$ shows that the solution to $4 - 2x < 3$ is $x > 0.5$.

37. Graphing

$$y_1 = \frac{-4x + 25}{5} - \frac{3x - 10}{10}$$

on the standard viewing rectangle shows that the solution is $x \leq 5.45$.

39. Graphing both $y_1 = -\frac{5}{2} - 0.75x - 2 = -0.75x - 4.5$ and $y_2 = 0.75x + 2 - 4 = 0.75x - 2$ on the same viewing rectangle shows that the solution to $-\frac{5}{2} < 0.75x + 2 < 4$ is $-3 < x < 2.67$.

41. Graphing

$$y_1 = \left| \frac{x - 3}{2} \right| - 5$$

on $[-10, 20] \times [-10, 10]$ shows that the solution is $x \leq -7$ or $x \geq 13$.

43. Graphing $y_1 = 2|x + 10| - 9$ on $[-20, 10] \times [-10, 10]$ shows that the solution is $x \leq -14.5$ or $x \geq -5.5$.

45. $|x| \leq 2$

47. $|x - 9| \geq 3$

49. $|x - 12| \leq 10$

51. $|x - (-3)| > 5$

        $|x + 3| > 5$

53.
$$x^2 \le 9$$
$$x^2 - 9 \le 0$$
$$(x+3)(x-3) \le 0$$
Critical numbers: $x = \pm 3$
Test intervals:
$$(-\infty,\ -3) \Rightarrow (x+3)(x-3) > 0$$
$$(-3,\ 3) \Rightarrow (x+3)(x-3) < 0$$
$$(3,\ \infty) \Rightarrow (x+3)(x-3) > 0$$
Solution interval: $[-3,\ 3]$

55.
$$x^2 + 4x + 4 \ge 9$$
$$x^2 + 4x - 5 \ge 0$$
$$(x+5)(x-1) \ge 0$$
Critical numbers: $x = -5,\ x = 1$
Test intervals:
$$(-\infty,\ -5) \Rightarrow (x+5)(x-1) > 0$$
$$(-5,\ 1) \Rightarrow (x+5)(x-1) < 0$$
$$(1,\ \infty) \Rightarrow (x+5)(x-1) > 0$$
Solution intervals: $(-\infty,\ -5] \cup [1,\ \infty)$

57.
$$x^2 + x < 6$$
$$x^2 + x - 6 < 0$$
$$(x+3)(x-2) < 0$$
Critical numbers: $x = -3,\ x = 2$
Test intervals:
$$(-\infty,\ -3) \Rightarrow (x+3)(x-2) > 0$$
$$(-3,\ 2) \Rightarrow (x+3)(x-2) < 0$$
$$(2,\ \infty) \Rightarrow (x+3)(x-2) > 0$$
Solution interval: $(-3,\ 2)$

59. $3(x-1)(x+1) > 0$
Critical numbers: $x = -1,\ x = 1$
Test intervals:
$$(-\infty,\ -1) \Rightarrow 3(x-1)(x+1) > 0$$
$$(-1,\ 1) \Rightarrow 3(x-1)(x+1) < 0$$
$$(1,\ \infty) \Rightarrow 3(x-1)(x+1) > 0$$
Solution intervals: $(-\infty,\ -1) \cup (1,\ \infty)$

61.
$$x^2 + 2x - 3 < 0$$
$$(x+3)(x-1) < 0$$
Critical numbers: $x = -3,\ x = 1$
Test intervals:
$$(-\infty,\ -3) \Rightarrow (x+3)(x-1) > 0$$
$$(-3,\ 1) \Rightarrow (x+3)(x-1) < 0$$
$$(1,\ \infty) \Rightarrow (x+3)(x-1) > 0$$
Solution interval: $(-3,\ 1)$

63.
$$4x^3 - 6x^2 < 0$$
$$2x^2(2x-3) < 0$$
Critical numbers: $x = 0,\ x = \frac{3}{2}$
Test intervals:
$$(-\infty,\ 0) \Rightarrow 2x^2(2x-3) < 0$$
$$\left(0,\ \tfrac{3}{2}\right) \Rightarrow 2x^2(2x-3) < 0$$
$$\left(\tfrac{3}{2},\ \infty\right) \Rightarrow 2x^2(2x-3) > 0$$
Solution intervals: $(-\infty,\ 0) \cup \left(0,\ \tfrac{3}{2}\right)$
Note: $x = 0$ is not a solution.

65.
$$x^3 - 4x \geq 0$$
$$x(x+2)(x-2) \geq 0$$

Critical numbers: $x = -2$, $x = 0$, $x = 2$

Test intervals:

$$(-\infty, -2) \Rightarrow x(x+2)(x-2) < 0$$
$$(-2, 0) \Rightarrow x(x+2)(x-2) > 0$$
$$(0, 2) \Rightarrow x(x+2)(x-2) < 0$$
$$(2, \infty) \Rightarrow x(x+2)(x-2) > 0$$

Solution intervals: $[-2, 0] \cup [2, \infty)$

67. Graphing $y_1 = (1/x) - x$ on the standard viewing rectangle, we see that $(1/x) - x > 0$ on $(-\infty, -1) \cup (0, 1)$. Algebraically:

$$\frac{1}{x} > x$$
$$\frac{1}{x} - x > 0$$
$$\frac{1 - x^2}{x} > 0$$
$$\frac{(1+x)(1-x)}{x} > 0$$

Critical numbers: $x = -1$, $x = 0$, $x = 1$

Analyzing the four test intervals, we obtain the same solution as before.

Solution intervals: $(-\infty, -1) \cup (0, 1)$

69. Graphing $y_1 = [(x+6)/(x+1)] - 2$ on the standard viewing rectangle, we see that $[(x+6)/(x+1)] - 2 < 0$ on $(-\infty, -1) \cup (4, \infty)$. Algebraically:

$$\frac{x+6}{x+1} < 2$$
$$\frac{x+6}{x+1} - 2 < 0$$
$$\frac{x+6-2(x+1)}{x+1} < 0$$
$$\frac{4-x}{x+1} < 0$$

Critical numbers: $x = -1$, $x = 4$

Test intervals:

$$(-\infty, -1) \Rightarrow \frac{4-x}{x+1} < 0$$
$$(-1, 4) \Rightarrow \frac{4-x}{x+1} > 0$$
$$(4, \infty) \Rightarrow \frac{4-x}{x+1} < 0$$

Solution intervals: $(-\infty, -1) \cup (4, \infty)$

71. Graphing $y_1 = [(3x-5)/(x-5)] - 4$ on the viewing rectangle $[-10, 20] \times [-5, 5]$, we see that $[(3x-5)/(x-5)] > 4$ on $(5, 15)$. Algebraically:

$$\frac{3x-5}{x-5} > 4$$
$$\frac{3x-5-4(x-5)}{x-5} > 0$$
$$\frac{15-x}{x-5} > 0$$

Critical numbers: $x = 5$, $x = 15$

Test intervals:

$$(-\infty, 5) \Rightarrow \frac{15-x}{x-5} < 0$$
$$(5, 15) \Rightarrow \frac{15-x}{x-5} > 0$$
$$(15, \infty) \Rightarrow \frac{15-x}{x-5} < 0$$

Solution interval: $(5, 15)$

73.
$$\frac{4}{x+5} > \frac{1}{2x+3}$$

$$\frac{4(2x+3) - 1(x+5)}{(x+5)(2x+3)} > 0$$

$$\frac{7x+7}{(x+5)(2x+3)} > 0$$

Critical numbers:
$$x = -5, \ x = -\tfrac{3}{2}, \ x = -1$$

Test intervals:

$$(-\infty, \ -5) \Rightarrow \frac{7x+7}{(x+5)(2x+3)} < 0$$

$$\left(-5, \ -\frac{3}{2}\right) \Rightarrow \frac{7x+7}{(x+5)(2x+3)} > 0$$

$$\left(-\frac{3}{2}, \ -1\right) \Rightarrow \frac{7x+7}{(x+5)(2x+3)} < 0$$

$$(-1, \ \infty) \Rightarrow \frac{7x+7}{(x+5)(2x+3)} > 0$$

Solution intervals: $\left(-5, \ -\frac{3}{2}\right) \cup (-1, \ \infty)$

75. $|x^2 - 4x + 5| < 2x^{-1} = \dfrac{2}{x}$

Graphing $y_1 = |x^2 - 4x + 5|$ and $y_2 = 2/x$ on the same viewing rectangle, we see that the solution satisfies $0 < x < 1$ or $1 < x < 2$.

77. $(x-1)^2(x+2)^3 \geq 0$

Using the zoom and trace features, we find that $x \geq -2$.

79. $-0.5x^2 + 12.5x + 1.6 > 0$

Using the zoom and trace features, we find that $-0.13 < x < 25.13$.

81. $\dfrac{5}{x-6} > \dfrac{3}{x+2}$

Using the zoom and trace features, we find that $x > 6$ or $-14 < x < -2$.

83. $\dfrac{3}{x-1} - \dfrac{2}{x+1} < 1$

Using the zoom and trace features, we find that $x < -2$ or $-1 < x < 1$ or $x > 3$.

85. The radicand of $\sqrt{3-x}$ is $3 - x$.

$$3 - x \geq 0$$
$$-x \geq -3$$
$$x \leq 3$$

Therefore, the interval is $(-\infty, \ 3]$.

87. The radicand of $\sqrt[4]{7-2x}$ is $7 - 2x$.

$$7 - 2x \geq 0$$
$$-2x \geq -7$$
$$x \leq \tfrac{7}{2}$$

Therefore, the interval is $\left(-\infty, \ \frac{7}{2}\right]$.

89. $4 - x^2 \geq 0$

$(2 - x)(2 + x) \geq 0$

Critical numbers: $x = 2$, $x = -2$
Test intervals:

$$(-\infty, -2) \Rightarrow (2 - x)(2 + x) < 0$$

$$(-2, 2) \Rightarrow (2 - x)(2 + x) > 0$$

$$(2, \infty) \Rightarrow (2 - x)(2 + x) < 0$$

Domain: $[-2, 2]$

91. $x^2 - 7x + 12 \geq 0$

$(x - 3)(x - 4) \geq 0$

Critical numbers: $x = 3$, $x = 4$
Test intervals:

$$(-\infty, 3) \Rightarrow (x - 3)(x - 4) > 0$$

$$(3, 4) \Rightarrow (x - 3)(x - 4) < 0$$

$$(4, \infty) \Rightarrow (x - 3)(x - 4) > 0$$

Domain: $(-\infty, 3] \cup [4, \infty)$

93. $12 - x - x^2 \geq 0$

$(4 + x)(3 - x) \geq 0$

Critical numbers: $x = -4$, $x = 3$
Test intervals:

$$(-\infty, -4) \Rightarrow (4 + x)(3 - x) < 0$$

$$(-4, 3) \Rightarrow (4 + x)(3 - x) > 0$$

$$(3, \infty) \Rightarrow (4 + x)(3 - x) < 0$$

Domain: $[-4, 3]$

95. $\dfrac{x}{x^2 - 9} \geq 0$

$\dfrac{x}{(x + 3)(x - 3)} \geq 0$

Critical numbers: $x = -3$, $x = 0$, $x = 3$
Test intervals:

$$(-\infty, -3) \Rightarrow \frac{x}{(x + 3)(x - 3)} < 0$$

$$(3, 0) \Rightarrow \frac{x}{(x + 3)(x - 3)} > 0$$

$$(0, 3) \Rightarrow \frac{x}{(x + 3)(x - 3)} < 0$$

$$(3, \infty) \Rightarrow \frac{x}{(x + 3)(x - 3)} > 0$$

Domain: $(-3, 0] \cup (3, \infty)$

97. $R > C$

$115.95x > 95x + 750$

$20.95x > 750$

$x > 35.7995$

$x \geq 36$ units

Using the zoom and trace features, we find
that $x = 35.80$.

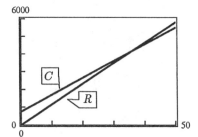

99. (a) $C = 1.45x + 150$

(b) $R = 2.95x$

(c) $P = R - C = 2.95x - (1.45x + 150)$

$$= 1.50x - 150$$

(d) If $50 \le P \le 200$, then

$$133.333 \le x \le 233.333$$

$$134 \le x \le 23.3$$

(e) Let x be the number of dozen *sold*. $C = 1.45(x + 10) + 150$, since there are 10 dozen unsold.

$$R = 2.95x$$

$$P = R - C = 1.50x - 164.5$$

If $50 \le P \le 200$, then $143 \le x \le 243$.

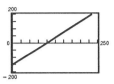

101. Subscribers $= 3.657t + 14.784$

$$3.657t + 14.784 > 55$$

Using the zoom and trace features, we find that $t = 1991$. Or, solving the inequality algebraically,

$$3.657t > 40.216$$

$$t > 10.997$$

$$(t = 1991)$$

103. $\left| \dfrac{h - 68.5}{2.7} \right| \le 1$

$$-1 \le \dfrac{h - 68.5}{2.7} \le 1$$

$$-2.7 \le h - 68.5 \le 2.7$$

$$65.8 \text{ inches } \le h \le 71.2 \text{ inches}$$

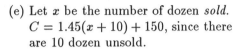

105. $s = -16t^2 + v_0 t + s_0 = -16t^2 + 160t = -16t(t - 10)$

  (a) $t - 10 = 0$

   $t = 10$ seconds later

  (b) $-16t^2 + 160t > 384$

   $t^2 - 10t + 24 < 0$

   $(t - 4)(t - 6) < 0$

   Critical numbers: $t = 4$, $t = 6$
   Test intervals: $(0, 4) \Rightarrow (t - 4)(t - 6) > 0$

   $(4, 6) \Rightarrow (t - 4)(t - 6) < 0$

   $(6, 10) \Rightarrow (t - 4)(t - 6) > 0$

   Solution interval: $(4, 6)$ or 4 sec $< t < 6$ sec

  Or, graphing $y_1 = -16t^2 + 160t$ and $y_2 = 384$ on the viewing rectangle $[0, 10] \times [0, 450]$, we can determine that $y_1 > y_2$ on the interval $(4, 6)$.

107. (a) $\dfrac{1}{R} = \dfrac{1}{R_1} + \dfrac{1}{R_2} = \dfrac{R_2 + R_1}{R_1 R_2}$

   $\Rightarrow R = \dfrac{R_1 R_2}{R_1 + R_2}$

  (b) If $R_2 = 2$, $R = \dfrac{R_1(2)}{R_1 + 2}$.

  (c) If $R \geq 1$, then

   $\dfrac{2R_1}{R_1 + 2} \geq 1 \Rightarrow 2R_1 \geq R_1 + 2 \Rightarrow R_1 \geq 2.$

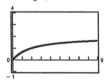

Section 2.6 Exploring Data: Linear Models and Scatter Plots

1.

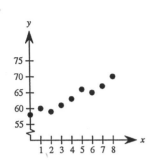

3. Using the points $(0, 58)$ and $(7, 67)$, a linear model for the data is

$$y - 58 = \frac{67 - 58}{7}(x - 0)$$

$$= \frac{9}{7}x$$

$$y = \frac{9}{7}x + 58$$

If $x = 10$ units of fertilizer are used,

$$y = \frac{9}{7}10 + 58 \approx 71 \text{ bushels.}$$

5.

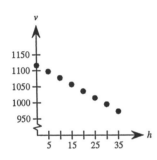

7. Using the points $(0, 1116)$ and $(30, 995)$, a linear model for the data is

$$v - 1116 = \frac{995 - 1116}{30}(h - 0)$$

$$v = -\frac{121}{30}h + 1116$$

when $h = 27$, $v = \frac{-121}{30}(27) + 1116 \approx 1007 \text{ ft/sec.}$

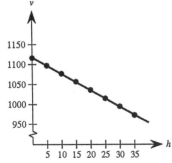

9. a.

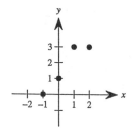

b. $y = x + 1$ fits the data well, and the sum of the squared differences is $0^2 + 0^2 + 1^2 + 0^2 = 1$.

c.

x	y	xy	x^2
-1	0	0	1
0	1	0	0
1	3	3	1
2	3	6	4
$\sum x_i = 2$	$\sum y_i = 7$	$\sum x_i y_i = 9$	$\sum x_i^2 = 6$

Using the formula for the least squares regression line with $n = 4$ produces

$$a = \frac{4(9) - 2(7)}{4(6) - (2)^2} = \frac{22}{20} = \frac{11}{10}$$

$$b = \frac{1}{4}\left(7 - \frac{11}{10}(2)\right) = \frac{1}{4}\left(\frac{48}{10}\right) = \frac{12}{10}$$

Thus the least square regression line is $y = \frac{11}{10}x + \frac{12}{10}$.

The sum of the squared differences is

$(.1 - 0)^2 + (1.2 - 1)^2 + (2.3 - 3)^2 + (3.4 - 3)^2 = 0.3$.

11. a.

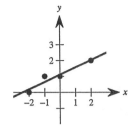

b.

x	y	xy	x^2
-2	0	0	4
-1	1	-1	1
0	1	0	0
2	2	4	4
$\sum x_i = -1$	$\sum y_i = 4$	$\sum x_i y_i = 3$	$\sum x_i{}^2 = 9$

$$a = \frac{4(3) - (-1)(4)}{4(9) - (-1)^2} = \frac{16}{35}$$

$$b = \frac{1}{4}\left(4 - \frac{16}{35}(-1)\right) = \frac{39}{35}$$

$$y = \frac{16}{35}x + \frac{39}{35}$$

13. a.

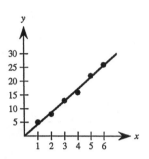

b.

x	y	xy	x^2
1	5	5	1
2	8	16	4
3	13	39	9
4	16	64	16
5	22	110	25
6	26	156	36
$\sum x_i = 21$	$\sum y_i = 90$	$\sum x_i y_i = 390$	$\sum x_i^2 = 91$

$$a = \frac{6(390) - 21(90)}{6(91) - (21)^2} \approx 4.2857$$

$$b = \frac{1}{6}\left(90 - 4.2857(21)\right) \approx 0$$

$$y = 4.2857x = \frac{30}{7}x$$

15.

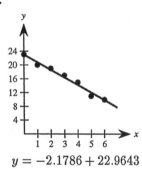

$$y = -2.1786 + 22.9643$$

17.

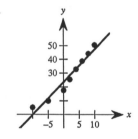

$$y = 2.3757x + 23.5456$$

19. a. $S = 21.1786x + 384.0714$
If $x = 4.5, S \approx 479.4$.

b.

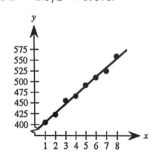

c. Correlation coefficient ≈ 0.9957.

Chapter 2   Review Exercises

1.
$$6 - (x-2)^2 = 2 + 4x - x^2$$
$$6 - (x^2 - 4x + 4) = 2 + 4x - x^2$$
$$2 + 4x - x^2 = 2 + 4x - x^2$$
$$0 = 0 \quad \text{Identity}$$

3. (a) $3(0)^2 + 7(0) + 5 \stackrel{?}{=} (0)^2 + 9$

$$5 \neq 9$$

$x = 0$ *is not* a solution.

(b) $3(-4)^2 + 7(-4) + 5 \stackrel{?}{=} (-4)^2 + 9$

$$25 = 25$$

$x = -4$ *is* a solution.

(c) $3\left(\dfrac{1}{2}\right)^2 + 7\left(\dfrac{1}{2}\right) + 5 \stackrel{?}{=} \left(\dfrac{1}{2}\right)^2 + 9$

$$\frac{37}{4} = \frac{37}{4}$$

$x = \frac{1}{2}$ *is* a solution.

(d) $3(-1)^2 + 7(-1) + 5 \stackrel{?}{=} (-1)^2 + 9$

$$1 \neq 10$$

$x = -1$ *is not* a solution.

5. $3x - 2(x+5) = 10$
$$3x - 2x - 10 = 10$$
$$x = 20$$

7. $3\left(1 - \dfrac{1}{5t}\right) = 0$
$$1 - \frac{1}{5t} = 0$$
$$1 = \frac{1}{5t}$$
$$5t = 1$$
$$t = \frac{1}{5}$$

9. $\qquad\qquad 6x^2 = 5x + 4$
$$6x^2 - 5x - 4 = 0$$
$$(3x - 4)(2x + 1) = 0$$
$$3x - 4 = 0 \;\Rightarrow\; x = \tfrac{4}{3}$$
$$2x + 1 = 0 \;\Rightarrow\; x = -\tfrac{1}{2}$$

11. $(x+4)^2 = 18$
$$x + 4 = \pm\sqrt{18}$$
$$x = -4 \pm 3\sqrt{2}$$

13. $x^2 - 12x + 30 = 0$
$$x = \frac{-(-12) \pm \sqrt{(-12)^2 - 4(1)(30)}}{2(1)}$$
$$x = 6 \pm \sqrt{6}$$

15. $4t^3 - 12t^2 + 8t = 0$

$4t(t^2 - 3t + 2) = 0$

$4t(t - 1)(t - 2) = 0$

$4t = 0 \Rightarrow t = 0$

$t - 1 = 0 \Rightarrow t = 1$

$t - 2 = 0 \Rightarrow t = 2$

17. $\dfrac{4}{(x - 4)^2} = 1$

$4 = (x - 4)^2$

$\pm 2 = x - 4$

$4 \pm 2 = x$

$x = 6 \quad \text{or} \quad x = 2$

19. $\sqrt{x + 4} = 3$

$(\sqrt{x + 4})^2 = (3)^2$

$x + 4 = 9$

$x = 5$

21. $2\sqrt{x} - 5 = 0$

$(2\sqrt{x})^2 = 5^2$

$4x = 25$

$x = \frac{25}{4}$

23. $(x - 1)^{2/3} - 25 = 0$

$(x - 1)^{2/3} = 25$

$x - 1 = \pm 25^{3/2}$

$x = 1 \pm 125$

$x = 126 \text{ or } x = -124$

25. $(x + 4)^{1/2} + 5x(x + 4)^{3/2} = 0$

$(x + 4)^{1/2}[1 + 5x(x + 4)] = 0$

$(x + 4)^{1/2}(5x^2 + 20x + 1) = 0$

$x + 4 = 0 \Rightarrow x = -4$

$5x^2 + 20x + 1 = 0 \Rightarrow x = \dfrac{-20 \pm \sqrt{380}}{10}$

$= -2 \pm \dfrac{\sqrt{95}}{5}$

27. $|x - 5| = 10$

$x - 5 = -10 \quad \text{or} \quad x - 5 = 10$

$x = -5 \qquad\qquad x = 15$

29. $x^2 + 6x - 3 = 0$

Using the zoom and trace features, we find that $x = 0.464,\ -6.464$.

31. $5\sqrt{x} - \sqrt{x - 1} = 6$

Using the zoom and trace features, we find that $x = 1.944$.

33. $\dfrac{1}{x} + \dfrac{1}{x + 1} = 2$

Using the zoom and trace features, we find that $x = \pm 0.707$.

35. $|x^2 - 3| = 2x$

Using the zoom and trace features, we find that $x = 1, 3$.

37. $V = \dfrac{1}{3}\pi r^2 h$

$$3V = \pi r^2 h$$

$$\dfrac{3V}{\pi h} = r^2$$

$$r = \sqrt{\dfrac{3V}{\pi h}}, \qquad \text{(assuming } r > 0\text{)}$$

39. $$L = \dfrac{k}{3\pi r^2 p}$$

$$3\pi r^2 p L = k$$

$$p = \dfrac{k}{3\pi r^2 L}$$

41. $-(6 - 2i) + (-8 + 3i) = -6 - 8 + (2 + 3)i$

$$= -14 + 5i$$

43. $5i(13 - 8i) = 65i - 40i^2$

$$= 40 + 65i$$

45. $\dfrac{6 + i}{i} = \dfrac{6 + i}{i} \cdot \dfrac{-i}{-i}$

$$= \dfrac{-6i + 1}{1}$$

$$= 1 - 6i$$

47. $f(x) = (x + 1)(x + 1)(3x - 1)(2x + 1)$

$$= (x^2 + 2x + 1)(6x^2 + x - 1)$$

$$= 6x^4 + 13x^3 + 7x^2 - x - 1$$

49. $f(x) = (3x - 2)(x - 4)(x - \sqrt{3}i)(x + \sqrt{3}i)$

$$= (3x^2 - 14x + 8)(x^2 + 3)$$

$$= 3x^4 - 14x^3 + 17x^2 - 42x + 24$$

51. $\frac{1}{2}(3 - x) > \frac{1}{3}(2 - 3x)$

$$3(3 - x) > 2(2 - 3x)$$

$$9 - 3x > 4 - 6x$$

$$3x > -5$$

$$x > -\tfrac{5}{3} \text{ or } \left(-\tfrac{5}{3}, \infty\right)$$

53. $\dfrac{x - 5}{3 - x} < 0$

Test intervals:

$$(-\infty, 3) \Rightarrow \dfrac{x - 5}{3 - x} < 0$$

$$(3, 5) \Rightarrow \dfrac{x - 5}{3 - x} > 0$$

$$(5, \infty) \Rightarrow \dfrac{x - 5}{3 - x} < 0$$

Solution intervals: $(-\infty, 3) \cup (5, \infty)$

55. $|x - 2| < 1$

$$-1 < x - 2 < 1$$

$$1 < x < 3 \text{ or } (1, 3)$$

57. $\left|x - \frac{3}{2}\right| \geq \frac{3}{2}$

$\qquad x - \frac{3}{2} \leq -\frac{3}{2} \quad$ or $\quad x - \frac{3}{2} \geq \frac{3}{2}$

$\qquad x \leq 0 \qquad\qquad x \geq 3$ or $(-\infty, \, 0] \cup [3, \, \infty)$

59. $\dfrac{x}{5} - 6 \leq -\dfrac{x}{2} + 6$

Using the zoom and trace features, we find that $x \leq 17.143$.

61. $(x - 4)|x| > 0$

Using the zoom and trace features, we find that $x = (4, \, \infty)$.

63. $2x - 10 \geq 0$

$\qquad 2x \geq 10$

$\qquad x \geq 5$ or $[5, \, \infty)$

65. September's profit $= x$

October's profit $= 1.12x$

$\qquad x + 1.12x = 689{,}000$

$\qquad 2.12x = 689{,}000$

$\qquad x = 325{,}000$

September's profit $= x = \$325{,}000$

October's profit $= 1.12x = \$364{,}000$

67. Let $x =$ the number of quarts of pure antifreeze.

$\qquad 30\%$ of $(10 - x) + 100\%$ of $x = 50\%$ of 10

$\qquad 0.30(10 - x) + 1.00x = 0.50(10)$

$\qquad 3 - 0.30x + 1.00x = 5$

$\qquad 0.70x = 2$

$\qquad x = \dfrac{2}{0.70}$

$\qquad \approx 2.857$ quarts

69. Since the angle is $45°$, the triangle is isosceles.

$\qquad x^2 + x^2 = 2000^2$

$\qquad 2x^2 = 4{,}000{,}000$

$\qquad x^2 = 2{,}000{,}000$

$\qquad x = 1000\sqrt{2} \approx 1414.21$ feet

71. Let $x = $ number of farmers in the group.

Cost per farmer: $48{,}000/x$

If two more farmers join the group, the cost per farmer will be $48{,}000/(x+2)$. Since this new cost is \$4000 less than the original cost:

$$\frac{48{,}000}{x} - 4000 = \frac{48{,}000}{x+2}$$

$$48{,}000(x+2) - 4000x(x+2) = 48{,}000x$$

$$12(x+2) - x(x+2) = 12x$$

$$12x + 24 - x^2 - 2x = 12x$$

$$0 = x^2 + 2x - 24$$

$$0 = (x+6)(x-4)$$

$x = -6$, extraneous or $x = 4$

Thus, $x = 4$ farmers. Or, using a graphing utility to graph

$$y_1 = \frac{48{,}000}{x} - 4000 - \frac{48{,}000}{x+2}$$

we see that the positive x-intercept is 4.00.

73.
$$29.95 = 42 - \sqrt{0.001x + 2}$$

$$\left(\sqrt{0.001x + 2}\right)^2 = (12.05)^2$$

$$0.001x + 2 = 145.2025$$

$$0.001x = 143.2025$$

$$x \approx 143{,}203$$

The demand would be for 143,203 units per day.

75.
$$R > C$$

$$125.95x > 92x + 1200$$

$$33.95x > 1200$$

$$x > 35.346$$

When $x \geq 36$ units, this product will return a profit.

CHAPTER 3

Polynomial and Rational Functions

Section 3.1   Quadratic Functions

You should know the following facts about parabolas.

- ■ $f(x) = ax^2 + bx + c$, $a \neq 0$, is a quadratic function and its graph is a parabola.
- ■ If $a > 0$, the parabola opens upward and the vertex is the minimum point. If $a < 0$, the parabola opens downward and the vertex is the maximum point.
- ■ The vertex is $(-b/2a,\ f(-b/2a))$.
- ■ To find the x-intercepts (if any), solve $ax^2 + bx + c = 0$.
- ■ The standard form of the equation of a parabola is $f(x) = a(x - h)^2 + k$, where $a \neq 0$.
  (a) The vertex is $(h,\ k)$.
  (b) The axis is the vertical line $x = h$.

---

1. $f(x) = (x - 3)^2$ opens upward and has vertex $(3, 0)$; graph (f)

```
RANGE
Xmin=-1
Xmax=6
Xscl=1
Ymin=-1
Ymax=5
Yscl=1
```

3. $f(x) = x^2 - 4$ opens upward and has vertex $(0, -4)$; graph (c)

```
RANGE
Xmin=-4
Xmax=4
Xscl=1
Ymin=-5
Ymax=2
Yscl=1
```

5. $f(x) = 4 - (x - 1)^2$ opens downward and has vertex $(1, 4)$; graph (b)

```
RANGE
Xmin=-3
Xmax=5
Xscl=1
Ymin=-2
Ymax=5
Yscl=1
```

7. (a) f is a parabola that opens upward and is broader than $y = x^2$.

(b) g is a parabola that opens downward and is narrower than $y = x^2$.

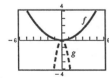

9. (a) f is shifted 3 units to the left, 3 units upward, and opens downward.

(b) g is shifted 4 units to the right and 3 units downward. It opens upward and is narrower than $y = x^2$.

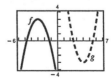

11. Vertex: $(2, 0)$

$y = a(x - 2)^2 + 0$

$(0, 4)$ is on graph

$4 = a(0 - 2)^2$

$a = 1$

$y = (x - 2)^2$

13. Vertex: $(-2, 4)$

$y = a(x + 2)^2 + 4$

$(0, 0)$ is on graph

$0 = a(0 + 2)^2 + 4$

$a = -1$

$y = -(x + 2)^2 + 4$

15. Vertex: $(-3, 3)$

$y = a(x + 3)^2 + 3$

$(-2, 1)$ is on graph

$1 = a(-2 + 3)^2 + 3$

$a = -2$

$y = -2(x + 3)^2 + 3$

17. $f(x) = x^2 - 5$

Vertex: $(0, -5)$

Intercepts: $(-\sqrt{5}, 0),\ (0, -5),\ (\sqrt{5}, 0)$

19. $f(x) = (x + 5)^2 - 6$

Vertex: $(-5, -6)$

Intercepts: $(-5 - \sqrt{6}, 0),$
$(-5 + \sqrt{6}, 0),\ (0, 19)$

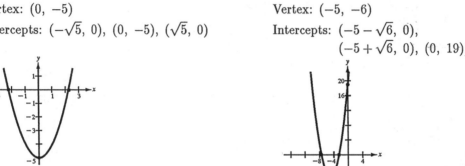

21. $h(x) = x^2 - 8x + 16 = (x - 4)^2$

Vertex: $(4, 0)$

Intercepts: $(0, 16),\ (4, 0)$

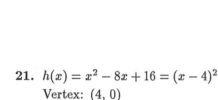

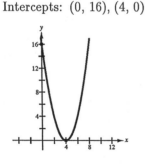

23. $f(x) = -x^2 + 2x + 5$

$\qquad = -(x^2 - 2x + 1) + 5 + 1$

$\qquad = -(x - 1)^2 + 6$

Vertex: $(1, 6)$

Intercepts: $(1 - \sqrt{6}, 0),\ (0, 5),\ (1 + \sqrt{6}, 0)$

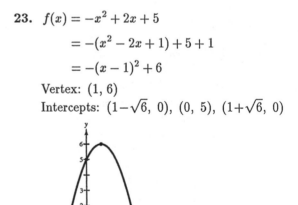

25. $h(x) = 4x^2 - 4x + 21$

$\quad = 4\left(x^2 - x + \frac{1}{4}\right) + 21 - 1$

$\quad = 4\left(x - \frac{1}{2}\right)^2 + 20$

Vertex: $\left(\frac{1}{2},\, 20\right)$

Intercept: $(0, 21)$

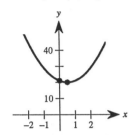

27. $f(x) = -(x^2 + 2x - 3)$

$\quad = -(x^2 + 2x + 1) + 3 + 1$

$\quad = -(x + 1)^2 + 4$

Vertex: $(-1, 4)$

Intercepts: $(1,\, 0),\ (-3,\, 0),\ (0,\, 3)$

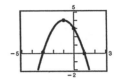

29. $f(x) = 2x^2 - 16x + 31$

$\quad = 2(x^2 - 8x + 16) + 31 - 32$

$\quad = 2(x - 4)^2 - 1$

Vertex: $(4, -1)$

Intercepts: $(3.29,\, 0),\ (4.71,\, 0),\ (0,\, 31)$

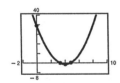

31. $y = a(x - 3)^2 + 4$

$\quad 2 = a(1 - 3)^2 + 4$

$\quad 4a = -2$

$\quad a = -\frac{1}{2}$

$\quad y = -\frac{1}{2}(x - 3)^2 + 4$

33. $y = a(x - 5)^2 + 12$

$\quad 15 = a(7 - 5)^2 + 12$

$\quad 4a = 3$

$\quad a = \frac{3}{4}$

$\quad y = \frac{3}{4}(x - 5)^2 + 12$

35. $y = (x + 1)(x - 3) = x^2 - 2x - 3$

$\quad y = -(x + 1)(x - 3) = -x^2 + 2x + 3$

37. $y = x(x - 10) = x^2 - 10x$

$\quad y = -x(x - 10) = -x^2 + 10x$

39. $y = (x + 3)(2x + 1) = 2x^2 + 7x + 3$

$\quad y = -(x + 3)(2x + 1) = -2x^2 - 7x - 3$

41. $f(x) = x(110 - x) = -x^2 + 110x = -(x^2 - 110x + 3025) + 3025 = -(x - 55)^2 + 3025$

Vertex: $(55, 3025)$

The two numbers are $x = 55$ and $110 - x = 55$. Or, by graphing $f(x) = -x^2 + 110x$, we see that the maximum value of f occurs at $(55, 3025)$.

43. (a) $2x + 2w = 100$

$$w = 50 - x$$

$$A(x) = xw = x(50 - x)$$

Domain: $0 < x < 50$

(c) $x = w = 25$ for maximum area (square)

(b)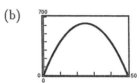

45. $4x + 3y = 200$

$$3y = 200 - 4x$$

$$y = \frac{200 - 4x}{3}$$

$$A = 2xy = 2x \left(\frac{200 - 4x}{3} \right)$$

$$= \frac{2}{3}(-4x^2 + 200x)$$

$$= -\frac{8}{3}(x^2 - 50x)$$

$$= -\frac{8}{3}(x^2 - 50x + 625) + \frac{5000}{3} = -\frac{8}{3}(x - 25)^2 + \frac{5000}{3}$$

The maximum area occurs at the vertex and is $5000/3$ square feet. This happens when $x = 25$ feet and $y = [200 - 4(25)]/3 = 100/3$ feet. The dimensions are $2x = 50$ feet by $33\frac{1}{3}$ feet.

47. $R = 900x - 0.1x^2 = -0.1(x^2 - 9000 + (4500)^2) + 2{,}025{,}000 = -0.1(x - 4500)^2 + 2{,}025{,}000$

Vertex: $(4500,\ 2{,}025{,}000)$

Maximum when $x = 4500$ units. Or, by graphing $R = 900x - 0.1x^2$, we see that the maximum value of R occurs at $(4500.00,\ 2{,}025{,}000.00)$.

49. $C = 4024.5 + 51.4t - 3.1t^2$, $(t = 0$ is 1960.$)$

(a) Yes, the average annual consumption dropped after 1968.

(b) $\dfrac{(4024.5)(116{,}530{,}000)}{48{,}500{,}000} = 9669.6$ cigarettes/smoker

$$\frac{9669.6}{365} = 26.5 \text{ cigarettes/day}$$

51. $y = -\frac{1}{12}x^2 + 2x + 4$

(a)

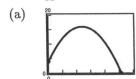

(b) $y = 4$ feet when $x = 0$.

(c) $y = 16$ feet is the maximum height (when $x = 12$).

(d) $x = 25.86$ feet when the ball strikes the ground $(y = 0)$.

53. $V = 0.77x^2 - 1.32x - 9.31, \quad 0 \le x \le 40$

(a)

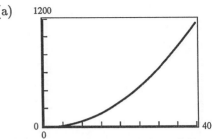

(b) If $x = 16, \quad V = 166.69$ board-feet.

(c) If $V = 500, \quad x = 26.59$ inches.

55. $f(x) = ax^2 + bx + c = a\left(x^2 + \dfrac{b}{a}x + \left(\dfrac{b}{2a}\right)^2\right) + c - \dfrac{b^2}{4a} = a\left(x + \dfrac{b}{2a}\right)^2 + \dfrac{4ac - b^2}{4a}$

Vertex: $\left(-\dfrac{b}{2a}, \ -\dfrac{b^2 - 4ac}{4a}\right)$

57. If $f(x) = ax^2 + bx + c$ has two real zeros, then by the Quadratic Formula they are

$x = \dfrac{-b \pm \sqrt{b^2 - 4ac}}{2a}$. The average of the zeros of f is

$\dfrac{\dfrac{-b - \sqrt{b^2 - 4ac}}{2a} + \dfrac{-b + \sqrt{b^2 - 4ac}}{2a}}{2} = \dfrac{\dfrac{-2b}{2a}}{2} = -\dfrac{b}{2a}$.

This is the x-coordinate of the vertex of the graph. (See Exercise 55.)

Section 3.2   Polynomial Functions of Higher Degree

You should know the following basic principles about polynomials.

■ $f(x) = a_n x^n + a_{n-1} x^{n-1} + \cdots + a_2 x^2 + a_1 x + a_0$, $a_n \neq 0$ is a polynomial function of degree n.

■ The graph of a polynomial function is continuous, as you can verify with a graphing utility.

■ If f is of odd degree and

    (a) $a_n > 0$, then: (b) $a_n < 0$, then:

         1. $f(x) \to \infty$ as $x \to \infty$ 1. $f(x) \to -\infty$ as $x \to \infty$

         2. $f(x) \to -\infty$ as $x \to -\infty$ 2. $f(x) \to \infty$ as $x \to -\infty$

■ If f is of even degree and

    (a) $a_n > 0$, then: (b) $a_n < 0$, then:

         1. $f(x) \to \infty$ as $x \to \infty$ 1. $f(x) \to -\infty$ as $x \to \infty$

         2. $f(x) \to \infty$ as $x \to -\infty$ 2. $f(x) \to -\infty$ as $x \to -\infty$

■ The following are equivalent for a polynomial function.

    (a) $x = a$ is a zero of a function.

    (b) $x = a$ is a solution of the polynomial equation $f(x) = 0$.

    (c) $(x - a)$ is a factor of the polynomial.

    (d) $(a, \ 0)$ is an x-intercept of the graph of f.

■ A polynomial of degree n has at most n distinct zeros. These can be found using a graphing utility.

■ If f is a polynomial function such that $a < b$ and $f(a) \neq f(b)$, then the Intermediate Value Theorem says that f takes on every value between $f(a)$ and $f(b)$ in the interval $[a, \ b]$.

■ If you can find a value where a polynomial is positive and another value where it is negative, then there is at least one real zero between the values. You can find this zero using a graphing utility.

1. (a) $f(x) = (x-2)^3$ is a right shift by 2 units of $y = x^3$.

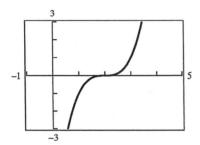

(b) $f(x) = x^3 - 2$ is a downward shift of 2 units of $y = x^3$.

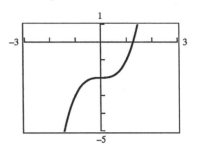

(c) $f(x) = (x-2)^3 - 2$ is a right shift of 2 units, and a downward shift of 2 units of $y = x^3$.

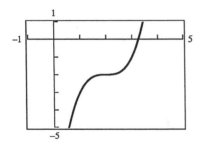

(d) $f(x) = -\frac{1}{2}x^3$ is a reflection in the x-axis, and wider, compared to $y = x^3$.

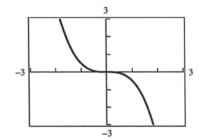

3. $f(x) = -3x + 5$ is a line with y-intercept $(0, 5)$; graph (e)

```
RANGE
Xmin=-3
Xmax=5
Xscl=1
Ymin=-1
Ymax=6
Yscl=1
```

5. $f(x) = -2x^2 - 8x - 9$ is a parabola opening downward; graph (b)

```
RANGE
Xmin=-5
Xmax=1
Xscl=1
Ymin=-12
Ymax=3
Yscl=3
```

7. $f(x) = -\frac{1}{3}x^3 + x - \frac{2}{3}$ is a cubic with y-intercept $\left(0, -\frac{2}{3}\right)$; graph (a)

```
RANGE
Xmin=-3
Xmax=3
Xscl=1
Ymin=-3
Ymax=2
Yscl=1
```

9. $f(x) = 3x^4 + 4x^3$ has intercepts $(0, 0)$ and $\left(-\frac{4}{3}, 0\right)$; graph (d)

```
RANGE
Xmin=-3
Xmax=2
Xscl=1
Ymin=-2
Ymax=4
Yscl=1
```

11.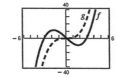

13.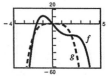

15. $f(x) = 2x^2 - 3x + 1$

The degree is even and the leading coefficient is positive. The graph rises to the left and right.

17. $h(t) = -\frac{2}{3}(t^2 - 5t + 3)$

The degree is even and the leading coefficient is negative. The graph falls to the left and right.

19. $f(x) = 6 - 2x + 4x^2 - 5x^3$

The degree is odd and the leading coefficient is negative. The graph rises to the left and falls to the right.

21. $f(x) = x^2 - 25$

$\quad = (x + 5)(x - 5)$

Thus, the real zeros are -5 and 5.

23. $h(t) = t^2 - 6t + 9$

$\quad = (t - 3)^2$

Thus, the real zero is 3.

25. $f(x) = x^2 + x - 2$

$\quad = (x + 2)(x - 1)$

Thus, the real zeros are -2 and 1.

27. $f(x) = 3x^2 - 12x + 3$

$\quad = 3(x^2 - 4x + 1)$

$\quad = \dfrac{4 \pm \sqrt{16 - 4}}{2} = 2 \pm \sqrt{3}$

Thus, the real zeros are $2 \pm \sqrt{3}$.

29. $f(t) = t^3 - 4t^2 + 4t$

$\quad = t(t - 2)^2$

Thus, the real zeros are 0 and 2.

31. $g(t) = \frac{1}{2}t^4 - \frac{1}{2}$

$\quad = \frac{1}{2}(t + 1)(t - 1)(t^2 + 1)$

Thus, the real zeros are -1 and 1.

33. $f(x) = 2x^4 - 2x^2 - 40$

$\qquad = 2(x^2 + 4)(x^2 - 5)$

$\qquad = 2(x^2 + 4)(x + \sqrt{5})(x - \sqrt{5})$

$\quad$ Thus, the real zeros are $-\sqrt{5}$ and $\sqrt{5}$.

35. $f(x) = 5x^4 + 15x^2 + 10$

$\qquad = 5(x^4 + 3x^2 + 2)$

$\qquad = 5(x^2 + 2)(x^2 + 1)$

No real zeros; or, by graphing f, we see the graph lies entirely above the x-axis.

37. $f(x) = (x - 0)(x - 10)$

$\qquad = x^2 - 10x$

39. $f(x) = (x - 2)(x + 6)$

$\qquad = x^2 + 4x - 12$

41. $f(x) = (x - 0)(x + 2)(x + 3)$

$\qquad = x(x^2 + 5x + 6)$

$\qquad = x^3 + 5x^2 + 6x$

43. $f(x) = (x - 4)(x + 3)(x - 3)(x - 0)$

$\qquad = (x^2 - 4x)(x^2 - 9)$

$\qquad = x^4 - 4x^3 - 9x^2 + 36x$

45. $f(x) = [x - (1 + \sqrt{3})][x - (1 - \sqrt{3})]$

$\qquad = [(x - 1) - \sqrt{3}][(x - 1) + \sqrt{3}]$

$\qquad = (x - 1)^2 - 3$

$\qquad = x^2 - 2x + 1 - 3$

$\qquad = x^2 - 2x - 2$

47.

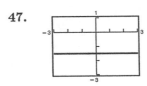

49.

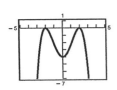

51.

53.

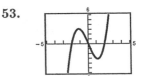

55.

57.

59.

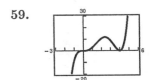

61.

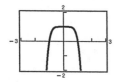

63. $f(x) = x^3 - 3x^2 + 3$
$[-1, 0], [1, 2], [2, 3]$

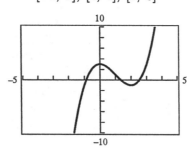

65. $g(x) = 3x^4 + 4x^3 - 3$
$[-2, -1], [0, 1]$

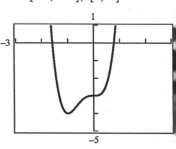

67. (a) Volume $= (12 - 2x)(12 - 2x)x$
$= 4x(6 - x)^2$

(b) Domain: $0 < x < 6$

(c) $V(x)$ is maximum for $x = 2.00$.

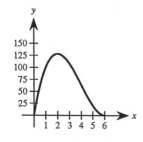

69. $R = \frac{1}{50,000}(-x^3 + 600x^2)$, $0 \le x \le 400$

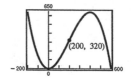

$x = 200$ is approximately the point where R is increasing most rapidly.

Section 3.3   Real Zeros of Polynomial Functions

> You should know the following basic techniques and principles of polynomial division.
>
> ■ The Division Algorithm (Long Division of Polynomials)
>
> ■ Synthetic Division
>
> ■ $f(k)$ is equal to the remainder of $f(x)$ divided by $(x - k)$.
>
> ■ $f(k) = 0$ if and only if $(x - k)$ is a factor of $f(x)$.

1.
$$
\begin{array}{r}
2x + 4 \\
x + 3 \overline{\smash{\big)}\ 2x^2 + 10x + 12} \\
\underline{2x^2 + 6x} \\
4x + 12 \\
\underline{4x + 12} \\
0
\end{array}
$$

3.
$$
\begin{array}{r}
x^2 - 3x + 1 \\
4x + 5 \overline{\smash{\big)}\ 4x^3 - 7x^2 - 11x + 5} \\
\underline{4x^3 + 5x^2} \\
-12x^2 - 11x \\
\underline{-12x^2 - 15x} \\
4x + 5 \\
\underline{4x + 5} \\
0
\end{array}
$$

5.
$$
\begin{array}{r}
x^3 + 3x^2 - 1 \\
x + 2 \overline{\smash{\big)}\ x^4 + 5x^3 + 6x^2 - x - 2} \\
\underline{x^4 + 2x^3} \\
3x^3 + 6x^2 \\
\underline{3x^3 + 6x^2} \\
-x - 2 \\
\underline{-x - 2} \\
0
\end{array}
$$

7.
$$
\begin{array}{r}
7 \\
x + 2 \overline{\smash{\big)}\ 7x + 3} \\
\underline{7x + 14} \\
-11
\end{array}
$$

$$
\frac{7x + 3}{x + 2} = 7 - \frac{11}{x + 2}
$$

9.
$$
\begin{array}{r}
3x + 5 \\
2x^2 + 1 \overline{\smash{\big)}\ 6x^3 + 10x^2 + x + 8} \\
\underline{6x^3 \qquad\quad + 3x} \\
10x^2 - 2x + 8 \\
\underline{10x^2 \qquad + 5} \\
-2x + 3
\end{array}
$$

$$
\frac{6x^3 + 10x^2 + x + 8}{2x^2 + 1} = 3x + 5 - \frac{2x - 3}{2x^2 + 1}
$$

11.

$$x^2 - 2x + 3\ \overline{)\ x^4\qquad + 3x^2\qquad\ + 1}$$

with the work:

$$\begin{array}{r} x^2 + 2x\ \ + 4 \\ \hline x^4\qquad + 3x^2\qquad + 1 \\ \underline{x^4 - 2x^3 + 3x^2} \\ 2x^3 \\ \underline{2x^3 - 4x^2 + 6x} \\ 4x^2 - 6x +\ 1 \\ \underline{4x^2 - 8x + 12} \\ 2x - 11 \end{array}$$

$$\Rightarrow \quad \frac{x^4 + 3x^2 + 1}{x^2 - 2x + 3} = x^2 + 2x + 4 + \frac{2x - 11}{x^2 - 2x + 3}$$

13. Observe that $(x - 1)^2 = x^2 - 2x + 1$.

$$\begin{array}{r} 2x \\ \hline x^2 - 2x + 1\ \overline{)\ 2x^3 - 4x^2 - 15x + 5} \\ \underline{2x^3 - 4x^2 +\ 2x} \\ -17x + 5 \end{array}$$

$$\Rightarrow \quad \frac{2x^3 - 4x^2 - 15x + 5}{(x - 1)^2} = 2x - \frac{17x - 5}{(x - 1)^2}$$

15.

5	3	−17	15	−25
		15	−10	25
	3	−2	5	0

$$(3x^3 - 17x^2 + 15x - 25) \div (x - 5)$$
$$= 3x^2 - 2x + 5$$

17.

−2	4	8	−9	−18
		−8	0	18
	4	0	−9	0

$$(4x^3 - 9x + 8x^2 - 18) \div (x + 2) = 4x^2 - 9$$

19.

−10	−1	0	75	−250
		10	−100	250
	−1	10	−25	0

$$(-x^3 + 75x - 250) \div (x + 10)$$
$$= -x^2 + 10x - 25$$

21.

4	5	−6	0	8
		20	56	224
	5	14	56	232

$$(5x^3 - 6x^2 + 8) \div (x - 4)$$
$$= 5x^2 + 14x + 56 + \frac{232}{x - 4}$$

23.

6	10	−50	0	0	−800
		60	60	360	2160
	10	10	60	360	1360

$$(10x^4 - 50x^3 - 800) \div (x - 6)$$
$$= 10x^3 + 10x^2 + 60x + 360 + \frac{1360}{x - 6}$$

25.

−8	1	0	0	512
		−8	64	−512
	1	−8	64	0

$$(x^3 + 512) \div (x + 8) = x^2 - 8x + 64$$

27. $2 \mid \begin{array}{ccccc} -3 & 0 & 0 & 0 & 0 \end{array}$

$ \begin{array}{ccccc} & -6 & -12 & -24 & -48 \end{array}$

$ \begin{array}{ccccc} -3 & -6 & -12 & -24 & -48 \end{array}$

$-3x^4 \div (x - 2)$

$\quad = -3x^3 - 6x^2 - 12x - 24 - \dfrac{48}{x-2}$

29. $-1 \mid \begin{array}{cccc} -1 & 2 & -3 & 5 \end{array}$

$ \begin{array}{cccc} & 1 & -3 & 6 \end{array}$

$ \begin{array}{cccc} -1 & 3 & -6 & 11 \end{array}$

$(5 - 3x + 2x^2 - x^3) \div (x + 1)$

$\quad = -x^2 + 3x - 6 + \dfrac{11}{x+1}$

31. $-\frac{1}{2} \mid \begin{array}{cccc} 4 & 16 & -23 & -15 \end{array}$

$\phantom{-\frac{1}{2} \mid} \begin{array}{cccc} & -2 & -7 & 15 \end{array}$

$\phantom{-\frac{1}{2} \mid} \begin{array}{cccc} 4 & 14 & -30 & 0 \end{array}$

$(4x^3 + 16x^2 - 23x - 15) \div \left(x + \frac{1}{2}\right)$

$\quad = 4x^2 + 14x - 30$

33. $2 \mid \begin{array}{cccc} 1 & 0 & -7 & 6 \end{array}$

$ \begin{array}{cccc} & 2 & 4 & -6 \end{array}$

$ \begin{array}{cccc} 1 & 2 & -3 & 0 \end{array}$

$x^3 - 7x + 6 = (x - 2)(x^2 + 2x - 3)$

$\quad = (x - 2)(x + 3)(x - 1)$

Real zeros: 2, -3, 1

35. $\frac{1}{2} \mid \begin{array}{cccc} 2 & -15 & 27 & -10 \end{array}$

$\phantom{\frac{1}{2} \mid} \begin{array}{cccc} & 1 & -7 & 10 \end{array}$

$\phantom{\frac{1}{2} \mid} \begin{array}{cccc} 2 & -14 & 20 & 0 \end{array}$

$2x^3 - 15x^2 + 27x - 10 = \left(x - \frac{1}{2}\right)(2x^2 - 14x + 20) = (2x - 1)(x - 2)(x - 5)$

Real zeros: $\frac{1}{2}$, 2, 5

37. $\sqrt{3} \mid \begin{array}{cccc} 1 & 2 & -3 & -6 \end{array}$

$\phantom{\sqrt{3} \mid} \begin{array}{cccc} & \sqrt{3} & 2\sqrt{3}+3 & 6 \end{array}$

$\phantom{\sqrt{3} \mid} \begin{array}{cccc} 1 & 2+\sqrt{3} & 2\sqrt{3} & 0 \end{array}$

$x^3 + 2x^2 - 3x - 6 = (x - \sqrt{3})(x^2 + (2+\sqrt{3})x + 2\sqrt{3}) = (x - \sqrt{3})(x + 2)(x + \sqrt{3})$

Real zeros: $\sqrt{3}$, -2, $-\sqrt{3}$

39. $f(x) = x^3 - x^2 - 14x + 11, \quad k = 4$

$$
\begin{array}{r|rrrr}
4 & 1 & -1 & -14 & 11 \\
  &   & 4 & 12 & -8 \\
\hline
  & 1 & 3 & -2 & 3
\end{array}
$$

$f(x) = (x - 4)(x^2 + 3x - 2) + 3$

$f(4) = (0)(26) + 3 = 3$

41. $f(x) = x^3 + 3x^2 - 2x - 14, \quad k = \sqrt{2}$

$$
\begin{array}{r|rrrr}
\sqrt{2} & 1 & 3 & -2 & -14 \\
         &   & \sqrt{2} & 2 + 3\sqrt{2} & 6 \\
\hline
         & 1 & 3 + \sqrt{2} & 3\sqrt{2} & -8
\end{array}
$$

$f(x) = (x - \sqrt{2})[x^2 + (3 + \sqrt{2})x + 3\sqrt{2}] - 8$

$f(\sqrt{2}) = (0)(4 + 6\sqrt{2}) - 8 = -8$

43. $f(x) = 4x^3 - 13x + 10$

(a)
$$
\begin{array}{r|rrrr}
1 & 4 & 0 & -13 & 10 \\
  &   & 4 & 4 & -9 \\
\hline
  & 4 & 4 & -9 & 1 \quad = f(1)
\end{array}
$$

(b)
$$
\begin{array}{r|rrrr}
-2 & 4 & 0 & -13 & 10 \\
   &   & -8 & 16 & -6 \\
\hline
   & 4 & -8 & 3 & 4 \quad = f(-2)
\end{array}
$$

(c)
$$
\begin{array}{r|rrrr}
\frac{1}{2} & 4 & 0 & -13 & 10 \\
            &   & 2 & 1 & -6 \\
\hline
            & 4 & 2 & -12 & 4 \quad = f(\tfrac{1}{2})
\end{array}
$$

(d)
$$
\begin{array}{r|rrrr}
8 & 4 & 0 & -13 & 10 \\
  &   & 32 & 256 & 1944 \\
\hline
  & 4 & 32 & 243 & 1954 \quad = f(8)
\end{array}
$$

45. $h(x) = 3x^3 + 5x^2 - 10x + 1$

(a)
$$
\begin{array}{r|rrrr}
3 & 3 & 5 & -10 & 1 \\
  &   & 9 & 42 & 96 \\
\hline
  & 3 & 14 & 32 & 97 \quad = h(3)
\end{array}
$$

(b)
$$
\begin{array}{r|rrrr}
\frac{1}{3} & 3 & 5 & -10 & 1 \\
            &   & 1 & 2 & -\frac{8}{3} \\
\hline
            & 3 & 6 & -8 & -\frac{5}{3} \quad = h(\tfrac{1}{3})
\end{array}
$$

(c)
$$
\begin{array}{r|rrrr}
-2 & 3 & 5 & -10 & 1 \\
   &   & -6 & 2 & 16 \\
\hline
   & 3 & -1 & -8 & 17 \quad = h(-2)
\end{array}
$$

(d)
$$
\begin{array}{r|rrrr}
-5 & 3 & 5 & -10 & 1 \\
   &   & -15 & 50 & -200 \\
\hline
   & 3 & -10 & 40 & -199 \quad = h(-5)
\end{array}
$$

47. $f(x) = x^3 + 3$

Sign variations: 0, positive zeros: 0

$f(-x) = -x^3 + 3$

Sign variations: 1, negative zeros: 1

49. $h(x) = 3x^4 + 2x^2 + 1$

Sign variations: 0, positive zeros: 0

$h(-x) = 3x^4 + 2x^2 + 1$

Sign variations: 0, negative zeros: 0

51. $g(x) = 2x^3 - 3x^2 - 3$
     Sign variations: 1, positive zeros: 1
     $g(-x) = -2x^3 - 3x^2 - 3$
     Sign variations: 0, negative zeros: 0

53. $f(x) = -5x^3 + x^2 - x + 5$
     Sign variations: 3, positive zeros: 3 or 1
     $f(-x) = 5x^3 + x^2 + x + 5$
     Sign variations: 0, negative zeros: 0

55. $h(x) = 4x^2 - 8x + 3$
     Sign variations: 2, positive zeros: 2 or 0
     $h(-x) = 4x^2 + 8x + 3$
     Sign variations: 0, negative zeros: 0

57. $f(x) = x^3 + x^2 - 4x - 4$
     Possible rational zeros: $\pm 1, \pm 2, \pm 4$
     $-2, -1, 2$ on graph

59. $f(x) = -4x^3 + 15x^2 - 8x - 3$
     Possible rational zeros: $\dfrac{\pm 1, \pm 3}{\pm 1, \pm 2, \pm 4} = \pm \dfrac{1}{4}, \pm \dfrac{1}{2}, \pm \dfrac{3}{4}, \pm 1, \pm \dfrac{3}{2}, \pm 3$

     $-\dfrac{1}{4}, 1, 3$ on graph

61. $f(x) = -2x^4 + 13x^3 - 21x^2 + 2x + 8$
     (a) Possible rational zeros:
         $\dfrac{\pm 1, \pm 2, \pm 4, \pm 8}{\pm 1, \pm 2}$
         $= \pm \dfrac{1}{2}, \pm 1, \pm 2, \pm 4, \pm 8$
     (c) $-\frac{1}{2}, 1, 2, 4$ on graph

(b)
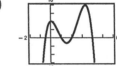

63. $f(x) = 32x^3 - 52x^2 + 17x + 3$
     (a) Possible rational zeros:
         $\pm \frac{1}{32}, \pm \frac{1}{16}, \pm \frac{3}{32}, \pm \frac{1}{8}, \pm \frac{3}{16}, \pm \frac{1}{4},$
         $\pm \frac{3}{8}, \pm \frac{1}{2}, \pm \frac{3}{4}, \pm 1, \pm \frac{3}{2}, \pm 3$
     (b)
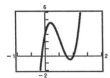

     (c) $-\frac{1}{8}, \frac{3}{4}, 1$ on graph

65. $f(x) = 4x^3 + 7x^2 - 11x - 18$
     (a) Possible rational zeros:
         $\pm \frac{1}{4}, \pm \frac{1}{2}, \pm \frac{3}{4}, \pm 1, \pm \frac{3}{2}, \pm \frac{9}{4},$
         $\pm \frac{9}{2}, \pm 2 \pm 3, \pm 6, \pm 9, \pm 18$
     (b)
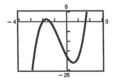

     (c) $-2, \dfrac{1 \pm \sqrt{145}}{8}$ on graph

67. $f(x) = x^4 - 4x^3 + 15$

(a) 4 | 1   −4   0   0   15
$$\begin{array}{r|rrrrr} 4 & 1 & -4 & 0 & 0 & 15 \\ & & 4 & 0 & 0 & 0 \\ \hline & 1 & 0 & 0 & 0 & 15 \end{array}$$

4 is an upper bound.

(b) $$\begin{array}{r|rrrrr} -1 & 1 & -4 & 0 & 0 & 15 \\ & & -1 & 5 & -5 & 5 \\ \hline & 1 & -5 & 5 & -5 & 20 \end{array}$$

−1 is a lower bound.

(c) $$\begin{array}{r|rrrrr} 3 & 1 & -4 & 0 & 0 & 15 \\ & & 3 & -3 & -9 & -27 \\ \hline & 1 & -1 & -3 & -9 & -12 \end{array}$$

3 is neither an upper nor lower bound.

69. $f(x) = x^4 - 4x^3 + 16x - 16$

(a) $$\begin{array}{r|rrrrr} -1 & 1 & -4 & 0 & 16 & -16 \\ & & -1 & 5 & -5 & -11 \\ \hline & 1 & -5 & 5 & 11 & -27 \end{array}$$

−1 is neither an upper nor lower bound.

(b) $$\begin{array}{r|rrrrr} -3 & 1 & -4 & 0 & 16 & -16 \\ & & -3 & 21 & -63 & 141 \\ \hline & 1 & -7 & 21 & -47 & 125 \end{array}$$

−3 is a lower bound.

(c) $$\begin{array}{r|rrrrr} 5 & 1 & -4 & 0 & 16 & -16 \\ & & 5 & 5 & 25 & 205 \\ \hline & 1 & 1 & 5 & 41 & 189 \end{array}$$

5 is an upper bound.

71. Possible rational zeros: $\pm 1, \pm 2, \pm 3, \pm 6$

$$\begin{array}{r|rrrr} 1 & 1 & -6 & 11 & -6 \\ & & 1 & -5 & 6 \\ \hline & 1 & -5 & 6 & 0 \end{array}$$

$$x^3 - 6x^2 + 11x - 6 = (x-1)(x^2 - 5x + 6)$$
$$= (x-1)(x-2)(x-3)$$

The zeros are 1, 2, and 3.

73. Possible rational zeros: $\pm 1, \pm 2, \pm 2$

$$\begin{array}{r|rrrr} 1 & 1 & -4 & -1 & 4 \\ & & 1 & -3 & -4 \\ \hline & 1 & -3 & -4 & 0 \end{array}$$

$$x^3 - 4x^2 - x + 4 = (x-1)(x^2 - 3x - 4)$$
$$= (x-1)(x-4)(x+1)$$

The zeros are −1, 1, and 4.

75. Possible rational zeros: $\pm 1, \pm 2, \pm 5, \pm 10$

$$\begin{array}{r|rrrr} -1 & 1 & 12 & 21 & 10 \\ & & -1 & -11 & -10 \\ \hline & 1 & 11 & 10 & 0 \end{array}$$

$$t^3 + 12t^2 + 21t + 10 = (t+1)(t^2 + 11t + 10) = (t+1)(t+1)(t+10)$$

The zeros are −1 and −10.

77. Possible rational zeros: ±1, ±2

$$1 \begin{array}{|rrrr} 1 & -4 & 5 & -2 \\ & 1 & -3 & 2 \\ \hline 1 & -3 & 2 & 0 \end{array}$$

$$x^3 - 4x^2 + 5x - 2 = (x-1)(x^2 - 3x + 2)$$
$$= (x-1)(x-1)(x-2)$$

The zeros are 1 and 2.

79. Possible rational zeros: ±1, ±$\frac{1}{2}$

$$-1 \begin{array}{|rrrr} 2 & 3 & 0 & -1 \\ & -2 & -1 & 1 \\ \hline 2 & 1 & -1 & 0 \end{array}$$

$$2x^3 + 3x^2 - 1 = (x+1)(2x^2 + x - 1)$$
$$= (x+1)(2x-1)(x+1)$$

The zeros are -1 and $\frac{1}{2}$.

81. Possible rational zeros: ±1, ±$\frac{1}{2}$, ±$\frac{1}{4}$

$$1 \begin{array}{|rrrr} 4 & 0 & -3 & -1 \\ & 4 & 4 & 1 \\ \hline 4 & 4 & 1 & 0 \end{array}$$

$$4x^3 - 3x - 1 = (x-1)(4x^2 + 4x + 1)$$
$$= (x-1)(2x+1)^2$$

The zeros are $-\frac{1}{2}$ and 1.

83. Possible rational zeros:

± 1, ±2, ±3, ±6,

±$\frac{1}{2}$, ±$\frac{3}{2}$, ±$\frac{1}{4}$, ±$\frac{3}{4}$

$$-\frac{3}{4} \begin{array}{|rrrr} 4 & 3 & 8 & 6 \\ & -3 & 0 & -6 \\ \hline 4 & 0 & 8 & 0 \end{array}$$

$$4y^3 + 3y^2 + 8y + 6 = \left(y + \frac{3}{4}\right)\left(4y^2 + 8\right)$$

The zero is $-\frac{3}{4}$.

85. $f(x) = x^4 - 3x^2 + 2$
$$= (x^2 - 1)(x^2 - 2)$$
$$= (x+1)(x-1)(x+\sqrt{2})(x-\sqrt{2})$$

The zeros are ±1 and ±$\sqrt{2}$.

87. $P(x) = x^4 - \frac{25}{4}x^2 + 9$
$$= \frac{1}{4}(4x^4 - 25x^2 + 36)$$

Possible rational zeros:

± $\frac{1}{4}$, ±$\frac{1}{2}$, ±$\frac{3}{4}$, ±1, ±$\frac{3}{2}$, ±2, ±$\frac{9}{4}$

± 3, ±4, ±$\frac{9}{2}$, ±6, ±9, ±12, ±18, ±36

$x = \pm2, \pm\frac{3}{2}$

89. $f(x) = x^3 - \frac{1}{4}x^2 - x + \frac{1}{4}$
$$= \frac{1}{4}(4x^3 - x^2 - 4x + 1)$$

Possible rational zeros: ±$\frac{1}{4}$, ±$\frac{1}{2}$, ±1

$x = -1, \frac{1}{4}, 1$

91. $f(x) = x^3 - 1 = (x-1)(x^2 + x + 1)$

Zeros: 1

One rational zero; zero irrational zeros

Matches (d)

93. $f(x) = x^3 - x = x(x^2 - 1) = x(x+1)(x-1)$

Zeros: $0, \pm 1$

Three rational zeros; no irrational zeros

Matches (b)

95. $f(x) = x^3 + x - 1$

(a) ± 1

(b)

(c) 0.68

97. $f(x) = x^4 - x - 3$

(a) $\pm 1, \pm 3$

(b)

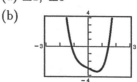

(c) $-1.16,\ 1.45$

99. $V = 18 = (9 - 2x)(5 - 2x)(x),\quad 0 < x < \dfrac{5}{2}$

$$x(45 - 28x + 4x^2) = 18$$

$$4x^3 - 28x^2 + 45x - 18 = 0$$

Using a graphing utility, we see that there are two solutions in the interval $\left(0, \frac{5}{2}\right)$: $x = 1.5$ and $x = 0.614$ or

$$(2x - 3)(2x^2 - 11x + 6) = 0$$

$$x = \frac{3}{2},\ \frac{11 - \sqrt{73}}{4}$$

$x = \dfrac{3}{2},\ 9 - 2x = 6,\ 5 - 2x = 2$

$x = \dfrac{11 - \sqrt{73}}{4} \approx 0.614,\ 9 - 2x = 7.77,\ 5 - 2x = 3.77$

Dimensions: $\frac{3}{2}$ inches $\times$ 2 inches $\times$ 6 inches or 0.614 in $\times$ 3.77 inches $\times$ 7.77 inches

101. $2{,}500{,}000 = -76x^3 + 4{,}830x^2 - 320{,}000$

$76x^3 - 4{,}830x^2 + 2{,}820{,}000 = 0$

Using a graphing utility with the viewing rectangle $[0, 50] \times [-10, 10]$, we see that there are two solutions, $x \approx 38.4$ or $x \approx 46.1$ which corresponds to \$384,000 or \$461,000 being spent on advertising. The smaller is 384,000.

103. $C = 100 \left(\dfrac{200}{x^2} + \dfrac{x}{x + 30} \right)$, $1 \le x$

$3x^3 - 40x^2 - 2400x - 36,000 = 0$

Graphing this function, we see that $x = 4000$. You can also graph C directly and zoom in on the minimum value.

105.

Iteration	a	c	b	$f(a)$	$f(c)$	$f(b)$	Error
1	0.0000	0.5000	1.0000	−8.0000	−0.5000	10.0000	0.5000
2	0.5000	0.7500	1.0000	−0.5000	4.1875	10.0000	0.2500
3	0.5000	0.6250	0.7500	−0.5000	1.7266	4.1875	0.1250
4	0.5000	0.5625	0.6250	−0.5000	0.5869	1.7266	0.0625
5	0.5000	0.5313	0.5625	−0.5000	0.0372	0.5869	0.0313
6	0.5000	0.5156	0.5313	−0.5000	−0.2329	0.0372	0.0156
7	0.5156	0.5234	0.5313	−0.2329	−0.0982	0.0372	0.0078
8	0.5234	0.5273	0.5313	−0.0982	−0.0306	0.0372	0.0039
9	0.5273	0.5293	0.5313	−0.0306	0.0033	0.0372	0.0020

The zero of f is approximately 0.53.

107.

Iteration	a	c	b	$f(a)$	$f(c)$	$f(b)$	Error
1	1.0000	1.5000	2.0000	−100.0000	−9.5625	56.0000	0.5000
2	1.5000	1.7500	2.0000	−9.5625	26.2461	56.0000	0.2500
3	1.5000	1.6250	1.7500	−9.5625	9.1345	26.2461	0.1250
4	1.5000	1.5625	1.6250	−9.5625	−0.0135	9.1345	0.0625
5	1.5625	1.5938	1.6250	−0.0135	4.6104	9.1345	0.0313
6	1.5625	1.5781	1.5938	−0.0135	2.3109	4.6104	0.0156
7	1.5625	1.5703	1.5781	−0.0135	1.1518	2.3109	0.0078
8	1.5625	1.5664	1.5703	−0.0135	0.5699	1.1518	0.0039
9	1.5625	1.5645	1.5664	−0.0135	0.2784	0.5699	0.0020
10	1.5625	1.5635	1.5645	−0.0135	0.1324	0.2784	0.0010

The zero of f is approximately 1.56.

Section 3.4   Complex Zeros and the Fundamental Theorem of Algebra

- You should know that if f is a polynomial of degree $n > 0$, then f has exactly n zeros (roots) in the complex number system.

- You should know that if $a + bi$ is a complex zero of a polynomial f, with real coefficients, then $a - bi$ is also a complex zero of f.

- You should know the difference between a factor that is irreducible over the rationals (such as $x^2 - 7$) and a factor that is irreducible over the reals (such as $x^2 + 9$).

1. $f(x) = x^2 + 25$
Zeros: $x = \pm 5i$
$f(x) = (x + 5i)(x - 5i)$

3. $h(x) = x^2 - 4x + 1$
Zeros: $x = \dfrac{4 \pm \sqrt{12}}{2} = 2 \pm \sqrt{3}$
$h(x) = (x - 2 + \sqrt{3})(x - 2 - \sqrt{3})$

5. $f(x) = x^4 - 81$
Zeros: $x = \pm 3, \ \pm 3i$
$f(x) = (x + 3)(x - 3)(x + 3i)(x - 3i)$

7. $f(z) = z^2 - 2z + 2$
Zeros: $z = \dfrac{2 \pm \sqrt{4}\,i}{2} = 1 \pm i$
$f(z) = (z - 1 + i)(z - 1 - i)$

9. $f(t) = t^3 - 3t^2 - 15t + 125$

-5	1	-3	-15	125
		-5	40	-125
	1	-8	25	0

Zeros: $t = -5, \ \dfrac{8 \pm \sqrt{36}\,i}{2} = 4 \pm 3i$
$f(t) = (t + 5)(t - 4 - 3i)(t - 4 + 3i)$

11. $f(x) = 16x^3 - 20x^2 - 4x + 15$

$-\frac{3}{4}$	16	-20	-4	15
		-12	24	-15
	16	-32	20	0

Zeros: $x = -\dfrac{3}{4}, \ \dfrac{32 \pm \sqrt{256}\,i}{32} = 1 \pm \dfrac{1}{2}i$
$f(x) = (4x + 3)(2x - 2 + i)(2x - 2 - i)$

13. $f(x) = 5x^3 - 9x^2 + 28x + 6$

$$
\begin{array}{r|rrrr}
-\frac{1}{5} & 5 & -9 & 28 & 6 \\
 & & -1 & 2 & -6 \\
\hline
 & 5 & -10 & 30 & 0
\end{array}
$$

$$x = -\frac{1}{5}, \quad \frac{10 \pm \sqrt{500}\,i}{10} = 1 \pm \sqrt{5}\,i$$

$$f(x) = (5x + 1)(x - 1 + \sqrt{5}\,i)(x - 1 - \sqrt{5}\,i)$$

15. $f(x) = x^4 + 10x^2 + 9$

$$= (x^2 + 9)(x^2 + 1)$$

Zeros: $x = \pm i, \ \pm 3i$

$$f(x) = (x + i)(x - i)(x + 3i)(x - 3i)$$

17. $g(x) = x^4 - 4x^3 + 8x^2 - 16x + 16$

$$
\begin{array}{r|rrrrr}
2 & 1 & -4 & 8 & -16 & 16 \\
 & & 2 & -4 & 8 & -16 \\
\hline
2 & 1 & -2 & 4 & -8 & 0 \\
 & & 2 & 0 & 8 & \\
\hline
 & 1 & 0 & 4 & 0 &
\end{array}
$$

Zeros: $x = 2, \ \pm 2i$

$$g(x) = (x - 2)^2(x + 2i)(x - 2i)$$

19. $f(x) = 2x^4 + 5x^3 + 4x^2 + 5x + 2$

$$= 2x^4 + 5x^3 + 2x^2 + 2x^2 + 5x + 2$$

$$= x^2(2x^2 + 5x + 2) + (2x^2 + 5x + 2)$$

$$= (x^2 + 1)(2x^2 + 5x + 2)$$

Zeros: $x = \pm i$

$$x = \frac{-5 \pm \sqrt{9}}{4} = -2, \ -\frac{1}{2}$$

$$f(x) = (2x + 1)(x + 2)(x + i)(x - i)$$

21. $f(x) = (x - 1)(x - 5i)(x + 5i)$

$$= (x - 1)(x^2 + 25)$$

$$= x^3 - x^2 + 25x - 25$$

23. $f(x) = (x - 2)(x - 4 - i)(x - 4 + i)$

$$= (x - 2)(x^2 - 8x + 17)$$

$$= x^3 - 10x^2 + 33x - 34$$

25. $f(x) = (x - i)(x + i)(x - 6i)(x + 6i) = (x^2 + 1)(x^2 + 36) = x^4 + 37x^2 + 36$

27. $f(x) = (x + 5)^2(x - 1 - \sqrt{3}\,i)(x - 1 + \sqrt{3}\,i)$

$$= (x^2 + 10x + 25)(x^2 - 2x + 4) = x^4 + 8x^3 + 9x^2 - 10x + 100$$

29. $f(x) = (4x - 3)(x + 2)(2x + 1 - 2i)(2x + 1 + 2i)$

$$= (4x^2 + 5x - 6)(4x^2 + 4x + 5) = 16x^4 + 36x^3 + 16x^2 + x - 30$$

31. $f(x) = x^4 + 6x^2 - 27$

(a) $f(x) = (x^2 + 9)(x^2 - 3)$

(b) $f(x) = (x^2 + 9)(x + \sqrt{3})(x - \sqrt{3})$

(c) $f(x) = (x + 3i)(x - 3i)(x + \sqrt{3})(x - \sqrt{3})$

33. $f(x) = x^4 - 4x^3 + 5x^2 - 2x - 6$

(a) $f(x) = (x^2 - 2x - 2)(x^2 - 2x + 3)$

(b) $f(x) = (x - 1 - \sqrt{3})(x - 1 + \sqrt{3})(x^2 - 2x + 3)$

(c) $f(x) = (x - 1 - \sqrt{3})(x - 1 + \sqrt{3})(x - 1 - \sqrt{2}\,i)(x - 1 + \sqrt{2}\,i)$

35.

$$
\begin{array}{r|rrrr}
5i & 2 & 3 & 50 & 75 \\
   &   & 10i & -50 + 15i & -75 \\
\hline
-5i & 2 & 3 + 10i & 15i & 0 \\
    &   & -10i & -15i & \\
\hline
   & 2 & 3 & 0 &
\end{array}
$$

Zeros: $-\frac{3}{2}$, $\pm 5i$

Since $5i$ is a zero, so is $-5i$. Using a graphing utility, we can determine that the real zero is -1.50.

37.

$$
\begin{array}{r|rrrrr}
2i & 2 & -1 & 7 & -4 & -4 \\
   &   & 4i & -8 - 2i & 4 - 2i & 4 \\
\hline
-2i & 2 & -1 + 4i & -1 - 2i & -2i & 0 \\
    &   & -4i & 2i & 2i & \\
\hline
1 & 2 & -1 & -1 & 0 & \\
  &   & 2 & 1 & & \\
\hline
  & 2 & 1 & 0 & &
\end{array}
$$

Zeros: $-\frac{1}{2}$, 1, $\pm 2i$

Since $2i$ is a zero, so is $-2i$. Using a graphing utility, we can determine that the real zeros are -0.50 and 1.00.

39.

$$
\begin{array}{r|rrrr}
-3 + i & 4 & 23 & 34 & -10 \\
       &   & -12 + 4i & -37 - i & 10 \\
\hline
-3 - i & 4 & 11 + 4i & -3 - i & 0 \\
       &   & -12 - 4i & 3 + i & \\
\hline
       & 4 & -1 & 0 &
\end{array}
$$

Zeros: $\frac{1}{4}$, $-3 \pm i$

41.

$$
\begin{array}{r|rrrrr}
-3 + \sqrt{2}\,i & 1 & 2 & -9 & -20 & 44 \\
                 &   & -3 + \sqrt{2}\,i & 1 - 4\sqrt{2}\,i & 32 + 4\sqrt{2}\,i & -44 \\
\hline
-3 - \sqrt{2}\,i & 1 & -1 + \sqrt{2}\,i & -8 - 4\sqrt{2}\,i & 12 + 4\sqrt{2}\,i & 0 \\
                 &   & -3 - \sqrt{2}\,i & 12 + 4\sqrt{2}\,i & -12 - 4\sqrt{2}\,i & \\
\hline
                 & 1 & -4 & 4 & 0 &
\end{array}
$$

Zeros: 2, $-3 \pm \sqrt{2}\,i$

43.

$$\dfrac{1-\sqrt{5}i}{2} \;\bigg|\; \begin{array}{cccc} 8 & -14 & 18 & -9 \\ & 4-4\sqrt{5}i & -15+3\sqrt{5}i & 9 \end{array}$$

$$\dfrac{1+\sqrt{5}i}{2} \;\bigg|\; \begin{array}{cccc} 8 & -10-4\sqrt{5}i & 3+3\sqrt{5}i & 0 \\ & 4+4\sqrt{5}i & -3-3\sqrt{5}i & \\ \hline 8 & -6 & 0 & \end{array}$$

Zeros: $\dfrac{3}{4}, \dfrac{1}{2} \pm \dfrac{\sqrt{5}}{2}i$

Since $\dfrac{1-\sqrt{5}i}{2}$ is a zero, so is $\dfrac{1+\sqrt{5}i}{2}$. Using a graphing utility, we can determine that the real zero is 0.75.

45. $\qquad -16t^2 + 48t = 64, \quad 0 \le t \le 3$

$-16t^2 + 48t - 64 = 0$

$$t = \dfrac{-48 \pm \sqrt{1792}i}{-32}$$

Since this results in imaginary roots, the ball will never reach a height of 64 feet. Verifying this with a graphing utility, we can graph $y_1 = h = -16t^2 + 48t$ and $y_2 = 64$ which do not intersect.

47. $f(x) = (x - \sqrt{b}i)(x + \sqrt{b}i)$

$\qquad\quad = x^2 + b$

Section 3.5   Rational Functions and Asymptotes

■ You should know the following basic facts about rational functions.

(a) A function of the form $f(x) = P(x)/Q(x)$, $Q(x) \neq 0$, where $P(x)$ and $Q(x)$ are polynomials, is called a rational function.

(b) The domain of a rational function is the set of all real numbers except those which make the denominator zero.

(c) If $f(x) = P(x)/Q(x)$ is in reduced form, and a is a value such that $Q(a) = 0$, then the line $x = a$ is a vertical asymptote of the graph of f.

(d) The line $y = b$ is a horizontal asymptote of the graph of f if $f(x) \to b$ as $x \to \infty$ or $x \to -\infty$.

■ Be able to graph rational functions with your graphing utility.

1. $f(x) = \dfrac{1}{x - 2}$

(a)

x	1	1.5	1.9	1.99	1.999
$f(x)$	-1	-2	-10	-100	-1000

x	3	2.5	2.1	2.01	2.001
$f(x)$	1	2	10	100	1000

x	3	5	10	100	1000
$f(x)$	1	0.3333	0.125	0.0102	0.0010

(b) Vertical asymptote: $x = 2$
Horizontal asymptote: $y = 0$

(c) Domain: $x \neq 2$

3. $f(x) = \dfrac{3x}{|x-2|}$

(a)

x	1	1.5	1.9	1.99	1.999
$f(x)$	3	9	57	597	5997

x	3	2.5	2.1	2.01	2.001
$f(x)$	9	15	63	603	6003

x	3	5	10	100	1000
$f(x)$	9	5	3.75	3.0612	3.0060

(b) Vertical asymptote: $x = 2$
Horizontal asymptote: $y = \pm 3$

(c) Domain: $x \neq 2$

5. $f(x) = \dfrac{3x^2}{x^2 - 4}$

(a)

x	1	1.5	1.9	1.99	1.999
$f(x)$	-1	-3.8571	-27.7692	-297.752	-2997.75

x	3	2.5	2.1	2.01	2.001
$f(x)$	5.4	8.3333	32.2683	302.2519	3002.25

x	3	5	10	100	1000
$f(x)$	5.4	3.5714	3.125	3.0012	3.0000

(b) Vertical asymptote:
$x = \pm 2$
Horizontal asymptote:
$y = 3$

(c) Domain: $x \neq \pm 2$

7. $f(x) = \dfrac{1}{x^2}$
Domain: all real numbers except 0
Vertical asymptote: $x = 0$
Horizontal asymptote: $y = 0$

9. $f(x) = \dfrac{2+x}{2-x} = \dfrac{x+2}{-x+2}$
Domain: all real numbers except 2
Vertical asymptote: $x = 2$
Horizontal asymptote: $y = -1$

11. $f(x) = \dfrac{x^3}{x^2 - 1} = x + \dfrac{x}{x^2 - 1}$
Domain: all real numbers except 1 and -1
Vertical asymptotes: $x = \pm 1$
No horizontal asymptote
(Slant asymptote: $y = x$)

13. $f(x) = \dfrac{3x^2 + 1}{x^2 + 9}$
Domain: all real numbers
Horizontal asymptote: $y = 3$

15. $f(x) = \dfrac{2}{x+1}$

Vertical asymptote:
$x = -1$
Horizontal asymptote:
$y = 0$
y-intercept: $(0, 2)$
Graph (f)

```
RANGE
Xmin=-5
Xmax=3
Xscl=1
Ymin=-3
Ymax=3
Yscl=1
```

17. $f(x) = \dfrac{x+1}{x}$

Vertical asymptote:
$x = 0$
Horizontal asymptote:
$y = 1$
x-intercept: $(-1,\ 0)$
Graph (a)

```
RANGE
Xmin=-3
Xmax=3
Xscl=1
Ymin=-1
Ymax=3
Yscl=1
```

19. $f(x) = \dfrac{x-2}{x-1}$

Vertical asymptote:
$x = 1$
Horizontal asymptote:
$y = 1$
x-intercept: $(2, 0)$
y-intercept: $(0, 2)$
Graph (c)

```
RANGE
Xmin=-2
Xmax=4
Xscl=1
Ymin=-1
Ymax=3
Yscl=1
```

21. $f(x) = \dfrac{x^2 - 4}{x + 2},\quad g(x) = x - 2$

(a) Domain of f: $x \neq -2$
   Domain of g: all x

(b) No vertical asymptote of f

(d) Some viewing rectangles will show the difference in domains. For instance, on the TI–81, use the standard viewing rectangle.

(c)

23. $f(x) = \dfrac{x-3}{x^2 - 3x},\quad g(x) = \dfrac{1}{x}$

(a) Domain of f: $x \neq 0,\ 3$
   Domain of g: $x \neq 0$

(b) f has a vertical asymptote at $x = 0$.

(d) Some viewing rectangles will show the difference in domains. For instance, on the TI–81, use the following range.

```
RANGE
Xmin=-4.5
Xmax=5
Xscl=1
Ymin=-2
Ymax=2
Yscl=1
```

(c)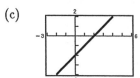

25. (a) $C = \dfrac{255(10)}{100 - 10} = 28\frac{1}{3}$

   The cost would be $28\frac{1}{3}$ million.

(b) $C = \dfrac{255(40)}{100 - 40} = 170$

   The cost would be $170 million.

(c) $C = \dfrac{255(75)}{100 - 75} = 765$

   The cost would be $765 million.

(d) No. The model is undefined for $p = 100$.

27. $N = \dfrac{10(5 + 3t)}{1 + 0.04t} = \dfrac{30t + 50}{0.04t + 1}$

(a) $N(5) \approx 167$ deer

   $N(10) = 250$ deer

   $N(25) = 400$ deer

(b) The herd is limited by a horizontal asymptote:

   $N = \dfrac{30}{0.04} = 750$ deer

   Verify this result by graphing N and $y = 750$ on the same viewing rectangle.

29. $P = \dfrac{0.5 + 0.9(n - 1)}{1 + 0.9(n - 1)}, \quad 0 < n$

(a)

n	1	2	3	4	5	6	7	8	9	10
P	0.50	0.74	0.82	0.86	0.89	0.91	0.92	0.93	0.94	0.95

(b) The percentage of correct responses is limited by a horizontal asymptote:

   $P = 0.9/0.9 = 1.0 = 100\%$. Verify this result by graphing P and $y = 1.0$ on the same viewing rectangle.

Section 3.6   Graphs of Rational Functions

- ■ You should know how to graph rational functions with a graphing utility.

- ■ Let $f(x) = p(x)/q(x)$ be a rational function, where $p(x)$ and $q(x)$ are polynomials with no common factors.

  (a) The y-intercept (if any) is the value $f(0)$.

  (b) The x-intercepts (if any) are the zeros of the numerator.

  (c) The vertical asymptotes (if any) are the zeros of the denominator.

  (d) The horizontal asymptote (if there is one) is the value that $f(x)$ approaches as x increases or decreases without bound.

- ■ You should be able to determine the behavior of the graph of a rational function between and beyond each x-intercept and vertical asymptote.

- ■ You should know how to determine whether or not a rational function has a slant asymptote.

---

1. $g(x) = f(x) + 1 = \dfrac{1}{x} + 1$

Vertical shift one unit upward

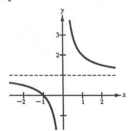

3. $g(x) = -f(x) = -\dfrac{1}{x}$

Reflection in the x-axis

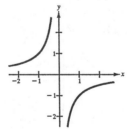

5. $g(x) = f(x) - 2 = \dfrac{4}{x^2} - 2$

Vertical shift two units downward

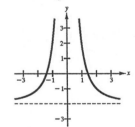

7. $g(x) = f(x - 2)$

$= \dfrac{4}{(x - 2)^2}$

Horizontal shift two units right

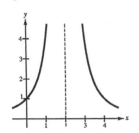

9. $g(x) = f(x + 2)$

$= \dfrac{8}{(x + 2)^3}$

Horizontal shift two units to the left

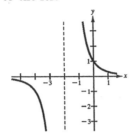

11. $g(x) = -f(x) = -\dfrac{8}{x^3}$

Reflection in the x-axis

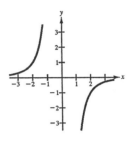

13. $f(x) = \dfrac{1}{x + 2}$

y-intercept: $\left(0, \frac{1}{2}\right)$

Vertical asymptote:

$x = -2$

Horizontal asymptote:

$y = 0$

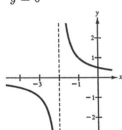

15. $h(x) = \dfrac{-1}{x + 2}$

y-intercept: $\left(0, -\frac{1}{2}\right)$

Vertical asymptote:

$x = -2$

Horizontal asymptote:

$y = 0$

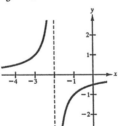

17. $C(x) = \dfrac{5 + 2x}{1 + x} = \dfrac{2x + 5}{x + 1}$

x-intercept: $\left(-\frac{5}{2}, 0\right)$

y-intercept: $(0, 5)$

Vertical asymptote:

$x = -1$

Horizontal asymptote:

$y = 2$

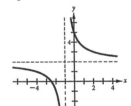

19. $g(x) = \dfrac{1}{x+2} + 2$

$= \dfrac{1 + 2(x+2)}{x+2}$

$= \dfrac{2x+5}{x+2}$

x-intercept: $\left(-\frac{5}{2},\, 0\right)$

y-intercept: $\left(0,\, \frac{5}{2}\right)$

Vertical asymptote: $x = -2$

Horizontal asymptote: $y = 2$

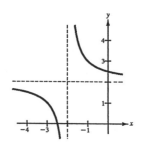

21. $f(x) = \dfrac{x^2}{x^2 + 9}$

Intercept: $(0, 0)$

Horizontal asymptote: $y = 1$

No vertical asymptotes

y-axis symmetry

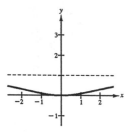

23. $h(x) = \dfrac{x^2}{x^2 - 9}$

Intercept: $(0, 0)$

Vertical asymptotes: $x = \pm 3$

Horizontal asymptote: $y = 1$

y-axis symmetry

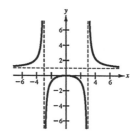

25. $g(x) = -\dfrac{1}{(x-2)^2} + 3$

$= \dfrac{-1 + 3(x-2)^2}{(x-2)^2}$

$= \dfrac{3x^2 - 12x + 11}{(x-2)^2}$

Using the quadratic formula, we see
that the solutions to $3x^2 - 12x + 11$ are
$2 \pm (\sqrt{3}/3) \approx 2.577,\ 1.423$.

Intercepts: $(2 \pm (\sqrt{3}/3),\, 0)$, $(0,\, 2.75)$

Vertical asymptote: $x = 2$

Horizontal asymptote: $y = 3$

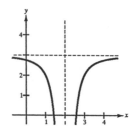

27. $f(x) = \dfrac{3x}{x^2 - x - 2}$

$= \dfrac{3x}{(x+1)(x-2)}$

Intercept: $(0, 0)$
Vertical asymptotes:
$x = -1, \ 2$
Horizontal asymptote:
$y = 0$

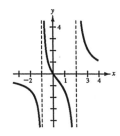

29. $f(x) = \dfrac{2+x}{1-x}$

Domain:
all real numbers $x \neq 1$
Range:
all real numbers $y \neq -1$

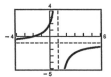

31. $f(t) = \dfrac{3t+1}{t}$

Domain:
all real numbers $t \neq 0$
Range:
all real numbers $y \neq 3$

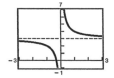

33. $h(t) = \dfrac{4}{t^2 + 1}$

Domain: all real numbers
Range: $0 < y \leq 4$

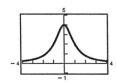

35. $f(x) = \dfrac{20x}{x^2 + 1} - \dfrac{1}{x}$

Domain:
all real numbers $x \neq 0$
Range: $-\infty < y < \infty$

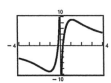

37. $f(x) = \dfrac{2x^2 + 1}{x} = 2x + \dfrac{1}{x}$

Vertical asymptote:
$x = 0$
Slant asymptote: $y = 2x$
Origin symmetry

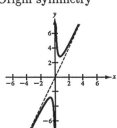

39. $g(x) = \dfrac{x^2+1}{x} = x + \dfrac{1}{x}$

Vertical asymptote:
   $x = 0$
Slant asymptote: $y = x$
Origin symmetry

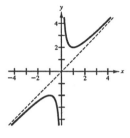

41. $f(x) = \dfrac{x^3}{x^2-1}$

$= x + \dfrac{x}{x^2-1}$

Intercept: $(0, 0)$
Vertical asymptotes:
   $x = \pm 1$
Slant asymptote: $y = x$
Origin symmetry

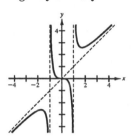

43. $f(x) = \dfrac{x^2-x+1}{x-1}$

$= x + \dfrac{1}{x-1}$

y-intercept: $(0, -1)$
Vertical asymptote:
   $x = 1$
Slant asymptote: $y = x$

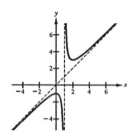

45. $f(x) = \dfrac{x^2+5x+8}{x+3}$

$= x + 2 + \dfrac{2}{x+3}$

y-intercept: $\left(0, \frac{8}{3}\right)$
Vertical asymptote:
   $x = -3$
Slant asymptote:
   $y = x + 2$

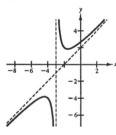

47. $h(x) = \dfrac{6x}{\sqrt{x^2+1}}$

Notice that the graph
has two horizontal
asymptotes:
   $y = \pm 6$

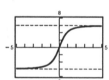

49. $f(x) = \dfrac{4(x-1)^2}{x^2-4x+5}$

Notice that the graph
crosses the horizontal
asymptote $y = 4$.

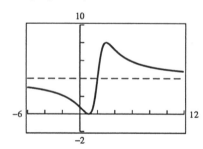

51.

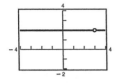

There is no vertical asymptote since

$$\frac{6 - 2x}{3 - x} = 2, \quad (x \neq 3).$$

53. $f(x) = \dfrac{3(x + 1)}{x^2 + x + 1}$

Relative maximum: $(0, \ 3)$

Relative minimum: $(-2, \ -1)$

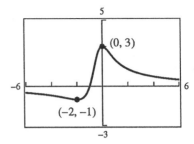

55. (a) $C = \dfrac{\text{Amount of brine}}{\text{Number of gallons}}$

$= \dfrac{\text{Original brine} + \text{added brine}}{\text{Original gallons} + \text{added gallons}}$

$= \dfrac{(5/2) + (3/4)x}{10 + x}$

$= \dfrac{3x + 10}{4(x + 10)}$

(b) Since the tank holds 250 gallons,
$0 \leq x \leq 240$.

(c)

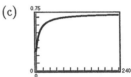

The rate of increase of brine gets
slower and approaches 0.75, or 75%.

57. (a) $(x - 2)(y - 4) = 30$ square inches of print $\Rightarrow$

$$y = \frac{30}{x - 2} + 4$$

$$= \frac{22 + 4x}{x - 2}$$

$$A = xy = x\left(\frac{22 + 4x}{x - 2}\right)$$

$$= \frac{2x(2x + 11)}{x - 2}$$

(b) Domain: $x > 2$

(c)

Minimum at $x = 5.87$ inches
and $y = 11.75$ inches

Chapter 3   Review Exercises

1. $y = \left(x + \dfrac{3}{2}\right)^2 + 1$

When $x = 0$, $y = \left(0 + \dfrac{3}{2}\right)^2 + 1 = \dfrac{13}{4}$.

Vertex: $\left(-\dfrac{3}{2},\ 1\right)$

Intercept: $\left(0,\ \dfrac{13}{4}\right)$

3. $y = \dfrac{1}{3}(x^2 + 5x - 4)$

$= \dfrac{1}{3}\left(x^2 + 5x + \dfrac{25}{4}\right) - \dfrac{4}{3} - \dfrac{25}{12}$

$= \dfrac{1}{3}\left(x + \dfrac{5}{2}\right)^2 - \dfrac{41}{12}$

When $x = 0$, $y = \dfrac{1}{3}\left(0 + \dfrac{5}{2}\right)^2 - \dfrac{41}{12} = -\dfrac{4}{3}$.

When $y = 0$,

$0 = \dfrac{1}{3}\left(x + \dfrac{5}{2}\right)^2 - \dfrac{41}{12} \Rightarrow x = \dfrac{-5 \pm \sqrt{41}}{2}$.

Vertex: $\left(-\dfrac{5}{2},\ -\dfrac{41}{12}\right)$

Intercepts: $\left(0,\ -\dfrac{4}{3}\right)$, $\left(\dfrac{-5 \pm \sqrt{41}}{2},\ 0\right)$

5. $f(x) = a(x - 1)^2 - 4$

$-3 = a(2 - 1)^2 - 4$

$1 = a$

$f(x) = (x - 1)^2 - 4$

7. $g(x) = x^2 - 2x$

$= (x^2 - 2x + 1) - 1$

$= (x - 1)^2 - 1$

Minimum: $(1,\ -1)$

9. $f(x) = 6x - x^2$

$= -(x^2 - 6x + 9) + 9$

$= -(x - 3)^2 + 9$

Maximum: $(3,\ 9)$

11. $f(t) = -2t^2 + 4t + 1$

$= -2(t^2 - 2t + 1) + 1 + 2$

$= -2(t - 1)^2 + 3$

Maximum: $(1,\ 3)$

13. $h(x) = x^2 + 5x - 4$

$$= \left(x^2 + 5x + \frac{25}{4} \right) - 4 - \frac{25}{4}$$

$$= \left(x + \frac{5}{2} \right)^2 - \frac{41}{4}$$

Minimum: $\left(-\frac{5}{2}, \ -\frac{41}{4} \right)$

15. $x + 2y - 6 = 0 \quad \Rightarrow \quad x = 6 - 2y$

$$A = xy = (6 - 2y)y = 6y - 2y^2$$

$$= -2 \left(y^2 - 3y + \frac{9}{4} \right) + \frac{9}{2}$$

$$= -2 \left(y - \frac{3}{2} \right)^2 + \frac{9}{2}$$

A is a maximum when

$$x = 6 - 2\left(\tfrac{3}{2}\right) = 3 \text{ and } y = \tfrac{3}{2}.$$

17. $R = 900x - 0.1x^2$

Using the zoom and trace features, the number of units that produces a maximum revenue is $x = 4500$.

19. $(50, 540), (49, 570)$

$$p - 540 = \frac{570 - 540}{49 - 50}(x - 50)$$

$$p = -30(x - 50) + 540 = -30x + 1500 + 540 = -30x + 2040$$

$$P = xp - C$$

$$P = x(-30x + 2040) - 18x = -30x^2 + 2022x$$

Graphing P on the viewing rectangle $[0, \ 60] \times [0, \ 40{,}000]$, and using the zoom and trace features, we see that $x = 33.70$ produces a maximum profit. Or, completing the square

$$P = -30 \left[x^2 - \frac{337}{5}x + \left(\frac{337}{10} \right)^2 \right] + \frac{(337)^2}{100} \cdot 30 = -30 \left(x - \frac{337}{10} \right)^2 + \frac{340{,}707}{10}.$$

P is maximum when $x = 33.7$. Therefore, to obtain a maximum profit, $p = -30(33.7) + 2040 = \$1029$ should be charged for rent.

21. $f(x) = -x^2 + 6x + 9$

Since the degree is even and the leading coefficient is negative, the graph falls to the left and falls to the right.

23. $g(x) = \frac{3}{4}(x^4 + 3x^2 + 2)$

Since the degree is even and the leading coefficient is positive, the graph rises to the left and rises to the right.

25. $f(x) = -(x-2)^3$

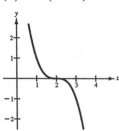

27. $g(x) = x^4 - x^3 - 2x^2$
$$= x^2(x^2 - x - 2)$$
$$= x^2(x-2)(x+1)$$

29. $f(t) = t^3 - 3t$
$$= t(t^2 - 3)$$
$$= t(t + \sqrt{3})(t - \sqrt{3})$$

31. $f(x) = x(x+3)^2$

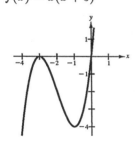

33.
$$\begin{array}{r} 8x\ +\ 5 \\ 3x-2\ \overline{)\ 24x^2 -\ \ x -\ 8} \\ \underline{24x^2 - 16x} \\ 15x -\ 8 \\ \underline{15x - 10} \\ 2 \end{array}$$

$$\frac{24x^2 - x - 8}{3x - 2} = 8x + 5 + \frac{2}{3x - 2}$$

35.
$$\begin{array}{r} x^2 - 2 \\ x^2-1\ \overline{)\ x^4 - 3x^2 + 2} \\ \underline{x^4 -\ \ x^2} \\ -2x^2 + 2 \\ \underline{-2x^2 + 2} \\ 0 \end{array}$$

$$\frac{x^4 - 3x^2 + 2}{x^2 - 1} = x^2 - 2$$

37.
$$\begin{array}{r} x^2 - 3x\ +2 \\ x^2+2\ \overline{)\ x^4 - 3x^3 + 4x^2 - 6x + 3} \\ \underline{x^4 + 2x^2} \\ -3x^3 + 2x^2 - 6x \\ \underline{-3x^3 -\ 6x} \\ 2x^2 +\ 3 \\ \underline{2x^2 +\ 4} \\ -1 \end{array}$$

$$\frac{x^4 - 3x^3 + 4x^2 - 6x + 3}{x^2 + 2}$$
$$= x^2 - 3x + 2 - \frac{1}{x^2 + 2}$$

39.

$$
\begin{array}{r|rrrrr}
2 & 0.25 & -4 & 0 & 0 & 0 \\
  &   & 0.5 & -7 & -14 & -28 \\
\hline
  & 0.25 & -3.5 & -7 & -14 & -28
\end{array}
$$

$$
\frac{0.25x^4 - 4x^3}{x - 2}
$$

$$
= 0.25x^3 - 3.5x^2 - 7x - 14 - \frac{28}{x-2}
$$

41.

$$
\begin{array}{r|rrrr}
1+2i & 2 & -5 & 12 & -5 \\
     &   & 2+4i & -11-2i & 5 \\
\hline
     & 2 & -3+4i & 1-2i & 0
\end{array}
$$

$$
\frac{2x^3 - 5x^2 + 12x - 5}{x - (1+2i)}
$$

$$
= 2x^2 + (-3+4i)x + (1-2i)
$$

43. $f(x) = 2x^3 + 3x^2 - 20x - 21$

(a) $x = 4$ is not a zero.

$$
\begin{array}{r|rrrr}
4 & 2 & 3 & -20 & -21 \\
  &   & 8 & 44 & 96 \\
\hline
  & 2 & 11 & 24 & 75
\end{array}
$$

(b) $x = -1$ is a zero.

$$
\begin{array}{r|rrrr}
-1 & 2 & 3 & -20 & -21 \\
   &   & -2 & -1 & 21 \\
\hline
   & 2 & 1 & -21 & 0
\end{array}
$$

(c) $x = -\frac{7}{2}$ is a zero.

$$
\begin{array}{r|rrrr}
-\frac{7}{2} & 2 & 3 & -20 & -21 \\
             &   & -7 & 14 & 21 \\
\hline
             & 2 & -4 & -6 & 0
\end{array}
$$

(d) $x = 0$ is not a zero.

$$
\begin{array}{r|rrrr}
0 & 2 & 3 & -20 & -21 \\
  &   & 0 & 0 & 0 \\
\hline
  & 2 & 3 & -20 & -21
\end{array}
$$

45. $f(x) = 2x^3 + 7x^2 - 18x - 30$

(a) $x = 1$ is not a zero.

$$
\begin{array}{r|rrrr}
1 & 2 & 7 & -18 & -30 \\
  &   & 2 & 9 & -9 \\
\hline
  & 2 & 9 & -9 & -39
\end{array}
$$

(b) $x = \frac{5}{2}$ is a zero.

$$
\begin{array}{r|rrrr}
\frac{5}{2} & 2 & 7 & -18 & -30 \\
            &   & 5 & 30 & 30 \\
\hline
            & 2 & 12 & 12 & 0
\end{array}
$$

(c) $x = -3 + \sqrt{3}$ is a zero.

$$
\begin{array}{r|rrrr}
-3+\sqrt{3} & 2 & 7 & -18 & -30 \\
            &   & -6+2\sqrt{3} & 3-5\sqrt{3} & 30 \\
\hline
            & 2 & 1+2\sqrt{3} & -15-5\sqrt{3} & 0
\end{array}
$$

(d) $x = 0$ is not a zero.

$$
\begin{array}{r|rrrr}
0 & 2 & 7 & -18 & -30 \\
  &   & 0 & 0 & 0 \\
\hline
  & 2 & 7 & -18 & -30
\end{array}
$$

47. $g(x) = 2x^4 - 17x^3 + 58x^2 - 77x + 26$

(a) -2

	2	-17	58	-77	26	
		-4	42	-200	554	
	2	-21	100	-277	580	$= g(-2)$

(b) $\frac{1}{2}$

	2	-17	58	-77	26	
		1	-8	25	-26	
	2	-16	50	-52	0	$= g\left(\frac{1}{2}\right)$

49. $f(x) = x^4 + 10x^3 - 24x^2 + 20x + 44$

(a) -3

	1	10	-24	20	44	
		-3	-21	135	-465	
	1	7	-45	155	-421	$= f(-3)$

(b) $\sqrt{2}\,i$

	1	10	-24	20	44
		$\sqrt{2}\,i$	$-2 + 10\sqrt{2}\,i$	$-20 - 26\sqrt{2}\,i$	52
	1	$10 + \sqrt{2}\,i$	$-26 + 10\sqrt{2}\,i$	$-26\sqrt{2}\,i$	96 $= f(\sqrt{2}\,i)$

51. $g(x) = 5x^3 + 3x^2 - 6x + 9$
Sign variations; 2, positive zeros: 2 or 0
$g(-x) = -5x^3 + 3x^2 + 6x + 9$
Sign variations; 1, negative zeros: 1

53. $f(x) = -4x^3 + 8x^2 - 3x + 15$
Possible rational zeros:
$$\frac{\pm 1, \ \pm 3, \ \pm 5, \ \pm 15}{\pm 1, \ \pm 2, \ \pm 4} = \pm 1, \ \pm 3, \ \pm 5, \ \pm 15,$$
$$\pm \frac{1}{2}, \ \pm\frac{3}{2}, \pm\frac{5}{2}, \ \pm\frac{15}{2},$$
$$\pm \frac{1}{4}, \ \pm\frac{3}{4}, \pm\frac{5}{4}, \ \pm\frac{15}{4}$$

55. $f(x) = 4x^3 - 11x^2 + 10x - 3$

1

	4	-11	10	-3
		4	-7	3
	4	-7	3	0

Zeros: $\frac{3}{4}$, 1

57. $f(x) = 6x^3 - 5x^2 + 24x - 20$

$\frac{5}{6}$

	6	-5	24	-20
		5	0	20
	6	0	24	0

Zeros: $\frac{5}{6}$, $\pm 2i$

59. $f(x) = 6x^4 - 25x^3 + 14x^2 + 27x - 18$

-1	6	-25	14	27	-18
		-6	31	-45	18
3	6	-31	45	-18	0
		18	-39	18	
	6	-13	6	0	

Zeros: -1, $\frac{2}{3}$, $\frac{3}{2}$, 3

61. $f(x) = x^4 + 2x - 1$

(a) ± 1

(b)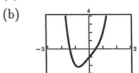

(c) -1.40, 0.47

63. $h(x) = x^3 - 6x^2 + 12x - 10$

(a) ± 1, ± 2, ± 5, ± 10

(b)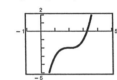

(c) 3.26

65. $3x^3 - 22{,}500x + 250{,}000 = 0$

Using a graphing utility, we find $x = 11.30$.

67. $f(x) = \dfrac{4}{x + 3}$

Domain: All real numbers except -3

Vertical asymptote: $x = -3$

Horizontal asymptote: $y = 0$

69. $g(x) = \dfrac{x^2}{x^2 - 4}$

Domain: All real numbers except ± 2

Vertical asymptotes: $x = -2$, $x = 2$

Horizontal asymptote: $y = 1$

71. $f(x) = \dfrac{-5}{x^2}$

y-axis symmetry

Vertical asymptote: $x = 0$

Horizontal asymptote: $y = 0$

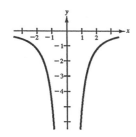

73. $g(x) = \dfrac{2+x}{1-x} = -\dfrac{x+2}{x-1}$

x-intercept: $(-2,\ 0)$

y-intercept: $(0,\ 2)$

Vertical asymptote: $x = 1$

Horizontal asymptote: $y = -1$

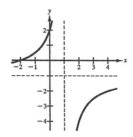

75. $P(x) = \dfrac{x^2}{x^2 + 1}$

Intercept: $(0,\ 0)$

y-axis symmetry

Horizontal asymptote: $y = 1$

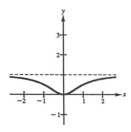

77. $y = \dfrac{x}{x^2 - 1}$

Intercept: $(0,\ 0)$

Origin symmetry

Vertical asymptotes: $x = -1,\ x = 1$

Horizontal asymptote: $y = 0$

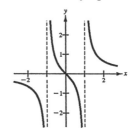

79. $f(x) = \dfrac{2x^3}{x^2+1}$

$= 2x - \dfrac{2x}{x^2+1}$

Intercept: $(0, \ 0)$

Origin symmetry

Slant asymptote: $y = 2x$

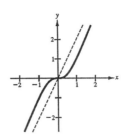

81. $s(x) = \dfrac{8x^2}{x^2+4}$

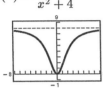

83. $g(x) = \dfrac{x^2+1}{x+1}$

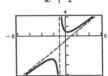

85. $\overline{C} = \dfrac{C}{x} = \dfrac{0.5x+500}{x}, \quad 0 < x$

$= 0.5 + \dfrac{500}{x}$

As x increases, the cost approaches the horizontal asymptote, $\overline{C} = 0.5$.

87. (a) When $p = 25$, $C = \dfrac{528(25)}{100-25} = \$176$ million.

(b) When $p = 50$, $C = \dfrac{528(50)}{100-50} = \$528$ million.

(c) When $p = 75$, $C = \dfrac{528(75)}{100-75} = \$1584$ million.

(d) As $p \Rightarrow 100$, C tends to infinity. No, it is not possible.

89. $y = \left(\dfrac{0.80-0.54x}{1+2.72x}\right)^2, \quad 0 < x$

For $y = 0.1$, $x = 0.35$ inches.

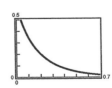

CHAPTER 4

Exponential and Logarithmic Functions

Section 4.1 Exponential Functions and Their Graphs

- You should know that a function of the form $y = a^x$, where $a > 0$, $a \neq 1$, is called an exponential function with base a.

- You should be able to graph exponential functions by hand and with a graphing utility.

- You should know the basic properties of exponential functions where $a > 0$ and $a \neq 1$.
  - (a) If $a^x = a^y$, then $x = y$.
  - (b) If $a^x = b^x$ and $x \neq 0$, then $a = b$.
  - (c) Domain: $(-\infty, \infty)$
  - (d) Range: $(0, \infty)$

- You should be familiar with the number e and the function e^x.

- You should know formulas for compound interest.
  - (a) For n compoundings per year: $A = P\left(1 + \dfrac{r}{n}\right)^{nt}$
  - (b) For continuous compoundings: $A = Pe^{rt}$.

- You should be able to use exponential functions in applications like radioactive decay and population growth.

---

1. $(3.4)^{5.6} \approx 946.852$

3. $1000(1.06)^{-5} \approx 747.258$

5. $5^{-\pi} \approx 0.006$

7. $100^{\sqrt{2}} \approx 673.639$

9. $e^{-3/4} \approx 0.472$

11. $f(x) = 3^x$

  y-intercept: $(0, 1)$

  3^x increases as x increases.

  Matches graph (g)

```
RANGE
Xmin=-3
Xmax=3
Xscl=1
Ymin=-1
Ymax=3
Yscl=1
```

13. $f(x) = 3^{-x}$

  y-intercept: $(0, 1)$

  3^{-x} decreases as x increases.

  Matches graph (b)

```
RANGE
Xmin=-3
Xmax=3
Xscl=1
Ymin=-1
Ymax=3
Yscl=1
```

15. $f(x) = 3^x - 4$

  y-intercept: $(0, -3)$

  $3^x - 4$ increases as x increases.

  Matches graph (d)

```
RANGE
Xmin=-3
Xmax=3
Xscl=1
Ymin=-5
Ymax=1
Yscl=1
```

17. $f(x) = -3^{x-2}$

  y-intercept: $\left(0, -\dfrac{1}{9}\right)$

  -3^{x-2} decreases as x increases.

  Point: $(2, -1)$

  Matches graph (f)

```
RANGE
Xmin=-1
Xmax=5
Xscl=1
Ymin=-5
Ymax=1
Yscl=1
```

19. $4^x < 3^x$ for $x < 0$

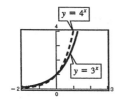

21. $g(x) = 5^x$

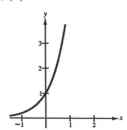

23. $f(x) = \left(\dfrac{1}{5}\right)^x = 5^{-x}$

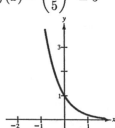

25. $h(x) = 5^{x-2}$

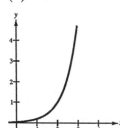

27. $g(x) = 5^{-x} - 3$

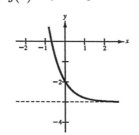

29. $f(x) = 3^{x-2} + 1$

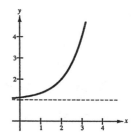

31. $y = 1.08^{-5x}$

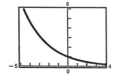

33. $s(t) = 2e^{0.12t}$

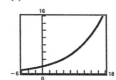

35. $g(x) = 1 + e^{-x}$

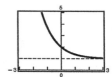

37. (a) $f(x) = 3^x$
(b) $g(x) = 3^{x-2}$
(c) $h(x) = -\frac{1}{2}(3^x)$
(d) $q(x) = 3^{-x} + 3$

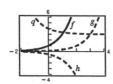

39. (a) $f(x) = x^2 e^{-x}$

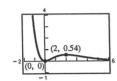

Increasing: $(0, 2)$
Decreasing: $(-\infty, 0)$, $(2, \infty)$
Relative maximum: $(2, 0.54)$
Relative minimum: $(0, 0)$

(b) $g(x) = x2^{3-x}$

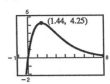

Increasing: $(-\infty, 1.44)$
Decreasing: $(1.44, \infty)$
Relative maximum: $(1.44, 4.25)$

41. $P = \$2500$, $r = 12\%$, $t = 10$ years

Compounded n times per year: $A = 2500\left(1 + \dfrac{0.12}{n}\right)^{10n}$

Compounded continuously: $A = 2500e^{0.12(10)}$

n	1	2	4	12	365	Continuous compounding
A	\$7,764.62	\$8,017.84	\$8,155.09	\$8,250.97	\$8,298.66	\$8,300.29

43. $P = \$2500$, $r = 12\%$, $t = 20$ years

Compounded n times per year: $A = 2500\left(1 + \dfrac{0.12}{n}\right)^{20n}$

Compounded continuously: $A = 2500e^{0.12(20)}$

n	1	2	4	12	365	Continuous compounding
A	\$24,115.73	\$25,714.29	\$26,602.23	\$27,231.38	\$27,547.07	\$27,557.94

45. $P = 100,000e^{-0.09t}$

t	1	10	20	30	40	50
P	\$91,393.12	\$40,656.97	\$16,529.89	\$6,720.55	\$2,732.37	\$1,110.90

47. $P = 100{,}000\left(1 + \dfrac{0.10}{12}\right)^{-12t}$

t	1	10	20	30	40	50
P	\$90,521.24	\$36,940.70	\$13,646.15	\$5,040.98	\$1,862.17	\$687.90

49. $A = 25{,}000e^{(0.0875)(25)} \approx \$222{,}822.57$

51. $p(x) = 500 - 0.5e^{0.004x}$

  (a) $x = 1000$

$$p = 500 - 0.5e^4 \approx \$472.70$$

  (b) $x = 1500$

$$p = 500 - 0.5e^6 \approx \$298.29$$

The graph of p is a decreasing function. Since $p \geq 0$, we see from graphing p that the domain is $(0,\ 1726.94)$ and the range is $(0,\ 499.50)$.

53. $P(t) = 100e^{0.2197t}$

  (a) $P(0) = 100e^{(0.2197)(0)} = 100$

  (b) $P(5) = 100e^{(0.2197)(5)} \approx 300$

  (c) $P(10) = 100e^{(0.2197)(10)} \approx 900$

55. $Q = 25\left(\dfrac{1}{2}\right)^{t/1620}$

  (a) When $t = 0$,

$$Q = 25\left(\dfrac{1}{2}\right)^{0/1620}$$

$$= 25(1)$$

$$= 25 \text{ units.}$$

  (b) When $t = 1000$,

$$Q = 25\left(\dfrac{1}{2}\right)^{1000/1620}$$

$$\approx 16.297 \text{ units.}$$

  (c)

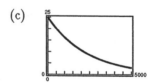

57. $y = \dfrac{300}{3 + 17e^{-1.57x}}$

(a)

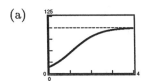

59. $V(t) = 20{,}000 \left(\dfrac{3}{4}\right)^t$

$V(2) = 20{,}000 \left(\dfrac{3}{4}\right)^2 = \$11{,}250$

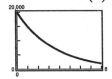

(b) If $x = 2$, $y = 80.3\%$.

(c) If $y = 66.67\%$, $x = 1.55$
   (1550 egg masses).

Section 4.2   Logarithmic Functions and Their Graphs

■ You should know that a function of the form $y = \log_a M$, where $a > 0$, $a \neq 1$, and $M > 0$, is called a logarithm of M to base a.

■ You should be able to convert from logarithmic form to exponential form and vice versa.

$$y = \log_a M \Longleftrightarrow a^y = M$$

■ You should know the following properties of logarithms.
(a) $\log_a 1 = 0$ (b) $\log_a a = 1$ (c) $\log_a a^x = x$
(d) Domain: $(0, \infty)$ (e) Range: $(-\infty, \infty)$

■ You should know the definition of the natural logarithmic function.

$$\log_e x = \ln x, \quad x > 0$$

■ You should know the properties of the natural logarithmic function.
(a) $\ln 1 = 0$ (b) $\ln e = 1$ (c) $\ln e^x = x$
(d) Domain: $(0, \infty)$ (e) Range: $(-\infty, \infty)$

■ You should be able to graph logarithmic functions by hand and with a graphing utility.

1. $\log_2 16 = \log_2 2^4 = 4$

3. $\log_{16} 4 = \log_{16} 16^{1/2} = \frac{1}{2}$

5. $\log_7 1 = \log_7 7^0 = 0$

7. $\log_{10} 0.01 = \log_{10} 10^{-2} = -2$

9. $\ln e^3 = 3$

11. $\log_a a^2 = 2$

13. $5^3 = 125$
$3 = \log_5 125$

15. $81^{1/4} = 3$
$\frac{1}{4} = \log_{81} 3$

17. $6^{-2} = \frac{1}{36}$
$-2 = \log_6 \left(\frac{1}{36}\right)$

19. $e^3 = 20.0855\ldots$
$3 = \ln 20.0855\ldots$

21. $\log_{10} 345 \approx 2.538$

23. $\log_{10}(0.48) \approx -0.319$

25. $\ln 18.42 \approx 2.913$

27. $f(x) = 3^x$, $g(x) = \log_3 x$

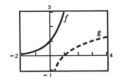

29. $f(x) = e^x$, $g(x) = \ln x$

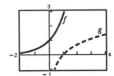

Notice that the graphs are symmetric with respect to the line $y = x$.

Notice that the graphs are symmetric with respect to the line $y = x$.

31. $f(x) = \ln x + 2$
Rises to the right
Vertical asymptote:
$x = 0$
Point on graph: $(1, 2)$
Graph (d)

```
RANGE
Xmin=-1
Xmax=4
Xscl=1
Ymin=-1
Ymax=3
Yscl=1
```

33. $f(x) = -\ln(x + 2)$
Falls to the right
Vertical asymptote:
$x = -2$
Intercepts:
$(-1, 0)$, $(0, -\ln 2)$
Graph (a)

```
RANGE
Xmin=-3
Xmax=3
Xscl=1
Ymin=-2
Ymax=2
Yscl=1
```

35. $f(x) = \ln(1 - x)$
Rises to the left
Vertical asymptote:
$x = 1$
Intercept: $(0, 0)$
Graph (f)

```
RANGE
Xmin=-3
Xmax=2
Xscl=1
Ymin=-2
Ymax=2
Yscl=1
```

37. $f(x) = \log_4 x$
Domain: $(0, \infty)$
Vertical asymptote: $x = 0$
Intercept: $(1, 0)$

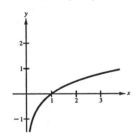

39. $y = -\log_3(x + 2)$
Domain: $x + 2 > 0 \Rightarrow x > -2$
Vertical asymptote: $x = -2$
x-intercept: $(-1, 0)$

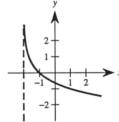

41. $f(x) = \ln(x - 2)$
    Domain: $(2, \infty)$
    Vertical asymptote: $x = 2$
    Intercept: $(3, 0)$

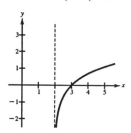

43. $f(x) = \frac{x}{2} - \ln\left(\frac{x}{4}\right)$
    Increasing: $(2, \infty)$
    Decreasing: $(0, 2)$
    Relative minimum: $(2, 1.693)$

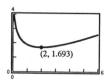

45. (a) $f(x) = \ln x$
    $g(x) = \sqrt{x}$

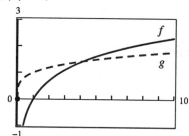

$\sqrt{x}$ increases more rapidly than $\ln x$.

(b) $f(x) = \ln x$
    $g(x) = \sqrt[4]{x}$

$\sqrt[4]{x}$ increases more rapidly than $\ln x$.

(The graphs of $\ln x$ and $\sqrt[4]{x}$ cross at approximately $x = 5504$.) The rate of growth of $\ln x$ is less than $\sqrt{x}$ and $\sqrt[4]{x}$ (and $\sqrt[8]{x}$) for large x.

47. $f(t) = 80 - 17 \log_{10}(t + 1), \quad 0 \le t \le 12$
    (a) $f(0) = 80 - 17 \log_{10}(0 + 1) = 80 - 17(0) = 80$
    (b) $f(4) = 80 - 17 \log_{10}(4 + 1) = 80 - 17(0.699) \approx 68.1$
    (c) $f(10) = 80 - 17 \log_{10}(10 + 1) = 80 - 17(1.041) \approx 62.3$

49. $t = \dfrac{\ln 2}{r}$

r	0.005	0.010	0.015	0.020	0.025	0.030
t	138.6	69.3	46.2	34.7	27.7	23.1

51. $y = 80.4 - 11 \ln x = 80.4 - 11 \ln 300$

$y \approx 17.658$ cubic feet per minute

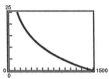

53. $t = \dfrac{5.315}{-6.7968 + \ln x}$, $1000 < x$

$\quad = \dfrac{5.315}{-6.7968 + \ln 1167.41}$

$t \approx 20$

The length of the mortgage will be about 20 years.

55. From Exercise 53, we know the length of the mortgage will be about 20 years. Thus, the total amount paid will be $12(20)(1167.41) = \$280{,}178.40$.

57. $W = 19{,}440(\ln 9 - \ln 3) \approx 21{,}357.023$ ft-lb

59. $f(x) = \dfrac{\ln x}{x}$

(a)

x	1	5	10	10^2	10^4	10^6
$f(x)$	0	0.322	0.230	0.046	0.00092	0.0000138

(b) As $x \Rightarrow \infty$, $f(x) \Rightarrow 0$.

(c)

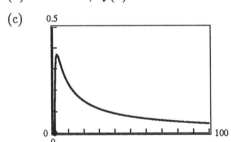

61. $y = 2 \ln x$ and $y = \ln x^2$ are not identical since the domain of the former is $(0, \infty)$, whereas, that of $y = \ln x^2$ is all $x \neq 0$. They are identical on $(0, \infty)$. You can verify this by graphing the two functions on the same viewing rectangle.

Section 4.3   Properties of Logarithms

■ You should know the following properties of logarithms.

(a) $\log_a(uv) = \log_a u + \log_a v$ (b) $\log_a(u/v) = \log_a u - \log_a v$

(c) $\log_a u^n = n \log_a u$ (d) $\log_a x = \dfrac{\log_b x}{\log_b a}$

Change of base

■ You should be able to rewrite logarithmic expressions.

---

1. $\log_3 5 = \dfrac{\log_{10} 5}{\log_{10} 3}$

3. $\log_2 x = \dfrac{\log_{10} x}{\log_{10} 2}$

5. $\log_3 5 = \dfrac{\ln 5}{\ln 3}$

7. $\log_2 x = \dfrac{\ln x}{\ln 2}$

9. $\log_3 7 = \dfrac{\log_{10} 7}{\log_{10} 3}$

$= \dfrac{\ln 7}{\ln 3}$

≈ 1.771

11. $\log_{1/2} 4 = \dfrac{\log_{10} 4}{\log_{10} \frac{1}{2}}$

$= \dfrac{\ln 4}{\ln \frac{1}{2}}$

$= -2.000$

13. $\log_9(0.4) = \dfrac{\log_{10} 0.4}{\log_{10} 9} = \dfrac{\ln 0.4}{\ln 9} \approx -0.417$

15. $\log_{15} 1250 = \dfrac{\log_{10} 1250}{\log_{10} 15} = \dfrac{\ln 1250}{\ln 15} \approx 2.633$

17. $\log_{10} 5x = \log_{10} 5 + \log_{10} x$

19. $\log_{10} \dfrac{5}{x} = \log_{10} 5 - \log_{10} x$

21. $\log_8 x^4 = 4 \log_8 x$

23. $\ln \sqrt{z} = \ln z^{1/2} = \frac{1}{2} \ln z$

25. $\ln xyz = \ln x + \ln y + \ln z$

27. $\ln \sqrt{a-1} = \ln(a-1)^{1/2}$

$= \frac{1}{2} \ln(a-1)$

29. $\ln z(z-1)^2 = \ln z + \ln(z-1)^2$

$= \ln z + 2 \ln(z-1)$

31. $\ln \sqrt[3]{\dfrac{x}{y}} = \ln \left(\dfrac{x}{y} \right)^{1/3} = \dfrac{1}{3} \ln \dfrac{x}{y} = \dfrac{1}{3} (\ln x - \ln y) = \dfrac{1}{3} \ln x - \dfrac{1}{3} \ln y$

33. $\ln \dfrac{x^4 \sqrt{y}}{z^5} = \ln x^4 + \ln \sqrt{y} - \ln z^5$

$= 4 \ln x + \dfrac{1}{2} \ln y - 5 \ln z$

35. $\log_b \dfrac{x^2}{y^2 z^3} = \log_b x^2 - (\log_b y^2 + \log_b z^3)$

$= 2 \log_b x - 2 \log_b y - 3 \log_b z$

37. $\ln x + \ln 2 = \ln 2x$

39. $\log_4 z - \log_4 y = \log_4 \dfrac{z}{y}$

41. $2\log_2(x+4) = \log_2(x+4)^2$

43. $\frac{1}{3}\log_3 5x = \log_3(5x)^{1/3} = \log_3 \sqrt[3]{5x}$

45. $\ln x - 3\ln(x+1) = \ln x - \ln(x+1)^3$
$$= \ln \frac{x}{(x+1)^3}$$

47. $\ln(x-2) - \ln(x+2) = \ln \dfrac{x-2}{x+2}$

49. $\ln x - 2[\ln(x+2) + \ln(x-2)] = \ln x - 2\ln(x^2-4) = \ln x - \ln(x^2-4)^2 = \ln \dfrac{x}{(x^2-4)^2}$

51. $\dfrac{1}{3}[2\ln(x+3) + \ln x - \ln(x^2-1)] = \dfrac{1}{3}\ln\dfrac{x(x+3)^2}{x^2-1} = \ln\sqrt[3]{\dfrac{x(x+3)^2}{x^2-1}}$

53. $\dfrac{1}{3}[\ln y + 2\ln(y+4)] - \ln(y-1) = \dfrac{1}{3}\ln y(y+4)^2 - \ln(y-1) = \ln\dfrac{\sqrt[3]{y(y+4)^2}}{y-1}$

55. $2\ln 3 - \dfrac{1}{2}\ln(x^2+1) = \ln 3^2 - \ln\sqrt{x^2+1} = \ln\dfrac{9}{\sqrt{x^2+1}}$

57. $\log_b 6 = \log_b(2 \cdot 3)$
$$= \log_b 2 + \log_b 3$$
$$\approx 0.3562 + 0.5646$$
$$= 0.9208$$

59. $\log_b 40 = \log_b(2^3 \cdot 5)$
$$= 3\log_b 2 + \log_b 5$$
$$= 3(0.3562) + 0.8271$$
$$= 1.8957$$

61. $\log_b\left(\dfrac{\sqrt{2}}{2}\right) = \log_b 2^{1/2} - \log_b 2$
$$= \dfrac{1}{2}\log_b 2 - \log_b 2$$
$$= -\dfrac{1}{2}\log_b 2$$
$$= -\dfrac{1}{2}(0.3562)$$
$$= -0.1781$$

63. $\log_b\sqrt{5b} = \dfrac{1}{2}[\log_b 5 + \log_b b]$
$$\approx \dfrac{1}{2}(0.8271 + 1)$$
$$= 0.9136$$

65. $\log_b\dfrac{(4.5)^3}{\sqrt{3}} = 3\log_b\dfrac{9}{2} - \dfrac{1}{2}\log_b 3 = 3(\log_b 3^2 - \log_b 2) - \dfrac{1}{2}\log_b 3$
$$= 3(2\log_b 3 - \log_b 2) - \dfrac{1}{2}\log_b 3 \approx 3[2(0.5646) - 0.3562] - \dfrac{1}{2}(0.5646) = 2.0367$$

67. $\log_3 9 = \log_3 3^2$

$\qquad = 2\log_3 3$

$\qquad = 2(1)$

$\qquad = 2$

69. $\log_4 16^{1.2} = 1.2\log_4 16$

$\qquad = 1.2\log_4 4^2$

$\qquad = 1.2(2)\log_4 4$

$\qquad = 1.2(2)(1)$

$\qquad = 2.4$

71. $\ln e^{4.5} = 4.5\ln e$

$\qquad = 4.5(1)$

$\qquad = 4.5$

73. $\log_4 8 = \log_4 2^3$

$\qquad = 3\log_4 2$

$\qquad = 3\log_4 \sqrt{4}$

$\qquad = 3\log_4 4^{1/2}$

$\qquad = 3\left(\frac{1}{2}\right)\log_4 4 = \frac{3}{2}$

75. $\log_7 \sqrt{70} = \frac{1}{2}\log_7(7 \cdot 10)$

$\qquad = \frac{1}{2}(\log_7 7 + \log_7 10)$

$\qquad = \frac{1}{2} + \frac{1}{2}\log_7 10$

77. $\log_5 \frac{1}{250} = \log_5 1 - \log_5 250$

$\qquad = 0 - \log_5(125 \cdot 2)$

$\qquad = -\log_5(5^3 \cdot 2)$

$\qquad = -[\log_5 5^3 + \log_5 2]$

$\qquad = -[3\log_5 5 + \log_5 2]$

$\qquad = -3 - \log_5 2$

79. $\ln(5e^6) = \ln 5 + \ln e^6 = 6 + \ln 5$

81. $\beta = 10\log_{10}\left(\dfrac{I}{10^{-16}}\right) = 10\left[\log_{10} I - \log_{10} 10^{-16}\right] = 10[\log_{10} I + 16] = 160 + 10\log_{10} I$

When $I = 10^{-10}$, we have $\beta = 160 + 10\log_{10} 10^{-10} = 160 + 10(-10) = 60$ decibels.

83. $f(x) = \ln\left(\dfrac{x}{2}\right)$

$g(x) = \dfrac{\ln x}{\ln 2}$

$h(x) = \ln x - \ln 2$

From the graphs, we see that $f(x) = h(x)$
and $f(x) \neq g(x)$!

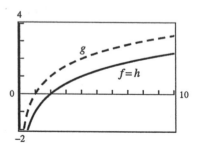

85. Let $x = \log_b u$, then $u = b^x$ and $u^n = (b^x)^n = b^{nx}$ and $\log_b u^n = \log_b b^{nx} = nx = n\log_b u$.

Section 4.4 Solving Exponential and Logarithmic Equations

- You should be able to solve exponential and logarithmic equations graphically and algebraically.
- To solve an exponential equation, take the logarithm of both sides.
- To solve a logarithmic equation, rewrite it in exponential form.
- Your graphing utility is especially helpful for checking answers.

1. $4^x = 16$

$4^x = 4^2$

$x = 2$

3. $7^x = \frac{1}{49}$

$7^x = 7^{-2}$

$x = -2$

5. $\left(\frac{3}{4}\right)^x = \frac{27}{64}$

$\left(\frac{3}{4}\right)^x = \left(\frac{3}{4}\right)^3$

$x = 3$

7. $\log_4 x = 3$

$x = 4^3 = 64$

9. $\log_{10} x = -1$

$x = 10^{-1} = \frac{1}{10}$

11. $\ln e^{x^2} = x^2$

13. $e^{\ln(5x+2)} = 5x + 2$

15. $e^{\ln x^2} = x^2$

17. $e^x = 10$

$x = \ln 10 \approx 2.303$

19. $7 - 2e^x = 5$

$-2e^x = -2$

$e^x = 1$

$x = \ln 1 = 0$

21. $e^{3x} = 12$

$3x = \ln 12$

$x = \frac{1}{3} \ln 12$

≈ 0.828

23. $500e^{-x} = 300$

$e^{-x} = \frac{3}{5}$

$-x = \ln \frac{3}{5}$

$x = -\ln \frac{3}{5}$

$= \ln \frac{5}{3} \approx 0.511$

25. $e^{2x} - 4e^x - 5 = 0$

   $(e^x + 1)(e^x - 5) = 0$

   $e^x + 1 = 0$ or $e^x - 5 = 0$

   $e^x = -1$ $e^x = 5$

   No solution $x = \ln 5$

                 ≈ 1.609

Checking with a graphing utility, the only
x-intercept is $x = 1.61$.

27. $20(100 - e^{x/2}) = 500$

   $100 - e^{x/2} = 25$

   $e^{x/2} = 75$

   $\dfrac{x}{2} = \ln 75$

   $x = 2\ln 75 \approx 8.635$

29. $10^x = 42$

   $x = \log_{10} 42$

     ≈ 1.623

31. $3^{2x} = 80$

   $\ln 3^{2x} = \ln 80$

   $2x \ln 3 = \ln 80$

   $x = \dfrac{\ln 80}{2 \ln 3}$

     ≈ 1.994

33. $5^{-t/2} = 0.20$

   $5^{-t/2} = \dfrac{1}{5}$

   $5^{-t/2} = 5^{-1}$

   $-\dfrac{t}{2} = -1$

   $t = 2$

35. $\left(1 + \dfrac{0.10}{12}\right)^{12t} = 2$

   $\ln\left(1 + \dfrac{0.10}{12}\right)^{12t} = \ln 2$

   $12t \ln\left(1 + \dfrac{0.10}{12}\right) = \ln 2$

   $t = \dfrac{\ln 2}{12 \ln\left(1 + \dfrac{0.10}{12}\right)} \approx 6.960$

37. $3e^{3x/2} = 962$

   $f(x) = 3e^{3x/2} - 962$

   $x = 3.847$

39. $e^{0.09t} = 3$

   $f(t) = e^{0.09t} - 3$

   $t = 12.207$

41. $8(10^{3x}) = 12$

   $f(x) = 8(10^{3x}) - 12$

   $x = 0.059$

43. $\left(1 + \dfrac{0.065}{365}\right)^{365t} = 4$

$$f(t) = \left(1 + \dfrac{0.065}{365}\right)^{365t} - 4$$

$$t = 21.330$$

45. $\ln x = -3 \Rightarrow e^{-3} = x \Rightarrow x \approx 0.050$

47. $\ln 2x = 2.4$

$2x = e^{2.4}$

$x = \dfrac{e^{2.4}}{2} \approx 5.512$

49. $\ln \sqrt{x+2} = 1$

$\sqrt{x+2} = e^1$

$x + 2 = e^2$

$x = -2 + e^2 \approx 5.389$

51. $\ln x + \ln(x - 2) = 1$

$\ln x(x - 2) = 1$

$x(x - 2) = e^1$

$x^2 - 2x - e = 0$

$$x = \frac{-(-2) \pm \sqrt{(-2)^2 - 4(1)(-e)}}{2(1)} = \frac{2 \pm 2\sqrt{1 + e}}{2} = 1 \pm \sqrt{1 + e}$$

$x = 1 + \sqrt{1 + e} \approx 2.928$

$x = 1 - \sqrt{1 + e} \approx -0.928$ extraneous

Checking with a graphing utility, the only solution to $y = \ln x + \ln(x - 2) - 1 = 0$ is $x = 2.93$.

53. $\log_{10}(z - 3) = 2$

$z - 3 = 10^2$

$z = 10^2 + 3 = 103$

55. $\log_{10}(x+4) - \log_{10} x = \log_{10}(x+2)$

$$\log_{10}\left(\frac{x+4}{x}\right) = \log_{10}(x+2)$$

$$\frac{x+4}{x} = x+2$$

$$x+4 = x^2 + 2x$$

$$0 = x^2 + x - 4$$

$$x = \frac{-1 \pm \sqrt{17}}{2} = -\frac{1}{2} \pm \frac{\sqrt{17}}{2}$$

$$x = -\frac{1}{2} + \frac{\sqrt{17}}{2} \approx 1.562$$

$$x = -\frac{1}{2} - \frac{\sqrt{17}}{2} \approx -2.562 \text{ extraneous}$$

Checking with a graphing utility, the only solution to $y = \log_{10}(x+4) - \log_{10} x - \log_{10}(x+2)$ is $x = 1.56$.

57. $\log_3 x + \log_3(x^2 - 8) = \log_3 8x$

$$\log_3 x(x^2 - 8) = \log_3 8x$$

$$x(x^2 - 8) = 8x$$

$$x^3 - 16x = 0$$

$$x(x+4)(x-4) = 0$$

$$x = 0 \text{ extraneous}$$

$$x + 4 = 0 \Rightarrow x = -4 \text{ extraneous}$$

$$x - 4 = 0 \Rightarrow x = 4$$

59. $\ln(x+5) = \ln(x-1) - \ln(x+1)$

$$\ln(x+5) = \ln\left(\frac{x-1}{x+1}\right)$$

$$x + 5 = \frac{x-1}{x+1}$$

$$(x+5)(x+1) = x - 1$$

$$x^2 + 6x + 5 = x - 1$$

$$x^2 + 5x + 6 = 0$$

$$(x+2)(x+3) = 0$$

$$x = -2 \text{ or } x = -3$$

Both of these solutions are extraneous, so the equation has no solution. The graph of $y = \ln(x+5) - \ln(x-1) + \ln(x+1)$ confirms that there are no solutions.

61. $2\ln x = 7$

$$f(x) = 2\ln x - 7$$

$$x = 33.115$$

63. $\ln x + \ln(x^2 + 1) = 8$

$$f(x) = \ln x + \ln(x^2 + 1) - 8$$

$$x = 14.369$$

65. $A = Pe^{rt}$

$2000 = 1000e^{0.085t}$

$2 = e^{0.085t}$

$\ln 2 = 0.085t$

$\dfrac{\ln 2}{0.085} = t$

$t \approx 8.2$ years

67. $A = Pe^{rt}$

$3000 = 1000e^{0.085t}$

$3 = e^{0.085t}$

$\ln 3 = 0.085t$

$\dfrac{\ln 3}{0.085} = t$

$t \approx 12.9$ years

69. $p = 500 - 0.5(e^{0.004x})$

  (a) $350 = 500 - 0.5(e^{0.004x})$

        $-150 = -0.5(e^{0.004x})$

          $300 = e^{0.004x}$

      $0.004x = \ln 300$

          $x = \dfrac{\ln 300}{0.004} \approx 1426$ units

  (b) $300 = 500 - 0.5(e^{0.004x})$

        $-200 = -0.5(e^{0.004x})$

          $400 = e^{0.004x}$

      $0.004x = \ln 400$

          $x = \dfrac{\ln 400}{0.004} \approx 1498$ units

71. $V = 6.7e^{-48.1/t}$

  (a)

  (b) The horizontal asymptote is $V = 6.7$.
      The horizontal asymptote represents
      the limiting yield per acre.

  (c) $1.3 = 6.7e^{-48.1/t}$

       $\dfrac{1.3}{6.7} = e^{-48.1/t}$

      $\ln \dfrac{1.3}{6.7} = -\dfrac{48.1}{t}$

           $t = -\dfrac{48.1}{\ln(1.3/6.7)}$

             ≈ 29.33 years

      Or, graphing
      $V - 1.3 = 6.7e^{-48.1/t} - 1.3$,
      we see that the t-intercept is
      $t = 29.33$.

73. (a)

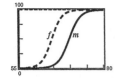

(b) The horizontal asymptote is $y = 100$ for each function.

(c) For males:

$$50 = \frac{100}{1 + e^{-0.6114(x-69.71)}}$$

$$1 + e^{-0.6114(x-69.71)} = \frac{100}{50}$$

$$e^{-0.6114(x-69.71)} = 1$$

$$-0.6114(x - 69.71) = \ln 1$$

$$x - 69.71 = 0$$

$$x = 69.71 \text{ in. for males}$$

For females:

$$50 = \frac{100}{1 + e^{-0.66607(x-64.51)}}$$

$$1 + e^{-0.66607(x-64.51)} = \frac{100}{50}$$

$$e^{-0.66607(x-64.51)} = 1$$

$$-0.66607(x - 64.51) = \ln 1$$

$$x - 64.51 = 0$$

$$x = 64.51 \text{ in. for females}$$

Or, you can determine the average height by using a graping utility to find the intersection of $m(x)$ (or $f(x)$) and $y = 50$.

Section 4.5 Applications of Exponential and Logarithmic Functions

■ You should be able to solve compound interest problems.

(a) Compound interest formulas:

1. $A = P\left(1 + \dfrac{r}{n}\right)^{nt}$ 2. $A = Pe^{rt}$

(b) Effective yield:

1. Effective yield $= \left(1 + \dfrac{r}{n}\right)^{n} - 1$, n compoundings per year

2. Effective yield $= e^{r} - 1$, continuous compounding

■ You should be able to solve growth and decay problems: $Q(t) = Ce^{kt}$

(a) If $k > 0$, the population grows.

(b) If $k < 0$, the population decays.

■ You should be able to solve logistics model problems: $y = \dfrac{a}{1 + be^{-(x-c)/d}}$

■ You should be able to solve intensity model problems: $S = K \log_{10} \dfrac{I}{I_0}$

	Initial investment	Annual % rate	Effective yield	Time to double	Amount after 10 yrs
1.	1000	12%	12.75%	5.78 yrs	3,320.12
3.	750	8.94%	9.35%	7.75 yrs	1,833.67
5.	500	9.5%	9.97%	7.30 yrs	1,292.85
7.	6392.79	11%	11.63%	6.30 yrs	19,205.00
9.	5000	8%	8.33%	8.66 yrs	11,127.70

Formulas used in Exercises 1–9:

Initial investment: $P = Ae^{-rt}$ Annual % rate: $r = \dfrac{\ln(A/P)}{t}$ or $r = \ln(1 + \text{effective yield})$

Effective yield $= e^{r} - 1$ Time to double $= \dfrac{\ln 2}{r}$

Amount after ten years $= Pe^{10r}$

11. $500,000 = P\left(1 + \dfrac{0.075}{12}\right)^{12(20)}$

$500,000 = P(1.00625)^{240}$

$P \approx \$112,087.09$

13. $P = 1000, \ r = 11\%$

(a) $n = 1$

$t = \dfrac{\ln 2}{\ln(1 + 0.11)} \approx 6.642$ years

(b) $n = 12$

$t = \dfrac{\ln 2}{12\ln\left(1 + \dfrac{0.11}{12}\right)} \approx 6.330$ years

(c) $n = 365$

$t = \dfrac{\ln 2}{365\ln\left(1 + \dfrac{0.11}{365}\right)} \approx 6.302$ years

(d) Continuously

$t = \dfrac{\ln 2}{0.11} \approx 6.301$ years

15. $3P = Pe^{rt}$

$3 = e^{rt}$

$rt = \ln 3$

$t = \dfrac{\ln 3}{r}$

r	2%	4%	6%	8%	10%	12%
t	54.93	27.47	18.31	13.73	10.99	9.16

17. $A = 1 + 0.075t$ (simple interest)

$A = e^{0.07t}$ (continuous compound interest)

Continuous compounding at 7% grows faster.

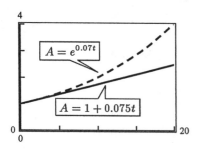

	Isotope	Half-life	Initial quantity	Amt. after 1000 yrs	Amt. after 10,000 yrs
19.	^{226}Ra	1620	10 grams	6.52 grams	0.14 grams
21.	^{14}C	5730	6.70 grams	5.95 grams	2 grams
23.	^{230}Pu	24,360	2.16 grams	2.1 grams	1.62 grams

Formula used in Exercises 19–23:

$Q(t) = Ce^{-(\ln 2/T)t}$

$Q(t) = $ amount, $C = $ initial amount, $T = $ half-life, $t = $ time

25. $y = e^{kt}$

$10 = e^{4k}$

$4k = \ln 10$

$k = \frac{1}{4}\ln 10 \approx 0.5756$

27. $y = e^{kt}$

$\frac{1}{4} = e^{4k}$

$4k = \ln \frac{1}{4}$

$k = \frac{1}{4}\ln \frac{1}{4} \approx -0.3466$

29. (a) If $t = 0$, $P = 105,300$.

(b) $150,000 = 105,300e^{0.015t}$

$$0.015t = \ln\left(\frac{150,000}{105,300}\right)$$

$$t = \frac{1}{0.015}\ln\left(\frac{150,000}{105,300}\right)$$

≈ 23.588 years

$1990 + 23 = 2013$

The city will have a population of 150,000 in the year 2013.

31. $1350 = 2500e^{k(-45)}$

$-45k = \ln\left(\frac{1350}{2500}\right)$

$k = \left(-\frac{1}{45}\right)\ln\left(\frac{1350}{2500}\right) \approx 0.0137$

$P = 2500e^{0.0137(20)} \approx 3288$

33. $P = Ce^{kt}$

$4.22 = Ce^{k(0)} \Rightarrow C = 4.22$

$6.49 = 4.22e^{10k}$

$\dfrac{6.49}{4.22} = e^{10k}$

$k = \dfrac{1}{10} \ln\left(\dfrac{6.49}{4.22}\right) \approx 0.0430$

$P = 4.22e^{0.0430}$

When $t = 20$, $P \approx 9.97$ million.

35. $N = 100e^{kt}$

$300 = 100e^{5k}$

$k = \dfrac{\ln 3}{5} \approx 0.2197$

$N = 100e^{0.2197t}$

$200 = 100e^{0.2197t}$

$t = \dfrac{\ln 2}{0.2197}$

≈ 3.15 hours

37. $Q(t) = Ce^{kt}$

$\tfrac{1}{2}C = Ce^{k(1620)}$

$\tfrac{1}{2} = e^{1620k}$

$k = \tfrac{1}{1620}\ln(\tfrac{1}{2}) \approx -0.000428$

$Q(t) = Ce^{-0.000428t}$

When $t = 100$,

$Q(100) \approx 0.958C$

$= 95.8\%$ of C.

39. $16{,}500 = 22{,}000e^{k(1)}$

$\tfrac{16{,}500}{22{,}000} = e^k$

$\ln\tfrac{3}{4} = k$

$k \approx -0.2877$

$y = 22{,}000e^{-0.2877(3)}$

$y \approx \$9{,}281$

41. $S(t) = 100(1 - e^{kt})$

(a) $15 = 100(1 - e^{k(1)})$

$-85 = -100e^k$

$k = \ln 0.85$

$k \approx -0.1625$

$S(t) = 100(1 - e^{-0.1625t})$

(b) $S(5) = 100(1 - e^{-0.1625(5)})$

$\approx 55.625 = 55{,}625$ units

43. $p = 0.166e^{-(x-64.5)^2/11.5}$

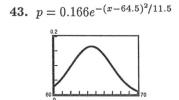

The average height is 64.5, the highest point on the graph.

45. $p(t) = \dfrac{10{,}000}{1 + 19e^{-t/5}}$

(a)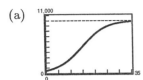

The larger horizontal asymptote is $p = 10{,}000$, which represents the carrying capacity of the lake for this species of fish.

(b) $p(5) = \dfrac{10{,}000}{1 + 19e^{-1}} \approx 1252$ fish

(c) $\quad 2000 = \dfrac{10{,}000}{1 + 19e^{-t/5}}$

$$1 + 19e^{-t/5} = 5$$

$$e^{-t/5} = \frac{4}{19}$$

$$-\frac{t}{5} = \ln\left(\frac{4}{19}\right)$$

$$t = -5\ln\left(\frac{4}{19}\right)$$

$$\approx 7.8 \text{ months}$$

Or, using a graphing utility to graph

$$y = \frac{10{,}000}{1 + 19e^{-t/5}} - 2000,$$

we see that the x-intercept is 7.79.

47. $S = 10(1 - e^{kx})$

(a) $2.5 = 10(1 - e^{k(5)})$

$\quad \frac{1}{4} = 1 - e^{5k}$

$\quad 5k = \ln\frac{3}{4}$

$\quad k = \frac{1}{5}\ln\frac{3}{4} \approx -0.0575$

$\quad S = 10(1 - e^{-0.0575x})$

(b) $S = 10\left(1 - e^{-0.0575(7)}\right)$

$\quad \approx 3.314$ or 3314 units

49. $R = \log_{10}\dfrac{I}{I_0} = \log_{10} I$ since $I_0 = 1$

(a) $R = \log_{10} 80{,}500{,}000 \approx 7.9$

(b) $R = \log_{10} 48{,}275{,}000 \approx 7.7$

51. $\beta(I) = 10 \log_{10} \dfrac{I}{I_0}$ where $I_0 = 10^{-16}$ watt/cm^2

(a) $\beta(10^{-14}) = 10 \log_{10} \dfrac{10^{-14}}{10^{-16}} = 10 \log_{10} 10^2 = 20$ decibels

(b) $\beta(10^{-9}) = 10 \log_{10} \dfrac{10^{-9}}{10^{-16}} = 10 \log_{10} 10^7 = 70$ decibels

(c) $\beta(10^{-6.5}) = 10 \log_{10} \dfrac{10^{-6.5}}{10^{-16}} = 10 \log_{10} 10^{9.5} = 95$ decibels

(d) $\beta(10^{-4}) = 10 \log_{10} \dfrac{10^{-4}}{10^{-16}} = 10 \log_{10} 10^{12} = 120$ decibels

53.
$$\beta = 10 \log_{10} \dfrac{I}{I_0}$$

$$\dfrac{\beta}{10} = \log_{10} \dfrac{I}{I_0}$$

$$10^{\beta/10} = \dfrac{I}{I_0}$$

$$I = I_0 10^{\beta/10}$$

$$\% \text{ decrease} = \dfrac{I_0 10^{93/10} - I_0 10^{80/10}}{I_0 10^{93/10}} \times 100 \approx 95\%$$

55. pH $= -\log_{10}[\mathrm{H}^+]$

$\qquad = -\log_{10}[2.3 \times 10^{-5}]$

$\qquad \approx 4.64$

57. pH $= -\log[\mathrm{H}^+]$

$\qquad 5.8 = -\log[\mathrm{H}^+]$

$\qquad [\mathrm{H}^+] = 10^{-5.8} \approx 1.6 \times 10^{-6}$

59. $\quad$ pH $= -\log_{10}[\mathrm{H}^+]$

$\qquad -\mathrm{pH} = \log_{10}[\mathrm{H}^+]$

$\quad 10^{-\mathrm{pH}} = [\mathrm{H}^+]$

$$\dfrac{\text{Hydrogen ion concentration of fruit}}{\text{Hydrogen ion concentration of tablet}} = \dfrac{10^{-2.5}}{10^{-9.5}} = 10^7$$

61. (a)

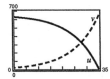

(b) In the early years of the mortgage, the larger part of the monthly payment goes for interest payments ($u > v$). Using the zoom feature, $u = v$ when $t = 27.7$ years.

63. $t = -2.5 \ln \left(\dfrac{T - 70}{98.6 - 70} \right)$

At 9:00 A.M. we have:

$$t = -2.5 \ln \left(\frac{85.7 - 70}{98.6 - 70} \right) \approx 1.5 \text{ hours.}$$

From this we can conclude that the person died at 7:30 A.M.

Section 4.6   Exploring Data: Nonlinear Models

1.

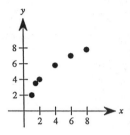

A logarithmic model seems best.

3.

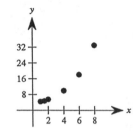

A exponential model seems best.

5.

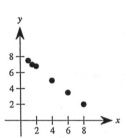

An exponential model seems best.

7. $y = 3.8073(1.3057)^x$

$= 3.8073e^{0.2667x}$

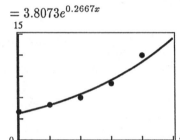

9. $y = 8.4629(0.7775)^x$

$= 8.4629e^{-.2517x}$

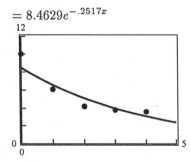

11. $y = 2.0829 + 1.2574 \ln x$

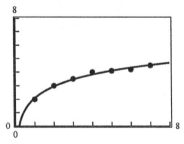

13. $y = 9.8262 - 4.0973 \ln x$

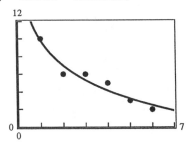

15. $y = 1.9847x^{0.7604}$

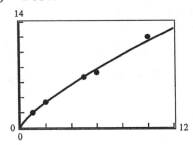

17. $y = 16.1033x^{-3.1738}$

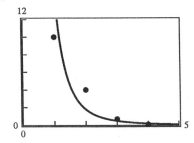

19. $y = 4.7539(6.7744)^x$

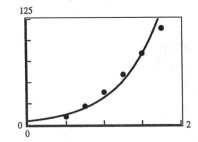

21. $y = 19.7523 + 3.5408 \ln t$

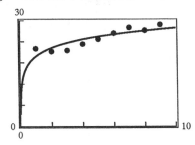

23. $y = 5.088x^{0.645}$

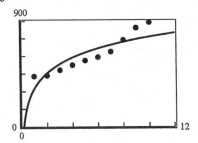

Chapter 4   Review Exercises

1. $f(x) = 2^x$

Horizontal asymptote: $y = 0$

y-intercept: $(0, 1)$

As x increases, $f(x)$ increases.

Matches (d)

```
RANGE
Xmin=-4
Xmax=3
Xscl=1
Ymin=-1
Ymax=4
Yscl=1
```

3. $f(x) = -2^x$

Horizontal asymptote: $y = 0$

y-intercept: $(0, -1)$

As x increases, $f(x)$ decreases.

Matches (a)

```
RANGE
Xmin=-4
Xmax=4
Xscl=1
Ymin=-5
Ymax=1
Yscl=1
```

5. $f(x) = \log_2 x$

Vertical asymptote: $x = 0$

x-intercept: $(1, 0)$

As x increases, $f(x)$ increases.

Matches (c)

```
RANGE
Xmin=-3
Xmax=6
Xscl=1
Ymin=-3
Ymax=3
Yscl=1
```

7. $f(x) = 6^x$

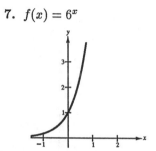

9. $g(x) = 6^{-x}$

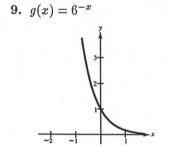

11. $h(x) = e^{-x/2}$

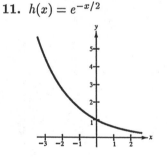

13. $f(x) = e^{x+2}$

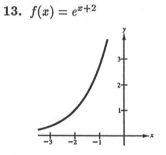

15. $n = 1$: $A = 3500(1 + 0.105)^{10}$ $\approx \$9,499.28$

$n = 2$: $A = 3500 \left(1 + \dfrac{0.105}{2}\right)^{20}$ $\approx \$9,738.91$

$n = 4$: $A = 3500 \left(1 + \dfrac{0.105}{4}\right)^{40}$ $\approx \$9,867.22$

$n = 12$: $A = 3500 \left(1 + \dfrac{0.105}{12}\right)^{120}$ $\approx \$9,956.20$

$n = 365$: $A = 3500 \left(1 + \dfrac{0.105}{365}\right)^{3650}$ $\approx \$10,000.27$

Continuous: $A = 3500e^{(0.105)(10)} \approx \$10,001.78$

17. $A = Pe^{rt}$

$P = Ae^{-rt} = 200{,}000e^{-0.08t}$

$t = 1$: $P = 200{,}000e^{-0.08} \approx \$184{,}623.27$

$t = 10$: $P = 200{,}000e^{-0.8} \approx \$89{,}865.79$

$t = 20$: $P = 200{,}000e^{-1.6} \approx \$40{,}379.30$

$t = 30$: $P = 200{,}000e^{-2.4} \approx \$18{,}143.59$

$t = 40$: $P = 200{,}000e^{-3.2} \approx \$8{,}152.44$

$t = 50$: $P = 200{,}000e^{-4.0} \approx \$3{,}663.13$

19. $A = 50{,}000e^{0.0875(35)}$

$\approx \$1{,}069{,}047.14$

21. $A = 500e^{-0.013t}$

$A = 500e^{-0.013(60)}$

≈ 229.2 units per milliliter
The algebraic solution is easier.

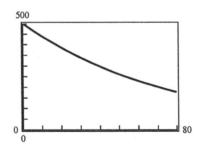

23. $y = 28e^{0.6-0.012s}$, $s \geq 50$

When $s = 50$, $y = 28e^{0.6-0.012(50)} = 28$ miles per gallon.

When $s = 55$, $y = 28e^{0.6-0.012(55)} \approx 26.4$ miles per gallon.

When $s = 60$, $y = 28e^{0.6-0.012(60)} \approx 24.8$ miles per gallon.

When $s = 65$, $y = 28e^{0.6-0.012(65)} \approx 23.4$ miles per gallon.

When $s = 70$, $y = 28e^{0.6-0.012(70)} \approx 22.0$ miles per gallon.

25. $g(x) = \log_3 x$

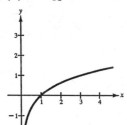

27. $f(x) = \ln x + 3$

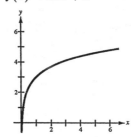

29. $h(x) = \ln(e^{x-1}) = x - 1$

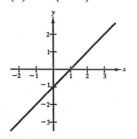

31. $4^3 = 64$

$3 = \log_4 64$

33. $\log_{10} 1000 = \log_{10} 10^3$

$= 3$

35. $\log_3 \frac{1}{9} = \log_3 3^{-2}$

$= -2$

37. $\ln e^7 = 7 \ln e$

$= 7(1)$

$= 7$

39. $\ln 1 = \ln e^0$

$= 0 \cdot \ln e$

$= 0$

41. $\log_4 9 = \dfrac{\log_{10} 9}{\log_{10} 4}$

$= \dfrac{\ln 9}{\ln 4}$

≈ 1.585

43. $\log_{12} 200 = \dfrac{\log_{10} 200}{\log_{10} 12}$

$= \dfrac{\ln 200}{\ln 12} \approx 2.132$

45. $\log_5 5x^2 = \log_5 5 + \log_5 x^2$

$= 1 + 2 \log_5 x$

47. $\log_{10} \dfrac{5\sqrt{y}}{x^2} = \log_{10} 5 + \log_{10} y^{1/2} - \log_{10} x^2 = \log_{10} 5 + \frac{1}{2} \log_{10} y - 2 \log_{10} x$

49. $\ln[(x^2 + 1)(x - 1)] = \ln(x^2 + 1) + \ln(x - 1)$

51. $\log_2 5 + \log_2 x = \log_2 5x$

53. $\dfrac{1}{2}\ln|2x-1|-2\ln|x+1|=\ln\sqrt{|2x-1|}-\ln(x+1)^2=\ln\dfrac{\sqrt{|2x-1|}}{(x+1)^2}$

55. $\ln 3+\dfrac{1}{3}\ln(4-x^2)-\ln x=\ln 3+\ln\sqrt[3]{4-x^2}-\ln x=\ln\dfrac{3\sqrt[3]{4-x^2}}{x}$

57. False. The domain is all $x>0$. Try using your graphing utility to graph $f(x)=\ln x$.

59. False
$$\ln(x+2)\neq\ln x+\ln 2$$
Try graphing $y_1=\ln(x+2)$ and $y_2=\ln x+\ln 2$. In fact, $\ln x+\ln 2=\ln 2x$.

61. $\log_b 25=\log_b 5^2$
$=2\log_b 5$
$\approx 2(0.8271)$
$=1.6542$

63. $\log_b\sqrt{3}=\log_b 3^{1/2}$
$=\dfrac{1}{2}\log_b 3$
$\approx\dfrac{1}{2}(0.5646)$
$=0.2823$

65. $s=25-\dfrac{13\ln\left(\frac{10}{12}\right)}{\ln 3}$
≈ 27.16 miles

67. $e^x=12$
$x=\ln 12\approx 2.485$

69. $3e^{-5x}=132$
$e^{-5x}=44$
$-5x=\ln 44$
$x=-\dfrac{1}{5}\ln 44\approx-0.757$

71. $e^{2x}-7e^x+10=0$
$(e^x-5)(e^x-2)=0$
$e^x-5=0\qquad\text{or}\quad e^x-2=0$
$x=\ln 5\qquad\qquad x=\ln 2$
$\approx 1.609\qquad\qquad \approx 0.693$

73. $\ln 3x=8.2$
$3x=e^{8.2}$
$x=\dfrac{1}{3}e^{8.2}$
≈ 1213.650

75. $\ln x-\ln 3=2$
$\ln\dfrac{x}{3}=2$
$\dfrac{x}{3}=e^2$
$x=3e^2$
≈ 22.167

77. $2=Ce^{k(0)}$
$2=Ce^0=C$
$3=2e^{k(4)}$
$\dfrac{3}{2}=e^{4k}$
$4k=\ln\dfrac{3}{2}$
$k=\dfrac{1}{4}\ln\dfrac{3}{2}$
≈ 0.1014
$y=2e^{0.1014t}$

79. $4=Ce^{k(0)}$
$4=Ce^0=C$
$\dfrac{1}{2}=4e^{k(5)}$
$\dfrac{1}{8}=e^{5k}$
$5k=\ln\dfrac{1}{8}$
$k=\dfrac{1}{5}\ln\dfrac{1}{8}$
≈ -0.4159
$y=4e^{-0.4159t}$

81. $p = 500 - 0.5e^{0.004x}$

(a) $p = 450$

$$450 = 500 - 0.5e^{0.004x}$$

$$0.5e^{0.004x} = 50$$

$$e^{0.004x} = 100$$

$$0.004x = \ln 100$$

$$x \approx 1151 \text{ units}$$

(b) $p = 400$

$$400 = 500 - 0.5e^{0.004x}$$

$$0.5e^{0.004x} = 100$$

$$e^{0.004x} = 200$$

$$0.004x = \ln 200$$

$$x \approx 1325 \text{ units}$$

83. (a) $\quad t = \dfrac{\ln 2}{r}$

$$7.75 = \dfrac{\ln 2}{r}$$

$$r = \dfrac{\ln 2}{7.75}$$

$$\approx 0.0894$$

or 8.94%

(b) $A = Pe^{rt}$

$$A = 750e^{[(\ln 2)/7.75](10)}$$

$$\approx \$1834.37$$

(c) $A = Pe^{[(\ln 2)/7.75](1)}$

$$\approx P(1.0936)$$

$$= P(1 + 0.0936)$$

Effective yield ≈ 0.0936

$$= 9.36\%$$

85.
$$\beta = 10\log_{10}\left(\dfrac{I}{10^{-16}}\right)$$

$$125 = 10\log_{10}\left(\dfrac{I}{10^{-16}}\right)$$

$$\dfrac{125}{10} = \log_{10}\left(\dfrac{I}{10^{-16}}\right)$$

$$10^{12.5} = \dfrac{I}{10^{-16}}$$

$$10^{12.5} = 10^{16}I$$

$$10^{12.5}10^{-16} = I$$

$$10^{-3.5} = I$$

87. $y = 234.6839(.8746)^x$

$$= 234.684e^{-0.134x}$$

CHAPTER 5

Trigonometric Functions

Section 5.1   Radian and Degree Measure

You should know the following basic facts about angles, their measurement, and their applications.

- Types of Angles:
  (a) Acute: Measure between 0° and 90°
  (b) Right: Measure 90°
  (c) Obtuse: Measure between 90° and 180°

- α and β are complementary if $\alpha + \beta = 90°$. They are supplementary if $\alpha + \beta = 180°$.

- Two angles in standard position that have the same terminal side are called coterminal angles.

- To convert degrees to radians, use $1° = \pi/180$ radians.

- To convert radians to degrees, use 1 radian $= (180/\pi)°$.

- $1' =$ one minute $= 1/60$ of $1°$.

- $1'' =$ one second $= 1/60$ of $1' = 1/3600$ of $1°$.

- The length of a circular arc is $s = r\theta$ where θ is measured in radians.

- Speed = distance/time

- Angular speed $= \theta/t = s/rt$

1. (a) $\dfrac{\pi}{5}$ Quadrant I

   (b) $\dfrac{7\pi}{5}$ Quadrant III

3. (a) -1 Quadrant IV
   (b) -2 Quadrant III

5. (a) 130°   Quadrant II
   (b) 285°   Quadrant IV

7. (a)

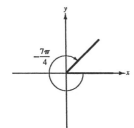

(b)

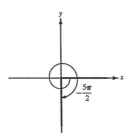

9. (a)

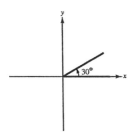

(b)

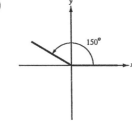

11. (a) $\dfrac{\pi}{9} + 2\pi = \dfrac{19\pi}{9}$

$\dfrac{\pi}{9} - 2\pi = -\dfrac{17\pi}{9}$

(b) $\dfrac{4\pi}{3} + 2\pi = \dfrac{10\pi}{3}$

$\dfrac{4\pi}{3} - 2\pi = -\dfrac{2\pi}{3}$

13. (a) $36° + 360° = 396°$

$36° - 360° = -324°$

(b) $-45° + 360° = 315°$

$-45° - 360° = -405°$

15. (a) $300° + 360° = 660°$

$300° - 360° = -60°$

(b) $740° - 720° = 20°$

$740° - 1080° = -340°$

17. (a) Complement: $\dfrac{\pi}{2} - \dfrac{\pi}{3} = \dfrac{\pi}{6}$

Supplement: $\pi - \dfrac{\pi}{3} = \dfrac{2\pi}{3}$

(b) Complement: None

Supplement: $\pi - \dfrac{3\pi}{4} = \dfrac{\pi}{4}$

19. (a) Complement: $90° - 18° = 72°$

Supplement: $180° - 18° = 162°$

(b) Complement: None

Supplement: $180° - 115° = 65°$

21. (a) $\dfrac{3\pi}{2} = \dfrac{3\pi}{2}\left(\dfrac{180}{\pi}\right) = 270°$

(b) $\dfrac{7\pi}{6} = \dfrac{7\pi}{6}\left(\dfrac{180}{\pi}\right) = 210°$

23. (a) $\dfrac{7\pi}{3} = \dfrac{7\pi}{3}\left(\dfrac{180}{\pi}\right) = 420°$

(b) $-\dfrac{11\pi}{30}\left(\dfrac{180}{\pi}\right) = -66°$

25. (a) $30° = 30\left(\dfrac{\pi}{180}\right)$

$= \dfrac{\pi}{6}$ radians

(b) $150° = 150\left(\dfrac{\pi}{180}\right)$

$= \dfrac{5\pi}{6}$ radians

27. (a) $-20° = -20\left(\dfrac{\pi}{180}\right)$

$= -\dfrac{\pi}{9}$ radians

(b) $-240° = -240\left(\dfrac{\pi}{180}\right)$

$= -\dfrac{4\pi}{3}$ radians

29. (a) $115° = 115\left(\dfrac{\pi}{180}\right) \approx 2.007$ radians

(b) $87.4° = 87.4\left(\dfrac{\pi}{180}\right) \approx 1.525$ radians

31. (a) $532° = 532\left(\dfrac{\pi}{180}\right) \approx 9.285$ radians

(b) $0.54° = 0.54\left(\dfrac{\pi}{180}\right) \approx 0.009$ radians

33. (a) $\dfrac{\pi}{7} = \dfrac{\pi}{7}\left(\dfrac{180}{\pi}\right) \approx 25.714°$

(b) $\dfrac{5\pi}{11} = \dfrac{5\pi}{11}\left(\dfrac{180}{\pi}\right) \approx 81.818°$

35. (a) $-4.2\pi = -4.2\pi\left(\dfrac{180}{\pi}\right) \approx -756.000°$

(b) $4.8 = 4.8\left(\dfrac{180}{\pi}\right) \approx 275.020°$

37. (a) $245°10' = 245\tfrac{10}{60} \approx 245.167°$

(b) $2°12' = 2\tfrac{12}{60} = 2.2°$

39. (a) $240.6° = 240° + (0.6)(60') = 240°36'$

(b) $-145.8° = -(145° + (0.8)(60'))$

$= -145°48'$

41. (a) $2.5 = 2.5\left(\dfrac{180}{\pi}\right)^{\!\circ}$

$\approx 143.23945°$

$= 143° + (0.23945)(60')$

$\approx 143°14' + (0.367)(60'')$

$= 143°14'22''$

(b) $-3.58 = -3.58\left(\dfrac{180}{\pi}\right)^{\!\circ}$

$\approx -205.1189°$

$= -(205° + (0.1189)(60'))$

$\approx -(205°7' + 0.1334(60''))$

$= -205°7'8''$

43. $\theta = \dfrac{s}{r} = \dfrac{4}{15}$

45. $r = 14.5$ cm, $s = 25$ cm

$$\theta = \frac{s}{r} = \frac{25}{14.5} \approx 1.724$$

47. $\theta = 180° \left(\dfrac{\pi}{180°}\right) = \pi$

$s = r\theta = 15(\pi) = 15\pi$ in.

≈ 47.12 in.

49. $s = r\theta = 6(2) = 12$ m

51. $\theta = 41°15'42'' - 32°47'9''$

$= 8°28'33'' \approx 0.1479$

$s \approx 4000(0.1479) \approx 591.72$ miles

53. $\theta = 42°7'15'' - 25°46'37''$

$= 16°20'38'' \approx 0.2853$

$s \approx 4000(0.2853) \approx 1141.02$ miles

55. $\theta = \frac{325}{4000} = 0.08125$ radian $\approx 4.655°$

57. $\theta = \dfrac{1/2}{2} = \dfrac{1}{4}$ radian $\approx 14.32°$

59. (a) 50 mi/hr $= \dfrac{50(5280)}{60} = 4400$ ft/min

Circumference $= 2.5\pi$ ft

$\dfrac{\text{Revolutions}}{\text{minute}} = \dfrac{4400}{2.5\pi} \approx 560.2$

(b) Angular speed $\approx 560.2(2\pi)$

≈ 3520 rad/min

61. Linear velocity for either pulley:

$1700(2\pi) = 3400\pi$ in./min

(a) Angular speed of motor pulley:

$\omega = \dfrac{v}{r} = \dfrac{3400\pi}{1} = 3400\pi$ rad/min

Angular speed of the saw arbor:

$\omega = \dfrac{v}{r} = \dfrac{3400\pi}{2} = 1700\pi$ rad/min

(b) Revolutions per minute of the saw arbor:

$\dfrac{1700\pi}{2\pi} = 850$ rev/min

63. (a) $\dfrac{\text{Revolutions}}{\text{Second}} = \dfrac{2400}{60} = 40$ rev/sec

Angular speed $= (2\pi)(40)$

$= 80\pi$ rad/sec

(b) Radius of saw blade $= \dfrac{7.5}{2} = 3.75$ in.

Radius in feet $= \dfrac{3.75 \text{ in.}}{12 \text{ in.}} = 0.3125$ ft

Speed $= \dfrac{s}{t} = \dfrac{r\theta}{t} = r\dfrac{\theta}{t}$

$= r(\text{angular speed})$

$= 0.3125(80\pi) = 78.54$ ft/sec

Section 5.2 The Trigonometric Functions and the Unit Circle

1. $t = \dfrac{\pi}{4} \Rightarrow \left(\dfrac{\sqrt{2}}{2}, \dfrac{\sqrt{2}}{2} \right)$

3. $t = \dfrac{5\pi}{6} \Rightarrow \left(-\dfrac{\sqrt{3}}{2}, \dfrac{1}{2} \right)$

5. $t = \dfrac{4\pi}{3} \Rightarrow \left(-\dfrac{1}{2}, -\dfrac{\sqrt{3}}{2} \right)$

7. $t = \dfrac{3\pi}{2} \Rightarrow (0, -1)$

9. $t = \dfrac{\pi}{4}$ corresponds to the point $\left(\dfrac{\sqrt{2}}{2}, \dfrac{\sqrt{2}}{2} \right)$.

$$\sin \frac{\pi}{4} = y = \frac{\sqrt{2}}{2}$$

$$\cos \frac{\pi}{4} = x = \frac{\sqrt{2}}{2}$$

$$\tan \frac{\pi}{4} = \frac{y}{x} = \frac{\sqrt{2}/2}{\sqrt{2}/2} = 1$$

11. $t = -\dfrac{5}{4}\pi$ corresponds to the point $\left(-\dfrac{\sqrt{2}}{2}, \dfrac{\sqrt{2}}{2} \right)$.

$$\sin \left(-\frac{5}{4}\pi \right) = y = \frac{\sqrt{2}}{2}$$

$$\cos \left(-\frac{5}{4}\pi \right) = x = -\frac{\sqrt{2}}{2}$$

$$\tan \left(-\frac{5}{4}\pi \right) = \frac{y}{x} = \frac{\sqrt{2}/2}{-\sqrt{2}/2} = -1$$

13. $t = \dfrac{11\pi}{6}$ corresponds to the point $\left(\dfrac{\sqrt{3}}{2}, -\dfrac{1}{2} \right)$.

$$\sin \left(\frac{11\pi}{6} \right) = y = -\frac{1}{2}$$

$$\cos \left(\frac{11\pi}{6} \right) = x = \frac{\sqrt{3}}{2}$$

$$\tan \left(\frac{11\pi}{6} \right) = \frac{y}{x} = \frac{-1/2}{\sqrt{3}/2} = -\frac{\sqrt{3}}{3}$$

15. $t = \dfrac{4\pi}{3}$ corresponds to the point $\left(-\dfrac{1}{2}, -\dfrac{\sqrt{3}}{2} \right)$.

$$\sin \frac{4\pi}{3} = y = -\frac{\sqrt{3}}{2}$$

$$\cos \frac{4\pi}{3} = x = -\frac{1}{2}$$

$$\tan \frac{4\pi}{3} = \frac{y}{x} = \frac{-\sqrt{3}/2}{-1/2} = \sqrt{3}$$

17. $t = \dfrac{3\pi}{4}$ corresponds to the point $\left(-\dfrac{\sqrt{2}}{2}, \dfrac{\sqrt{2}}{2} \right)$.

$$\sin \frac{3\pi}{4} = y = \frac{\sqrt{2}}{2}$$

$$\cos \frac{3\pi}{4} = x = -\frac{\sqrt{2}}{2}$$

$$\tan \frac{3\pi}{4} = \frac{y}{x} = \frac{\sqrt{2}/2}{-\sqrt{2}/2} = -1$$

$$\csc \frac{3\pi}{4} = \frac{1}{y} = \frac{1}{\sqrt{2}/2} = \sqrt{2}$$

$$\sec \frac{3\pi}{4} = \frac{1}{x} = \frac{1}{-\sqrt{2}/2} = -\sqrt{2}$$

$$\cot \frac{3\pi}{4} = \frac{x}{y} = \frac{-\sqrt{2}/2}{\sqrt{2}/2} = -1$$

19. $t = \dfrac{\pi}{2}$ corresponds to the point $(0, 1)$.

$$\sin \frac{\pi}{2} = y = 1 \qquad\qquad \csc \frac{\pi}{2} = \frac{1}{y} = 1$$

$$\cos \frac{\pi}{2} = x = 0 \qquad\qquad \sec \frac{\pi}{2} \text{ is undefined.}$$

$$\tan \frac{\pi}{2} \text{ is undefined.} \qquad \cot \frac{\pi}{2} = \frac{x}{y} = \frac{0}{1} = 0$$

21. $t = -\dfrac{4\pi}{3}$ corresponds to the point $\left(-\dfrac{1}{2}, \dfrac{\sqrt{3}}{2}\right)$.

$$\sin\left(-\frac{4\pi}{3}\right) = y = \frac{\sqrt{3}}{2} \qquad\qquad \csc\left(-\frac{4\pi}{3}\right) = \frac{1}{y} = \frac{1}{\sqrt{3}/2} = \frac{2\sqrt{3}}{3}$$

$$\cos\left(-\frac{4\pi}{3}\right) = x = -\frac{1}{2} \qquad\qquad \sec\left(-\frac{4\pi}{3}\right) = \frac{1}{x} = \frac{1}{-1/2} = -2$$

$$\tan\left(-\frac{4\pi}{3}\right) = \frac{y}{x} = \frac{\sqrt{3}/2}{-1/2} = -\sqrt{3} \qquad \cot\left(-\frac{4\pi}{3}\right) = \frac{x}{y} = \frac{-1/2}{\sqrt{3}/2} = -\frac{\sqrt{3}}{3}$$

23. $\sin 3\pi = \sin \pi = 0$

25. $\cos \dfrac{8\pi}{3} = \cos \dfrac{2\pi}{3} = -\dfrac{1}{2}$

27. $\cos \dfrac{19\pi}{6} = \cos \dfrac{7\pi}{6} = -\dfrac{\sqrt{3}}{2}$

29. $\sin\left(-\dfrac{9\pi}{4}\right) = \sin \dfrac{7\pi}{4} = -\dfrac{\sqrt{2}}{2}$

31. (a) $\sin(-t) = -\sin t = -\dfrac{1}{3}$

(b) $\csc(-t) = -\csc t$

$$= -\frac{1}{\sin t} = -3$$

33. (a) $\cos t = \cos(-t) = -\dfrac{7}{8}$

(b) $\sec(-t) = \dfrac{1}{\cos(-t)} = -\dfrac{8}{7}$

35. (a) $\sin(\pi - t) = \sin t = \frac{4}{5}$

(b) $\sin(t + \pi) = -\sin t = -\frac{4}{5}$

37. $\sin \dfrac{\pi}{4} \approx 0.7071$

39. $\cos(-3) \approx -0.9900$

41. $\cos(-1.7) \approx -0.1288$

43. $\csc 0.8 \approx 1.3940$

45. (a)

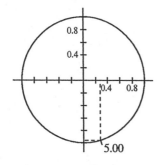

The approximate point corresponding to
$t = 5$ radians is $(0.3, -1)$.

$$\sin 5 \approx -1$$

(b)

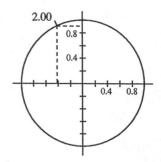

The approximate point corresponding to
$t = 2$ radians is $(-0.4, 0.9)$.

$$\cos 2 \approx -0.4$$

47. (a)

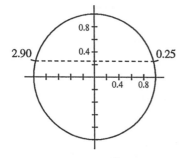

$$\sin t = 0.25 = y$$

$$t \approx 0.25 \text{ or } t \approx 2.90$$

(b)

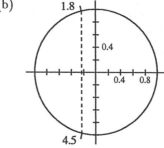

$$\cos t = -0.25 = x$$

$$t \approx 1.8 \text{ or } t \approx 4.5$$

49. $y(t) = \frac{1}{4}\cos 6t$

(a) $y(0) = \frac{1}{4}\cos(6 \cdot 0) = 0.2500$ ft

(b) $y\left(\frac{1}{4}\right) = \frac{1}{4}\cos\left(6 \cdot \frac{1}{4}\right) \approx 0.0177$ ft

(c) $y\left(\frac{1}{2}\right) = \frac{1}{4}\cos\left(6 \cdot \frac{1}{2}\right) \approx -0.2475$ ft

51. $I = 5e^{-2(0.7)}\sin 0.7 \approx 0.794$

Section 5.3   Trigonometric Functions and Right Triangles

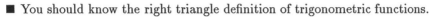

- You should know the right triangle definition of trigonometric functions.

  (a) $\sin \theta = \dfrac{\text{opp}}{\text{hyp}}$

  (b) $\cos \theta = \dfrac{\text{adj}}{\text{hyp}}$

  (c) $\tan \theta = \dfrac{\text{opp}}{\text{adj}}$

  (d) $\cot \theta = \dfrac{\text{adj}}{\text{opp}}$

  (e) $\sec \theta = \dfrac{\text{hyp}}{\text{adj}}$

  (f) $\csc \theta = \dfrac{\text{hyp}}{\text{opp}}$

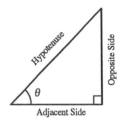

- You should know the following identities.

  (a) $\csc \theta = \dfrac{1}{\sin \theta}$

  (b) $\sec \theta = \dfrac{1}{\cos \theta}$

  (c) $\cot \theta = \dfrac{1}{\tan \theta}$

  (d) $\sin \theta = \dfrac{1}{\csc \theta}$

  (e) $\cos \theta = \dfrac{1}{\sec \theta}$

  (f) $\tan \theta = \dfrac{1}{\cot \theta}$

  (g) $\tan \theta = \dfrac{\sin \theta}{\cos \theta}$

  (h) $\cot \theta = \dfrac{\cos \theta}{\sin \theta}$

  (i) $\sin^2 \theta + \cos^2 \theta = 1$

  (j) $1 + \tan^2 \theta = \sec^2 \theta$

  (k) $1 + \cot^2 \theta = \csc^2 \theta$

- You should know that two acute angles α and β are complementary if $\alpha + \beta = 90°$, and cofunctions of complementary angles are equal.

- You should know the function values of $30°$, $45°$, and $60°$, or be able to construct triangles from which you can determine them.

- You should be able to evaluate trigonometric functions with a calculator. Be sure your calculator is set in the appropriate mode—degree or radian.

1.

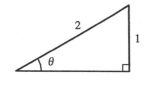

$$b = \sqrt{2^2 - 1^2} = \sqrt{3}$$

$$\sin\theta = \frac{1}{2} \qquad\qquad \csc\theta = 2$$

$$\cos\theta = \frac{\sqrt{3}}{2} \qquad\qquad \sec\theta = \frac{2}{\sqrt{3}} = \frac{2\sqrt{3}}{3}$$

$$\tan\theta = \frac{1}{\sqrt{3}} = \frac{\sqrt{3}}{3} \qquad \cot\theta = \frac{3}{\sqrt{3}} = \sqrt{3}$$

3.

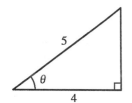

$$a = \sqrt{5^2 - 4^2} = 3$$

$$\sin\theta = \tfrac{3}{5} \qquad \csc\theta = \tfrac{5}{3}$$

$$\cos\theta = \tfrac{4}{5} \qquad \sec\theta = \tfrac{5}{4}$$

$$\tan\theta = \tfrac{3}{4} \qquad \cot\theta = \tfrac{4}{3}$$

5.

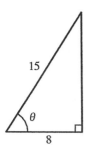

$$a = \sqrt{15^2 - 8^2} = \sqrt{161}$$

$$\sin\theta = \frac{\sqrt{161}}{15} \qquad \csc\theta = \frac{15}{\sqrt{161}} = \frac{15\sqrt{161}}{161}$$

$$\cos\theta = \frac{8}{15} \qquad \sec\theta = \frac{15}{8}$$

$$\tan\theta = \frac{\sqrt{161}}{8} \qquad \cot\theta = \frac{8}{\sqrt{161}} = \frac{8\sqrt{161}}{161}$$

7.

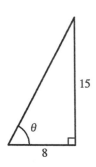

$$c = \sqrt{8^2 + 15^2} = 17$$

$$\sin\theta = \tfrac{15}{17} \qquad \csc\theta = \tfrac{17}{15}$$

$$\cos\theta = \tfrac{8}{17} \qquad \sec\theta = \tfrac{17}{8}$$

$$\tan\theta = \tfrac{15}{8} \qquad \cot\theta = \tfrac{8}{15}$$

9. Given: $\sin \theta = \dfrac{2}{3}$

$2^2 + (\text{adj})^2 = 3^2$

$\text{adj} = \sqrt{5}$

$\cos \theta = \dfrac{\sqrt{5}}{3}$

$\tan \theta = \dfrac{2\sqrt{5}}{5}$

$\cot \theta = \dfrac{\sqrt{5}}{2}$

$\sec \theta = \dfrac{3\sqrt{5}}{5}$

$\csc \theta = \dfrac{3}{2}$

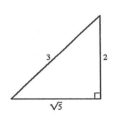

11. Given: $\sec \theta = 2$

$(\text{opp})^2 + 1^2 = 2^2$

$\text{opp} = \sqrt{3}$

$\sin \theta = \dfrac{\sqrt{3}}{2}$

$\cos \theta = \dfrac{1}{2}$

$\tan \theta = \sqrt{3}$

$\cot \theta = \dfrac{\sqrt{3}}{3}$

$\csc \theta = \dfrac{2\sqrt{3}}{3}$

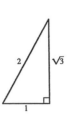

13. Given: $\tan \theta = 3$

$3^2 + 1^2 = (\text{hyp})^2$

$\text{hyp} = \sqrt{10}$

$\sin \theta = \dfrac{3\sqrt{10}}{10}$

$\cos \theta = \dfrac{\sqrt{10}}{10}$

$\cot \theta = \dfrac{1}{3}$

$\sec \theta = \sqrt{10}$

$\csc \theta = \dfrac{\sqrt{10}}{3}$

15. Given: $\cot\theta = \dfrac{3}{2}$

$$2^2 + 3^2 = (\text{hyp})^2$$

$$\text{hyp} = \sqrt{13}$$

$$\sin\theta = \frac{2}{\sqrt{13}} = \frac{2\sqrt{13}}{13}$$

$$\cos\theta = \frac{3}{\sqrt{13}} = \frac{3\sqrt{13}}{13}$$

$$\tan\theta = \frac{2}{3}$$

$$\csc\theta = \frac{\sqrt{13}}{2}$$

$$\sec\theta = \frac{\sqrt{13}}{3}$$

17. $\sin 60° = \dfrac{\sqrt{3}}{2}$, $\cos 60° = \dfrac{1}{2}$

(a) $\tan 60° = \dfrac{\sin 60°}{\cos 60°} = \sqrt{3}$

(b) $\sin 30° = \cos 60° = \dfrac{1}{2}$

(c) $\cos 30° = \sin 60° = \dfrac{\sqrt{3}}{2}$

(d) $\cot 60° = \dfrac{\cos 60°}{\sin 60°} = \dfrac{1}{\sqrt{3}} = \dfrac{\sqrt{3}}{3}$

19. $\csc\theta = 3$, $\sec\theta = \dfrac{3\sqrt{2}}{4}$

(a) $\sin\theta = \dfrac{1}{\csc\theta} = \dfrac{1}{3}$

(b) $\cos\theta = \dfrac{1}{\sec\theta} = \dfrac{2\sqrt{2}}{3}$

(c) $\tan\theta = \dfrac{\sin\theta}{\cos\theta} = \dfrac{1/3}{(2\sqrt{2})/3} = \dfrac{\sqrt{2}}{4}$

(d) $\sec(90° - \theta) = \csc\theta = 3$

21. (a) $\cos 60° = \dfrac{1}{2}$

(b) $\tan\dfrac{\pi}{4} = \dfrac{\sin 45°}{\cos 45°} = \dfrac{\sqrt{2}/2}{\sqrt{2}/2} = 1$

23. (a) $\cot 45° = 1$

(b) $\cos 45° = \dfrac{\sqrt{2}}{2}$

25. (a) $\sin 10° \approx 0.1736$

(b) $\cos 80° \approx 0.1736$

27. (a) $\sin 16.35° \approx 0.2815$

(b) $\csc 16.35° \approx 3.5523$

29. (a) $\sec 42°12' \approx 1.3499$

(b) $\csc 48°7' \approx 1.3432$

31. (a) $\cot\dfrac{\pi}{16} \approx 5.0273$

(b) $\tan\dfrac{\pi}{16} \approx 0.1989$

33. (a) $\csc 1 \approx 1.1884$

(b) $\sec\left(\dfrac{\pi}{2} - 1\right) = \csc 1 \approx 1.1884$

35. (a) $\sin\theta = \dfrac{1}{2} \Rightarrow \theta = 30° = \dfrac{\pi}{6}$

(b) $\csc\theta = 2 \Rightarrow \theta = 30° = \dfrac{\pi}{6}$

37. (a) $\sec\theta = 2 \Rightarrow \theta = 60° = \dfrac{\pi}{3}$

(b) $\cot\theta = 1 \Rightarrow \theta = 45° = \dfrac{\pi}{4}$

39. (a) $\csc\theta = \dfrac{2\sqrt{3}}{3} \Rightarrow \theta = 60° = \dfrac{\pi}{3}$

(b) $\sin\theta = \dfrac{\sqrt{2}}{2} \Rightarrow \theta = 45° = \dfrac{\pi}{4}$

41. (a) $\sin\theta = 0.8191 \Rightarrow$

$\theta \approx 55° \approx 0.96$ radians

(b) $\cos\theta = 0.0175 \Rightarrow$

$\theta \approx 89° \approx 1.55$ radians

43. (a) $\tan\theta = 1.1920 \Rightarrow$

$\theta \approx 50° \approx 0.873$ radians

(b) $\tan\theta = 0.4663 \Rightarrow$

$\theta \approx 25° \approx 0.436$ radians

45. $\tan 30° = \dfrac{y}{100}$

$y = 100\tan 30° \approx 57.74$

47. $\cot 60° = \dfrac{x}{25}$

$x = \dfrac{25}{\tan 60°} = \dfrac{25\sqrt{3}}{3} \approx 14.4$

49. $\csc 40° = \dfrac{r}{10}$

$r = \dfrac{10}{\sin 40°} \approx 15.56$

51. $\sin 50° = \dfrac{y}{12}$

$y \approx 12\sin 50 \approx 9.19$

53. $\tan\theta = \dfrac{6}{8} = \dfrac{h}{20}$

$h = 15$ ft

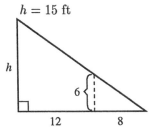

55. Let $h =$ the distance up the side of the house.

$\sin 75° = \dfrac{h}{20}$

$h = 20\sin 75° \approx 19.32$ ft

57. Let $d =$ the distance from the shoreline.

$\cot 4° = \dfrac{d}{150}$

$d = 150\cot 4° \approx 2145.10$ ft

59.

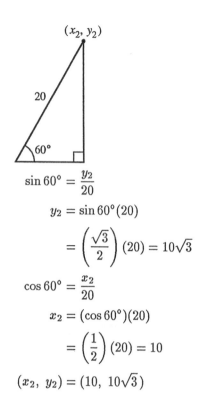

$$\sin 30^\circ = \frac{y_1}{20}$$

$$y_1 = (\sin 30^\circ)(20)$$

$$= \left(\frac{1}{2}\right)(20) = 10$$

$$\cos 30^\circ = \frac{x_1}{20}$$

$$x_1 = \cos 30^\circ (20)$$

$$= \frac{\sqrt{3}}{2}(20) = 10\sqrt{3}$$

$$(x_1,\ y_1) = (10\sqrt{3},\ 10)$$

$$\sin 60^\circ = \frac{y_2}{20}$$

$$y_2 = \sin 60^\circ (20)$$

$$= \left(\frac{\sqrt{3}}{2}\right)(20) = 10\sqrt{3}$$

$$\cos 60^\circ = \frac{x_2}{20}$$

$$x_2 = (\cos 60^\circ)(20)$$

$$= \left(\frac{1}{2}\right)(20) = 10$$

$$(x_2,\ y_2) = (10,\ 10\sqrt{3})$$

61. $\sin 25^\circ \approx 0.42$

$\cos 25^\circ \approx 0.91$

$\tan 25^\circ \approx 0.47$

$\csc 25^\circ \approx 2.37$

$\sec 25^\circ \approx 1.10$

$\cot 25^\circ \approx 2.14$

63. True

$$\csc x = \frac{1}{\sin x} \Rightarrow$$

$$\sin 60^\circ \csc 60^\circ = \sin 60^\circ \frac{1}{\sin 60^\circ} = 1$$

65. False, $\dfrac{\sqrt{2}}{2} + \dfrac{\sqrt{2}}{2} = \sqrt{2} \neq 1$

67. False

$$\frac{\sin 60^\circ}{\sin 30^\circ} = \frac{\cos 30^\circ}{\sin 30^\circ} = \cot 30^\circ$$

$$\approx 1.7321$$

$$\neq \sin 2^\circ = 0.0349$$

Section 5.4   Trigonometric Functions of Any Angle

■ You should know the signs of the trigonometric functions in each quadrant.

■ You should know the trigonometric function values of the quadrant angles 0, $\pi/2$, π, and $3\pi/2$.

■ You should be able to find reference angles.

■ You should be able to evaluate trigonometric functions of any angle. (Use reference angles.)

■ You should know that the period of sine and cosine is 2π.

■ You should know which trigonometric functions are odd and even.

1. (a) $(x, y) = (3, 4)$

$$r = \sqrt{9 + 16} = 5$$

$\sin\theta = \dfrac{y}{r} = \dfrac{4}{5} \qquad \csc\theta = \dfrac{r}{y} = \dfrac{5}{4}$

$\cos\theta = \dfrac{x}{r} = \dfrac{3}{5} \qquad \sec\theta = \dfrac{r}{x} = \dfrac{5}{3}$

$\tan\theta = \dfrac{y}{x} = \dfrac{4}{3} \qquad \cot\theta = \dfrac{x}{y} = \dfrac{3}{4}$

(b) $(x, y) = (8, -15)$

$$r = \sqrt{64 + 225} = 17$$

$\sin\theta = \dfrac{y}{r} = -\dfrac{15}{17} \qquad \csc\theta = \dfrac{r}{y} = -\dfrac{17}{15}$

$\cos\theta = \dfrac{x}{r} = \dfrac{8}{17} \qquad \sec\theta = \dfrac{r}{x} = \dfrac{17}{8}$

$\tan\theta = \dfrac{y}{x} = -\dfrac{15}{8} \qquad \cot\theta = \dfrac{x}{y} = -\dfrac{8}{15}$

3. (a) $(x, y) = (-\sqrt{3}, 1)$

$$r = \sqrt{3 + 1} = 2$$

$\sin\theta = \dfrac{y}{r} = \dfrac{1}{2} \qquad \csc\theta = \dfrac{r}{y} = 2$

$\cos\theta = \dfrac{x}{r} = -\dfrac{\sqrt{3}}{2} \qquad \sec\theta = \dfrac{r}{x} = -\dfrac{2\sqrt{3}}{3}$

$\tan\theta = \dfrac{y}{x} = -\dfrac{\sqrt{3}}{3} \qquad \cot\theta = \dfrac{x}{y} = -\sqrt{3}$

(b) $(x, y) = (-2, -2)$

$$r = \sqrt{4 + 4} = 2\sqrt{2}$$

$\sin\theta = \dfrac{y}{r} = -\dfrac{\sqrt{2}}{2} \qquad \csc\theta = \dfrac{r}{y} = -\sqrt{2}$

$\cos\theta = \dfrac{x}{r} = -\dfrac{\sqrt{2}}{2} \qquad \sec\theta = \dfrac{r}{x} = -\sqrt{2}$

$\tan\theta = \dfrac{y}{x} = 1 \qquad \cot\theta = \dfrac{x}{y} = 1$

5. (a) $(x, y) = (7, 24)$

$$r = \sqrt{49 + 576} = 25$$

$\sin\theta = \dfrac{y}{r} = \dfrac{24}{25} \qquad \csc\theta = \dfrac{r}{y} = \dfrac{25}{24}$

$\cos\theta = \dfrac{x}{r} = \dfrac{7}{25} \qquad \sec\theta = \dfrac{r}{x} = \dfrac{25}{7}$

$\tan\theta = \dfrac{y}{x} = \dfrac{24}{7} \qquad \cot\theta = \dfrac{x}{y} = \dfrac{7}{24}$

(b) $(x, y) = (7, -24)$

$$r = \sqrt{49 + 576} = 25$$

$\sin\theta = \dfrac{y}{r} = -\dfrac{24}{25} \qquad \csc\theta = \dfrac{r}{y} = -\dfrac{25}{24}$

$\cos\theta = \dfrac{x}{r} = \dfrac{7}{25} \qquad \sec\theta = \dfrac{r}{x} = \dfrac{25}{7}$

$\tan\theta = \dfrac{y}{x} = -\dfrac{24}{7} \qquad \cot\theta = \dfrac{x}{y} = -\dfrac{7}{24}$

7. (a) $(x,\ y) = (-4,\ 10)$

$r = \sqrt{16+100} = 2\sqrt{29}$

$$\sin\theta = \frac{y}{r} = \frac{5\sqrt{29}}{29} \qquad \csc\theta = \frac{r}{y} = \frac{\sqrt{29}}{5}$$

$$\cos\theta = \frac{x}{r} = -\frac{2\sqrt{29}}{29} \qquad \sec\theta = \frac{r}{x} = -\frac{\sqrt{29}}{2}$$

$$\tan\theta = \frac{y}{x} = -\frac{5}{2} \qquad \cot\theta = \frac{x}{y} = -\frac{2}{5}$$

(b) $(x,\ y) = (3,\ -5)$

$r = \sqrt{9+25} = \sqrt{34}$

$$\sin\theta = \frac{y}{r} = -\frac{5\sqrt{34}}{34} \qquad \csc\theta = \frac{r}{y} = -\frac{\sqrt{34}}{5}$$

$$\cos\theta = \frac{x}{r} = \frac{3\sqrt{34}}{34} \qquad \sec\theta = \frac{r}{x} = \frac{\sqrt{34}}{3}$$

$$\tan\theta = \frac{y}{x} = -\frac{5}{3} \qquad \cot\theta = \frac{x}{y} = -\frac{3}{5}$$

9. $a_1 = 3,\ \ b_1 = 4,\ \ a_2 = 9$

(a) $c_1 = \sqrt{a_1{}^2 + b_1{}^2} = 5$

$$b_2 = \frac{a_2}{a_1}b_1 = 3(4) = 12$$

$$c_2 = \frac{a_2}{a_1}c_1 = 3(5) = 15$$

(b) $\sin\alpha_1 = \dfrac{a_1}{c_1} = \dfrac{3}{5} = \dfrac{a_2}{c_2} = \sin\alpha_2$

$\cos\alpha_1 = \dfrac{b_1}{c_1} = \dfrac{4}{5} = \dfrac{b_2}{c_2} = \cos\alpha_2$

$\tan\alpha_1 = \dfrac{a_1}{b_1} = \dfrac{3}{4} = \dfrac{a_2}{b_2} = \tan\alpha_2$

$\csc\alpha_1 = \dfrac{c_1}{a_1} = \dfrac{5}{3} = \dfrac{c_2}{a_2} = \csc\alpha_2$

$\sec\alpha_1 = \dfrac{c_1}{b_1} = \dfrac{5}{4} = \dfrac{c_2}{b_2} = \sec\alpha_2$

$\cot\alpha_1 = \dfrac{b_1}{a_1} = \dfrac{4}{3} = \dfrac{b_2}{a_2} = \cot\alpha_2$

11. $a_1 = 1,\ \ c_1 = 2,\ \ b_2 = 5$

(a) $b_1 = \sqrt{c_1{}^2 - a_1{}^2} = \sqrt{3}$

$$a_2 = \frac{b_2}{b_1}a_1 = \frac{5}{\sqrt{3}}(1) = \frac{5\sqrt{3}}{3}$$

$$c_2 = \frac{b_2}{b_1}c_1 = \frac{5}{\sqrt{3}}(2) = \frac{10\sqrt{3}}{3}$$

(b) $\sin\alpha_1 = \dfrac{a_1}{c_1} = \dfrac{1}{2} = \dfrac{a_2}{c_2} = \sin\alpha_2$

$\cos\alpha_1 = \dfrac{b_1}{c_1} = \dfrac{\sqrt{3}}{2} = \dfrac{b_2}{c_2} = \cos\alpha_2$

$\tan\alpha_1 = \dfrac{a_1}{b_1} = \dfrac{\sqrt{3}}{3} = \dfrac{a_2}{b_2} = \tan\alpha_2$

$\csc\alpha_1 = \dfrac{c_1}{a_1} = 2 = \dfrac{c_2}{a_2} = \csc\alpha_2$

$\sec\alpha_1 = \dfrac{c_1}{b_1} = \dfrac{2\sqrt{3}}{3} = \dfrac{c_2}{b_2} = \sec\alpha_2$

$\cot\alpha_1 = \dfrac{b_1}{a_1} = \sqrt{3} = \dfrac{b_2}{a_2} = \cot\alpha_2$

13. (a) $\sin\theta < 0$ and $\cos\theta < 0$
in Quadrant III

(b) $\sin\theta > 0$ and $\cos\theta < 0$
in Quadrant II

15. (a) $\sin\theta > 0$ and $\tan\theta < 0$
in Quadrant II

(b) $\cos\theta > 0$ and $\tan\theta < 0$
in Quadrant IV

17. $\sin\theta = \dfrac{y}{r} = \dfrac{3}{5} \Rightarrow |x| = 4$

θ in Quadrant II $\Rightarrow x = -4$

$\sin\theta = \dfrac{y}{r} = \dfrac{3}{5}$ $\csc\theta = \dfrac{r}{y} = \dfrac{5}{3}$

$\cos\theta = \dfrac{x}{r} = -\dfrac{4}{5}$ $\sec\theta = \dfrac{r}{x} = -\dfrac{5}{4}$

$\tan\theta = \dfrac{y}{x} = -\dfrac{3}{4}$ $\cot\theta = \dfrac{x}{y} = -\dfrac{4}{3}$

19. $\sin\theta < 0 \Rightarrow y < 0$

$\tan\theta = \dfrac{y}{x} = \dfrac{-15}{8} \Rightarrow r = 17$

$\sin\theta = \dfrac{y}{r} = -\dfrac{15}{17}$ $\csc\theta = \dfrac{r}{y} = -\dfrac{17}{15}$

$\cos\theta = \dfrac{x}{r} = \dfrac{8}{17}$ $\sec\theta = \dfrac{r}{x} = \dfrac{17}{8}$

$\tan\theta = \dfrac{y}{x} = -\dfrac{15}{8}$ $\cot\theta = \dfrac{x}{y} = -\dfrac{8}{15}$

21. $\sec\theta = \dfrac{r}{x} = \dfrac{2}{-1} \Rightarrow |y| = \sqrt{3}$

$\sin\theta > 0 \Rightarrow y = \sqrt{3}$

$\sin\theta = \dfrac{y}{r} = \dfrac{\sqrt{3}}{2}$ $\csc\theta = \dfrac{r}{y} = \dfrac{2\sqrt{3}}{3}$

$\cos\theta = \dfrac{x}{r} = -\dfrac{1}{2}$ $\sec\theta = \dfrac{r}{x} = -2$

$\tan\theta = \dfrac{y}{x} = -\sqrt{3}$ $\cot\theta = \dfrac{x}{y} = -\dfrac{\sqrt{3}}{3}$

23. $\sin\theta = 0 \Rightarrow \theta = n\pi$

$\sec\theta = -1 \Rightarrow \theta = \pi$

$\sin\theta = \dfrac{y}{r} = \dfrac{0}{r} = 0$ $\csc\theta = \dfrac{r}{y}$, undefined

$\cos\theta = \dfrac{x}{r} = \dfrac{-r}{r} = -1$ $\sec\theta = \dfrac{r}{x} = -1$

$\tan\theta = \dfrac{y}{x} = \dfrac{0}{x} = 0$ $\cot\theta = \dfrac{x}{y}$, undefined

25. θ in Quadrant III and $(x,\,y)$ satisfies $(x,\,2x) \Rightarrow r^2 = x^2 + 4x^2$ and $x < 0$. Thus, $r = \sqrt{5}\,|x| = -\sqrt{5}\,x$.

$\sin\theta = \dfrac{y}{r} = -\dfrac{2x}{\sqrt{5}\,x} = -\dfrac{2\sqrt{5}}{5}$ $\csc\theta = \dfrac{r}{y} = -\dfrac{\sqrt{5}}{2}$

$\cos\theta = \dfrac{x}{r} = -\dfrac{x}{\sqrt{5}\,x} = -\dfrac{\sqrt{5}}{5}$ $\sec\theta = \dfrac{r}{x} = -\sqrt{5}$

$\tan\theta = \dfrac{y}{x} = \dfrac{2x}{x} = 2$ $\cot\theta = \dfrac{x}{y} = \dfrac{1}{2}$

27. (a) $\theta = 203°$

$\theta' = 203° - 180° = 23°$

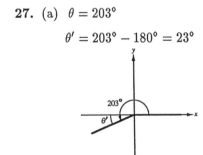

(b) $\theta = 127°$

$\theta' = 180° - 127° = 53°$

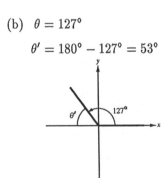

29. (a) $\qquad \theta = -245°$

$360° - 245° = 115°$

(coterminal angle)

$\theta' = 180° - 115° = 65°$

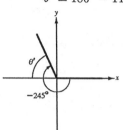

(b) $\theta = -72°$

$\theta' = 72°$

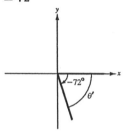

31. (a) $\theta = \dfrac{2\pi}{3}$

$\theta' = \pi - \dfrac{2\pi}{3} = \dfrac{\pi}{3}$

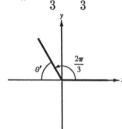

(b) $\theta = \dfrac{7\pi}{6}$

$\theta' = \dfrac{7\pi}{6} - \pi = \dfrac{\pi}{6}$

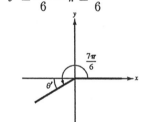

33. (a) $\theta = 3.5$

$\theta' = 3.5 - \pi \approx 0.3584$

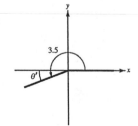

(b) $\theta = 5.8$

$\theta' = 2\pi - 5.8 \approx 0.4832$

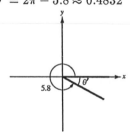

35. (a) $\theta = 225°$, $\theta' = 45°$, Quadrant III

$$\sin 225° = -\sin 45° = -\frac{\sqrt{2}}{2}$$

$$\cos 225° = -\cos 45° = -\frac{\sqrt{2}}{2}$$

$$\tan 225° = \tan 45° = 1$$

(b) $\theta = -225°$, $\theta' = 45°$, Quadrant II

$$\sin(-225°) = \sin 45° = \frac{\sqrt{2}}{2}$$

$$\cos(-225°) = -\cos 45° = -\frac{\sqrt{2}}{2}$$

$$\tan(-225°) = -\tan 45° = -1$$

37. (a) $\theta = 750°$, $\theta' = 30°$, Quadrant I

$$\sin 750° = \sin 30° = \frac{1}{2}$$

$$\cos 750° = \cos 30° = \frac{\sqrt{3}}{2}$$

$$\tan 750° = \tan 30° = \frac{\sqrt{3}}{3}$$

(b) $\theta = 510°$, $\theta' = 30°$, Quadrant II

$$\sin 510° = \sin 30° = \frac{1}{2}$$

$$\cos 510° = -\cos 30° = -\frac{\sqrt{3}}{2}$$

$$\tan 510° = -\tan 30° = -\frac{\sqrt{3}}{3}$$

39. (a) $\theta = \frac{4\pi}{3}$, $\theta' = \frac{\pi}{3}$, Quadrant III

$$\sin \frac{4\pi}{3} = -\sin \frac{\pi}{3} = -\frac{\sqrt{3}}{2}$$

$$\cos \frac{4\pi}{3} = -\cos \frac{\pi}{3} = -\frac{1}{2}$$

$$\tan \frac{4\pi}{3} = \tan \frac{\pi}{3} = \sqrt{3}$$

(b) $\theta = \frac{2\pi}{3}$, $\theta' = \frac{\pi}{3}$, Quadrant II

$$\sin \frac{2\pi}{3} = \sin \frac{\pi}{3} = \frac{\sqrt{3}}{2}$$

$$\cos \frac{2\pi}{3} = -\cos \frac{\pi}{3} = -\frac{1}{2}$$

$$\tan \frac{2\pi}{3} = -\tan \frac{\pi}{3} = -\sqrt{3}$$

41. (a) $\theta = -\frac{\pi}{6}$, $\theta' = \frac{\pi}{6}$, Quadrant IV

$$\sin \left(-\frac{\pi}{6}\right) = -\sin \frac{\pi}{6} = -\frac{1}{2}$$

$$\cos \left(-\frac{\pi}{6}\right) = \cos \frac{\pi}{6} = \frac{\sqrt{3}}{2}$$

$$\tan \left(-\frac{\pi}{6}\right) = -\tan \frac{\pi}{6} = -\frac{\sqrt{3}}{3}$$

(b) $\theta = \frac{5\pi}{6}$, $\theta' = \frac{\pi}{6}$, Quadrant II

$$\sin \frac{5\pi}{6} = \sin \frac{\pi}{6} = \frac{1}{2}$$

$$\cos \frac{5\pi}{6} = -\cos \frac{\pi}{6} = -\frac{\sqrt{3}}{2}$$

$$\tan \frac{5\pi}{6} = -\tan \frac{\pi}{6} = -\frac{\sqrt{3}}{3}$$

43. (a) $\theta = \dfrac{11\pi}{4}$, $\theta' = \dfrac{\pi}{4}$,   Quadrant II

$$\sin \frac{11\pi}{4} = \sin \frac{\pi}{4} = \frac{\sqrt{2}}{2}$$

$$\cos \frac{11\pi}{4} = -\cos \frac{\pi}{4} = -\frac{\sqrt{2}}{2}$$

$$\tan \frac{11\pi}{4} = -\tan \frac{\pi}{4} = -1$$

(b) $\theta = -\dfrac{13\pi}{6}$, $\theta' = \dfrac{\pi}{6}$,   Quadrant IV

$$\sin \left(-\frac{13\pi}{6} \right) = -\sin \frac{\pi}{6} = -\frac{1}{2}$$

$$\cos \left(-\frac{13\pi}{6} \right) = \cos \frac{\pi}{6} = \frac{\sqrt{3}}{2}$$

$$\tan \left(-\frac{13\pi}{6} \right) = -\tan \frac{\pi}{6} = -\frac{\sqrt{3}}{3}$$

45. (a) $\sin 10° \approx 0.1736$
    (b) $\csc 10° \approx 5.7588$

47. (a) $\cos(-110°) \approx -0.3420$
    (b) $\cos 250° \approx -0.3420$

49. (a) $\tan 240° \approx 1.7321$
    (b) $\cot 210° \approx 1.7321$

51. (a) $\tan \dfrac{\pi}{9} \approx 0.3640$

    (b) $\tan \dfrac{10\pi}{9} \approx 0.3640$

53. (a) $\sin \theta = \dfrac{1}{2} \Rightarrow$ reference angle is $30°$ or $\dfrac{\pi}{6}$ and θ is in Quadrant I or Quadrant II.

Values in degrees: $30°$, $150°$

Values in radian: $\dfrac{\pi}{6}$, $\dfrac{5\pi}{6}$

(b) $\sin \theta = -\dfrac{1}{2} \Rightarrow$ reference angle is $30°$ or $\dfrac{\pi}{6}$ and θ is in Quadrant III or IV.

Values in degrees: $210°$, $330°$

Values in radians: $\dfrac{7\pi}{6}$, $\dfrac{11\pi}{6}$

55. (a) $\csc \theta = \dfrac{2\sqrt{3}}{3} \Rightarrow$ reference angle is $60°$ or $\dfrac{\pi}{3}$ and θ is in Quadrant I or II.

Values in degrees: $60°$, $120°$

Values in radians: $\dfrac{\pi}{3}$, $\dfrac{2\pi}{3}$

(b) $\cot \theta = -1 \Rightarrow$ reference angle is $45°$ or $\dfrac{\pi}{4}$ and θ is in Quadrant II or IV.

Values in degrees: $135°$, $315°$

Values in radians: $\dfrac{3\pi}{4}$, $\dfrac{7\pi}{4}$

57. (a) $\tan \theta = 1 \Rightarrow$ reference angle is $45°$ or $\dfrac{\pi}{4}$ and θ is in Quadrant I or III.

Values in degrees: $45°$, $225°$

Values in radians: $\dfrac{\pi}{4}$, $\dfrac{5\pi}{4}$

(b) $\cot \theta = -\sqrt{3} \Rightarrow$ reference angle is $30°$ or $\dfrac{\pi}{6}$ and θ is in Quadrant II or IV.

Values in degrees: $150°$, $330°$

Values in radians: $\dfrac{5\pi}{6}$, $\dfrac{11\pi}{6}$

59. (a) $\sin \theta = 0.8191$

Quadrant I:
$\theta = \sin^{-1} 0.8191 \approx 54.99°$

Quadrant II:
$\theta = 180° - \sin^{-1} 0.8191 \approx 125.01°$

(b) $\sin \theta = -0.2589 \Rightarrow \theta' \approx 15.00°$

Quadrant III:
$\theta = 180° + \theta' \approx 195.00°$

Quadrant IV:
$\theta = 360° - \theta' \approx 345.00°$

61. (a) $\cos \theta = 0.9848 \Rightarrow \theta' \approx 0.175$

Quadrant I:
$\theta = \cos^{-1}(0.9848) \approx 0.175$

Quadrant IV:
$\theta = 2\pi - \theta' \approx 6.109$

(b) $\cos \theta = -0.5890 \Rightarrow \theta' \approx 0.941$

Quadrant II:
$\theta = \cos^{-1}(-0.5890) \approx 2.201$

Quadrant III:
$\theta = \pi + \theta' \approx 4.083$

63. (a) $\tan \theta = 1.192 \Rightarrow \theta' \approx 0.873$

Quadrant I: $\theta = \tan^{-1} 1.192 \approx 0.873$

Quadrant III: $\theta = \pi + \theta' \approx 4.014$

(b) $\tan \theta = -8.144 \Rightarrow \theta' \approx 1.449$

Quadrant II: $\theta = \pi - \theta' \approx 1.693$

Quadrant IV: $\theta = 2\pi - \theta' \approx 4.835$

65.
$$\sin \theta = -\tfrac{3}{5}$$
$$\sin^2 \theta + \cos^2 \theta = 1$$
$$\cos^2 \theta = 1 - \sin^2 \theta$$
$$\cos^2 \theta = 1 - \left(-\frac{3}{5}\right)^2$$
$$\cos^2 \theta = 1 - \frac{9}{25}$$
$$\cos^2 \theta = \frac{16}{25}$$
$\cos \theta > 0$ in Quadrant IV.
$$\cos \theta = \frac{4}{5}$$

67.
$$\csc \theta = -2$$
$$\cot^2 \theta + 1 = \csc^2 \theta$$
$$\cot^2 \theta = \csc^2 \theta - 1$$
$$\cot^2 \theta = (-2)^2 - 1$$
$$\cot^2 \theta = 3$$
$\cot \theta < 0$ in Quadrant IV.
$$\cot \theta = -\sqrt{3}$$

69. $\sin^2\theta + \cos^2\theta = 1$

$\sin^2 2 + \cos^2 2 = 1$

71. $T = 45 - 23\cos\left[\dfrac{2\pi}{365}(t - 32)\right]$

(a) $T = 45 - 23\cos\left[\dfrac{2\pi}{365}(1 - 32)\right]$

  $\approx 25.2°$

(b) $T = 45 - 23\cos\left[\dfrac{2\pi}{365}(185 - 32)\right]$

  $\approx 65.1°$

(c) $T = 45 - 23\cos\left[\dfrac{2\pi}{365}(291 - 32)\right]$

  $\approx 50.8°$

73. (a) $\sin 30° = \dfrac{5}{d}$

$d = \dfrac{5}{\sin 30°}$

$= \dfrac{5}{1/2} = 10 \text{ miles}$

(b) $\sin 75° = \dfrac{5}{d}$

$d = \dfrac{5}{\sin 75°}$

$\approx 5.18 \text{ miles}$

(c) $\sin 90° = \dfrac{5}{d}$

$d = \dfrac{5}{\sin 90°} = \dfrac{5}{1} = 5$

Section 5.5   Graphs of Sine and Cosine Functions

- You should be able to graph sine and cosine functions with your graphing utility. Be sure you have set the calculator in radian mode.
- You should be able to graph $y = a \sin(bx - c)$ and $y = a \cos(bx - c)$.
- Amplitude: $|a|$
- Period: $\dfrac{2\pi}{|b|}$
- Shift: Solve $bx - c = 0$ and $bx - c = 2\pi$.

1. $y = 2 \sin 2x$

Amplitude: $|2| = 2$

Period: $\dfrac{2\pi}{|2|} = \pi$

```
RANGE
Xmin=0
Xmax=3π
Xscl=π/2
Ymin=-3
Ymax=3
Yscl=1
```

3. $y = \dfrac{3}{2} \cos \dfrac{x}{2}$

Amplitude: $\left|\dfrac{3}{2}\right| = \dfrac{3}{2}$

Period: $\dfrac{2\pi}{|1/2|} = 4\pi$

```
RANGE
Xmin=0
Xmax=4π
Xscl=π
Ymin=-2
Ymax=2
Yscl=1
```

5. $y = \dfrac{1}{2} \sin \pi x$

Amplitude: $\left|\dfrac{1}{2}\right| = \dfrac{1}{2}$

Period: $\dfrac{2\pi}{|\pi|} = 2$

```
RANGE
Xmin=0
Xmax=6
Xscl=1
Ymin=-2
Ymax=2
Yscl=0.5
```

7. $y = -3 \sin 10x$

Amplitude: $|-3| = 3$

Period: $\dfrac{2\pi}{|10|} = \dfrac{\pi}{5}$

9. $y = 3 \sin 4\pi x$

Amplitude: $|3| = 3$

Period: $\dfrac{2\pi}{|4\pi|} = \dfrac{1}{2}$

11. $f(x) = \sin x$

$g(x) = \sin(x - \pi)$

The graph of g is a horizontal shift to the right π units of the graph of f (a phase shift). Verify this by graphing f and g on the same viewing rectangle.

13. $f(x) = \cos 2x$

$g(x) = -\cos 2x$

The graph of g is a reflection in the x-axis of the graph of f. Verify this by graphing f and g on the same viewing rectangle.

15. $f(x) = \sin x$

$g(x) = 2 + \sin x$

The graph of g is a vertical shift upward of 2 units of the graph of f. Verify this by graphing f and g on the same viewing rectangle.

17. $f(x) = -2\sin x$

$g(x) = 4\sin x$

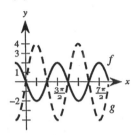

19. $f(x) = \cos x$

$g(x) = 1 + \cos x$

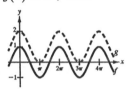

21. $f(x) = -\dfrac{1}{2}\sin\dfrac{x}{2}$

$g(x) = 3 - \dfrac{1}{2}\sin\dfrac{x}{2}$

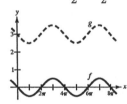

23. $f(x) = 2\cos x$

$g(x) = 2\cos(x + \pi)$

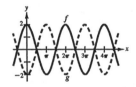

25. $f(x) = \sin x$

$g(x) = \cos\left(x - \dfrac{\pi}{2}\right)$

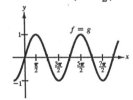

27. $f(x) = \cos x$

$g(x) = -\sin\left(x - \dfrac{\pi}{2}\right)$

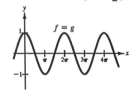

29. $y = -2\sin 6x$

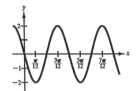

31. $y = \cos 2\pi x$

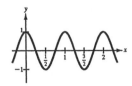

33. $y = -\sin \dfrac{2\pi x}{3}$

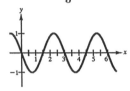

35. $y = 2 - \sin \dfrac{2\pi x}{3}$

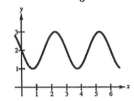

37. $y = \sin \left(x - \dfrac{\pi}{4}\right)$

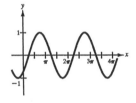

39. $y = 3\cos(x + \pi)$

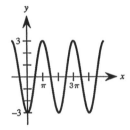

41. $y = \frac{1}{10}\cos(60\pi x)$

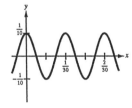

43. $y = 3\cos(x + \pi) - 3$

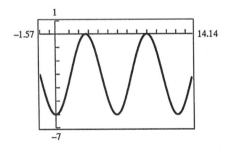

45. $y = \dfrac{2}{3} \cos \left(\dfrac{x}{2} - \dfrac{\pi}{4} \right)$

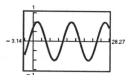

47. $y = -2 \sin(4x + \pi)$

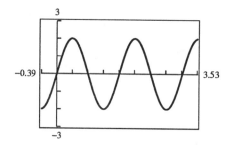

49. $y = \cos \left(2\pi x - \dfrac{\pi}{2} \right) + 1$

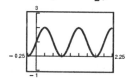

51. $y = -0.1 \sin \left(\dfrac{\pi x}{10} + \pi \right)$

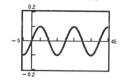

53. $y = 5 \cos(\pi - 2x) + 2$

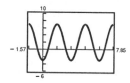

55. $f(x) = \sin x$

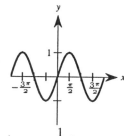

$\sin x = -\dfrac{1}{2}$ for

$x = -\dfrac{5\pi}{6}, \ -\dfrac{\pi}{6}, \ \dfrac{7\pi}{6}, \ \dfrac{11\pi}{6}$

57.

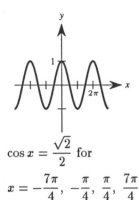

$$\cos x = \frac{\sqrt{2}}{2} \text{ for}$$

$$x = -\frac{7\pi}{4}, \ -\frac{\pi}{4}, \ \frac{\pi}{4}, \ \frac{7\pi}{4}$$

59. $f(x) = a \cos x + d$
Amplitude: $a = 2$
Vertical shift upwards 2 units: $d = 2$
$f(x) = 2 \cos x + 2$
Verify this result using your graphing
utility.

61. $y = a \sin(bx - c)$
Amplitude: $a = 2$
Period: $\dfrac{\pi}{2} = \dfrac{2\pi}{4} \Rightarrow b = 4$
Phase shift: $c = 0$
$y = 2 \sin 4x$
Verify this result using your graphing
utility.

63. $y = a \cos(bx - c)$
Amplitude: $a = 1$
Period: $\pi = \dfrac{2\pi}{2} \Rightarrow b = 2$
Phase shift: $-\dfrac{\pi}{4} = \dfrac{c}{b} \Rightarrow c = -\dfrac{\pi}{2}$
$y = \cos\left(2x + \dfrac{\pi}{2}\right)$
Verify using your graphing utility.

65. $f(x) = 2e^x, \quad g(x) = 5 \cos x$
There are two points of intersection.
Using the zoom and trace features, we
obtain $(-1.480, 0.455)$ and $(0.672, 3.914)$.

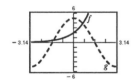

67. $v = 0.85 \sin \dfrac{\pi t}{3}$

(a) Period: $\dfrac{2\pi}{\pi/3} = 6$

(b) $\dfrac{60}{6} = 10$ cycles/min

(c)

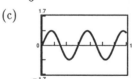

69. $y = 0.001 \sin 880\pi t$

(a) Period: $\dfrac{2\pi}{880\pi} = \dfrac{1}{440}$

(b) Frequency:

$\dfrac{1}{1/440} = 440$

(c)

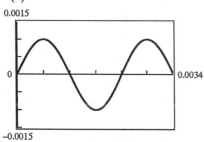

71. $S = 22.3 - 3.4 \cos \dfrac{\pi t}{6}$

The maximum sales occur in June $(t = 6)$ and the minimum sales in December $(t = 12)$.

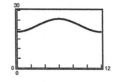

73. $g(x) = 2f(x)$

75. $g(x) = f(x - \pi)$

Section 5.6   Other Trigonometric Graphs

■ You should be able to obtain all the graphs of the trigonometric functions with your graphing utility.

■ You should be able to graph:
$$y = a\tan(bx - c) \qquad y = a\cot(bx - c)$$
$$y = a\sec(bx - c) \qquad y = a\csc(bx - c)$$

■ When graphing $y = a\sec(bx - c)$ or $y = a\csc(bx - c)$ you should know to first graph $y = a\cos(bx - c)$ or $y = a\sin(bx - c)$ since
(a) The intercepts of sine and cosine are vertical asymptotes of cosecant and secant.
(b) The maximums of sine and cosine are local minimums of cosecant and secant.
(c) The minimums of sine and cosine are local maximums of cosecant and secant.

1. $y = \sec 2x$ matches graph (c)

```
RANGE
Xmin=-π/2
Xmax=3π/2
Xscl=π/4
Ymin=-3
Ymax=3
Yscl=1
```

3. $y = \tan\dfrac{x}{2}$ matches graph (e)

```
RANGE
Xmin=-2π
Xmax=2π
Xscl=π/2
Ymin=-3
Ymax=3
Yscl=1
```

5. $y = \cot \pi x$ matches graph (d)

```
RANGE
Xmin=-1
Xmax=4
Xscl=1
Ymin=-2
Ymax=2
Yscl=1
```

7. $y = -\sec x$ matches graph (b)

```
RANGE
Xmin=-π
Xmax=2π
Xscl=π/2
Ymin=-3
Ymax=3
Yscl=1
```

9. $y = \frac{1}{3}\tan x$

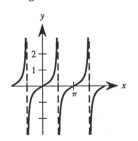

11. $y = \tan 2x$

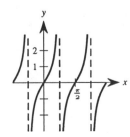

13. $y = -\frac{1}{2} \sec x$

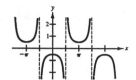

15. $y = -\sec \pi x$

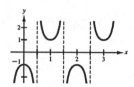

17. $y = \sec \pi x - 1$

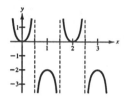

19. $y = \csc \dfrac{x}{2}$

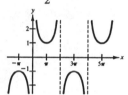

21. $y = \cot \dfrac{x}{2}$

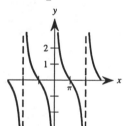

23. $y = \frac{1}{2} \sec 2x$

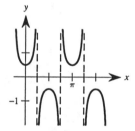

25. $y = \tan \dfrac{\pi x}{4}$

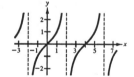

27. $y = \csc(\pi - x)$

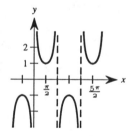

29. $y = \dfrac{1}{4} \csc \left(x + \dfrac{\pi}{4} \right)$

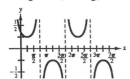

31. $y = \tan \dfrac{x}{3}$

33. $y = -2 \sec 4x$

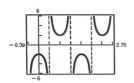

35. $y = \tan \left(x - \dfrac{\pi}{4} \right)$

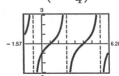

37. $y = \dfrac{1}{4} \cot \left(x - \dfrac{\pi}{2} \right)$

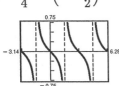

39. $y = 2 \sec(2x - \pi)$

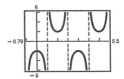

41. $f(x) = \tan x$

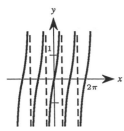

$\tan x = 1$ for

$$x = -\frac{7\pi}{4}, \ -\frac{3\pi}{4}, \ \frac{\pi}{4}, \ \frac{5\pi}{4}$$

43. $f(x) = \sec x$

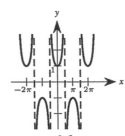

$\sec x = -2$ for

$$x = -\frac{4\pi}{3}, \ -\frac{2\pi}{3}, \ \frac{2\pi}{3}, \ \frac{4\pi}{3}$$

45. The function $f(x) = \sec x = 1/\cos x$ is even since its graph is symmetric about the y-axis.

47. $f(x) = 2 \sin x$ and $g(x) = \frac{1}{2} \csc x$, $0 < x < \pi$

(a)

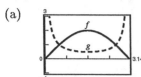

(b) $f > g$ on the interval
   (0.524, 2.618).

(c) As x approaches π, f
   approaches 0 and g increases
   without bound. g is the
   reciprocal of f:

$$g(x) = \frac{1}{2} \csc x = \frac{1}{2 \sin x} = \frac{1}{f(x)}$$

49. $y = 2 - 2 \sin \dfrac{x}{2}$

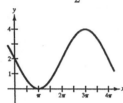

51. $y = 4 - 2 \cos \pi x$

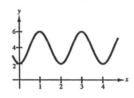

53. $y = 1 + \csc x$

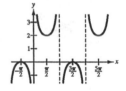

55. $y = \sin x + \cos x$

Period: 2π

Relative maximum: (0.785, 1.414)

Relative minimum: (3.927, −1.414)

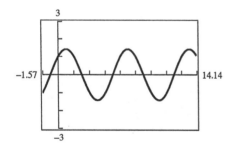

57. $f(x) = 2 \sin x + \sin 2x$

Period: 2π

Relative maximum: (1.047, 2.598)

Relative minimum: (5.236, −2.598)

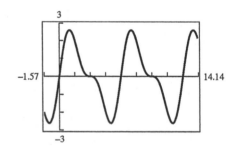

59. $g(x) = \cos x - \cos \dfrac{x}{2}$

Period: 4π

Relative maximum: $(0,\ 0)$, $(2\pi,\ 2)$

Relative minimum:

$(2.636,\ -1.125)$, $(9.930,\ -1.125)$

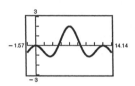

61. $h(x) = \sin x + \frac{1}{3}\sin 5x$

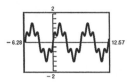

63. $y = -3 + \cos x + 2\sin 2x$

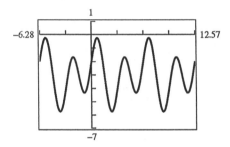

65. $y_1 = x + \sin x$

$y_2 = x$

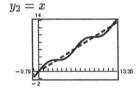

67. $y_1 = \frac{1}{2}x - 2\cos x$

$y_2 = \frac{1}{2}x$

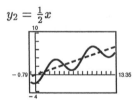

69. $y_1 = -t + \sin \dfrac{\pi t}{2}$

$y_2 = -t$

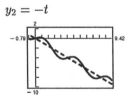

71. $y_1 = \dfrac{x^2}{8} + \sin\left(\dfrac{\pi x}{2}\right)$

$y_2 = \dfrac{x^2}{8}$

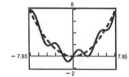

73. $y_1 = 2^{-x/4} \cos \pi x$

$y_2 = 2^{-x/4}, \quad y_3 = -2^{-x/4}$

The functional values approach 0 as x increases without bound.

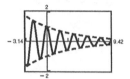

75. $y_1 = e^{-x^2/2} \sin x$

$y_2 = e^{-x^2/2}, \quad y_3 = -e^{-x^2/2}$

The functional values approach 0 as x increases without bound.

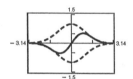

77. $y_1 = x \cos x$

$y_2 = x$

$y_3 = -x$

The functional values approach 0 as x approaches 0.

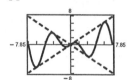

79. $y_1 = |x| \sin x$

$y_2 = x$

$y_3 = -x$

The functional values approach 0 as x approaches 0.

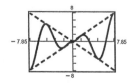

81. $y = \dfrac{6}{x} + \cos x, \quad x > 0$

y increases without bound as x approaches 0.

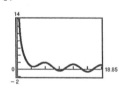

83. $g(x) = \dfrac{\sin x}{x}$

g approaches the value of 1 as x approaches 0.

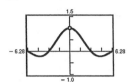

85. $f(x) = \sin\left(\dfrac{1}{x}\right)$

f oscillates between -1 and 1 as x approaches 0.

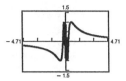

87. $f(x) = \sin x + \cos\left(x + \dfrac{\pi}{2}\right)$

$g(x) = 0$

$f = g$

(The functions are identically 0.)

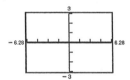

89. $f(x) = \sin^2 x$

$g(x) = \frac{1}{2}(1 - \cos 2x)$

$f = g$

(The functions are equal.)

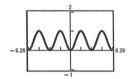

91. $f(t) = t^2 \sin t$, $[0, \, 2\pi]$

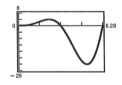

93. $f(x) = \sin x - \frac{1}{3}\sin 3x + \frac{1}{5}\sin 5x$, $[0, \, \pi]$

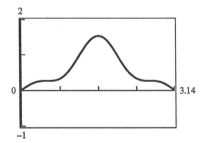

95. $\tan x = \dfrac{6}{d}$

$\qquad d = \dfrac{6}{\tan x}$

$\qquad d = 6\cot x$

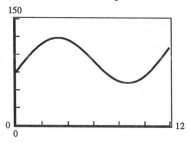

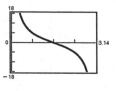

97. $S = 74 + 3t + 40\sin\dfrac{\pi t}{6}$

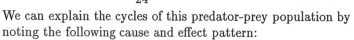

99. $P = 10{,}000 + 3000\sin\dfrac{2\pi t}{24}$

$\qquad p = 15{,}000 + 5000\cos\dfrac{2\pi t}{24}$

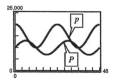

We can explain the cycles of this predator-prey population by noting the following cause and effect pattern:

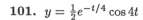

Predator population increase	Prey population decrease	Predator population decrease	Prey population increase

101. $y = \frac{1}{2}e^{-t/4}\cos 4t$

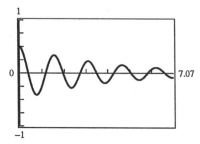

Section 5.7   Inverse Trigonometric Functions

■ You should know the definitions, domains, and ranges of $y = \arcsin x$, $y = \arccos x$, and $y = \arctan x$.

■ You should know the inverse properties of the inverse trigonometric functions.

■ You should be able to use the triangle technique to convert trigonometric expressions into algebraic expressions.

■ You should be able to produce the graphs of the inverse trigonometric functions with your graphing utility.

---

1. $y = \arcsin \dfrac{1}{2} \Rightarrow \sin y = \dfrac{1}{2}$ for $-\dfrac{\pi}{2} \le y \le \dfrac{\pi}{2} \Rightarrow y = \dfrac{\pi}{6}$

3. $y = \arccos \dfrac{1}{2} \Rightarrow \cos y = \dfrac{1}{2}$ for $0 \le y \le \pi \Rightarrow y = \dfrac{\pi}{3}$

5. $y = \arctan \dfrac{\sqrt{3}}{3} \Rightarrow \tan y = \dfrac{\sqrt{3}}{3}$ for $-\dfrac{\pi}{2} < y < \dfrac{\pi}{2} \Rightarrow y = \dfrac{\pi}{6}$

7. $y = \arccos \left(-\dfrac{\sqrt{3}}{2} \right) \Rightarrow \cos y = -\dfrac{\sqrt{3}}{2}$ for $0 \le y \le \pi \Rightarrow y = \dfrac{5\pi}{6}$

9. $y = \arctan(-\sqrt{3}) \Rightarrow \tan y = -\sqrt{3}$ for $-\dfrac{\pi}{2} < y < \dfrac{\pi}{2} \Rightarrow y = -\dfrac{\pi}{3}$

11. $y = \arccos \left(-\dfrac{1}{2} \right) \Rightarrow \cos y = -\dfrac{1}{2}$ for $0 \le y \le \pi \Rightarrow y = \dfrac{2\pi}{3}$

13. $y = \arcsin \dfrac{\sqrt{3}}{2} \Rightarrow \sin y = \dfrac{\sqrt{3}}{2}$ for $-\dfrac{\pi}{2} \le y \le \dfrac{\pi}{2} \Rightarrow y = \dfrac{\pi}{3}$

15. $y = \arctan 0 \Rightarrow \tan y = 0$ for $-\dfrac{\pi}{2} < y < \dfrac{\pi}{2} \Rightarrow y = 0$

17. $\arccos 0.28 \approx 1.29$ **19.** $\arcsin(-0.75) \approx -0.85$ **21.** $\arctan(-2) \approx -1.11$

23. $\arcsin 0.31 \approx 0.32$ **25.** $\arccos(-0.41) \approx 1.99$ **27.** $\arctan 0.92 \approx 0.74$

29. $f(x) = \tan x, \quad -\dfrac{\pi}{2} < x < \dfrac{\pi}{2}$

$g(x) = \arctan x$

$y = x$

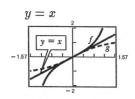

31. $y = \sin(\arcsin 0.3) = 0.3$

33. $\cos[\arccos(-0.1)] = -0.1$

35. $\arcsin(\sin 3\pi) = \arcsin 0 = 0$

37. $y = \arctan \frac{3}{4}$

$\sin y = \sin\left(\arctan \frac{3}{4}\right)$

$= \frac{3}{5}$

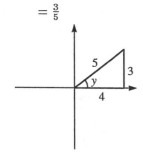

39. $y = \arctan 2$

$\cos y = \cos(\arctan 2)$

$= \dfrac{1}{\sqrt{5}} = \dfrac{\sqrt{5}}{5}$

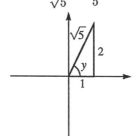

41. $y = \arcsin \frac{5}{13}$

$\cos y = \cos \left(\arcsin \frac{5}{13}\right)$

$= \frac{12}{13}$

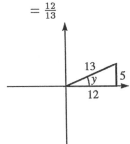

43. $y = \arctan \left(-\frac{3}{5}\right)$

$\sec y = \sec \left[\arctan \left(-\frac{3}{5}\right)\right] = \frac{\sqrt{34}}{5}$

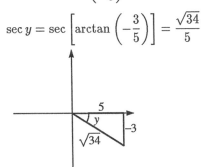

45. $f(x) = \sin(\arctan 2x)$

$g(x) = \dfrac{2x}{\sqrt{1 + 4x^2}}$

Asymptotes: $y = \pm 1$

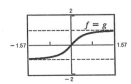

47. $y = \arctan x$

$\cot y = \cot(\arctan x) = \dfrac{1}{x}$

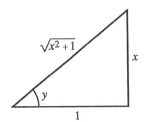

49. $y = \arcsin 2x$

$\cos y = \cos(\arcsin 2x) = \sqrt{1 - 4x^2}$

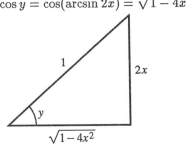

51. $y = \arccos x$

$\sin y = \sin(\arccos x) = \sqrt{1 - x^2}$

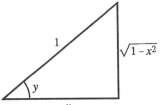

53. $y = \arccos \dfrac{x}{3}$

$\tan y = \tan\left(\arccos \dfrac{x}{3}\right) = \dfrac{\sqrt{9 - x^2}}{x}$

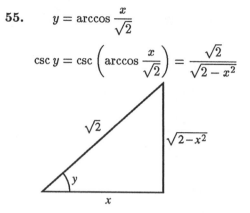

55. $y = \arccos \dfrac{x}{\sqrt{2}}$

$\csc y = \csc\left(\arccos \dfrac{x}{\sqrt{2}}\right) = \dfrac{\sqrt{2}}{\sqrt{2 - x^2}}$

57. $\arctan \dfrac{9}{x} = \arcsin \dfrac{9}{\sqrt{x^2 + 81}}$

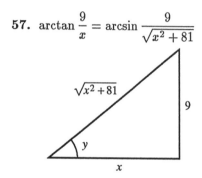

59. $\arccos \dfrac{3}{\sqrt{x^2 - 2x + 10}}$

$= \arcsin \dfrac{|x - 1|}{\sqrt{x^2 - 2x + 10}}$

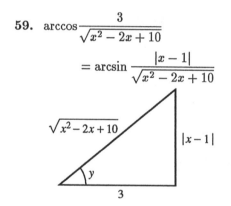

61. $f(x) = \arcsin(x - 1)$

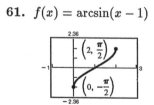

63. $f(x) = \arctan 2x$

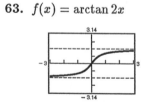

65. $f(t) = 3\cos 2t + 3\sin 2t$

$w = 2$, $A = 3$, $B = 3$

$$= \sqrt{9+9}\sin\left(2t + \arctan\left(\frac{3}{3}\right)\right)$$

$$= 3\sqrt{2}\sin\left(2t + \frac{\pi}{4}\right)$$

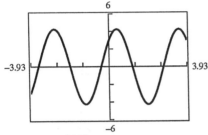

67. $\beta = \arctan\dfrac{4x}{x^2+5}$

(a)
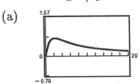

(b) When $x = 2.236$, β is a maximum (0.730).

(c) $\beta = 0$ is a horizontal asymptote. As the distance from the picture increases without bound, the angle β approaches 0.

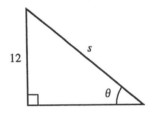

69. $\theta = \arcsin\left(\dfrac{12}{s}\right)$

(a) $\theta = \arcsin\left(\dfrac{12}{48}\right) \Rightarrow$

$\sin\theta = \dfrac{1}{4} \Rightarrow \theta = 14.5°$

(b) $\theta = \arcsin\left(\dfrac{12}{24}\right) \Rightarrow$

$\sin\theta = \dfrac{1}{2} \Rightarrow \theta = 30.0°$

71. $y = \operatorname{arccot} x$ if and only if $\cot y = x$ where $-\infty < x < \infty$ and $0 < y < \pi$. The domain of $y = \operatorname{arccot} x$ is $(-\infty,\ \infty)$ and the range is $(0,\ \pi)$.

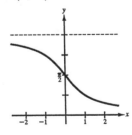

73. $y = \operatorname{arccsc} x$ if and only if $\csc y = x$ where $x \le -1 \cup x \ge 1$ and $-\pi/2 \le y < 0$ and $0 < y \le \pi/2$. The domain of $y = \operatorname{arccsc} x$ is $(-\infty,\ -1] \cup [1,\ \infty)$ and the range is $[-\pi/2,\ 0) \cup (0,\ \pi/2]$.

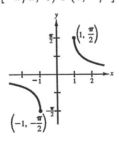

75. $y = \arcsin(-x), \quad -1 \le x \le 1$

$\sin y = -x, \quad -\dfrac{\pi}{2} \le y \le \dfrac{\pi}{2}$

$-\sin y = x$

$\sin(-y) = x$

(The sine function is odd.)

$-y = \arcsin x$

$y = -\arcsin x$

77. $y = \pi - \arccos x$

$\cos y = \cos(\pi - \arccos x)$

$\cos y = \cos \pi \cos(\arccos x) + \sin \pi \sin(\arccos x)$

$\cos y = -x$

$y = \arccos(-x)$

79. $y_2 = \dfrac{\pi}{2} - y_1$

$\arcsin x + \arccos x = y_1 + y_2$

$= y_1 + \left(\dfrac{\pi}{2} - y_1 \right)$

$= \dfrac{\pi}{2}$

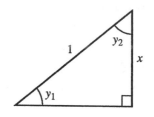

Section 5.8 Applications of Trigonometry

- You should be able to solve right triangles.
- You should be able to solve right triangle applications.
- You should be able to solve applications of simple harmonic motion.

1. Given: $A = 20°$, $b = 10$

$$\tan A = \frac{a}{b} \Rightarrow a = b \tan A = 10 \tan 20°$$

$$\approx 3.6397$$

$$\cos A = \frac{a}{c} \Rightarrow c = \frac{a}{\cos A} = \frac{10}{\cos 20°}$$

$$\approx 10.642$$

$$B = 90° - 20° = 70°$$

3. Given: $B = 71°$, $b = 24$

$$\tan B = \frac{b}{a} \Rightarrow a = \frac{b}{\tan B} = \frac{24}{\tan 71°}$$

$$\approx 8.2639$$

$$\sin B = \frac{b}{c} \Rightarrow c = \frac{b}{\sin B} = \frac{24}{\sin 71°}$$

$$\approx 25.383$$

$$A = 90° - 71° = 19°$$

5. Given: $A = 12°15'$, $c = 430.5$

$$\sin A = \frac{a}{c} \Rightarrow a = c \sin A$$

$$= 430.5 \sin 12.25°$$

$$\approx 91.342$$

$$\cos A = \frac{b}{c} \Rightarrow b = c \cos A$$

$$= 430.5 \cos 12.25°$$

$$\approx 420.70$$

$$B = 90° - 12°15' = 77°45'$$

7. Given: $a = 6$, $b = 10$

$$c^2 = a^2 + b^2 \Rightarrow$$

$$c = \sqrt{36 + 100} = 2\sqrt{34} \approx 11.662$$

$$\tan A = \frac{a}{b} = \frac{6}{10} \Rightarrow$$

$$A = \arctan \frac{3}{5} \approx 30.96°$$

$$B \approx 90° - 30.964° = 59.04°$$

9. Given: $b = 16$, $c = 52$

$$a^2 = c^2 - b^2 \Rightarrow a = \sqrt{2704 - 256} = 12\sqrt{17} \approx 49.477$$

$$\cos A = \frac{b}{c} = \frac{16}{52} \Rightarrow A = \arccos \frac{4}{13} \approx 72.08°$$

$$B \approx 90° - 72.080° = 17.92°$$

11. $\tan\theta = \dfrac{h}{\frac{1}{2}b} \Rightarrow h = \dfrac{1}{2}b\tan\theta$

$h = \dfrac{1}{2}b\tan\theta$

$h = \dfrac{1}{2}(4)\tan 52° \approx 2.56 \text{ in.}$

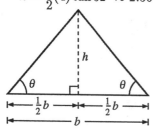

13. $\tan 30° = \dfrac{70}{x}$

$x = \dfrac{70}{\tan 30°}$

$\approx 121.2 \text{ ft}$

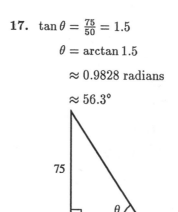

15. $\sin 74° = \dfrac{h}{16}$

$h = 16\sin 74°$

$\approx 15.4 \text{ ft}$

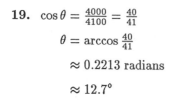

17. $\tan\theta = \frac{75}{50} = 1.5$

$\theta = \arctan 1.5$

$\approx 0.9828 \text{ radians}$

$\approx 56.3°$

19. $\cos\theta = \frac{4000}{4100} = \frac{40}{41}$

$\theta = \arccos\frac{40}{41}$

$\approx 0.2213 \text{ radians}$

$\approx 12.7°$

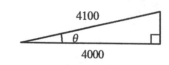

21. Since the airplane speed is

$$\left(275\frac{\text{ft}}{\text{sec}}\right)\left(60\frac{\text{sec}}{\text{min}}\right) = 16{,}500\frac{\text{ft}}{\text{min}},$$

after one minute its distance travelled is 16,500 feet.

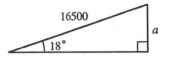

$$\sin 18° = \frac{a}{16{,}500}$$

$$a = 16{,}500 \sin 18°$$

$$\approx 5099 \text{ ft}$$

23. $\tan 47°40' = \dfrac{b}{50}$

$$b = 50 \tan 47°40'$$

$$\tan 35° = \frac{a}{50}$$

$$a = 50 \tan 35°$$

Height of steeple $= b - a$

$$= 50 \tan 47°40' - 50 \tan 35°$$

$$\approx 19.9 \text{ ft}$$

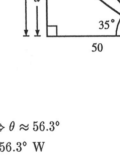

25. 550 mph for 1.5 hours takes the plane 825 miles from its point of departure.

$$\sin 38° = \frac{a}{825} \Rightarrow a \approx 508 \text{ miles north}$$

$$\cos 38° = \frac{b}{825} \Rightarrow b \approx 650 \text{ miles east}$$

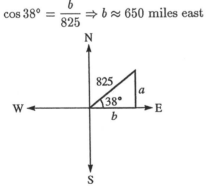

27. $\tan \theta = \frac{45}{30} \Rightarrow \theta \approx 56.3°$

Bearing: N 56.3° W

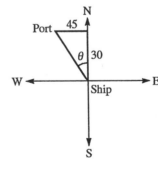

29. $\theta = 32°,\quad \phi = 68°$

    (a) $\alpha = 90° - 32° = 58°$

        Bearing from A to C: N 58° E

    (b) $\beta = \theta = 32°$

$$\gamma = 90° - \phi = 22°$$

$$C = \beta + \gamma = 54°$$

$$\tan C = \frac{d}{50} \Rightarrow$$

$$\tan 54° = \frac{d}{50} \Rightarrow d \approx 68.8 \text{ yd}$$

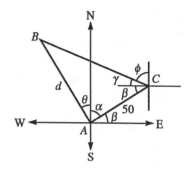

31. $\cot 6.5° = \dfrac{d}{300} \Rightarrow d \approx 2633.07 \text{ ft}$

$$\cot 4° = \frac{D}{300} \Rightarrow D \approx 4290.20 \text{ ft}$$

Distance between ships:

$$D - d \approx 4290.20 - 2633.07$$

$$= 1657.13 \text{ ft}$$

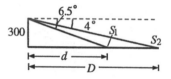

33. $\tan 57° = \dfrac{a}{x} \Rightarrow x = a \cot 57°$

$$\tan 16° = \frac{a}{x + (55/6)}$$

$$\tan 16° = \frac{a}{a \cot 57° + (55/6)}$$

$$\cot 16° = \frac{a \cot 57° + (55/6)}{a}$$

$$a \cot 16° - a \cot 57° = \frac{55}{6}$$

$$a \approx 3.23 \text{ miles}$$

$$\approx 17{,}054 \text{ ft}$$

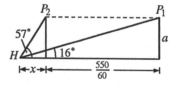

35. $\sin 36° = \dfrac{d}{25} \Rightarrow d \approx 14.6946$

Length of side: $2d \approx 29.389$ inches

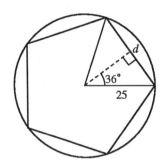

37. $\cos 30° = \dfrac{b}{r}$

$b = \cos 30° \, r$

$b = \dfrac{\sqrt{3}\, r}{2}$

$y = 2b = 2\left(\dfrac{\sqrt{3}\, r}{2}\right) = \sqrt{3}\, r$

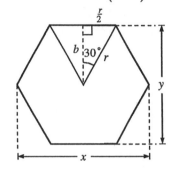

39. $\tan 35° = \dfrac{a}{10}$

$a = 10 \tan 35° \approx 7$

$\cos 35° = \dfrac{10}{c}$

$c = \dfrac{10}{\cos 35°} \approx 12.2$

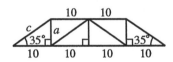

41. $d = 4 \cos 8\pi t$

(a) Maximum displacement = amplitude = 4

(b) Frequency $= \dfrac{1}{\text{period}} = \dfrac{1}{1/4} = 4$ cycles/unit of time

(c) $8\pi t = \dfrac{\pi}{2} \Rightarrow t = \dfrac{1}{16}$

43. $d = \dfrac{1}{16} \sin 120\pi t$

   (a) Maximum displacement = amplitude = $\dfrac{1}{16}$

   (b) Frequency $= \dfrac{1}{\text{period}} = \dfrac{1}{1/60} = 60$ cycles/unit of time

   (c) $120\pi t = \pi \Rightarrow t = \dfrac{1}{120}$

45. $d = a \sin \omega t$

   Period $= \dfrac{2\pi}{\omega} = \dfrac{1}{\text{frequency}}$

          $\dfrac{2\pi}{\omega} = \dfrac{1}{264}$

          $\omega = 2\pi(264) = 528\pi$

Chapter 5 Review Exercises

1. $\theta = \dfrac{11\pi}{4}$

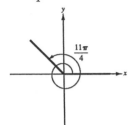

3. $\theta = -110°$

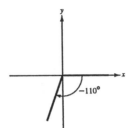

Coterminal angles: $\dfrac{3\pi}{4}, -\dfrac{5\pi}{4}$

Coterminal angles: $250°, -470°$

5. $135°16'45'' = 135 + \frac{16}{60} + \frac{45}{3600} \approx 135.28°$

7. $5°22'53'' = 5 + \frac{22}{60} + \frac{53}{3600} \approx 5.38°$

9. $135.27 = 135° + (0.27)(60)$
$= 135° + 16' + 0.2(60)$
$= 135°16'12''$

11. $-85.15° = -[85° + (0.15)(60)] = -85°9'$

13. $\dfrac{5\pi \text{ rad}}{7} = \dfrac{5\pi \text{ rad}}{7} \cdot \dfrac{180°}{\pi \text{ rad}} \approx 128.57°$

15. $-3.5 \text{ rad} = -3.5 \text{ rad} \cdot \dfrac{180°}{\pi \text{ rad}} \approx -200.54°$

17. $480° = 480° \cdot \dfrac{\pi \text{ rad}}{180°}$
$= \dfrac{8\pi}{3} \text{ rad}$
$\approx 8.3776 \text{ rad}$

19. $-33°45' = -33.75°$
$= -33.75° \cdot \dfrac{\pi \text{ rad}}{180°}$
$= -\dfrac{3\pi}{16} \text{ rad}$
$\approx -0.5890 \text{ rad}$

21. $252°$ is in Quadrant III.
Reference angle: $252° - 180° = 72°$

23. $-\dfrac{6\pi}{5}$ is in Quadrant II; coterminal to $\dfrac{4\pi}{5}$
Reference angle: $\pi - \dfrac{4\pi}{5} = \dfrac{\pi}{5}$

25. $x = 12$, $y = 16$

$r = \sqrt{144 + 256} = \sqrt{400} = 20$

$\sin\theta = \frac{4}{5}$ $\csc\theta = \frac{5}{4}$

$\cos\theta = \frac{3}{5}$ $\sec\theta = \frac{5}{3}$

$\tan\theta = \frac{4}{3}$ $\cot\theta = \frac{3}{4}$

27. $x = -7$, $y = 2$, $r = \sqrt{49 + 4} = \sqrt{53}$

$\sin\theta = \frac{y}{r} = \frac{2}{\sqrt{53}} = \frac{2\sqrt{53}}{53}$ $\csc\theta = \frac{\sqrt{53}}{2}$

$\cos\theta = \frac{x}{r} = -\frac{7}{\sqrt{53}} = -\frac{7\sqrt{53}}{53}$ $\sec\theta = -\frac{\sqrt{53}}{7}$

$\tan\theta = \frac{y}{x} = -\frac{2}{7}$ $\cot\theta = -\frac{7}{2}$

29. $x = -4$, $y = -6$, $r = \sqrt{16 + 36} = 2\sqrt{13}$

$\sin\theta = \frac{y}{r} = \frac{-6}{2\sqrt{13}} = -\frac{3\sqrt{13}}{13}$ $\csc\theta = -\frac{\sqrt{13}}{3}$

$\cos\theta = \frac{x}{r} = \frac{-4}{2\sqrt{13}} = -\frac{2\sqrt{13}}{13}$ $\sec\theta = -\frac{\sqrt{13}}{2}$

$\tan\theta = \frac{y}{x} = \frac{-6}{-4} = \frac{3}{2}$ $\cot\theta = \frac{2}{3}$

31. $\sec\theta = \frac{6}{5}$, $\tan\theta < 0 \Rightarrow \theta$ is in Quadrant IV.

$r = 6$, $x = 5$, $y = -\sqrt{36 - 25} = -\sqrt{11}$

$\sin\theta = \frac{y}{r} = -\frac{\sqrt{11}}{6}$ $\csc\theta = -\frac{6\sqrt{11}}{11}$

$\cos\theta = \frac{x}{r} = \frac{5}{6}$ $\sec\theta = \frac{6}{5}$

$\tan\theta = \frac{y}{x} = -\frac{\sqrt{11}}{5}$ $\cot\theta = -\frac{5\sqrt{11}}{11}$

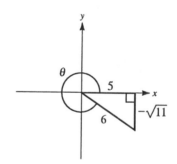

33. $\sin\theta = \dfrac{3}{8}, \quad \cos\theta < 0 \Rightarrow \theta$ is in Quadrant II.

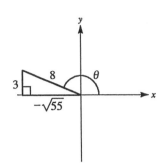

$y = 3, \quad r = 8, \quad x = -\sqrt{55}$

$\sin\theta = \dfrac{y}{r} = \dfrac{3}{8}$ $\qquad\qquad$ $\csc\theta = \dfrac{8}{3}$

$\cos\theta = \dfrac{x}{r} = -\dfrac{\sqrt{55}}{8}$ $\qquad$ $\sec\theta = -\dfrac{8}{\sqrt{55}} = -\dfrac{8\sqrt{55}}{55}$

$\tan\theta = \dfrac{y}{x} = -\dfrac{3}{\sqrt{55}} = -\dfrac{3\sqrt{55}}{55}$ $\qquad$ $\cot\theta = -\dfrac{\sqrt{55}}{3}$

35. $\tan\dfrac{\pi}{3} = \sqrt{3}$

37. $\sin\dfrac{5\pi}{3} = -\sin\dfrac{\pi}{3}$

$= -\dfrac{\sqrt{3}}{2}$

39. $\cos 495° = -\cos 45°$

$= -\dfrac{\sqrt{2}}{2}$

41. $\tan 33° \approx 0.65$

43. $\sec\dfrac{12\pi}{5} \approx 3.24$

45. $\cos\theta = -\dfrac{\sqrt{2}}{2} \Rightarrow \theta$ is in Quadrant II or III.

Reference angle: $\dfrac{\pi}{4}$

$\theta = \dfrac{3\pi}{4}, \dfrac{5\pi}{4}$ or $\theta = 135°, 225°$

47. $\csc\theta = -2 \Rightarrow \theta$ is in Quadrant III or IV.

Reference angle: $\dfrac{\pi}{6}$

$\theta = \dfrac{7\pi}{6}, \dfrac{11\pi}{6}$ or $\theta = 210°, 330°$

49. $\sin\theta = 0.8387 \Rightarrow \theta$ is in Quadrant I or II.

$\qquad = \arcsin 0.8387$

$\theta \approx 0.9949$ rad or $0.9949 \cdot \dfrac{180}{\pi} = 57.0°$

$\theta \approx \pi - 0.9949 \approx 2.1467$ rad or

$2.1467 \cdot \dfrac{180}{\pi} = 123.0°$

51. $\sec\theta = -1.0353, \ \theta$ is in Quadrant II or III.

Reference angle: $15.0°$

$\theta = 165.0°$ or $165° \cdot \dfrac{\pi}{180°} \approx 2.8798$ rad

$\theta = 195.0°$ or $195° \cdot \dfrac{\pi}{180°} \approx 3.4034$ rad

53. $\sec[\arcsin(x-1)] = \sec\theta$

$$= \frac{1}{\sqrt{-x^2+2x}}$$

$$= \frac{\sqrt{-x^2+2x}}{-x^2+2x}$$

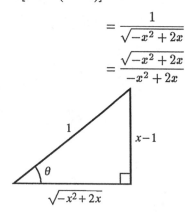

55. $\sin\left(\arccos\dfrac{x^2}{4-x^2}\right) = \sin\theta$

$$= \frac{2\sqrt{4-2x^2}}{4-x^2}$$

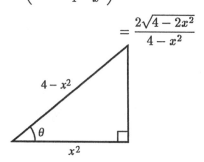

57. $y = 3\cos 2\pi x$

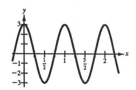

59. $f(x) = 5\sin\dfrac{2x}{5}$

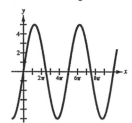

61. $f(x) = -\dfrac{1}{4}\cos\dfrac{\pi x}{4}$

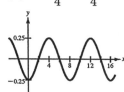

63. $g(t) = \frac{5}{2}\sin(t-\pi)$

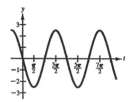

65. $h(t) = \tan\left(t - \dfrac{\pi}{4}\right)$

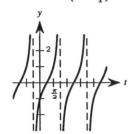

67. $f(t) = \csc\left(3t - \dfrac{\pi}{2}\right)$

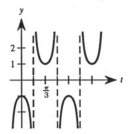

69. $f(\theta) = \cot\dfrac{\pi\theta}{8}$

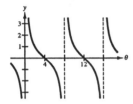

71. $f(x) = \dfrac{x}{4} - \sin x$

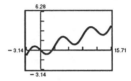

73. $y = \dfrac{x}{3} + \cos\pi x$

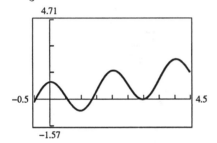

75. $h(\theta) = \theta\sin\pi\theta$

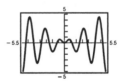

77. $y = \arcsin\dfrac{x}{2}$

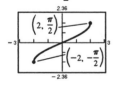

79. $f(x) = \dfrac{\pi}{2} + \arctan x$

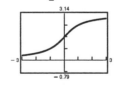

81. $f(x) = e^{\sin x}$

The function is periodic with period 2π.

Relative maximum: $(1.571, 2.718)$

Relative minimum: $(4.712, 0.368)$

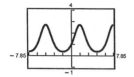

83. $g(x) = 2 \sin x \cos^2 x$

The function is periodic with period 2π.

Relative maxima:

$(0.615, 0.770)$, $(2.526, 0.770)$, $(4.712, 0)$

Relative minima:

$(1.571, 0)$, $(3.757, -0.770)$, $(5.668, -0.770)$

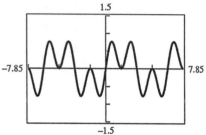

85. $\sin 50° = \dfrac{h}{10} \Rightarrow h = 10 \sin 50°$

≈ 7.66 m

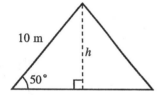

87. $\tan 28° = \dfrac{h}{2.5}$

$h = 2.5 \tan 28° \approx 1.33$ mi

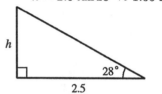

89. $\tan 1°10' = \dfrac{a}{2.5}$

$a = 2.5 \tan(1.167°)$

$a \approx 0.051$ miles ≈ 268.8 feet

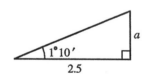

91. (a) $\sin x \approx x - \dfrac{x^3}{3!} + \dfrac{x^5}{5!} - \dfrac{x^7}{7!}$

(b)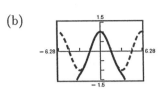

$\cos x \approx 1 - \dfrac{x^2}{2!} + \dfrac{x^4}{4!} - \dfrac{x^6}{6!}$

(c) The next term for $\sin x$ is $x^9/9!$, while that for $\cos x$ is $x^8/8!$. The accuracy increases with additional terms.

CHAPTER 6

Additional Topics in Trigonometry

Section 6.1   Applications of Fundamental Identities

■ You should know the fundamental trigonometric identities.

(a) Reciprocal Identities

$$\sin u = \frac{1}{\csc u} \qquad\qquad \csc u = \frac{1}{\sin u}$$

$$\cos u = \frac{1}{\sec u} \qquad\qquad \sec u = \frac{1}{\cos u}$$

$$\tan u = \frac{1}{\cot u} = \frac{\sin u}{\cos u} \qquad \cot u = \frac{1}{\tan u} = \frac{\cos u}{\sin u}$$

(b) Pythagorean Identities

$$\sin^2 u + \cos^2 u = 1$$

$$1 + \tan^2 u = \sec^2 u$$

$$1 + \cot^2 u = \csc^2 u$$

(c) Cofunction Identities

$$\sin\left(\frac{\pi}{2} - u\right) = \cos u \qquad \cos\left(\frac{\pi}{2} - u\right) = \sin u$$

$$\tan\left(\frac{\pi}{2} - u\right) = \cot u \qquad \cot\left(\frac{\pi}{2} - u\right) = \tan u$$

$$\sec\left(\frac{\pi}{2} - u\right) = \csc u \qquad \csc\left(\frac{\pi}{2} - u\right) = \sec u$$

(d) Even–Odd Identities

$$\sin(-x) = -\sin x \qquad \csc(-x) = -\csc x$$

$$\cos(-x) = \cos x \qquad \sec(-x) = \sec x$$

$$\tan(-x) = -\tan x \qquad \cot(-x) = -\cot x$$

■ You should be able to use these fundamental identities to find function values.

■ You should be able to convert trigonometric expressions to equivalent forms by factoring and using the fundamental identities.

■ You should be able to verify trigonometric identities using your graphing utilities.

1. $\sin x = \dfrac{1}{2}$

$\cos x = \dfrac{\sqrt{3}}{2} \Rightarrow x$ is in Quadrant I.

$\tan x = \dfrac{\sin x}{\cos x} = \dfrac{1/2}{\sqrt{3}/2} = \dfrac{1}{\sqrt{3}} = \dfrac{\sqrt{3}}{3}$

$\cot x = \dfrac{1}{\tan x} = \sqrt{3}$

$\sec x = \dfrac{1}{\cos x} = \dfrac{2}{\sqrt{3}} = \dfrac{2\sqrt{3}}{3}$

$\csc x = \dfrac{1}{\sin x} = 2$

3. $\sec\theta = \sqrt{2}$

$\sin\theta = -\dfrac{\sqrt{2}}{2} \Rightarrow \theta$ is in Quadrant IV.

$\cos\theta = \dfrac{1}{\sec\theta} = \dfrac{1}{\sqrt{2}} = \dfrac{\sqrt{2}}{2}$

$\tan\theta = \dfrac{\sin\theta}{\cos\theta} = \dfrac{-\sqrt{2}/2}{\sqrt{2}/2} = -1$

$\cot\theta = \dfrac{1}{\tan\theta} = -1$

$\csc\theta = -\sqrt{2}$

5. $\sin(-x) = -\sin x = -\dfrac{2}{3} \Rightarrow \sin x = \dfrac{2}{3}$

$\sin x = \dfrac{2}{3}$

$\tan x = -\dfrac{2\sqrt{5}}{5} \Rightarrow x$ is in Quadrant II.

$\cos x = -\sqrt{1 - \sin^2 x}$

$ = -\sqrt{1 - \dfrac{4}{9}} = -\dfrac{\sqrt{5}}{3}$

$\cot x = \dfrac{1}{\tan x} = -\dfrac{\sqrt{5}}{2}$

$\sec x = \dfrac{1}{\cos x} = -\dfrac{3\sqrt{5}}{5}$

$\csc x = \dfrac{1}{\sin x} = \dfrac{3}{2}$

7. $\tan\theta = 2$

$\sin\theta < 0 \Rightarrow \theta$ is in Quadrant III.

$\sec\theta = -\sqrt{\tan^2\theta + 1}$

$ = -\sqrt{4 + 1} = -\sqrt{5}$

$\cos\theta = \dfrac{1}{\sec\theta} = -\dfrac{1}{\sqrt{5}} = -\dfrac{\sqrt{5}}{5}$

$\sin\theta = -\sqrt{1 - \cos^2\theta}$

$ = -\sqrt{1 - \dfrac{1}{5}} = -\dfrac{2}{\sqrt{5}} = -\dfrac{2\sqrt{5}}{5}$

$\csc\theta = \dfrac{1}{\sin\theta} = -\dfrac{\sqrt{5}}{2}$

$\cot\theta = \dfrac{1}{\tan\theta} = \dfrac{1}{2}$

9. $\sin\theta = -1, \quad \cot\theta = 0 \Rightarrow \theta = \dfrac{3\pi}{2}$

$\cos\theta = \sqrt{1 - \sin^2\theta} = 0$

$\sec\theta$ is undefined.

$\tan\theta$ is undefined.

$\csc\theta = -1$

11. $\sec x \cos x = \sec x \cdot \dfrac{1}{\sec x} = 1$

The expression is matched with (d).

13. $\tan^2 x - \sec^2 x = \tan^2 x - (\tan^2 x + 1) = -1$

The expression is matched with (a).

15. $\cot x \sin x = \dfrac{\cos x}{\sin x} \cdot \sin x = \cos x$

The expression is matched with (b).

17. $\sin x \sec x = \sin x \cdot \dfrac{1}{\cos x} = \tan x$

The expression is matched with (b).

19. $\dfrac{\sec^2 x - 1}{\sin^2 x} = \dfrac{\tan^2 x}{\sin^2 x}$

$$= \dfrac{\sin^2 x}{\cos^2 x} \cdot \dfrac{1}{\sin^2 x} = \sec^2 x$$

The expression is matched with (e).

21. $\sec^4 x - \tan^4 x = (\sec^2 + \tan^2 x)(\sec^2 x - \tan^2 x) = (\sec^2 + \tan^2 x)(1) = \sec^2 x + \tan^2 x$

The expression is matched with (f).

23. $\tan \phi \csc \phi = \dfrac{\sin \phi}{\cos \phi} \cdot \dfrac{1}{\sin \phi}$

$$= \dfrac{1}{\cos \phi} = \sec \phi$$

25. $\cos \beta \tan \beta = \cos \beta \left(\dfrac{\sin \beta}{\cos \beta} \right)$

$$= \sin \beta$$

27. $\dfrac{\cot x}{\csc x} = \dfrac{\cos x / \sin x}{1 / \sin x}$

$$= \dfrac{\cos x}{\sin x} \cdot \dfrac{\sin x}{1} = \cos x$$

29. $\sec^2 x (1 - \sin^2 x) = \sec^2 x \cdot \cos^2 x$

$$= \dfrac{1}{\cos^2 x} \cdot \cos^2 x$$

$$= 1$$

31. $\dfrac{\sin(-x)}{\cos x} = -\dfrac{\sin x}{\cos x} = -\tan x$

33. $\cos \left(\dfrac{\pi}{2} - x \right) \sec x = (\sin x)(\sec x)$

$$= (\sin x) \left(\dfrac{1}{\cos x} \right)$$

$$= \dfrac{\sin x}{\cos x}$$

$$= \tan x$$

35. $\dfrac{\cos^2 y}{1 - \sin y} = \dfrac{1 - \sin^2 y}{1 - \sin y} = \dfrac{(1 + \sin y)(1 - \sin y)}{1 - \sin y} = 1 + \sin y$

37. $\tan^2 x - \tan^2 x \sin^2 x = \tan^2 x (1 - \sin^2 x) = \tan^2 x \cos^2 x = \dfrac{\sin^2 x}{\cos^2 x} \cdot \cos^2 x = \sin^2 x$

39. $\sin^2 x \sec^2 x - \sin^2 x = \sin^2 x (\sec^2 x - 1)$

$$= \sin^2 x \tan^2 x$$

41. $\tan^4 x + 2 \tan^2 x + 1 = (\tan^2 x + 1)^2$

$$= (\sec^2 x)^2$$

$$= \sec^4 x$$

43. $\sin^4 x - \cos^4 x = (\sin^2 x + \cos^2 x)(\sin^2 x - \cos^2 x) = (1)(\sin^2 x - \cos^2 x) = \sin^2 x - \cos^2 x$

45. $(\sin x + \cos x)^2 = \sin^2 x + 2 \sin x \cos x + \cos^2 x$

$$= (\sin^2 x + \cos^2 x) + 2 \sin x \cos x = 1 + 2 \sin x \cos x$$

47. $(\sec x + 1)(\sec x - 1) = \sec^2 x - 1 = \tan^2 x$

49. $\dfrac{1}{1+\cos x} + \dfrac{1}{1-\cos x} = \dfrac{1 - \cos x + 1 + \cos x}{(1+\cos x)(1-\cos x)} = \dfrac{2}{1-\cos^2 x} = \dfrac{2}{\sin^2 x} = 2 \csc^2 x$

51. $\dfrac{\cos x}{1+\sin x} + \dfrac{1+\sin x}{\cos x} = \dfrac{\cos^2 x + (1+\sin x)^2}{\cos x (1+\sin x)}$

$$= \dfrac{2 + 2\sin x}{\cos x(1+\sin x)} = \dfrac{2(1+\sin x)}{\cos x(1+\sin x)} = \dfrac{2}{\cos x} = 2 \sec x$$

53. $\dfrac{\sin^2 y}{1-\cos y} = \dfrac{1 - \cos^2 y}{1 - \cos y} = \dfrac{(1+\cos y)(1-\cos y)}{1 - \cos y} = 1 + \cos y$

55. $\dfrac{3}{\sec x - \tan x} \cdot \dfrac{\sec x + \tan x}{\sec x + \tan x} = \dfrac{3(\sec x + \tan x)}{\sec^2 x - \tan^2 x} = \dfrac{3(\sec x + \tan x)}{1} = 3(\sec x + \tan x)$

57. $y_1 = \csc x$

$y_2 = \cot \dfrac{x}{2} - \cot x$

The graphs of y_1 and y_2 appear to be equal. The equation is an identity.

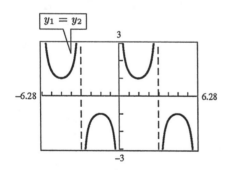

59. $y_1 = \sin 2x$

$y_2 = 2 \sin x$

The graphs of y_1 and y_2 are different. The equation is not an identity.

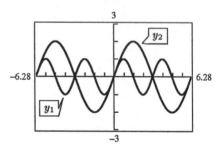

61. $y_1 = \cos x$

$y_2 = \sqrt{1 - \sin^2 x}$

(a) The graphs of y_1 and y_2 coincide on $[0,\ \pi/2]$ and $[3\pi/2,\ 2\pi]$. The graphs of $y_1 = \cos x$ and $y_2 = -\sqrt{1 - \sin^2 x}$ coincide on $[\pi/2,\ 3\pi/2]$.

63. $\sqrt{25 - x^2} = \sqrt{25 - (5\sin\theta)^2}, \quad x = 5 \sin\theta$

$$= \sqrt{25 - 25 \sin^2 \theta}$$

$$= \sqrt{25(1 - \sin^2 \theta)}$$

$$= \sqrt{25 \cos^2 \theta}$$

$$= 5 \cos \theta$$

65. $\sqrt{x^2 - 9} = \sqrt{(3\sec\theta)^2 - 9}, \quad x = 3\sec\theta$

$= \sqrt{9\sec^2\theta - 9}$

$= \sqrt{9(\sec^2\theta - 1)}$

$= \sqrt{9\tan^2\theta}$

$= 3\tan\theta$

67. $\sqrt{x^2 + 25} = \sqrt{(5\tan\theta)^2 + 25}, \quad x = 5\tan\theta$

$= \sqrt{25\tan^2\theta + 25}$

$= \sqrt{25(\tan^2\theta + 1)}$

$= \sqrt{25\sec^2\theta}$

$= 5\sec\theta$

69. $\sqrt{1 - (x-1)^2} = \sqrt{1 - (\sin\theta)^2}, \quad x - 1 = \sin\theta$

$= \sqrt{\cos^2\theta}$

$= \cos\theta$

71. $\sqrt{(9 + x^2)^3} = \sqrt{[9 + (3\tan\theta)^2]^3}, \quad x = 3\tan\theta$

$= \sqrt{(9 + 9\tan^2\theta)^3} = \sqrt{[9(1 + \tan^2\theta)]^3}$

$= \sqrt{(9\sec^2\theta)^3} = \left(\sqrt{9\sec^2\theta}\right)^3$

$= (3\sec\theta)^2 = 27\sec^3\theta$

73. $\sec\theta = \sqrt{1 + \tan^2\theta}$ is valid for θ in Quadrant I, $0 \le \theta < \pi/2$, and Quadrant IV, $3\pi/2 < \theta \le 2\pi$.

75. $\ln|\cos\theta| - \ln|\sin\theta| = \ln\left|\dfrac{\cos\theta}{\sin\theta}\right|$

$= \ln|\cot\theta|$

77. False, $\dfrac{\sin k\theta}{\cos k\theta} = \tan k\theta \ne \tan\theta$ in general.

79. True; $\sin\theta\csc\theta = \sin\theta\left(\dfrac{1}{\sin\theta}\right) = 1$, provided $\sin\theta \ne 0$.

81. $\csc^2 - \cot^2\theta = 1$

(a) $\theta = 132°$

$\csc^2 132° - \cot^2 132° \approx 1.8107 - 0.8107 = 1$

(b) $\theta = \dfrac{2\pi}{7}$

$\csc^2 \dfrac{2\pi}{7} - \cot^2 \dfrac{2\pi}{7} \approx 1.6360 - 0.6360 = 1$

83. $\cos\left(\dfrac{\pi}{2} - \theta\right) = \sin\theta$

(a) $\theta = 80°$

$\cos(90° - 80°) = \sin 80°$

$0.9848 = 0.9848$

(b) $\theta = 0.8$

$\cos\left(\dfrac{\pi}{2} - 0.8\right) = \sin 0.8$

$0.7174 = 0.7174$

85. $\cos\theta = \pm\sqrt{1 - \sin^2\theta}$

$\tan\theta = \dfrac{\sin\theta}{\cos\theta} = \pm\dfrac{\sin\theta}{\sqrt{1 - \sin^2\theta}}$

$\cot\theta = \dfrac{\cos\theta}{\sin\theta} = \pm\dfrac{\sqrt{1 - \sin^2\theta}}{\sin\theta}$

$\sec\theta = \dfrac{1}{\cos\theta} = \pm\dfrac{1}{\sqrt{1 - \sin^2\theta}}$

$\csc\theta = \dfrac{1}{\sin\theta}$

Section 6.2   Verifying Trigonometric Identities

- You should know the difference between an expression, a conditional equation, and an identity.

- You should be able to solve trigonometric identities, using the following techniques.
  - (a) Work with *one* side at a time. Do not "cross" the equal sign.
  - (b) Use algebraic techniques such as combining fractions, factoring expressions, rationalizing denominators, and squaring binomials.
  - (c) Use the fundamental identities.
  - (d) Convert all the terms into sines and cosines.

- You can verify trigonometric identities by graphing both sides with your graphing utility.

1. $\sin t \csc t = \sin t \left(\dfrac{1}{\sin t} \right) = 1$

3. $(1 + \sin \alpha)(1 - \sin \alpha) = (1 - \sin^2 \alpha)$
$$= \cos^2 \alpha$$

5. $\cos^2 \beta - \sin^2 \beta = (1 - \sin^2 \beta) - \sin^2 \beta$
$$= 1 - 2 \sin^2 \beta$$

7. $\tan^2 \theta + 4 = (\sec^2 \theta - 1) + 4$
$$= \sec^2 \theta + 3$$

9. $\sin^2 \alpha - \sin^4 \alpha = (1 - \cos^2 \alpha) - (1 - \cos^2 \alpha)^2$
$$= 1 - \cos^2 \alpha - 1 + 2 \cos^2 \alpha - \cos^4 \alpha = \cos^2 \alpha - \cos^4 \alpha$$

11. $\dfrac{\sec^2 x}{\tan x} = \dfrac{1}{\cos^2 x} \cdot \dfrac{\cos x}{\sin x}$
$$= \dfrac{1}{\cos x} \cdot \dfrac{1}{\sin x}$$
$$= \sec x \csc x$$

13. $\dfrac{\cot^2 t}{\csc t} = \dfrac{\cos^2 t}{\sin^2 t} \cdot \sin t$
$$= \dfrac{\cos^2 t}{\sin t}$$
$$= \dfrac{1 - \sin^2 t}{\sin t}$$
$$= \csc t - \sin t$$

15. $\sin^{1/2} x \cos x - \sin^{5/2} x \cos x = \sin^{1/2} x \cos x (1 - \sin^2 x) = \sin^{1/2} x \cos x \cdot \cos^2 x = \cos^3 x \sqrt{\sin x}$

17. $\dfrac{1}{\sec x \tan x} = \cos x \cdot \dfrac{\cos x}{\sin x}$

$$= \dfrac{\cos^2 x}{\sin x}$$

$$= \dfrac{1 - \sin^2 x}{\sin x}$$

$$= \dfrac{1}{\sin x} - \sin x$$

$$= \csc x - \sin x$$

19. $\csc x - \sin x = \dfrac{1}{\sin x} - \sin x$

$$= \dfrac{1 - \sin^2 x}{\sin x}$$

$$= \dfrac{\cos^2 x}{\sin x}$$

$$= \cos x \cdot \dfrac{\cos x}{\sin x}$$

$$= \cos x \cot x$$

21. $\dfrac{1}{\tan x} + \dfrac{1}{\cot x} = \dfrac{\cot x + \tan x}{\tan x \cot x}$

$$= \dfrac{\cot x + \tan x}{1}$$

$$= \tan x + \cot x$$

23. $\dfrac{\cos \theta \cot \theta}{1 - \sin \theta} - 1 = \dfrac{\cos \theta \cot \theta - (1 - \sin \theta)}{1 - \sin \theta}$

$$= \dfrac{\cos \theta (\cos \theta / \sin \theta) - 1 + \sin \theta}{1 - \sin \theta}$$

$$= \dfrac{\cos^2 \theta - \sin \theta + \sin^2 \theta}{\sin \theta (1 - \sin \theta)}$$

$$= \dfrac{1 - \sin \theta}{\sin \theta (1 - \sin \theta)}$$

$$= \dfrac{1}{\sin \theta}$$

$$= \csc \theta$$

25. $2 \sec^2 x - 2 \sec^2 x \sin^2 x - \sin^2 x - \cos^2 x = 2 \sec^2 x (1 - \sin^2 x) - (\sin^2 x + \cos^2 x)$

$$= 2 \sec^2 x (\cos^2 x) - 1$$

$$= 2 \cdot \dfrac{1}{\cos^2 x} \cdot \cos^2 x - 1$$

$$= 2 - 1$$

$$= 1$$

27. $2 + \cos^2 x - 3 \cos^4 x = (1 - \cos^2 x)(2 + 3 \cos^2 x) = \sin^2 x (2 + 3 \cos^2 x)$

29. $\sec^4 \theta - \tan^4 \theta = (\sec^2 \theta + \tan^2 \theta)(\sec^2 \theta - \tan^2 \theta)$

$$= (1 + \tan^2 \theta + \tan^2 \theta)(1) = 1 + 2 \tan^2 \theta$$

31. $\dfrac{\sin \beta}{1 - \cos \beta} \cdot \dfrac{1 + \cos \beta}{1 + \cos \beta} = \dfrac{\sin \beta (1 + \cos \beta)}{1 - \cos^2 \beta}$

$$= \dfrac{1 + \cos \beta}{\sin \beta}$$

33. $\cos \left(\dfrac{\pi}{2} - x \right) \csc x = \sin x \csc x$

$$= \dfrac{1}{\csc x} \cdot \csc x = 1$$

35. $\dfrac{\csc(-x)}{\sec(-x)} = \dfrac{1/\sin(-x)}{1/\cos(-x)}$

$\phantom{\dfrac{\csc(-x)}{\sec(-x)}} = \dfrac{\cos(-x)}{\sin(-x)}$

$\phantom{\dfrac{\csc(-x)}{\sec(-x)}} = \dfrac{\cos x}{-\sin x}$

$\phantom{\dfrac{\csc(-x)}{\sec(-x)}} = -\cot x$

37. $\dfrac{\cos(-\theta)}{1 + \sin(-\theta)} = \dfrac{\cos\theta}{1 - \sin\theta} \cdot \dfrac{1 + \sin\theta}{1 + \sin\theta}$

$\phantom{\dfrac{\cos(-\theta)}{1 + \sin(-\theta)}} = \dfrac{\cos\theta(1 + \sin\theta)}{1 - \sin^2\theta}$

$\phantom{\dfrac{\cos(-\theta)}{1 + \sin(-\theta)}} = \dfrac{\cos\theta(1 + \sin\theta)}{\cos^2\theta}$

$\phantom{\dfrac{\cos(-\theta)}{1 + \sin(-\theta)}} = \dfrac{1 + \sin\theta}{\cos\theta}$

$\phantom{\dfrac{\cos(-\theta)}{1 + \sin(-\theta)}} = \dfrac{1}{\cos\theta} + \dfrac{\sin\theta}{\cos\theta}$

$\phantom{\dfrac{\cos(-\theta)}{1 + \sin(-\theta)}} = \sec\theta + \tan\theta$

39. $\sin^2 x + \sin^2\left(\dfrac{\pi}{2} - x\right) = \sin^2 x + \cos^2 x$

$\phantom{\sin^2 x + \sin^2\left(\dfrac{\pi}{2} - x\right)} = 1$

41. $\sqrt{\dfrac{1 + \sin\theta}{1 - \sin\theta}} = \sqrt{\dfrac{1 + \sin\theta}{1 - \sin\theta} \cdot \dfrac{1 + \sin\theta}{1 + \sin\theta}}$

$\phantom{\sqrt{\dfrac{1 + \sin\theta}{1 - \sin\theta}}} = \sqrt{\dfrac{(1 + \sin\theta)^2}{1 - \sin^2\theta}}$

$\phantom{\sqrt{\dfrac{1 + \sin\theta}{1 - \sin\theta}}} = \sqrt{\dfrac{(1 + \sin\theta)^2}{\cos^2\theta}}$

$\phantom{\sqrt{\dfrac{1 + \sin\theta}{1 - \sin\theta}}} = \dfrac{1 + \sin\theta}{|\cos\theta|}$

43. $\dfrac{\sin x \cos y + \cos x \sin y}{\cos x \cos y - \sin x \sin y} = \dfrac{\dfrac{\sin x \cos y}{\cos x \cos y} + \dfrac{\cos x \sin y}{\cos x \cos y}}{\dfrac{\cos x \cos y}{\cos x \cos y} - \dfrac{\sin x \sin y}{\cos x \cos y}} = \dfrac{\tan x + \tan y}{1 - \tan x \tan y}$

45. $\dfrac{\tan x + \cot y}{\tan x \cot y} = \dfrac{\dfrac{1}{\cot x} + \dfrac{1}{\tan y}}{\dfrac{1}{\cot x} \cdot \dfrac{1}{\tan y}} \cdot \dfrac{\cot x \tan y}{\cot x \tan y} = \tan y + \cot x$

47. $\ln|\tan\theta| = \ln\left|\dfrac{\sin\theta}{\cos\theta}\right| = \ln|\sin\theta| - \ln|\cos\theta|$

49. $\ln(1 - \cos\theta) - 2\ln|\sin\theta| = \ln(1 - \cos\theta) - \ln(\sin^2\theta) = \ln\left(\dfrac{1 - \cos\theta}{\sin^2\theta}\right) = \ln\left(\dfrac{1 - \cos\theta}{1 - \cos^2\theta}\right)$

$ = \ln\left(\dfrac{1 - \cos\theta}{(1 - \cos\theta)(1 + \cos\theta)}\right) = \ln\left(\dfrac{1}{1 + \cos\theta}\right) = -\ln(1 + \cos\theta)$

51. True Identity: $\sin\theta = \pm\sqrt{1 - \cos^2\theta}$

$\sin\theta = \sqrt{1 - \cos^2\theta}$ is not true for $\pi < \theta < 2\pi$. For instance, let $\theta = 7\pi/4$.

53. True Identity: $\pm\sqrt{\tan^2 x} = \tan x$

$\sqrt{\tan^2 x} = \tan x$ is not true for $\pi/2 < \theta < \pi$ or $3\pi/2 < \theta < 2\pi$. For instance, let $\theta = 3\pi/4$.

55. $\mu W \cos\theta = W \sin\theta$

$$\mu = \frac{W \sin\theta}{W \cos\theta} = \frac{\sin\theta}{\cos\theta} = \tan\theta$$

Section 6.3 Solving Trigonometric Equations

- You should be able to identify and solve trigonometric equations. Use your graphing utility to check your answers.
- A trigonometric equation is a conditional equation. It is true for a specific set of values.
- To solve trigonometric equations, use algebraic techniques such as collecting like terms, taking square roots, factoring, squaring, converting to quadratic form, and using formulas.
- Your graphing utility is especially useful in solving trigonometric equations.

1. $2\cos x - 1 = 0$

    (a) $2\cos\dfrac{\pi}{3} - 1 = 2\left(\dfrac{1}{2}\right) - 1 = 0$
                  (b) $2\cos\dfrac{5\pi}{3} - 1 = 2\left(\dfrac{1}{2}\right) - 1 = 0$

3. $3\tan^2 2x - 1 = 0$

    (a) $3\left[\tan 2\left(\dfrac{\pi}{12}\right)\right]^2 - 1 = 3\tan^2\dfrac{\pi}{6} - 1 = 3\left(\dfrac{1}{\sqrt{3}}\right)^2 - 1 = 0$

    (b) $3\left[\tan 2\left(\dfrac{5\pi}{12}\right)\right]^2 - 1 = 3\tan^2\dfrac{5\pi}{6} - 1 = 3\left(-\dfrac{1}{\sqrt{3}}\right)^2 - 1 = 0$

5. $2\sin^2 x - \sin x - 1 = 0$

    (a) $2\sin^2\dfrac{\pi}{2} - \sin\dfrac{\pi}{2} - 1 = 2(1)^2 - 1 - 1 = 0$

    (b) $2\sin^2\dfrac{7\pi}{6} - \sin\dfrac{7\pi}{6} - 1 = 2\left(-\dfrac{1}{2}\right)^2 - \left(-\dfrac{1}{2}\right) - 1 = \dfrac{1}{2} + \dfrac{1}{2} - 1 = 0$

7. $2\cos x + 1 = 0$

$$2\cos x = -1$$
$$\cos x = -\dfrac{1}{2}$$
$$x = \dfrac{2\pi}{3} + 2n\pi$$
$$\text{or } x = \dfrac{4\pi}{3} + 2n\pi$$

9. $\sqrt{3}\csc x - 2 = 0$

$$\sqrt{3}\csc x = 2$$
$$\csc x = \dfrac{2}{\sqrt{3}}$$
$$x = \dfrac{\pi}{3} + 2n\pi$$
$$\text{or } x = \dfrac{2\pi}{3} + 2n\pi$$

11. $2\sin^2 x = 1$

$$\sin x = \pm\frac{\sqrt{2}}{2}$$

$$x = \frac{\pi}{4} + \frac{n\pi}{2}$$

13. $3\sec^2 x - 4 = 0$

$$\sec x = \pm\frac{2}{\sqrt{3}}$$

$$x = \frac{\pi}{6} + n\pi$$

$$\text{or } x = \frac{5\pi}{6} + n\pi$$

15. $\tan x(\tan x - 1) = 0$

$\tan x = 0 \quad$ or $\tan x - 1 = 0$

$x = n\pi \qquad\qquad \tan x = 1$

$$x = \frac{\pi}{4} + n\pi$$

17. $\sin x(\sin x + 1) = 0$

$\sin x = 0 \quad$ or $\sin x = -1$

$x = n\pi \qquad\qquad x = \frac{3\pi}{2} + 2n\pi$

19.
$$\sin^2 x = 3\cos^2 x$$

$$\sin^2 x - 3(1 - \sin^2 x) = 0$$

$$4\sin^2 x = 3$$

$$\sin x = \pm\frac{\sqrt{3}}{2}$$

$$x = \frac{\pi}{3} + n\pi$$

$$\text{or } x = \frac{2\pi}{3} + n\pi$$

21. $\sec x \csc x - 2\csc x = 0$

$$\csc x(\sec x - 2) = 0$$

$\csc x = 0 \quad$ or $\sec x - 2 = 0$

No solution $\qquad \sec x = 2$

$$x = \frac{\pi}{3}, \frac{5\pi}{3}$$

23. $2\sin^2 x + 3\sin x + 1 = 0$

$$(2\sin x + 1)(\sin x + 1) = 0$$

$2\sin x + 1 = 0 \qquad$ or $\sin x + 1 = 0$

$$\sin x = -\frac{1}{2} \qquad\qquad \sin x = -1$$

$$x = \frac{7\pi}{6}, \frac{11\pi}{6} \qquad\qquad x = \frac{3\pi}{2}$$

25. $2\sec^2 x + \tan^2 x - 3 = 0$

$$2(\tan^2 x + 1) + \tan^2 x - 3 = 0$$

$$3\tan^2 x - 1 = 0$$

$$\tan x = \pm\frac{\sqrt{3}}{3}$$

$$x = \frac{\pi}{6}, \frac{5\pi}{6}, \frac{7\pi}{6}, \frac{11\pi}{6}$$

27. $2 \sin x + \csc x = 0$

$2 \sin x + \dfrac{1}{\sin x} = 0$

$2 \sin^2 x + 1 = 0$

Since $2 \sin^2 x + 1 > 0$, there are no solutions.

29. $\sin 2x = -\dfrac{\sqrt{3}}{2}$

$2x = \dfrac{4\pi}{3} + 2n\pi \quad$ or $\quad 2x = \dfrac{5\pi}{3} + 2n\pi$

$x = \dfrac{2\pi}{3} + n\pi \qquad\qquad x = \dfrac{5\pi}{6} + n\pi$

$x = \dfrac{2\pi}{3}, \dfrac{5\pi}{3} \qquad\qquad x = \dfrac{5\pi}{6}, \dfrac{11\pi}{6}$

31. $\cos\left(\dfrac{x}{2}\right) = \dfrac{\sqrt{2}}{2}$

$\dfrac{x}{2} = \dfrac{\pi}{4} + 2n\pi$

$x = \dfrac{\pi}{2} + 4n\pi$

$x = \dfrac{\pi}{2}$

33. $6y^2 - 13y + 6 = 0$

$(3y - 2)(2y - 3) = 0$

$3y - 2 = 0 \quad$ or $\quad 2y - 3 = 0$

$y = \frac{2}{3} \qquad\qquad y = \frac{3}{2}$

$6 \cos^2 x - 13 \cos x + 6 = 0$

$(3 \cos x - 2)(2 \cos x - 3) = 0$

$3 \cos x - 2 = 0 \qquad\qquad$ or $\qquad 2 \cos x - 3 = 0$

$\cos x = \frac{2}{3} \qquad\qquad\qquad\qquad \cos x = \frac{3}{2}$

$x \approx 0.8411, \ 5.4421 \qquad\qquad$ (No solution)

35. $y^2 - 8y + 13 = 0$

$y = \dfrac{8 \pm \sqrt{64 - 52}}{2}$

$= \dfrac{8 \pm \sqrt{12}}{2}$

$= \dfrac{8 \pm 2\sqrt{3}}{2}$

$= 4 \pm \sqrt{3}$

$\tan^2 x - 8 \tan x + 13 = 0$

$\tan x = \dfrac{8 \pm \sqrt{64 - 52}}{2} \approx 5.73205, \ 2.26795$

$\tan x = 5.73205 \qquad$ or $\qquad \tan x = 2.26795$

$x \approx 1.3981, \ 4.5397 \qquad\qquad x \approx 1.1555, \ 4.2971$

37. The graph of $y = 2\cos x - \sin x$ has two x-intercepts: $x = 1.107$ and $x = 4.249$.

39. The graph of

$$y = \frac{1 + \sin x}{\cos x} + \frac{\cos x}{1 + \sin x} - 4$$

has two x-intercepts: $x = 1.047$ and $x = 5.236$.

41. The graph of $y = 2\sin x - x$ has two x-intercepts: $x = 0$ and $x = 1.895$.

43. The graph of $y = \sec^2 x + 0.5\tan x - 1$ has five x-intercepts: $x = 0$, $x = 2.678$, $x = 3.142$, $x = 5.820$, and $x = 6.283$.

45. The graph of $y = 2\tan^2 x + 7\tan x - 15$ has four x-intercepts: $x = 0.983$, $x = 1.768$, $x = 4.124$, and $x = 4.910$.

47. The graph of $y = 12\sin^2 x - 13\sin x + 3$ has four x-intercepts: $x = 0.340$, $x = 0.848$, $x = 2.294$, and $x = 2.802$.

49. The graph of $\sin^2 x + 2\sin x - 1$ has two x-intercepts: $x = 0.427$ and $x = 2.715$.

51. (a) $f(x) = \sin x + \cos x$

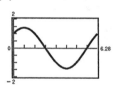

Maximum at $(0.785, 1.414)$

Minimum at $(3.927, -1.414)$

(b) The graph of $y = \cos x - \sin x$ has the same two x-intercepts: $x = 0.785$, $x = 3.927$.

53.

$$\cos x = x$$

$$\cos 0.5 = 0.8775825619$$

$$\cos(0.8775825619) = 0.6390124942$$

$$\cos(0.6390124942) = 0.8026851007$$

$$\vdots$$

$$\cos(0.7390851332) = 0.7390851332$$

You could also solve the equation $\cos x = x$ by finding the solution to $\cos x - x = 0$ using a graphing utility.

55. $A = 2x \cos x, \quad -\dfrac{\pi}{2} < x < \dfrac{\pi}{2}$

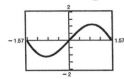

The area of the largest rectangle is 1.122, corresponding to $x = 0.860$.

57.

$$y = \frac{1}{4}(\cos 8t - 3 \sin 8t)$$

$$\frac{1}{4}(\cos 8t - 3 \sin 8t) = 0$$

$$\cos 8t = 3 \sin 8t$$

$$\frac{1}{3} = \tan 8t$$

$$8t = 0.32175 + n\pi$$

$$t = 0.04 + \frac{n\pi}{8}$$

In the interval $0 \le t \le 1$, $t = 0.04$, 0.43, and 0.83.

59. $r = \frac{1}{32}{v_0}^2 \sin 2\theta, \quad r = 300, \ v_0 = 100$

$300 = \frac{1}{32}(100)^2 \sin 2\theta$

$\sin 2\theta = 0.96$

$2\theta \approx 1.287 \qquad$ or $\quad 2\theta = \pi - 1.287 \approx 1.855$

$\theta \approx 0.6435 \approx 37° \qquad \quad \theta \approx 0.928 \approx 53°$

61. $f(x) = \tan\left(\dfrac{\pi x}{4}\right) = x$

Solving $\tan(\pi x/4) - x = 0$, we see that $x = 1.0$.

63. $f(x) = \dfrac{4x - x^2 + 2}{4} = x$

Solving

$$\frac{4x - x^2 + 2}{4} - x = 0$$

we see that $x = 1.414$ or $x = \sqrt{2}$.

Section 6.4   Sum and Difference Formulas

■ You should memorize the sum and difference formulas.

$\sin(u \pm v) = \sin u \cos v \pm \cos u \sin v$

$\cos(u \pm v) = \cos u \cos v \mp \sin u \sin v$

$\tan(u \pm v) = \dfrac{\tan u \pm \tan v}{1 \mp \tan u \tan v}$

■ You should be able to use these formulas to find the values of the trigonometric functions of angles whose sums or differences are special angles.

■ You should be able to use these formulas to solve trigonometric equations.

1. $\sin 75° = \sin(30° + 45°)$

$= \sin 30° \cos 45° + \sin 45° \cos 30° = \dfrac{1}{2} \cdot \dfrac{\sqrt{2}}{2} + \dfrac{\sqrt{2}}{2} \cdot \dfrac{\sqrt{3}}{2} = \dfrac{\sqrt{2}}{4}(1 + \sqrt{3})$

$\cos 75° = \cos(30° + 45°)$

$= \cos 30° \cos 45° - \sin 30° \sin 45° = \dfrac{\sqrt{3}}{2} \cdot \dfrac{\sqrt{2}}{2} - \dfrac{1}{2} \cdot \dfrac{\sqrt{2}}{2} = \dfrac{\sqrt{2}}{4}(\sqrt{3} - 1)$

$\tan 75° = \tan(30° + 45°)$

$= \dfrac{\tan 30° + \tan 45°}{1 - \tan 30° \tan 45°} = \dfrac{(\sqrt{3}/3) + 1}{1 - (\sqrt{3}/3)} = \sqrt{3} + 2$

3. $\sin 105° = \sin(60° + 45°)$

$= \sin 60° \cos 45° + \sin 45° \cos 60° = \dfrac{\sqrt{3}}{2} \cdot \dfrac{\sqrt{2}}{2} + \dfrac{\sqrt{2}}{2} \cdot \dfrac{1}{2} = \dfrac{\sqrt{2}}{4}(\sqrt{3} + 1)$

$\cos 105° = \cos(60° + 45°)$

$= \cos 60° \cos 45° - \sin 60° \sin 45° = \dfrac{1}{2} \cdot \dfrac{\sqrt{2}}{2} - \dfrac{\sqrt{3}}{2} \cdot \dfrac{\sqrt{2}}{2} = \dfrac{\sqrt{2}}{4}(1 - \sqrt{3})$

$\tan 105° = \tan(60° + 45°)$

$= \dfrac{\tan 60° + \tan 45°}{1 - \tan 60° \tan 45°} = \dfrac{\sqrt{3} + 1}{1 - \sqrt{3}} = -2 - \sqrt{3}$

5. $\sin 195° = \sin(225° - 30°) = \sin 225° \cos 30° - \sin 30° \cos 225°$

$$= -\sin 45° \cos 30° + \sin 30° \cos 45° = -\frac{\sqrt{2}}{2} \cdot \frac{\sqrt{3}}{2} + \frac{1}{2} \cdot \frac{\sqrt{2}}{2} = \frac{\sqrt{2}}{4}(1 - \sqrt{3})$$

$\cos 195° = \cos(225° - 30°) = \cos 225° \cos 30° + \sin 225° \sin 30°$

$$= -\cos 45° \cos 30° - \sin 45° \sin 30° = -\frac{\sqrt{2}}{2} \cdot \frac{\sqrt{3}}{2} - \frac{\sqrt{2}}{2} \cdot \frac{1}{2} = -\frac{\sqrt{2}}{4}(\sqrt{3} + 1)$$

$\tan 195° = \tan(225° - 30°)$

$$= \frac{\tan 225° - \tan 30°}{1 + \tan 225° \tan 30°} = \frac{\tan 45° - \tan 30°}{1 + \tan 45° \tan 30°} = \frac{1 - (\sqrt{3}/3)}{1 + (\sqrt{3}/3)} = 2 - \sqrt{3}$$

7. $\sin \dfrac{11\pi}{12} = \sin \left(\dfrac{3\pi}{4} + \dfrac{\pi}{6} \right)$

$$= \sin \frac{3\pi}{4} \cos \frac{\pi}{6} + \sin \frac{\pi}{6} \cos \frac{3\pi}{4} = \frac{\sqrt{2}}{2} \cdot \frac{\sqrt{3}}{2} + \frac{1}{2} \left(-\frac{\sqrt{2}}{2} \right) = \frac{\sqrt{2}}{4}(\sqrt{3} - 1)$$

$\cos \dfrac{11\pi}{12} = \cos \left(\dfrac{3\pi}{4} + \dfrac{\pi}{6} \right)$

$$= \cos \frac{3\pi}{4} \cos \frac{\pi}{6} - \sin \frac{3\pi}{4} \sin \frac{\pi}{6} = -\frac{\sqrt{2}}{2} \cdot \frac{\sqrt{3}}{2} - \frac{\sqrt{2}}{2} \cdot \frac{1}{2} = -\frac{\sqrt{2}}{4}(\sqrt{3} + 1)$$

$\tan \dfrac{11\pi}{12} = \tan \left(\dfrac{3\pi}{4} + \dfrac{\pi}{6} \right)$

$$= \frac{\tan(3\pi/4) + \tan(\pi/6)}{1 - \tan(3\pi/4) \tan(\pi/6)} = \frac{-1 + (\sqrt{3}/3)}{1 - (-1)(\sqrt{3}/3)} = -2 + \sqrt{3}$$

9. $\sin \dfrac{17\pi}{12} = \sin \left(\dfrac{9\pi}{4} - \dfrac{5\pi}{6} \right)$

$$= \sin \frac{9\pi}{4} \cos \frac{5\pi}{6} - \sin \frac{5\pi}{6} \cos \frac{9\pi}{4} = \frac{\sqrt{2}}{2} \left(-\frac{\sqrt{3}}{2} \right) - \left(\frac{1}{2} \right) \left(\frac{\sqrt{2}}{2} \right) = -\frac{\sqrt{2}}{4}(\sqrt{3} + 1)$$

$\cos \dfrac{17\pi}{12} = \cos \left(\dfrac{9\pi}{4} - \dfrac{5\pi}{6} \right)$

$$= \cos \frac{9\pi}{4} \cos \frac{5\pi}{6} + \sin \frac{9\pi}{4} \sin \frac{5\pi}{6} = \frac{\sqrt{2}}{2} \left(-\frac{\sqrt{3}}{2} \right) + \frac{\sqrt{2}}{2} \left(\frac{1}{2} \right) = \frac{\sqrt{2}}{4}(1 - \sqrt{3})$$

$\tan \dfrac{17\pi}{12} = \tan \left(\dfrac{9\pi}{4} - \dfrac{5\pi}{6} \right)$

$$= \frac{\tan(9\pi/4) - \tan(5\pi/6)}{1 + \tan(9\pi/4) \tan(5\pi/6)} = \frac{1 - (-\sqrt{3}/3)}{1 + (-\sqrt{3}/3)} = 2 + \sqrt{3}$$

11. $\cos 25° \cos 15° - \sin 25° \sin 15° = \cos(25° + 15°) = \cos 40°$

13. $\sin 230° \cos 30° - \cos 230° \sin 30° = \sin(230° - 30°) = \sin 200°$

15. $\dfrac{\tan 325° - \tan 86°}{1 + \tan 325° \tan 86°} = \tan(325° - 86°) = \tan 239°$

17. $\sin 3 \cos 1.2 - \cos 3 \sin 1.2 = \sin(3 - 1.2) = \sin 1.8$

19. $\dfrac{\tan 2x + \tan x}{1 - \tan 2x \tan x} = \tan(2x + x) = \tan 3x$

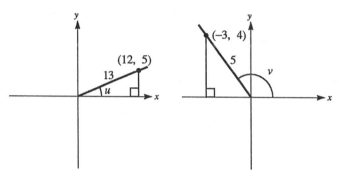

FIGURES FOR EXERCISES 21 AND 23

21. $\sin(u + v) = \sin u \cos v + \cos u \sin v$

$\quad = \left(\frac{5}{13}\right)\left(-\frac{3}{5}\right) + \left(\frac{12}{13}\right)\left(\frac{4}{5}\right)$

$\quad = \frac{-15}{65} + \frac{48}{65}$

$\quad = \frac{33}{65}$

23. $\cos(v + u) = \cos v \cos u - \sin v \sin u$

$\quad = \left(-\frac{3}{5}\right)\left(\frac{12}{13}\right) - \left(\frac{4}{5}\right)\left(\frac{5}{13}\right)$

$\quad = \frac{-36}{65} - \frac{20}{65}$

$\quad = -\frac{56}{65}$

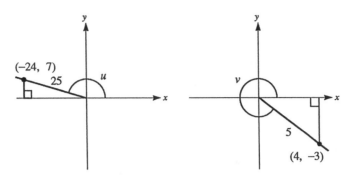

FIGURES FOR EXERCISES 25 AND 27

25. $\cos(u + v) = \cos u \cos v - \sin u \sin v$

$= \left(-\frac{24}{25}\right)\left(\frac{4}{5}\right) = \left(\frac{7}{25}\right)\left(\frac{-3}{5}\right)$

$= -\frac{96}{125} + \frac{21}{125}$

$= -\frac{75}{125}$

$= -\frac{3}{5}$

27. $\sin(v - u) = \sin v \cos u - \cos v \sin u$

$= \left(-\frac{3}{5}\right)\left(-\frac{24}{25}\right) - \left(\frac{4}{5}\right)\left(\frac{7}{25}\right)$

$= \frac{72}{125} - \frac{28}{125}$

$= \frac{44}{125}$

29. $\sin\left(\dfrac{\pi}{2} + x\right) = \sin\dfrac{\pi}{2}\cos x + \sin x \cos\dfrac{\pi}{2} = (1)(\cos x) + (\sin x)(0) = \cos x$

31. $\sin\left(\dfrac{\pi}{6} + x\right) = \sin\dfrac{\pi}{6}\cos x + \sin x \cos\dfrac{\pi}{6} = \dfrac{1}{2}(\cos x + \sqrt{3}\,\sin x)$

33. $\cos(\pi - \theta) + \sin\left(\dfrac{\pi}{2} + \theta\right) = \cos\pi\cos\theta + \sin\pi\sin\theta + \sin\dfrac{\pi}{2}\cos\theta + \sin\theta\cos\dfrac{\pi}{2}$

$= (-1)(\cos\theta) + (0)(\sin\theta) + (1)(\cos\theta) + (\sin\theta)(0)$

$= -\cos\theta + \cos\theta$

$= 0$

35. $\cos(x + y)\cos(x - y) = (\cos x \cos y - \sin x \sin y)(\cos x \cos y + \sin x \sin y)$

$= \cos^2 x \cos^2 y - \sin^2 x \sin^2 y$

$= \cos^2 x(1 - \sin^2 y) - \sin^2 x \sin^2 y$

$= \cos^2 x - \cos^2 x \sin^2 y - \sin^2 x \sin^2 y$

$= \cos^2 x - \sin^2 y(\cos^2 x + \sin^2 x)$

$= \cos^2 x - \sin^2 y$

37. $\sin(x + y) + \sin(x - y) = \sin x \cos y + \sin y \cos x + \sin x \cos y - \sin y \cos x$

$= 2\sin x \cos y$

39. $\cos(n\pi + \theta) = \cos n\pi \cos \theta - \sin n\pi \sin \theta$

$$= (-1)^n(\cos \theta) - (0)(\sin \theta) = (-1)^n(\cos \theta), \text{ where } n \text{ is an integer}$$

41. $C = \arctan \dfrac{b}{a} \Rightarrow \sin C = \dfrac{b}{\sqrt{a^2 + b^2}}, \quad \cos C \dfrac{a}{\sqrt{a^2 + b^2}}$

$$\sqrt{a^2 + b^2}\sin(B\theta + C) = \sqrt{a^2 + b^2}\left(\sin B\theta \cdot \dfrac{a}{\sqrt{a^2 + b^2}} + \dfrac{b}{\sqrt{a^2 + b^2}} \cdot \cos B\theta\right)$$

$$= a \sin B\theta + b \cos B\theta$$

43. $y_1 = \cos\left(\dfrac{3\pi}{2} - x\right)$

$y_2 = -\sin x$

The graphs of y_1 and y_2 coincide.

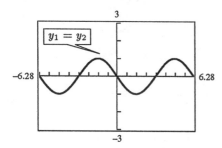

45. $y_1 = \sin\left(\dfrac{3\pi}{2} + \theta\right) + \sin(\pi - \theta)$

$y_2 = \sin \theta - \cos \theta$

The graphs of y_1 and y_2 coincide.

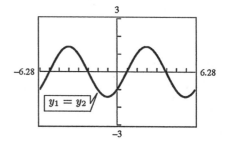

47. $\sin \theta + \cos \theta$

$a = 1, \quad b = 1, \quad B = 1$

(a) $C = \arctan \dfrac{b}{a} = \arctan 1 = \dfrac{\pi}{4}$

$$\sin \theta + \cos \theta = \sqrt{a^2 + b^2}\sin(B\theta + C) = \sqrt{2}\sin\left(\theta + \dfrac{\pi}{4}\right)$$

(b) $C = \arctan \dfrac{a}{b} = \arctan 1 = \dfrac{\pi}{4}$

$$\sin \theta + \cos \theta = \sqrt{a^2 + b^2}\cos(B\theta - C) = \sqrt{2}\cos\left(\theta - \dfrac{\pi}{4}\right)$$

49. $12\sin 3\theta + 5\cos 3\theta$

$a = 12, \quad b = 5, \quad B = 3$

(a) $C = \arctan \dfrac{b}{a} = \arctan \dfrac{5}{12} \approx 0.3948$

$12\sin 3\theta + 5\cos 3\theta = \sqrt{a^2 + b^2}\,\sin(B\theta + C) \approx 13\sin(3\theta + 0.3948)$

(b) $C = \arctan \dfrac{a}{b} = \arctan \dfrac{12}{5} \approx 1.1760$

$12\sin 3\theta + 5\cos 3\theta = \sqrt{a^2 + b^2}\,\cos(B\theta - C) \approx 13\cos(3\theta - 1.1760)$

51. $C = \arctan \dfrac{b}{a} = \dfrac{\pi}{4} \Rightarrow a = b$

$\sqrt{a^2 + b^2} = 2 \Rightarrow a = b = \sqrt{2}$

$B = 1$

$2\sin\left(\theta + \dfrac{\pi}{4}\right) = \sqrt{2}\,\sin\theta + \sqrt{2}\,\cos\theta$

53. $\sin(\arcsin x + \arccos x) = \sin(\arcsin x)\cos(\arccos x) + \sin(\arccos x)\cos(\arcsin x)$

$$= x \cdot x + \sqrt{1 - x^2} \cdot \sqrt{1 - x^2}$$

$$= x^2 + 1 - x^2$$

$$= 1$$

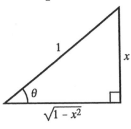

$\theta = \arcsin x$

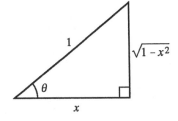

$\theta = \arccos x$

55.

$$\sin\left(x + \dfrac{\pi}{3}\right) + \sin\left(x - \dfrac{\pi}{3}\right) = 1$$

$$\sin x \cos \dfrac{\pi}{3} + \cos x \sin \dfrac{\pi}{3} + \sin x \cos \dfrac{\pi}{3} - \cos x \sin \dfrac{\pi}{3} = 1$$

$$2\sin x(0.5) = 1$$

$$\sin x = 1$$

$$x = \dfrac{\pi}{2}$$

57.
$$\cos\left(x + \frac{\pi}{4}\right) + \cos\left(x - \frac{\pi}{4}\right) = 1$$

$$\cos x \cos\frac{\pi}{4} - \sin x \sin\frac{\pi}{4} + \cos x \cos\frac{\pi}{4} + \sin x \sin\frac{\pi}{4} = 1$$

$$2\cos x \left(\frac{\sqrt{2}}{2}\right) = 1$$

$$\sqrt{2}\cos x = 1$$

$$\cos x = \frac{1}{\sqrt{2}}$$

$$\cos x = \frac{\sqrt{2}}{2}$$

$$x = \frac{\pi}{4}, \frac{7\pi}{4}$$

59. $\cos\left(x + \frac{\pi}{4}\right) - \cos\left(x - \frac{\pi}{4}\right) = 1$

Graphing

$$y = \cos\left(x + \frac{\pi}{4}\right) - \cos\left(x - \frac{\pi}{4}\right) - 1$$

we see that there are two x-intercepts in the interval $[0, \ 2\pi)$: $x = 3.927$ and $x = 5.498$.

61.
$$y_1 = A\cos 2\pi\left(\frac{t}{T} - \frac{x}{\lambda}\right)$$

$$y_2 = A\cos 2\pi\left(\frac{t}{T} + \frac{x}{\lambda}\right)$$

$$y_1 + y_2 = A\cos 2\pi\left(\frac{t}{T} - \frac{x}{\lambda}\right) + A\cos 2\pi\left(\frac{t}{T} + \frac{x}{\lambda}\right)$$

$$y_1 + y_2 = A\left[\cos 2\pi\frac{t}{T}\cos 2\pi\frac{x}{\lambda} + \sin 2\pi\frac{t}{T}\sin 2\pi\frac{x}{\lambda}\right] + A\left[\cos 2\pi\frac{t}{T}\cos 2\pi\frac{x}{\lambda} - \sin 2\pi\frac{t}{T}\sin 2\pi\frac{x}{\lambda}\right]$$

$$= 2A\cos 2\pi\frac{t}{T}\cos 2\pi\frac{x}{\lambda}$$

63. $\dfrac{\cos(x + h) - \cos x}{h} = \dfrac{\cos x \cdot \cos h - \sin x \cdot \sin h - \cos x}{h}$

$$= \cos x \left(\frac{\cos h - 1}{h}\right) - \sin x \left(\frac{\sin h}{h}\right)$$

Section 6.5   Multiple-Angle and Product-to-Sum Formulas

■ You should know the following double-angle formulas.

(a) $\sin 2u = 2 \sin u \cos u$ (b) $\cos 2u = \cos^2 u - \sin^2 u$ (c) $\tan 2u = \dfrac{2 \tan u}{1 - \tan^2 u}$

$$= 2\cos^2 u - 1$$

$$= 1 - 2\sin^2 u$$

■ You should be able to reduce the power of a trigonometric function.

(a) $\sin^2 u = \dfrac{1 - \cos 2u}{2}$ (b) $\cos^2 u = \dfrac{1 + \cos 2u}{2}$ (c) $\tan^2 u = \dfrac{1 - \cos 2u}{1 + \cos 2u}$

■ You should be able to use the half-angle formulas.

(a) $\sin \dfrac{u}{2} = \pm\sqrt{\dfrac{1 - \cos u}{2}}$ (b) $\cos \dfrac{u}{2} = \pm\sqrt{\dfrac{1 + \cos u}{2}}$ (c) $\tan \dfrac{u}{2} = \dfrac{1 - \cos u}{\sin u}$

$$= \dfrac{\sin u}{1 + \cos u}$$

■ You should be able to use the product-sum formulas.

(a) $\sin u \sin v = \dfrac{1}{2}[\cos(u - v) - \cos(u + v)]$

(b) $\cos u \cos v = \dfrac{1}{2}[\cos(u - v) + \cos(u + v)]$

(c) $\sin u \cos v = \dfrac{1}{2}[\sin(u + v) + \sin(u - v)]$

(d) $\cos u \sin v = \dfrac{1}{2}[\sin(u + v) - \sin(u - v)]$

■ You should be able to use the sum-product formulas.

(a) $\sin x + \sin y = 2 \sin \left(\dfrac{x + y}{2}\right) \cos \left(\dfrac{x - y}{2}\right)$

(b) $\sin x - \sin y = 2 \cos \left(\dfrac{x + y}{2}\right) \sin \left(\dfrac{x - y}{2}\right)$

(c) $\cos x + \cos y = 2 \cos \left(\dfrac{x + y}{2}\right) \cos \left(\dfrac{x - y}{2}\right)$

(d) $\cos x - \cos y = -2 \sin \left(\dfrac{x + y}{2}\right) \sin \left(\dfrac{x - y}{2}\right)$

1. $f(x) = \sin 2x - \sin x$

Graphing the function on the interval $[0,\ 2\pi)$, we find the zeros are $x = 0$, 1.047, 3.142, and 5.236. Algebraically:

$$\sin 2x - \sin x = 0$$

$$2\sin x \cos x - \sin x = 0$$

$$\sin x (2\cos x - 1) = 0$$

$$\sin x = 0 \qquad \text{or} \quad 2\cos x - 1 = 0$$

$$x = 0,\ \pi \qquad\qquad \cos x = \frac{1}{2}$$

$$x = \frac{\pi}{3},\ \frac{5\pi}{3}$$

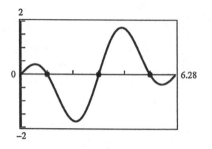

3. $g(x) = 4\sin x \cos x - 1$

Graphing the function on the interval $[0,\ 2\pi)$, we find the zeros are $x = 0.262$, 1.309, 3.403, and 4.451. Algebraically:

$$4\sin x \cos x = 1$$

$$2\sin 2x = 1$$

$$\sin 2x = \frac{1}{2}$$

$$2x = \frac{\pi}{6} + 2n\pi \quad \text{or} \quad 2x = \frac{5\pi}{6} + 2n\pi$$

$$x = \frac{\pi}{12} + n\pi \qquad\qquad x = \frac{5\pi}{12} + n\pi$$

$$x = \frac{\pi}{12},\ \frac{13\pi}{12} \qquad\qquad x = \frac{5\pi}{12},\ \frac{17\pi}{12}$$

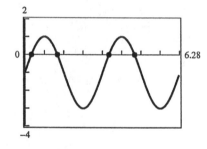

5. $h(x) = \cos 2x - \cos x$

Graphing the function on the interval $[0,\ 2\pi)$, we find the zeros are $x = 0$, 2.094, and 4.189.

—CONTINUED ON NEXT PAGE—

5. —CONTINUED—

Algebraically:

$$\cos 2x = \cos x$$

$$\cos^2 x - \sin^2 x = \cos x$$

$$\cos^2 x - (1 - \cos^2 x) - \cos x = 0$$

$$2\cos^2 x - \cos x - 1 = 0$$

$$(2\cos x + 1)(\cos x - 1) = 0$$

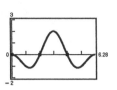

$$2\cos x + 1 = 0 \qquad \text{or} \quad \cos x - 1 = 0$$

$$\cos x = -\frac{1}{2} \qquad\qquad \cos x = 1$$

$$\qquad\qquad\qquad x = 0$$

$$x = \frac{2\pi}{3},\ \frac{4\pi}{3}$$

7. $y = \tan 2x - \cot x$

Graphing the function on the interval $[0,\ 2\pi)$, we find the zeros are $x = 0.524,\ 1.571,\ 2.618,$ $3.665,\ 4.712,$ and $5.760.$ Algebraically:

$$\tan 2x - \cot x = 0$$

$$\frac{2\tan x}{1 - \tan^2 x} = \cot x$$

$$2\tan x = \cot x(1 - \tan^2 x)$$

$$2\tan x = \cot x - \cot x \tan^2 x$$

$$2\tan x = \cot x - \tan x$$

$$3\tan x = \cot x$$

$$3\tan x - \cot x = 0$$

$$3\tan x - \frac{1}{\tan x} = 0$$

$$\frac{3\tan^2 x - 1}{\tan x} = 0$$

$$\frac{1}{\tan x}(3\tan^2 x - 1) = 0$$

$$\cot x(3\tan^2 x - 1) = 0$$

$$\cot x = 0 \qquad \text{or} \quad 3\tan^2 x - 1 = 0$$

$$x = \frac{\pi}{2},\ \frac{3\pi}{2} \qquad\qquad \tan^2 x = \frac{1}{3}$$

$$\tan x = \pm\frac{\sqrt{3}}{3}$$

$$x = \frac{\pi}{6},\ \frac{5\pi}{6},\ \frac{7\pi}{6},\ \frac{11\pi}{6}$$

9. $h(t) = \sin 4t + 2\sin 2t$

Graphing the function on the interval $[0, \ 2\pi)$, we find the zeros are $x = 0$, 1.571, 3.142, and 4.712. Algebraically:

$$\sin 4t + 2\sin 2t = 0$$

$$2\sin 2t \cos 2t + 2\sin 2t = 0$$

$$2\sin 2t(\cos 2t + 1) = 0$$

$$2\sin 2t = 0 \qquad \text{or} \quad \cos 2t + 1 = 0$$

$$\sin 2t = 0 \qquad \qquad \cos 2t = -1$$

$$2t = n\pi \qquad \qquad 2t = \pi + 2n\pi$$

$$t = \frac{n}{2}\pi \qquad \qquad t = \frac{\pi}{2} + n\pi$$

$$t = 0, \ \frac{\pi}{2}, \ \pi, \ \frac{3\pi}{2} \qquad \qquad t = \frac{\pi}{2}, \ \frac{3\pi}{2}$$

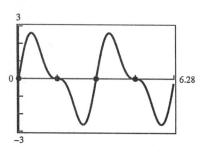

11. $f(x) = 6\sin x \cos x$

$\qquad = 3(2\sin x \cos x)$

$\qquad = 3\sin 2x$

Relative maxima: $(0.785, \ 3)$, $(3.927, \ 3)$

Relative minima:

$(2.356, \ -3)$, $(5.498, \ -3)$

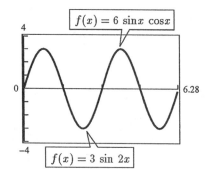

13. $g(x) = 4 - 8\sin^2 x$

$\qquad = 4(1 - 2\sin^2 x)$

$\qquad = 4\cos 2x$

Relative maxima: $(0, \ 4)$, $(3.142, \ 4)$

Relative minima:

$(1.571, \ -4)$, $(4.712, \ -4)$

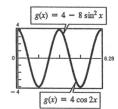

15. $\sin 2u = 2 \sin u \cos u$

$$= 2 \cdot \frac{3}{5} \cdot \frac{4}{5} = \frac{24}{25}$$

$\cos 2u = \cos^2 u - \sin^2 u$

$$= \frac{16}{25} - \frac{9}{25} = \frac{7}{25}$$

$\tan 2u = \dfrac{2 \tan u}{1 - \tan^2 u}$

$$= \frac{2(3/4)}{1 - (9/16)} = \frac{24}{7}$$

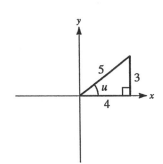

17. $\sin 2u = 2 \sin u \cos u$

$$= 2 \left(-\frac{1}{\sqrt{5}} \right) \left(-\frac{2}{\sqrt{5}} \right) = \frac{4}{5}$$

$\cos 2u = \cos^2 u - \sin^2 u$

$$= \left(-\frac{2}{\sqrt{5}} \right)^2 - \left(-\frac{1}{\sqrt{5}} \right)^2 = \frac{3}{5}$$

$\tan 2u = \dfrac{2 \tan u}{1 - \tan^2 u} = \dfrac{2(1/2)}{1 - (1/4)} = \dfrac{4}{3}$

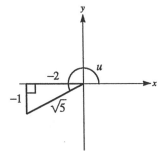

19. $\sin 2u = 2 \sin u \cos u$

$$= 2 \left(\frac{\sqrt{21}}{5} \right) \left(-\frac{2}{5} \right) = -\frac{4\sqrt{21}}{25}$$

$\cos 2u = \cos^2 u - \sin^2 u$

$$= \left(-\frac{2}{5} \right)^2 - \left(\frac{\sqrt{21}}{5} \right)^2 = -\frac{17}{25}$$

$\tan 2u = \dfrac{2 \tan u}{1 - \tan^2 u}$

$$= \frac{2(-\sqrt{21}/2)}{1 - (-\sqrt{21}/2)^2} = \frac{4\sqrt{21}}{17}$$

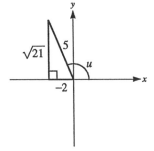

21. $\cos^4 x = (\cos^2 x)(\cos^2 x) = \left(\dfrac{1 + \cos 2x}{2} \right) \left(\dfrac{1 + \cos 2x}{2} \right) = \dfrac{1 + 2\cos 2x + \cos^2 2x}{4}$

$$= \frac{1 + 2\cos 2x + (1 + \cos 4x)/2}{4} = \frac{2 + 4\cos 2x + 1 + \cos 4x}{8} = \frac{3 + 4\cos 2x + \cos 4x}{8}$$

23. $\sin^2 x (\cos^2 x) = \dfrac{1 - \cos 2x}{2} \cdot \dfrac{1 + \cos 2x}{2}$

$$= \dfrac{1 - \cos^2 2x}{4} = \dfrac{1}{4}\left(1 - \dfrac{1 + \cos 4x}{2}\right) = \dfrac{1}{8}(2 - 1 - \cos 4x) = \dfrac{1}{8}(1 - \cos 4x)$$

25. $\sin^2 x \cos^4 x = \sin^2 x \cos^2 x \cos^2 x$

$$= \left(\dfrac{1 - \cos 2x}{2}\right)\left(\dfrac{1 + \cos 2x}{2}\right)\left(\dfrac{1 + \cos 2x}{2}\right)$$

$$= \dfrac{1}{8}(1 - \cos 2x)(1 + \cos 2x)(1 + \cos 2x)$$

$$= \dfrac{1}{8}(1 - \cos^2 2x)(1 + \cos 2x)$$

$$= \dfrac{1}{8}(1 + \cos 2x)\left(1 - \left(\dfrac{1 + \cos 4x}{2}\right)\right)$$

$$= \dfrac{1}{16}(1 + \cos 2x)(1 - \cos 4x)$$

27. $\sin 105° = \sin\left(\dfrac{1}{2} \cdot 210°\right) = \sqrt{\dfrac{1 - \cos 210°}{2}} = \sqrt{\dfrac{1 + (\sqrt{3}/2)}{2}} = \dfrac{1}{2}\sqrt{2 + \sqrt{3}}$

$\cos 105° = \cos\left(\dfrac{1}{2} \cdot 210°\right) = -\sqrt{\dfrac{1 + \cos 210°}{2}} = -\sqrt{\dfrac{1 - (\sqrt{3}/2)}{2}} = -\dfrac{1}{2}\sqrt{2 - \sqrt{3}}$

$\tan 105° = \tan\left(\dfrac{1}{2} \cdot 210°\right) = \dfrac{\sin 210°}{1 + \cos 210°} = \dfrac{-1/2}{1 - (\sqrt{3}/2)} = -2 - \sqrt{3}$

29. $\sin 112°30' = \sin\left(\dfrac{1}{2} \cdot 225°\right) = \sqrt{\dfrac{1 - \cos 225°}{2}} = \sqrt{\dfrac{1 + (\sqrt{2}/2)}{2}} = \dfrac{1}{2}\sqrt{2 + \sqrt{2}}$

$\cos 112°30' = \cos\left(\dfrac{1}{2} \cdot 225°\right) = -\sqrt{\dfrac{1 + \cos 225°}{2}} = -\sqrt{\dfrac{1 - (\sqrt{2}/2)}{2}} = -\dfrac{1}{2}\sqrt{2 - \sqrt{2}}$

$\tan 112°30' = \tan\left(\dfrac{1}{2} \cdot 225°\right) = \dfrac{\sin 225°}{1 + \cos 225°} = \dfrac{-\sqrt{2}/2}{1 - (\sqrt{2}/2)} = -1 - \sqrt{2}$

31. $\sin\dfrac{\pi}{8} = \sin\left[\dfrac{1}{2}\left(\dfrac{\pi}{4}\right)\right] = \sqrt{\dfrac{1 - \cos(\pi/4)}{2}} = \dfrac{1}{2}\sqrt{2 - \sqrt{2}}$

$\cos\dfrac{\pi}{8} = \cos\left[\dfrac{1}{2}\left(\dfrac{\pi}{4}\right)\right] = \sqrt{\dfrac{1 + \cos(\pi/4)}{2}} = \dfrac{1}{2}\sqrt{2 + \sqrt{2}}$

$\tan\dfrac{\pi}{8} = \tan\left[\dfrac{1}{2}\left(\dfrac{\pi}{4}\right)\right] = \dfrac{\sin(\pi/4)}{1 + \cos(\pi/4)} = \dfrac{\sqrt{2}/2}{1 + (\sqrt{2}/2)} = \sqrt{2} - 1$

33. $\sin\left(\dfrac{u}{2}\right) = \sqrt{\dfrac{1-\cos u}{2}} = \sqrt{\dfrac{1+(12/13)}{2}} = \dfrac{5\sqrt{26}}{26}$

$\cos\left(\dfrac{u}{2}\right) = \sqrt{\dfrac{1+\cos u}{2}} = \sqrt{\dfrac{1-(12/13)}{2}} = \dfrac{\sqrt{26}}{26}$

$\tan\left(\dfrac{u}{2}\right) = \dfrac{\sin u}{1+\cos u} = \dfrac{5/13}{1-(12/13)} = \dfrac{5}{1} = 5$

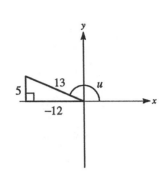

35. $\sin\left(\dfrac{u}{2}\right) = \sqrt{\dfrac{1-\cos u}{2}} = \sqrt{\dfrac{1-(8/\sqrt{89})}{2}}$

$= \sqrt{\dfrac{\sqrt{89}-8}{2\sqrt{89}}}$

$\cos\left(\dfrac{u}{2}\right) = -\sqrt{\dfrac{1+\cos u}{2}} = -\sqrt{\dfrac{1+(8/\sqrt{89})}{2}}$

$= -\sqrt{\dfrac{\sqrt{89}+8}{2\sqrt{89}}}$

$\tan\left(\dfrac{u}{2}\right) = \dfrac{1-\cos u}{\sin u} = \dfrac{1-(8/\sqrt{89})}{-5/\sqrt{89}}$

$= \dfrac{8-\sqrt{89}}{5}$

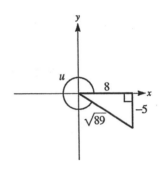

37. $\sin\left(\dfrac{u}{2}\right) = \sqrt{\dfrac{1-\cos u}{2}} = \sqrt{\dfrac{1+(4/5)}{2}} = \dfrac{3\sqrt{10}}{10}$

$\cos\left(\dfrac{u}{2}\right) = -\sqrt{\dfrac{1+\cos u}{2}} = -\sqrt{\dfrac{1-(4/5)}{2}} = -\dfrac{\sqrt{10}}{10}$

$\tan\left(\dfrac{u}{2}\right) = \dfrac{1-\cos u}{\sin u} = \dfrac{1+(4/5)}{-3/5} = -3$

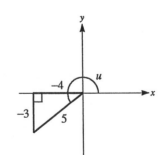

39. $\sqrt{\dfrac{1 - \cos 6x}{2}} = |\sin 3x|$

41. $-\sqrt{\dfrac{1 - \cos 8x}{1 + \cos 8x}} = -\dfrac{\sqrt{(1 - \cos 8x)/2}}{\sqrt{(1 + \cos 8x)/2}}$

$$= -\dfrac{\sin 4x}{\cos 4x}$$

$$= -|\tan 4x|$$

43. $f(x) = \sin \dfrac{x}{2} + \cos x$

Graphing the function on the interval $[0, \ 2\pi)$, we find the zero is $x = 3.142$. Algebraically:

$$\sin \dfrac{x}{2} + \cos x = 0$$

$$\sin \dfrac{x}{2} = -\cos x$$

$$\pm\sqrt{\dfrac{1 - \cos x}{2}} = -\cos x$$

$$\dfrac{1 - \cos x}{2} = \cos^2 x$$

$$1 - \cos x = 2\cos^2 x$$

$$2\cos^2 x + \cos x - 1 = 0$$

$$(2\cos x - 1)(\cos x + 1) = 0$$

$$2\cos x - 1 = 0 \qquad \text{or} \quad \cos x = -1$$

$$\cos x = \dfrac{1}{2} \qquad\qquad x = \pi$$

$$x = \dfrac{\pi}{3}, \ \dfrac{5\pi}{3}$$

$\pi/3$ and $5\pi/3$ are extraneous solutions. π is the only solution.

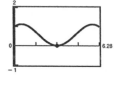

45. $h(x) = \cos \dfrac{x}{2} - \sin x$

Graphing the function on the interval $[0,\ 2\pi)$, we find the zeros are $x = 1.047,\ 3.142,$ and 5.236. Algebraically:

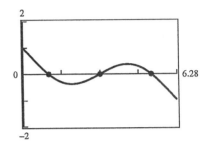

$$\cos \dfrac{x}{2} - \sin x = 0$$

$$\pm\sqrt{\dfrac{1 + \cos x}{2}} = \sin x$$

$$\dfrac{1 + \cos x}{2} = \sin^2 x$$

$$1 + \cos x = 2 \sin^2 x$$

$$1 + \cos x = 2 - 2 \cos^2 x$$

$$2 \cos^2 x + \cos x - 1 = 0$$

$$(2 \cos x - 1)(\cos x + 1) = 0$$

$$2 \cos x - 1 = 0 \qquad \text{or} \quad \cos x + 1 = 0$$

$$\cos x = \dfrac{1}{2} \qquad\qquad \cos x = -1$$

$$\qquad\qquad\qquad\qquad x = \pi$$

$$x = \dfrac{\pi}{3},\ \dfrac{5\pi}{3}$$

$\pi/3$, π, and $5\pi/3$ are all solutions to the equation.

47. $6 \sin \dfrac{\pi}{4} \cos \dfrac{\pi}{4} = 6 \cdot \dfrac{1}{2} \left[\sin \left(\dfrac{\pi}{4} + \dfrac{\pi}{4} \right) + \sin \left(\dfrac{\pi}{4} - \dfrac{\pi}{4} \right) \right] = 3 \left(\sin \dfrac{\pi}{2} + \sin 0 \right)$

49. $\sin 5\theta \cos 3\theta = \dfrac{1}{2}[\sin(5\theta + 3\theta) + \sin(5\theta - 3\theta)] = \dfrac{1}{2}(\sin 8\theta + \sin 2\theta)$

51. $5 \cos(-5\beta) \cos 3\beta = 5 \cdot \dfrac{1}{2}[\cos(-5\beta - 3\beta) + \cos(-5\beta + 3\beta)]$

$$= \dfrac{5}{2}[\cos(-8\beta) + \cos(-2\beta)] = \dfrac{5}{2}(\cos 8\beta + \cos 2\beta)$$

53. $\sin(x + y) \sin(x - y) = \dfrac{1}{2}(\cos 2y - \cos 2x)$ **55.** $\sin(\theta + \pi) \cos(\theta - \pi) = \dfrac{1}{2}(\sin 2\theta + \sin 2\pi)$

57. $\sin 60° + \sin 30° = 2 \sin \left(\dfrac{60° + 30°}{2} \right) \cos \left(\dfrac{60° - 30°}{2} \right) = 2 \sin 45° \cos 15°$

59. $\cos \dfrac{3\pi}{4} - \cos \dfrac{\pi}{4} = -2 \sin \left(\dfrac{(3\pi/4) + (\pi/4)}{2} \right) + \left(\dfrac{(3\pi/4) - (\pi/4)}{2} \right) = -2 \sin \dfrac{\pi}{2} \sin \dfrac{\pi}{4}$

61. $\cos 6x + \cos 2x = 2 \cos \left(\dfrac{6x + 2x}{2} \right) \cos \left(\dfrac{6x - 2x}{2} \right) = 2 \cos 4x \cos 2x$

63. $\sin(\alpha + \beta) - \sin(\alpha - \beta) = 2\cos\left(\dfrac{\alpha + \beta + \alpha - \beta}{2}\right)\sin\left(\dfrac{\alpha + \beta - \alpha + \beta}{2}\right) = 2\cos\alpha\sin\beta$

65. $\cos(\phi + 2\pi) + \cos\phi = 2\cos\left(\dfrac{\phi + 2\pi + \phi}{2}\right)\cos\left(\dfrac{\phi + 2\pi - \phi}{2}\right) = 2\cos(\phi + \pi)\cos\pi$

67. $g(x) = \sin 6x + \sin 2x$

Graphing the function on the interval $[0,\ 2\pi)$, we find the zeros are $x = 0,\ 0.785,\ 1.571,\ 2.356,$ 3.142, 3.927, 4.712, and 5.498. Algebraically:

$$\sin 6x + \sin 2x = 0$$

$$2\sin 4x \cos 2x = 0$$

$$\sin 4x = 0 \qquad\qquad \text{or} \qquad \cos 2x = 0$$

$$4x = n\pi \qquad\qquad\qquad\qquad 2x = \frac{\pi}{2} + n\pi$$

$$x = \frac{n\pi}{4} \qquad\qquad\qquad\qquad x = \frac{\pi}{4} + \frac{n\pi}{2}$$

$$x = 0,\ \frac{\pi}{4},\ \frac{\pi}{2},\ \frac{3\pi}{4}, \qquad\qquad x = \frac{\pi}{4},\ \frac{3\pi}{4},\ \frac{5\pi}{4},\ \frac{7\pi}{4}$$

$$\pi,\ \frac{5\pi}{4},\ \frac{3\pi}{2},\ \frac{7\pi}{4}$$

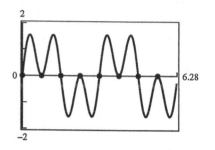

69. $f(x) = \dfrac{\cos 2x}{\sin 3x - \sin x} - 1$

Graphing the function on the interval $[0,\ 2\pi)$, we find the zeros are $x = 0.524$ and 2.618. Algebraically:

$$\frac{\cos 2x}{\sin 3x - \sin x} = 1$$

$$\frac{\cos 2x}{2\cos 2x \sin x} = 1$$

$$2\sin x = 1$$

$$\sin x = \frac{1}{2}$$

$$x = \frac{\pi}{6},\ \frac{5\pi}{6}$$

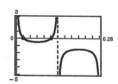

71. $\csc 2\theta = \dfrac{1}{\sin 2\theta}$

$\qquad = \dfrac{1}{2 \sin \theta \cos \theta}$

$\qquad = \dfrac{1}{\sin \theta} \cdot \dfrac{1}{2 \cos \theta}$

$\qquad = \dfrac{\csc \theta}{2 \cos \theta}$

73. $\cos^2 2\alpha - \sin^2 2\alpha = \cos[2(2\alpha)]$

$\qquad\qquad\qquad\qquad\quad = \cos 4\alpha$

75. $(\sin x + \cos x)^2 = \sin^2 x + 2 \sin x \cos x + \cos^2 x$

$\qquad\qquad\qquad\quad = (\sin^2 x + \cos^2 x) + 2 \sin x \cos x = 1 + \sin 2x$

77. $\cos 3\beta = \cos(2\beta + \beta)$

$\qquad = \cos 2\beta \cos \beta - \sin 2\beta \sin \beta$

$\qquad = (\cos^2 \beta - \sin^2 \beta) \cos \beta - 2 \sin \beta \cos \beta \sin \beta$

$\qquad = \cos^3 \beta - \sin^2 \beta \cos \beta - 2 \sin^2 \beta \cos \beta$

$\qquad = \cos^3 \beta - 3 \sin^2 \beta \cos \beta$

79. $1 + \cos 10y = 1 + \cos^2 5y - \sin^2 5y = 1 + \cos^2 5y - (1 - \cos^2 5y) = 2 \cos^2 5y$

81. $\sec \dfrac{u}{2} = \pm\sqrt{\dfrac{1}{\cos(u/2)}} = \pm\sqrt{\dfrac{2}{1 + \cos u}} = \pm\sqrt{\dfrac{2 \sin u}{\sin u(1 + \cos u)}} = \pm\sqrt{\dfrac{2 \sin u}{\sin u + \sin u \cos u}}$

$\qquad = \pm\sqrt{\dfrac{(2 \sin u)/(\cos u)}{(\sin u)/(\cos u) + (\sin u \cos u)/(\cos u)}} = \pm\sqrt{\dfrac{2 \tan u}{\tan u + \sin u}}$

83. $\dfrac{\cos 4x + \cos 2x}{\sin 4x + \sin 2x} = \dfrac{2 \cos\left(\dfrac{4x + 2x}{2}\right) \cos\left(\dfrac{4x - 2x}{2}\right)}{2 \sin\left(\dfrac{4x + 2x}{2}\right) \cos\left(\dfrac{4x - 2x}{2}\right)} = \dfrac{2 \cos 3x \cos x}{2 \sin 3x \cos x} = \cot 3x$

85. $\dfrac{\cos 4x - \cos 2x}{2 \sin 3x} = \dfrac{-2 \sin\left(\dfrac{4x + 2x}{2}\right) \sin\left(\dfrac{4x - 2x}{2}\right)}{2 \sin 3x} = \dfrac{-2 \sin 3x \sin x}{2 \sin 3x} = -\sin x$

87.
$$\frac{\cos t + \cos 3t}{\sin 3t - \sin t} = \frac{2\cos\left(\frac{4t}{2}\right)\cos\left(-\frac{2t}{2}\right)}{2\cos\left(\frac{4t}{2}\right)\sin\left(\frac{2t}{2}\right)}$$

$$= \frac{\cos(-t)}{\sin(t)}$$

$$= \frac{\cos(t)}{\sin(t)}$$

$$= \cot t$$

89. $\sin^2 x = \dfrac{1 - \cos 2x}{2} = \dfrac{1}{2} - \dfrac{\cos 2x}{2}$

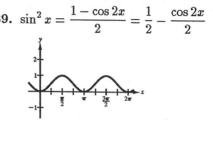

91. $\sin(2\arcsin x) = 2\sin(\arcsin x)\cos(\arcsin x) = 2x\sqrt{1 - x^2}$

93. $\frac{1}{2}[\sin(u + v) - \sin(u - v)] = \frac{1}{2}[\sin u \cos v + \sin v \cos u - (\sin u \cos v - \sin v \cos u)]$

$$= \frac{1}{2}(2\sin v \cos u)$$

$$= \cos u \sin v$$

95. (a) $A = \dfrac{1}{2}bh$

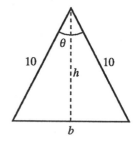

$$\cos\frac{\theta}{2} = \frac{h}{10} \Rightarrow h = 10\cos\frac{\theta}{2}$$

$$\sin\frac{\theta}{2} = \frac{(1/2)b}{10} \Rightarrow \frac{1}{2}b = 10\sin\frac{\theta}{2}$$

$$A = 10\sin\frac{\theta}{2}10\cos\frac{\theta}{2} \Rightarrow A = 100\sin\frac{\theta}{2}\cos\frac{\theta}{2}$$

(b) $A = 100\sin\dfrac{\theta}{2}\cos\dfrac{\theta}{2}$

$$A = 50\left(2\sin\frac{\theta}{2}\cos\frac{\theta}{2}\right)$$

$$A = 50\sin\theta$$

When $\theta = \pi/2$, $\sin\theta = 1 \Rightarrow$ the area is a maximum.

$$A = 50\sin\frac{\pi}{2} = 50(1) = 50 \text{ square feet}$$

Section 6.6   Law of Sines

- If ABC is any oblique triangle with sides a, b, and c, then
$$\frac{a}{\sin A} = \frac{b}{\sin B} = \frac{c}{\sin C}.$$

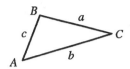

- You should be able to use the Law of Sines to solve an oblique triangle for the remaining three parts, given:
  (a) Two angles and any side (AAS or ASA)
  (b) Two sides and an angle opposite one of them (SSA)
    1. If A is acute and:
       (a) $a < h$, no triangle is possible.
       (b) $a = h$ or $a > b$, one triangle is possible.
       (c) $h < a < b$, two triangles are possible.
    2. If A is obtuse and:
       (a) $a \le b$, no triangle is possible.
       (b) $a > b$, one triangle is possible.

- The area of any triangle equals one-half the product of the lengths of two sides times the sine of their included angle.
$$A = \tfrac{1}{2}ab \sin C = \tfrac{1}{2}ac \sin B = \tfrac{1}{2}bc \sin A$$

1. Given: $A = 30°$, $B = 45°$, $a = 10$

$C = 180° - A - B = 105°$

$$b = \frac{a}{\sin A}(\sin B) = \frac{10 \sin 45°}{\sin 30°} = 10\sqrt{2} \approx 14.14$$

$$c = \frac{a}{\sin A}(\sin C) = \frac{10 \sin 105°}{\sin 30°} \approx 19.32$$

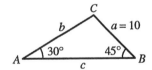

3. Given: $A = 10°$, $B = 60°$, $a = 4.5$

$C = 180° - A - B = 110°$

$$b = \frac{a}{\sin A}(\sin B) = \frac{4.5}{\sin 10°}(\sin 60°) \approx 22.44$$

$$c = \frac{a}{\sin A}(\sin C) = \frac{4.5}{\sin 10°}(\sin 110°) \approx 24.35$$

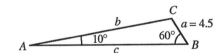

5. Given: $A = 36°$, $a = 8$, $b = 5$

$$\sin B = \frac{b \sin A}{a} = \frac{5 \sin 36°}{8}$$

$$\approx 0.3674 \Rightarrow B \approx 21.6°$$

$$C = 180 - A - B$$

$$\approx 180° - 36° - 21.6° = 122.4°$$

$$c = \frac{a}{\sin A}(\sin C)$$

$$= \frac{8}{\sin 36°}(\sin 122.4°) \approx 11.49$$

7. Given: $A = 150°$, $C = 20°$, $a = 200$

$$B = 180° - A - C$$

$$= 180° - 150° - 20° = 10°$$

$$b = \frac{a}{\sin A}(\sin B)$$

$$= \frac{200}{\sin 150°}(\sin 10°) \approx 69.46$$

$$c = \frac{a}{\sin A}(\sin C)$$

$$= \frac{200}{\sin 150°}(\sin 20°) \approx 136.8$$

9. Given: $A = 83°20'$, $C = 54.6°$, $c = 18.1$

$$B = 180° - A - C$$

$$= 180° - 80°20' - 54°36' = 42°4'$$

$$a = \frac{c}{\sin C}(\sin A)$$

$$= \frac{18.1}{\sin 54.6°}(\sin 83°20') \approx 22.05$$

$$b = \frac{c}{\sin C}(\sin B)$$

$$= \frac{18.1}{\sin 54.6°}(\sin 42.1°) \approx 14.89$$

11. Given: $B = 15°30'$, $a = 4.5$, $b = 6.8$

$$\sin A = \frac{a \sin B}{b} = \frac{4.5 \sin 15°30'}{6.8}$$

$$\approx 0.1768 \Rightarrow A \approx 10.2°$$

$$C = 180° - A - B$$

$$\approx 180° - 10.2° - 15.5° = 154.3°$$

$$c = \frac{b}{\sin B}(\sin C)$$

$$\approx \frac{6.8}{\sin 15°30'}(\sin 154.3°) \approx 11.03$$

13. Given: $C = 145°$, $b = 4$, $c = 14$

$$\sin B = \frac{b \sin C}{c}$$

$$= \frac{4 \sin 145°}{14} \approx 0.1639 \Rightarrow B \approx 9.43°$$

$$A = 180° - B - C$$

$$\approx 180° - 9.43° - 145° = 25.6°$$

$$a = \frac{c}{\sin C}(\sin A)$$

$$\approx \frac{14}{\sin 145°}(\sin 25.6°) \approx 10.53$$

15. Given: $A = 110°15'$, $a = 48$, $b = 16$

$$\sin B = \frac{b \sin A}{a} = \frac{16 \sin 110°15'}{48}$$

$$\approx 0.3127 \Rightarrow B = 18.22°$$

$$C = 180° - A - B$$

$$\approx 180° - 110.25° - 18.22° \approx 51.53°$$

$$c = \frac{a}{\sin A}(\sin C)$$

$$\approx \frac{48}{\sin 110°15'}(\sin 51.53°) \approx 40.05$$

17. Given: $a = 4.5$, $b = 12.8$, $A = 58°$

$$h = 12.8 \sin 58° \approx 10.86$$

Since $a < h$, no triangle is formed.

19. Given: $a = 4.5$, $b = 5$, $A = 58°$

$$\sin B = \frac{b \sin A}{a} = \frac{5 \sin 58°}{4.5} \approx 0.9423 \Rightarrow B = 70.4° \text{ or } B = 109.6°$$

Case 1	Case 2

Case 1

$B \approx 70.4°$

$C \approx 180° - 70.4° - 58° = 51.6°$

$c \approx \dfrac{4.5}{\sin 58°}(\sin 51.6°) \approx 4.16$

Case 2

$B \approx 109.6°$

$C \approx 180° - 109.6° - 58° = 12.4°$

$c \approx \dfrac{4.5}{\sin 58°}(\sin 12.4°) \approx 1.14$

21. Given: $a = 125$, $b = 200$, $A = 110°$

No triangle is formed because A is obtuse and $a < b$.

23. Given: $A = 36°$, $a = 5$

(a) One solution if $b \leq 5$ or $b = \dfrac{5}{\sin 36°}$

(b) Two solutions if $5 < b < \dfrac{5}{\sin 36°}$

(c) No solution is $b > \dfrac{5}{\sin 36°}$

25. Area $= \frac{1}{2}ab \sin C$

$= \frac{1}{2}(4)(6) \sin 120° \approx 10.39$

27. Area $= \frac{1}{2}bc \sin A$

$= \frac{1}{2}(57)(85) \sin 43°45' \approx 1675$

29. Area $= \frac{1}{2}ac \sin B = \frac{1}{2}(62)(20) \sin 130° \approx 474.9$

31. $\sin B = \dfrac{5\sin 30°}{3} \approx 0.8333 \Rightarrow B \approx 56.4°$

$D \approx 180° - 30° - 56.4° = 93.6°$

$d \approx \dfrac{3}{\sin 30°}(\sin 93.6°) \approx 6 \text{ ft}$

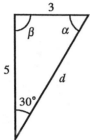

33. Given: $A = 74° - 28° = 46°,$

$B = 180° - 41° - 74° = 65°,$

$c = 100$

$C = 180° - 46° - 65° = 69°$

$a = \dfrac{c}{\sin C}(\sin A) = \dfrac{100}{\sin 69°}(\sin 46°)$

$\approx 77 \text{ yds}$

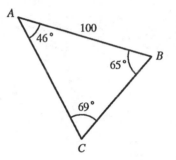

35. $C = 180° - 51° - 68° = 61°$

$a = \dfrac{c}{\sin C}(\sin A)$

$= \dfrac{6}{\sin 61°}(\sin 51°) \approx 5.33$

$h = a\sin B \approx 5.33(\sin 68°)$

$\approx 4.94 \approx 5 \text{ mi}$

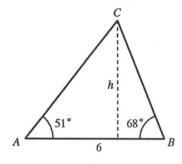

37. $A = 65° - 28° = 37°$

$c = 18.5$

$B = 180° - 16.5° - 65° = 98.5°$

$C = 180° - 37° - 98.5° = 44.5°$

$$a = \frac{c}{\sin C}(\sin A) = \frac{18.5}{\sin 44.5°}(\sin 37°)$$

≈ 15.9 miles to B

$$b = \frac{c}{\sin C}(\sin B) = \frac{18.5}{\sin 44.5°}(\sin 98.5°)$$

≈ 26.1 miles to A

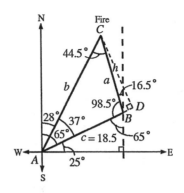

39. $A = 90° - 62° = 28°$,

$B = 90° + 38° = 128°$, $c = 5$

$C = 180° - 128° - 28° = 24°$

$$a = \frac{c}{\sin C}(\sin A)$$

$$= \frac{5}{\sin 24°}(\sin 28°) \approx 5.77$$

$d = a\sin(90° - 38°)$

$\approx 5.77 \sin 52° \approx 4.55$ miles

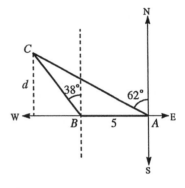

41. $h = b\sin A = 450 \sin 30° = 225$ ft

$a = 120$ ft

Since $a < h$, no such triangle is possible.

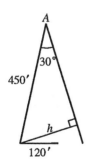

Section 6.7   Law of Cosines

■ If ABC is any oblique triangle with sides a, b, and c, the following equations are valid.

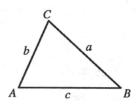

(a) $a^2 = b^2 + c^2 - 2bc \cos A$ or $\cos A = \dfrac{b^2 + c^2 - a^2}{2bc}$

(b) $b^2 = a^2 + c^2 - 2ac \cos B$ or $\cos B = \dfrac{a^2 + c^2 - b^2}{2ac}$

(c) $c^2 = a^2 + b^2 - 2ab \cos C$ or $\cos C = \dfrac{a^2 + b^2 - c^2}{2ab}$

■ You should be able to use the Law of Cosines to solve
an oblique triangle for the remaining three parts, given:
(a) Three sides (SSS)
(b) Two sides and their included angle (SAS)

■ Given any triangle with sides of length a, b, and c, then the area of the triangle is

$$\text{Area} = \sqrt{s(s-a)(s-b)(s-c)}, \text{ where } s = \dfrac{a+b+c}{2}. \quad \text{(Heron's Formula)}$$

1. Given: $a = 5$, $b = 7$, $c = 10$

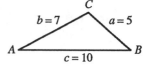

$\cos C = \dfrac{a^2 + b^2 - c^2}{2ab} = \dfrac{25 + 49 - 100}{2(5)(7)} \approx -0.3714 \Rightarrow C \approx 111.8°$

$\sin A = \dfrac{a \sin C}{c} \approx \dfrac{5 \sin 111.8°}{10} \approx 0.4642 \Rightarrow A \approx 27.7°$

$B \approx 180° - 111.8° - 27.7° = 40.5°$

3. Given: $A = 30°$, $b = 10$, $c = 20$

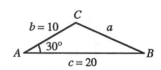

$a^2 = b^2 + c^2 - 2bc \cos A$

$\approx 100 + 400 - 2(10)(20)(0.8660) \approx 153.6 \Rightarrow a \approx 12.39$

$\cos C = \dfrac{a^2 + b^2 - c^2}{2ab} = \dfrac{153.6 + 100 - 400}{2(12.39)(10)}$

$\approx -0.5907 \Rightarrow C \approx 126.2°$

$B \approx 180° - 30° - 126.2° = 23.8°$

5. Given: $a = 9$, $b = 12$, $c = 15$

$$\cos C = \frac{a^2 + b^2 - c^2}{2ab} = \frac{81 + 144 - 225}{2(9)(12)} = 0 \Rightarrow C = 90°$$

$$\sin A = \frac{9}{15} = \frac{3}{5} \Rightarrow A \approx 36.9°$$

$$B \approx 180° - 90° - 36.9° = 53.13°$$

7. Given: $a = 75.4$, $b = 52$, $c = 52$

$$\cos A = \frac{b^2 + c^2 - a^2}{2bc} = \frac{52^2 + 52^2 - 75.4^2}{2(52)(52)} \approx -0.05125 \Rightarrow A \approx 92.9°$$

$$\sin B = \frac{b \sin A}{a} \approx \frac{52(0.9987)}{75.4} \approx 0.68875 \Rightarrow B \approx 43.5°$$

$$C = B \approx 43.5°$$

9. Given: $A = 120°$, $b = 3$, $c = 10$

$$a^2 = b^2 + c^2 - 2bc \cos A = 9 + 100 - 60 \cos 120° = 139 \Rightarrow a \approx 11.79$$

$$\sin B = \frac{b \sin A}{a} \approx \frac{3 \sin 120°}{11.79} \approx 0.2204 \Rightarrow B \approx 12.73°$$

$$C \approx 180° - 120° - 12.73° = 47.27°$$

11. Given: $B = 8°45'$, $a = 25$, $c = 15$

$$b^2 = a^2 + c^2 - 2ac \cos B \approx 625 + 225 - 2(25)(15)(0.9884) \approx 108.7 \Rightarrow b \approx 10.43$$

$$\sin C = \frac{c \sin B}{b} = \frac{15(0.1521)}{10.43} \approx 0.2188 \Rightarrow C \approx 12.64°$$

$$A \approx 180° - 8.75° - 12.64° = 158.61°$$

13. Given: $C = 125°40'$, $a = 32$, $b = 32$

$$c^2 = a^2 + b^2 - 2ab \cos C \approx 32^2 + 32^2 - 2(32)(32)(-0.5831) \approx 3242.1 \Rightarrow c \approx 56.94$$

$$A = B \Rightarrow 2A = 180° - 125°40' = 54°20' \Rightarrow A = B = 27°10'$$

15.

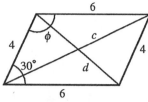

$$d^2 = 4^2 + 6^2 - 2(4)(6)\cos 30°$$

$$d \approx 3.23$$

$$2\phi = 360° - 2(30°)$$

$$\phi = 150°$$

$$c^2 = 4^2 + 6^2 - 2(4)(6)\cos 150°$$

$$c \approx 9.67$$

17.

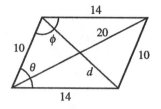

$$\cos\phi = \frac{10^2 + 14^2 - 20^2}{2(10)(14)}$$

$$\phi \approx 111.80°$$

$$2\theta \approx 360° - 2(111.80°)$$

$$\theta = 68.2°$$

$$d^2 = 10^2 + 14^2 - 2(10)(14)\cos 68.2°$$

$$d \approx 13.86$$

19.

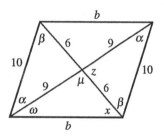

$$\cos\alpha = \frac{(9)^2 + (10)^2 - (6)^2}{2(9)(10)}$$

$$\alpha \approx 36.3°$$

$$\cos\beta = \frac{6^2 + 10^2 - 9^2}{2(6)(10)}$$

$$\beta \approx 62.7°$$

$$z = 180° - \alpha - \beta \approx 81.0°$$

$$\mu = 180° - z \approx 99.0°$$

$$b^2 = 9^2 + 6^2 - 2(9)(6)(\cos 99.0°)$$

$$b \approx 11.57$$

$$\cos\omega = \frac{9^2 + 11.57^2 - 6^2}{2(9)(11.57)}$$

$$\omega \approx 30.8°$$

$$\theta = \alpha + \omega \approx 67.1°$$

$$\cos x = \frac{6^2 + 11.57^2 - 9^2}{2(6)(11.57)}$$

$$x \approx 50.2°$$

$$\phi = \beta + x \approx 112.9°$$

21. $a = 5$, $b = 7$, $c = 10 \Rightarrow s = \dfrac{a + b + c}{2} = 11$

Area $= \sqrt{s(s - a)(s - b)(s - c)} = \sqrt{11(6)(4)(1)} \approx 16.25$

23. $a = 12$, $b = 15$, $c = 9 \Rightarrow s = \dfrac{12 + 15 + 9}{2} = 18$

Area $= \sqrt{18(6)(3)(9)} = 54$

25. $a = 20$, $b = 20$, $c = 10 \Rightarrow s = \dfrac{20 + 20 + 10}{2} = 25$

Area $= \sqrt{25(5)(5)(15)} \approx 96.82$

27. $a = 400$, $b = 500$, $c = 700 \Rightarrow s = \dfrac{a + b + c}{2} = 800$

Area $= \sqrt{s(s - a)(s - b)(s - c)} = \sqrt{800(400)(300)(100)} \approx 97{,}979.6 \ \text{ft}^2$

29. $\cos B = \dfrac{3500^2 + 8000^2 - 6500^2}{2(3500)(8000)}$

$B = 52.62° \Rightarrow 52°37' \Rightarrow$ N $52°37'$ E

$\cos C = \dfrac{3500^2 + 6500^2 - 8000^2}{2(3500)(6500)}$

$C = 102.05°$

$\alpha = 180° - 52.62° - 102.05° = 25.33°$

$\beta = 90° - \alpha = 64.67° \Rightarrow 64°40' \Rightarrow$ S $64°40'$ E

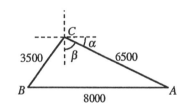

31. $C = 180° - 53° - 67° = 60°$

$c^2 = a^2 + b^2 - 2ab \cos C$

$\quad = 36^2 + 48^2 - 2(36)(48)(0.5)$

$\quad = 1872$

$c \approx 43.3 \ \text{mi}$

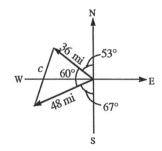

33. $\overline{AC} = \sqrt{800^2 + 950^2 - 2(800)(950)\cos 100°}$

$\approx \sqrt{1{,}806{,}445.23} \approx 1344$ ft

35. $4.25^2 = 2^2 + 3^2 - 2(2)(3)\cos\theta$

$\cos\theta = \dfrac{2^2 + 3^2 - 4.25^2}{2(2)(3)} \approx -0.4219$

$\theta \approx 114.95°$

37. $\overline{RS} = \sqrt{8^2 + 10^2} = \sqrt{164} = 2\sqrt{41} \approx 12.8$ ft

$\overline{PQ} = \frac{1}{2}\sqrt{16^2 + 10^2} = \frac{1}{2}\sqrt{356} = \sqrt{89} \approx 9.4$ ft

$\tan P = \frac{10}{16}$

$P = \arctan\frac{5}{8} \approx 32.0°$

$\overline{QS} = \sqrt{8^2 + 9.4^2 - 2(8)(9.4)\cos 32°} \approx \sqrt{24.82} \approx 5.0$ ft

39. Bearing from O to D: N θ W

Bearing from N to D: S ϕ W

$\cos\phi = \dfrac{(9.25)^2 + 7^2 - (10.75)^2}{2(9.25)(7)} \approx 0.1467 \Rightarrow \phi \approx 81.6°$

$\cos\theta = 0.5249 \Rightarrow \theta \approx 58.3°$

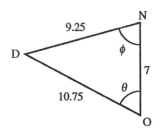

41. (a) $d^2 = 60^2 + 90^2 - 2(60)(90)\cos 45°$

$\approx 4063.25 \Rightarrow d \approx 63.74$ ft

(b) $\cos\alpha = \dfrac{d^2 + 60^2 - 90^2}{2d(60)} \approx -0.0571$

$\Rightarrow \alpha \approx 93.3°$

$\Rightarrow \angle HTP \approx 41.7°$

$\Rightarrow \angle STP \approx 48.3°$

$d_1{}^2 = 45^2 + 4063.25 - 2(45)(63.74)\cos 48.3°$

$\approx 2272 \Rightarrow d_1 \approx 47.7$ ft

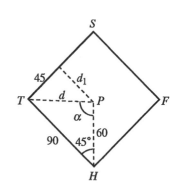

43. $A = 180° - 40° - 25° = 115°$

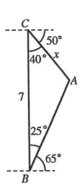

$$\frac{x}{\sin 25°} = \frac{7}{\sin 115°} \Rightarrow$$

$$x = \frac{7 \sin 25°}{\sin 115°} = 3.26 \text{ feet}$$

45. $a = 25,\ b = 55,\ c = 72 \Rightarrow s = \dfrac{25 + 55 + 72}{2} = 76$

(a) Area of triangle $= \sqrt{s(s-a)(s-b)(s-c)} = \sqrt{76(51)(21)(4)} \approx 570.6$

(b) $\cos C = \dfrac{a^2 + b^2 - c^2}{2ab} = \dfrac{25^2 + 55^2 - 72^2}{2(25)(55)} \approx -0.5578 \Rightarrow C \approx 123.9°$

$2R = \dfrac{c}{\sin C} = \dfrac{72}{0.8300} \approx 86.75 \Rightarrow R \approx 43.4$

Area of the circumscribed circle: $A = \pi R^2 \approx 5911$

(c) $r = \sqrt{\dfrac{(s-a)(s-b)(s-c)}{s}} = \sqrt{\dfrac{(51)(21)(4)}{76}} \approx 7.51$

Area of inscribed circle: $A = \pi r^2 \approx 177.1$

47. $a^2 = b^2 + c^2 - 2bc \cos A$

$$\cos A = \frac{b^2 + c^2 - a^2}{2bc}$$

$$1 + \cos A = \frac{b^2 + 2bc + c^2 - a^2}{2bc}$$

$$\frac{1}{2} bc(1 + \cos A) = \frac{(b+c)^2 - a^2}{4} = \left(\frac{a+b+c}{2}\right)\left(\frac{-a+b+c}{2}\right)$$

Section 6.8   DeMoivre's Theorem and nth Roots

> ■ You should be able to graphically represent complex numbers and know the following facts about them.
>
> ■ The absolute value of the complex number $z = a + bi$ is $|z| = \sqrt{a^2 + b^2}$.
>
> ■ The trigonometric form of the complex number $z = a + bi$ is $z = r(\cos\theta + i\sin\theta)$ where
> (a) $a = r\cos\theta$.
> (b) $b = r\sin\theta$.
> (c) $r = \sqrt{a^2 + b^2}$; r is called the modulus of z.
> (d) $\tan\theta = b/a$; θ is called the argument of z.
>
> ■ Given $z_1 = r_1(\cos\theta_1 + i\sin\theta_1)$ and $z_2 = r_2(\cos\theta_2 + i\sin\theta_2)$:
> (a) $z_1 z_2 = r_1 r_2[\cos(\theta_1 + \theta_2) + i\sin(\theta_1 + \theta_2)]$
> (b) $\dfrac{z_1}{z_2} = \dfrac{r_1}{r_2}[\cos(\theta_1 - \theta_2) + i\sin(\theta_1 - \theta_2)], \quad z_2 \neq 0$

1. $|-5i| = \sqrt{0^2 + (-5)^2}$

$\qquad = \sqrt{25} = 5$

3. $|-4 + 4i| = \sqrt{(-4)^2 + (4)^2}$

$\qquad = \sqrt{32} = 4\sqrt{2}$

5. $|6 - 7i| = \sqrt{6^2 + (-7)^2}$

$\qquad = \sqrt{85}$

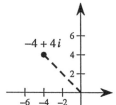

7. $z = 4i$

$\quad r = \sqrt{0^2 + 4^2} = \sqrt{16} = 4$

$\quad \tan\theta = \dfrac{4}{0}, \quad \text{undefined} \Rightarrow \theta = \dfrac{\pi}{2}$

$\quad z = 4\left(\cos\dfrac{\pi}{2} + i\sin\dfrac{\pi}{2}\right)$

9. $z = -3 - 3i$

$\quad r = \sqrt{(-3)^2 + (-3)^2} = \sqrt{18} = 3\sqrt{2}$

$\quad \tan\theta = \dfrac{-3}{-3} = 1 \Rightarrow \theta = \dfrac{5\pi}{4}$

$\quad z = 3\sqrt{2}\left(\cos\dfrac{5\pi}{4} + i\sin\dfrac{5\pi}{4}\right)$

11. $z = 3 - 3i$

$r = \sqrt{3^2 + (-3)^2} = \sqrt{18} = 3\sqrt{2}$

$\tan\theta = \dfrac{-3}{3} = -1 \Rightarrow \theta = \dfrac{7\pi}{4}$

$z = 3\sqrt{2}\left(\cos\dfrac{7\pi}{4} + i\sin\dfrac{7\pi}{4}\right)$

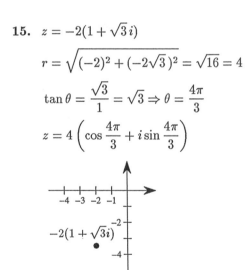

13. $z = \sqrt{3} + i$

$r = \sqrt{(\sqrt{3})^2 + 1^2} = \sqrt{4} = 2$

$\tan\theta = \dfrac{1}{\sqrt{3}} = \dfrac{\sqrt{3}}{3} \Rightarrow \theta = \dfrac{\pi}{6}$

$z = 2\left(\cos\dfrac{\pi}{6} + i\sin\dfrac{\pi}{6}\right)$

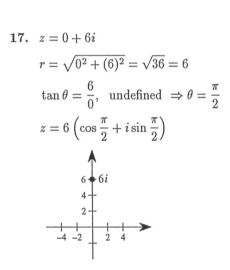

15. $z = -2(1 + \sqrt{3}\,i)$

$r = \sqrt{(-2)^2 + (-2\sqrt{3})^2} = \sqrt{16} = 4$

$\tan\theta = \dfrac{\sqrt{3}}{1} = \sqrt{3} \Rightarrow \theta = \dfrac{4\pi}{3}$

$z = 4\left(\cos\dfrac{4\pi}{3} + i\sin\dfrac{4\pi}{3}\right)$

17. $z = 0 + 6i$

$r = \sqrt{0^2 + (6)^2} = \sqrt{36} = 6$

$\tan\theta = \dfrac{6}{0}, \;\; \text{undefined} \Rightarrow \theta = \dfrac{\pi}{2}$

$z = 6\left(\cos\dfrac{\pi}{2} + i\sin\dfrac{\pi}{2}\right)$

19. $z = -7 + 4i$

$r = \sqrt{(-7)^2 + (4)^2} = \sqrt{65}$

$\tan\theta = \dfrac{4}{-7} \Rightarrow \theta \approx 2.62$

$z \approx \sqrt{65}(\cos 2.62 + i\sin 2.62)$

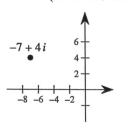

21. $z = 7 + 0i$

$r = \sqrt{(7)^2 + (0)^2}$

$= \sqrt{49} = 7$

$\tan\theta = \frac{0}{7} = 0 \Rightarrow \theta = 0$

$z = 7(\cos 0 + i\sin 0)$

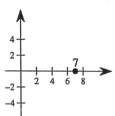

23. $z = 1 + 6i$

$r = \sqrt{1^2 + (6)^2} = \sqrt{37}$

$\tan\theta = \dfrac{6}{1} = 6 \Rightarrow \theta \approx 1.41$

$z \approx \sqrt{37}(\cos 1.41 + i\sin 1.41)$

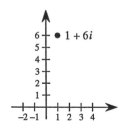

25. $z = -3 - i$

$r = \sqrt{(-3)^2 + (-1)^2} = \sqrt{10}$

$\tan\theta = \dfrac{-1}{-3} = \dfrac{1}{3} \Rightarrow \theta \approx 3.46$

$z \approx \sqrt{10}(\cos 3.46 + i\sin 3.46)$

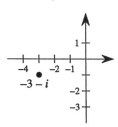

27. $2(\cos 150° + i\sin 150°)$

$= 2\left[-\dfrac{\sqrt{3}}{2} + i\left(\dfrac{1}{2}\right)\right]$

$= -\sqrt{3} + i$

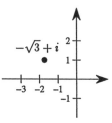

29. $\dfrac{3}{2}(\cos 300° + i\sin 300°)$

$$= \dfrac{3}{2}\left[\dfrac{1}{2} + i\left(-\dfrac{\sqrt{3}}{2}\right)\right]$$

$$= \dfrac{3}{4} - \dfrac{3\sqrt{3}}{4}i$$

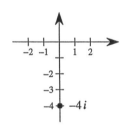

31. $3.75\left(\cos\dfrac{3\pi}{4} + i\sin\dfrac{3\pi}{4}\right)$

$$= -\dfrac{15\sqrt{2}}{8} + \dfrac{15\sqrt{2}}{8}i$$

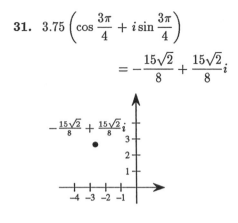

33. $4\left(\cos\dfrac{3\pi}{2} + i\sin\dfrac{3\pi}{2}\right) = 4(0 - i)$

$$= -4i$$

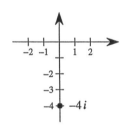

35. $3[\cos(18°45') + i\sin(18°45')]$

$$\approx 2.841 + 0.9643i$$

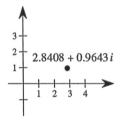

37. $\left[3\left(\cos\dfrac{\pi}{3} + i\sin\dfrac{\pi}{3}\right)\right]\left[4\left(\cos\dfrac{\pi}{6} + i\sin\dfrac{\pi}{6}\right)\right] = (3)(4)\left[\cos\left(\dfrac{\pi}{3} + \dfrac{\pi}{6}\right) + i\sin\left(\dfrac{\pi}{6} + \dfrac{\pi}{3}\right)\right]$

$$= 12\left(\cos\dfrac{\pi}{2} + i\sin\dfrac{\pi}{2}\right)$$

39. $\left[\dfrac{5}{3}(\cos 140° + i\sin 140°)\right]\left[\dfrac{2}{3}(\cos 60° + i\sin 60°)\right] = \left(\dfrac{5}{3}\right)\left(\dfrac{2}{3}\right)[\cos(140° + 60°) + i\sin(140° + 60°)]$

$$= \dfrac{10}{9}(\cos 200° + i\sin 200°)$$

41. $[0.45(\cos 310° + i \sin 310°)][0.60(\cos 200° + i \sin 200°)]$

$$= (0.45)(0.60)[\cos(310° + 200°) + i \sin(310° + 200°)]$$

$$= 0.27(\cos 510° + i \sin 510°)$$

$$= 0.27(\cos 150° + i \sin 150°)$$

43. $\dfrac{2(\cos 120° + i \sin 120°)}{4(\cos 40° + i \sin 40°)} = \dfrac{2}{4}[\cos(120° - 40°) + i \sin(120° - 40°)] = \dfrac{1}{2}(\cos 80° + i \sin 80°)$

45. $\dfrac{\cos(5\pi/3) + i \sin(5\pi/3)}{\cos \pi + i \sin \pi} = \cos\left(\dfrac{5\pi}{3} - \pi\right) + i \sin\left(\dfrac{5\pi}{3} - \pi\right) = \cos\left(\dfrac{2\pi}{3}\right) + i \sin\left(\dfrac{2\pi}{3}\right)$

47. $\dfrac{12(\cos 52° + i \sin 52°)}{3(\cos 110° + i \sin 110°)} = 4[\cos(52° - 110°) + i \sin(52° - 110°)]$

$$= 4[\cos(-58°) + i \sin(-58°)] = 4[\cos 302° + i \sin 302°]$$

49. (a) $2 + 2i = 2\sqrt{2}(\cos 45° + i \sin 45°)$

$\qquad 1 - i = \sqrt{2}[\cos(-45°) + i \sin(-45°)]$

(b) $(2 + 2i)(1 - i) = [2\sqrt{2}(\cos 45° + i \sin 45°)][\sqrt{2}(\cos(-45°) + i \sin(-45°))]$

$$= 4(\cos 0° + i \sin 0°) = 4$$

(c) $(2 + 2i)(1 - i) = 2 - 2i + 2i - 2i^2 = 2 + 2 = 4$

51. (a) $\quad -2i = 2(\cos 270° + i \sin 270°)$

$\qquad 1 + i = \sqrt{2}(\cos 45° + i \sin 45°)$

(b) $-2(1 + i) = [2(\cos 270° + i \sin 270°)][\sqrt{2}(\cos 45° + i \sin 45°)]$

$$= 2\sqrt{2}(\cos 315° + i \sin 315°) = 2 - 2i$$

(c) $-2i(1 + i) = -2i - 2i^2 = -2i + 2 = 2 - 2i$

53. (a) $\qquad 5 = 5(\cos 0° + i \sin 0°)$

$\qquad 2 + 3i = \sqrt{13}(\cos 56.31° + i \sin 56.31°)$

(b) $\dfrac{5}{2 + 3i} = \dfrac{5(\cos 0° + i \sin 0°)}{\sqrt{13}(\cos 56.3° + i \sin 56.3°)} = \dfrac{5\sqrt{13}}{13}(\cos 303.7° + i \sin 303.7°) \approx 0.7694 - 1.154i$

(c) $\dfrac{5}{2 + 3i} = \dfrac{5}{2 + 3i} \cdot \dfrac{2 - 3i}{2 - 3i} = \dfrac{10 - 15i}{13} = \dfrac{10}{13} - \dfrac{15}{13}i \approx 0.7694 - 1.154i$

55. $\dfrac{z_1}{z_2} = \dfrac{r_1(\cos\theta_1 + i\sin\theta_1)}{r_2(\cos\theta_2 + i\sin\theta_2)} \cdot \dfrac{\cos\theta_2 - i\sin\theta_2}{\cos\theta_2 - i\sin\theta_2}$

$$= \dfrac{r_1}{r_2(\cos^2\theta_2 + \sin^2\theta_2)}[\cos\theta_1\cos\theta_2 + \sin\theta_1\sin\theta_2 + i(\sin\theta_1\cos\theta_2 - \sin\theta_2\cos\theta_1)]$$

$$= \dfrac{r_1}{r_2}[\cos(\theta_1 - \theta_2) + i\sin(\theta_1 - \theta_2)]$$

57. (a) $z\bar{z} = [r(\cos\theta + i\sin\theta)][r(\cos(-\theta) + i\sin(-\theta))]$

$$= r^2[\cos(\theta - \theta) + i\sin(\theta - \theta)] = r^2[\cos 0 + i\sin 0] = r^2$$

(b) $\dfrac{z}{\bar{z}} = \dfrac{r(\cos\theta + i\sin\theta)}{r[\cos(-\theta) + i\sin(-\theta)]} = \dfrac{r}{r}[\cos(\theta - (-\theta)) + i\sin(\theta - (-\theta))] = \cos 2\theta + i\sin 2\theta$

59. Let $z = x + iy$ such that:

$$|z| = 2 \Rightarrow 2 = \sqrt{x^2 + y^2}$$

$$\Rightarrow 4 = x^2 + y^2 :$$

circle with radius of 2

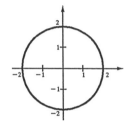

61. $(1 + i)^5 = \left[\sqrt{2}\left(\cos\dfrac{\pi}{4} + i\sin\dfrac{\pi}{4}\right)\right]^5$

$$= (\sqrt{2})^5\left(\cos\dfrac{5\pi}{4} + i\sin\dfrac{5\pi}{4}\right) = 4\sqrt{2}\left(-\dfrac{\sqrt{2}}{2} - \dfrac{\sqrt{2}}{2}i\right) = -4 - 4i$$

63. $(-1 + i)^{10} = \left[\sqrt{2}\left(\cos\dfrac{3\pi}{4} + i\sin\dfrac{3\pi}{4}\right)\right]^{10}$

$$= (\sqrt{2})^{10}\left(\cos\dfrac{30\pi}{4} + i\sin\dfrac{30\pi}{4}\right) = 32\left[\cos\left(\dfrac{3\pi}{2} + 6\pi\right) + i\sin\left(\dfrac{3\pi}{2} + 6\pi\right)\right]$$

$$= 32\left(\cos\dfrac{3\pi}{2} + i\sin\dfrac{3\pi}{2}\right) = 32[0 + i(-1)] = -32i$$

65. $2(\sqrt{3}+i)^7 = 2\left[2\left(\cos\dfrac{\pi}{6}+i\sin\dfrac{\pi}{6}\right)\right]^7$

$$= 2\left[2^7\left(\cos\dfrac{7\pi}{6}+i\sin\dfrac{7\pi}{6}\right)\right]$$

$$= 256\left(-\dfrac{\sqrt{3}}{2}-\dfrac{1}{2}i\right)$$

$$= -128\sqrt{3}-128i$$

67. $[5(\cos 20° + i\sin 20°)]^3 = 5^3(\cos 60° + i\sin 60°)$

$$= \dfrac{125}{2}+\dfrac{125\sqrt{3}}{2}i$$

69. $\left(\cos\dfrac{5\pi}{4}+i\sin\dfrac{5\pi}{4}\right)^{10} = \cos\dfrac{25\pi}{2}+i\sin\dfrac{25\pi}{2}$

$$= \cos\left(12\pi+\dfrac{\pi}{2}\right)+i\sin\left(12\pi+\dfrac{\pi}{2}\right) = \cos\dfrac{\pi}{2}+i\sin\dfrac{\pi}{2} = i$$

71. $[5(\cos 3.2 + i\sin 3.2)]^4 = 5^4(\cos 12.8 + i\sin 12.8)$

$$\approx 625(0.9728+0.2315i) \approx 608.0 + 144.7i$$

73. (a) Square roots of $9(\cos 120° + i\sin 120°)$:   (b)

$$\sqrt{9}\left[\cos\left(\dfrac{120°+360°k}{2}\right)+i\sin\left(\dfrac{120°+360°k}{2}\right)\right], \quad k = 0,\ 1$$

$$3(\cos 60° + i\sin 60°)$$

$$3(\cos 240° + i\sin 240°)$$

(c) $\dfrac{3}{2}+\dfrac{3\sqrt{3}}{2}i,\quad -\dfrac{3}{2}-\dfrac{3\sqrt{3}}{2}i$

75. (a) Fourth roots of $16\left(\cos\dfrac{4\pi}{3}+i\sin\dfrac{4\pi}{3}\right)$:

$$\sqrt[4]{16}\left[\cos\left(\dfrac{(4\pi/3)+2k\pi}{4}\right)+i\sin\left(\dfrac{(4\pi/3)+2k\pi}{4}\right)\right], \quad k = 0,\ 1,\ 2,\ 3$$

$$2\left(\cos\dfrac{\pi}{3}+i\sin\dfrac{\pi}{3}\right)$$

$$2\left(\cos\dfrac{5\pi}{6}+i\sin\dfrac{5\pi}{6}\right)$$

$$2\left(\cos\dfrac{4\pi}{3}+i\sin\dfrac{4\pi}{3}\right)$$

$$2\left(\cos\dfrac{11\pi}{6}+i\sin\dfrac{11\pi}{6}\right)$$

(b)

(c) $1+\sqrt{3}i,\quad -\sqrt{3}+i,\quad -1-\sqrt{3}i,\quad \sqrt{3}-i$

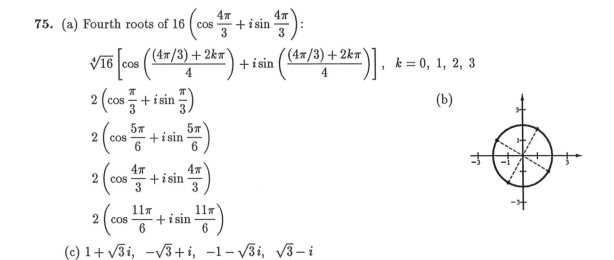

77. (a) Square roots of $-25i = 25\left(\cos\dfrac{3\pi}{2} + i\sin\dfrac{3\pi}{2}\right)$:

$$\sqrt{25}\left[\cos\left(\dfrac{(3\pi/2) + 2k\pi}{2}\right) + i\sin\left(\dfrac{(3\pi/2) + 2k\pi}{2}\right)\right], \quad k = 0,\ 1$$

$$5\left(\cos\dfrac{3\pi}{4} + i\sin\dfrac{3\pi}{4}\right)$$

$$5\left(\cos\dfrac{7\pi}{4} + i\sin\dfrac{7\pi}{4}\right)$$

(c) $-\dfrac{5\sqrt{2}}{2} + \dfrac{5\sqrt{2}}{2}i,\ \dfrac{5\sqrt{2}}{2} - \dfrac{5\sqrt{2}}{2}i$

(b)

79. (a) Cube roots of $-\dfrac{125}{2}(1 + \sqrt{3}\,i) = 125\left(\cos\dfrac{4\pi}{3} + i\sin\dfrac{4\pi}{3}\right)$:

$$\sqrt[3]{125}\left[\cos\left(\dfrac{(4\pi/3) + 2k\pi}{3}\right) + i\sin\left(\dfrac{(4\pi/3) + 2k\pi}{3}\right)\right], \quad k = 0,\ 1,\ 2$$

$$5\left(\cos\dfrac{4\pi}{9} + i\sin\dfrac{4\pi}{9}\right)$$

$$5\left(\cos\dfrac{10\pi}{9} + i\sin\dfrac{10\pi}{9}\right)$$

$$5\left(\cos\dfrac{16\pi}{9} + i\sin\dfrac{16\pi}{9}\right)$$

(c) $0.8682 + 4.924i,\ -4.698 - 1.710i,\ 3.830 - 3.214i$

(b)

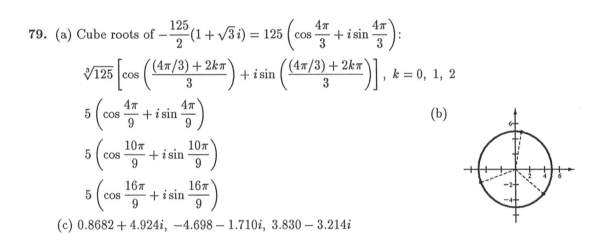

81. (a) Cube roots of $8 = 8(\cos 0 + i \sin 0)$:

$$\sqrt[3]{8}\left[\cos\left(\frac{2k\pi}{3}\right) + i\sin\left(\frac{2k\pi}{3}\right)\right], \quad k = 0,\ 1,\ 2$$

$$2(\cos 0 + i\sin 0)$$

$$2\left(\cos\frac{2\pi}{3} + i\sin\frac{2\pi}{3}\right)$$

$$2\left(\cos\frac{4\pi}{3} + i\sin\frac{4\pi}{3}\right)$$

(c) $2,\ -1 + \sqrt{3}\,i,\ -1 - \sqrt{3}\,i$

(b)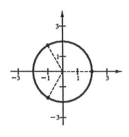

83. (a) Fifth roots of $1 = \cos 0 + i\sin 0$:

$$\cos\frac{2k\pi}{5} + i\sin\frac{2k\pi}{5}, \quad k = 0,\ 1,\ 2,\ 3,\ 4$$

$$\cos 0 + i\sin 0$$

$$\cos\frac{2\pi}{5} + i\sin\frac{2\pi}{5}$$

$$\cos\frac{4\pi}{5} + i\sin\frac{4\pi}{5}$$

$$\cos\frac{6\pi}{5} + i\sin\frac{6\pi}{5}$$

$$\cos\frac{8\pi}{5} + i\sin\frac{8\pi}{5}$$

(c) $1,\ 0.3090 + 0.9511i,\ -0.8090 + 0.5878i,$

$-0.8090 - 0.5878i,\ 0.3090 - 0.9511i$

(b)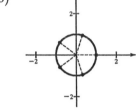

85. $x^4 - i = 0$

$\qquad x^4 = i$

The solutions are the fourth roots of $i = \cos \dfrac{\pi}{2} + i \sin \dfrac{\pi}{2}$.

$\sqrt[4]{1} \left[\cos \left(\dfrac{(\pi/2) + 2k\pi}{4} \right) + i \sin \left(\dfrac{(\pi/2) + 2k\pi}{4} \right) \right]$, $k = 0,\ 1,\ 2,\ 3$

$\qquad \cos \dfrac{\pi}{8} + i \sin \dfrac{\pi}{8} \approx 0.9239 + 0.3827i$

$\qquad \cos \dfrac{5\pi}{8} + i \sin \dfrac{5\pi}{8} \approx -0.3827 + 0.9239i$

$\qquad \cos \dfrac{9\pi}{8} + i \sin \dfrac{9\pi}{8} \approx -0.9239 - 0.3827i$

$\qquad \cos \dfrac{13\pi}{8} + i \sin \dfrac{13\pi}{8} \approx 0.3827 - 0.9239i$

87. $x^5 + 243 = 0$

$\qquad x^5 = -243$

The solutions are the fifth roots of -243:

$\sqrt[5]{243} \left[\cos \left(\dfrac{\pi + 2k\pi}{5} \right) + i \sin \left(\dfrac{\pi + 2k\pi}{5} \right) \right]$, $k = 0,\ 1,\ 2,\ 3,\ 4$

$\qquad 3 \left(\cos \dfrac{\pi}{5} + i \sin \dfrac{\pi}{5} \right) \approx 2.427 + 1.763i$

$\qquad 3 \left(\cos \dfrac{3\pi}{5} + i \sin \dfrac{3\pi}{5} \right) \approx -0.9271 + 2.853i$

$\qquad 3 \left(\cos \pi + i \sin \pi \right) = -3$

$\qquad 3 \left(\cos \dfrac{7\pi}{5} + i \sin \dfrac{7\pi}{5} \right) \approx -0.9271 - 2.853i$

$\qquad 3 \left(\cos \dfrac{9\pi}{5} + i \sin \dfrac{9\pi}{5} \right) \approx 2.427 - 1.763i$

89. $x^3 + 64i = 0$

$$x^3 = -64i$$

The solutions are the cube roots of $-64i$:

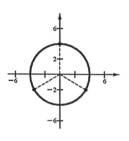

$$\sqrt[3]{64}\left[\cos\left(\frac{(3\pi/2) + 2k\pi}{3}\right) + i\sin\left(\frac{(3\pi/2) + 2k\pi}{3}\right)\right],\ k = 0,\ 1,\ 2$$

$$4\left(\cos\frac{\pi}{2} + i\sin\frac{\pi}{2}\right) = 4i$$

$$4\left(\cos\frac{7\pi}{6} + i\sin\frac{7\pi}{6}\right) = -2\sqrt{3} - 2i$$

$$4\left(\cos\frac{11\pi}{6} + i\sin\frac{11\pi}{6}\right) = 2\sqrt{3} - 2i$$

91. $x^3 - (1 - i) = 0$

$$x^3 = 1 - i = \sqrt{2}(\cos 315° + i\sin 315°)$$

The solutions are the cube roots of $1 - i$:

$$\sqrt[3]{\sqrt{2}}\left[\cos\left(\frac{315° + 360°k}{3}\right) + i\sin\left(\frac{315° + 360°k}{3}\right)\right],\ k = 0,\ 1,\ 2$$

$$\sqrt[6]{2}(\cos 105° + i\sin 105°) \approx -0.2905 + 1.0842i$$

$$\sqrt[6]{2}(\cos 225° + i\sin 225°) \approx -0.7937 - 0.7937i$$

$$\sqrt[6]{2}(\cos 345° + i\sin 345°) \approx 1.0842 - 0.2905i$$

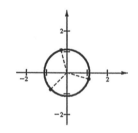

Chapter 6   Review Exercises

1. $\dfrac{1}{\cos^2 x + 1} = \dfrac{1}{\csc^2 x} = \sin^2 x$

3. $\dfrac{\sin^2 \alpha - \cos^2 \alpha}{\sin^2 \alpha - \sin \alpha \cos \alpha} = \dfrac{(\sin \alpha + \cos \alpha)(\sin \alpha - \cos \alpha)}{\sin \alpha(\sin \alpha - \cos \alpha)} = \dfrac{\sin \alpha + \cos \alpha}{\sin \alpha} = 1 + \cot \alpha$

5. $\cos^2 \beta + \cos^2 \beta \tan^2 \beta = \cos^2 \beta(1 + \tan^2 \beta)$

$\qquad\qquad = \cos^2 \beta \sec^2 \beta$

$\qquad\qquad = 1$

7. $\tan^2 \theta(\csc^2 \theta - 1) = \tan^2 \theta \cot^2 \theta = 1$

9. $1 - 4\sin^2 x \cos^2 x = 1 - (2 \sin x \cos x)^2$

$\qquad\qquad = 1 - \sin^2 2x$

$\qquad\qquad = \cos^2 2x$

11. $\tan x(1 - \sin^2 x) = \tan x \cos^2 x$

$\qquad\qquad = \dfrac{\sin x}{\cos x} \cdot \cos^2 x$

$\qquad\qquad = \sin x \cos x$

$\qquad\qquad = \dfrac{1}{2}(2 \sin x \cos x)$

$\qquad\qquad = \dfrac{1}{2} \sin 2x$

13. $\sec^2 x \cot x - \cot x = \cot x(\sec^2 x - 1) = \cot x \tan^2 x = \dfrac{1}{\tan x} \tan^2 x = \tan x$

15. $\sin^5 x \cos^2 x = \sin^4 x \cos^2 x \sin x$

$\qquad\qquad = (1 - \cos^2 x)^2 \cos^2 x \sin x = (\cos^2 x - 2 \cos^4 x + \cos^6 x) \sin x$

17. Using a product-sum formula, we have

$\qquad \sin 3\theta \sin \theta = \frac{1}{2}(\cos 2\theta - \cos 4\theta).$

19. $\sqrt{\dfrac{1 - \sin \theta}{1 + \sin \theta}} = \sqrt{\dfrac{1 - \sin \theta}{1 + \sin \theta} \cdot \dfrac{1 - \sin \theta}{1 - \sin \theta}}$

$\qquad\qquad = \dfrac{1 - \sin \theta}{|\cos \theta|}$

21. $\cos 3x = \cos(2x + x) = \cos 2x \cos x - \sin 2x \sin x$

$\qquad\qquad = (\cos^2 x - \sin^2 x) \cos x - 2 \sin x \cos x \sin x = \cos^3 x - 3 \sin^2 x \cos x$

$\qquad\qquad = \cos^3 x - 3 \cos x(1 - \cos^2 x) = \cos^3 x - 3 \cos x + 3 \cos^3 x = 4 \cos^3 x - 3 \cos x$

23. $\cot\left(\dfrac{\pi}{2} - x\right) = \dfrac{\cos[(\pi/2) - x]}{\sin[(\pi/2) - x]} = \dfrac{\cos(\pi/2) \cos x + \sin(\pi/2) \sin x}{\sin(\pi/2) \cos x - \sin x \cos(\pi/2)} = \dfrac{\sin x}{\cos x} = \tan x$

25. $\dfrac{\sec x - 1}{\tan x} = \dfrac{(1/\cos x) - 1}{\sin x / \cos x}$

$\qquad = \dfrac{1 - \cos x}{\sin x} = \tan \dfrac{x}{2}$

27. $\dfrac{\cos 3x - \cos x}{\sin 3x - \sin x} = \dfrac{-2 \sin 2x \sin x}{2 \cos 2x \sin x} = -\tan 2x$

29. $2 \sin y \cos y \sec 2y = (\sin 2y)(\sec 2y) = \dfrac{\sin 2y}{\cos 2y} = \tan 2y$

31. $y_1 = \sin\left(x - \dfrac{3\pi}{2}\right)$

$\quad y_2 = \cos x$

The graphs of y_1 and y_2 coincide.

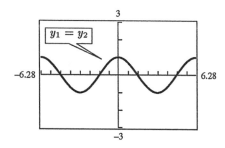

33. $y_1 = \tan^2 x$

$\quad y_2 = \dfrac{1 - \cos 2x}{1 + \cos 2x}$

The graphs of y_1 and y_2 coincide.

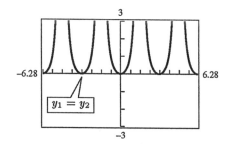

35. $y_1 = 1 + \cos 2x + \cos 4x + \cos 6x$

$\quad y_2 = 4 \cos x \cos 2x \cos 3x$

The graphs of y_1 and y_2 coincide.

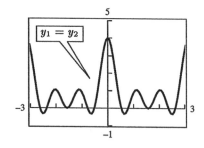

37. $\sin \dfrac{5\pi}{12} = \sin \left(\dfrac{2\pi}{3} - \dfrac{\pi}{4} \right)$

$$= \sin \left(\dfrac{2\pi}{3} \right) \cos \left(\dfrac{\pi}{4} \right) - \cos \dfrac{2\pi}{3} \sin \left(\dfrac{\pi}{4} \right)$$

$$= \left(\dfrac{\sqrt{3}}{2} \right) \left(\dfrac{\sqrt{2}}{2} \right) - \left(-\dfrac{1}{2} \right) \left(\dfrac{\sqrt{2}}{2} \right)$$

$$= \dfrac{\sqrt{2}}{4}(\sqrt{3}+1)$$

39. $\cos 157° 30' = \cos \left(\dfrac{315°}{2} \right)$

$$= -\sqrt{\dfrac{1 + \cos 315°}{2}}$$

$$= -\dfrac{\sqrt{2 + \sqrt{2}}}{2}$$

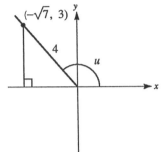
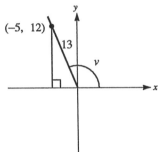

FIGURES FOR EXERCISES 37 AND 39

41. $\sin(u + v) = \sin u \cos v + \cos u \sin v$

$$= \left(\dfrac{3}{4} \right) \left(-\dfrac{5}{13} \right) + \left(-\dfrac{\sqrt{7}}{4} \right) \left(\dfrac{12}{13} \right) = -\dfrac{15}{52} - \dfrac{12\sqrt{7}}{52} = \dfrac{-3(5 + 4\sqrt{7})}{52}$$

43. $\cos(u - v) = \cos u \cos v + \sin u \sin v = \left(-\dfrac{\sqrt{7}}{4} \right) \left(-\dfrac{5}{13} \right) + \left(\dfrac{3}{4} \right) \left(\dfrac{12}{13} \right) = \dfrac{5\sqrt{7} + 36}{52}$

45. $\cos \dfrac{u}{2} = \sqrt{\dfrac{1 + \cos u}{2}}$

$$= \sqrt{\dfrac{1 + (-\sqrt{7}/4)}{2}}$$

$$= \sqrt{\dfrac{4 - \sqrt{7}}{8}}$$

$$= \dfrac{1}{4}\sqrt{2(4 - \sqrt{7})}$$

47. If $\dfrac{\pi}{2} < \theta < \pi$, then $\cos \dfrac{\theta}{2} < 0$. False, if

$$\dfrac{\pi}{2} < \theta < \pi \Rightarrow \dfrac{\pi}{4} < \dfrac{\theta}{2} < \dfrac{\pi}{2},$$

which is in Quadrant I $\Rightarrow \cos(\theta/2) > 0$.
For example, let $\theta = 3\pi/4$. Then,

$$\cos \dfrac{\theta}{2} = 0.3827 > 0.$$

49. $4 \sin(-x) \cos(-x) = -2 \sin 2x$. True.

$$4 \sin(-x) \cos(-x) = 4(-\sin x)(\cos x) = -4 \sin x \cos x = -2(2 \sin x \cos x) = -2 \sin 2x$$

51. $f(x) = \sin x - \tan x$

Graphing the function on the interval $[0,\ 2\pi)$, we find the zeros are $x = 0$ and 3.142. Algebraically:

$$\sin x - \tan x = 0$$

$$\sin x - \frac{\sin x}{\cos x} = 0$$

$$\sin x \cos x - \sin x = 0$$

$$\sin x(\cos x - 1) = 0$$

$\sin x = 0$ \qquad or $\cos x - 1 = 0$

$x = 0,\ \pi$ \qquad\qquad $\cos x = 1$

\qquad\qquad\qquad\qquad $x = 0$

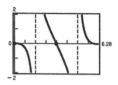

53. $g(x) = \sin 2x + \sqrt{2}\sin x$

Graphing the function on the interval $[0,\ 2\pi)$, we find the zeros are $x = 0$, 2.356, 3.142, and 3.927. Algebraically:

$$\sin 2x + \sqrt{2}\sin x = 0$$

$$2\sin x \cos x + \sqrt{2}\sin x = 0$$

$$\sin x(2\cos x + \sqrt{2}) = 0$$

$\sin x = 0$ \qquad or \quad $2\cos x + \sqrt{2} = 0$

$x = 0,\ \pi$

\qquad\qquad\qquad $\cos x = -\dfrac{\sqrt{2}}{2}$

\qquad\qquad\qquad $x = \dfrac{3\pi}{4},\ \dfrac{5\pi}{4}$

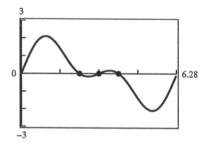

55. $h(x) = \cos^2 x + \sin x - 1$

Graphing the function on the interval $[0,\ 2\pi)$, we find the zeros are $x = 0$, 1.571 and 3.142. Algebraically:

$$\cos^2 x + \sin x = 1$$

$$1 - \sin^2 x + \sin x = 1$$

$$\sin x(\sin x - 1) = 0$$

$\sin x = 0$ \qquad or \quad $\sin x = 1$

$x = 0,\ \pi$ \qquad\qquad $x = \dfrac{\pi}{2}$

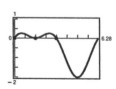

57. $y = \dfrac{1 + \sin x}{\cos x} + \dfrac{\cos x}{1 + \sin x} - 4$

Graphing the function on the interval $[0,\ 2\pi)$, we find the zeros are $x = 1.047$ and 5.236.
Algebraically:

$$\frac{1 + \sin x}{\cos x} + \frac{\cos x}{1 + \sin x} = 4$$

$$(1 + \sin x)^2 + \cos^2 x = 4\cos x(1 + \sin x)$$

$$1 + 2\sin x + \sin^2 x + \cos^2 x = 4\cos x(1 + \sin x)$$

$$2 + 2\sin x - 4\cos x(1 + \sin x) = 0$$

$$2(1 + \sin x)(1 - 2\cos x) = 0$$

$1 + \sin x = 0$ or $1 - 2\cos x = 0$

$\sin x = -1$ $\cos x = \dfrac{1}{2}$

$x = \dfrac{3\pi}{2}$ $x = \dfrac{\pi}{3},\ \dfrac{5\pi}{3}$

(extraneous solution)

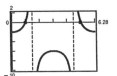

59. $g(t) = \tan^3 t - \tan^2 t + 3\tan t - 3$

Graphing the function on the interval $[0,\ 2\pi)$, we find the zeros are $x = 0.785$ and 3.927.
Algebraically:

$$\tan^3 t - \tan^2 t + 3\tan t - 3 = 0$$

$$\tan^2 t(\tan t - 1) + 3(\tan t - 1) = 0$$

$$(\tan^2 t + 3)(\tan t - 1) = 0$$

$\tan^2 t + 3 = 0$ or $\tan t - 1 = 0$

(No solution) $\tan t = 1$

$t = \dfrac{\pi}{4},\ \dfrac{5\pi}{4}$

61. $\cos 3\theta + \cos 2\theta = 2\cos\dfrac{5\theta}{2}\cos\dfrac{\theta}{2}$

63. $\sin 3\alpha(\sin 2\alpha) = \frac{1}{2}[\cos(3\alpha - 2\alpha) - \cos(3\alpha + 2\alpha)] = \frac{1}{2}(\cos\alpha - \cos 5\alpha)$

65. $\cos(2\arccos 2x) = \cos 2\theta$

$$= \cos^2\theta - \sin^2\theta$$

$$= (2x)^2 - (\sqrt{1-4x^2})^2$$

$$= 4x^2 - (1-4x^2)$$

$$= 8x^2 - 1$$

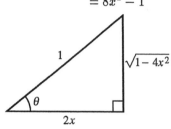

67. $\sin^{-1/2}\cos x = \dfrac{\cos x}{\sin^{1/2}x}$

$$= \dfrac{\cos x}{\sqrt{\sin x}} \cdot \dfrac{\sqrt{\sin x}}{\sqrt{\sin x}}$$

$$= \dfrac{\cos x}{\sin x}\sqrt{\sin x}$$

$$= \cot x\sqrt{\sin x}$$

69. $y = 1.5\sin 8t - 0.5\cos 8t$

  (a) $a = \dfrac{3}{2}, \ b = \dfrac{1}{2}, \ B = 8, \ C = \arctan\left(\dfrac{1/2}{3/2}\right)$

  $y = \sqrt{(3/2)^2 + (1/2)^2}\,\sin\left(8t + \arctan\dfrac{1}{3}\right)$

  $y = \dfrac{1}{2}\sqrt{10}\,\sin\left(8t + \arctan\dfrac{1}{3}\right)$

  (c) Amplitude $= \sqrt{a^2 + b^2} = \dfrac{1}{2}\sqrt{10}$

  (d) Frequency $= \dfrac{B}{\text{period}} = \dfrac{8}{2\pi} = \dfrac{4}{\pi}$

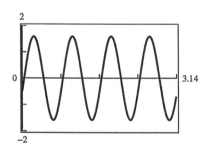

71. Given: $a = 5, \ b = 8, \ c = 10$

  $\cos C = \dfrac{a^2 + b^2 - c^2}{2ab} = \dfrac{25 + 64 - 100}{80} \approx -0.1375 \Rightarrow C \approx 97.9°$

  $\sin A = \dfrac{a\sin C}{c} \approx \dfrac{5(0.9905)}{10} \approx 0.4953 \Rightarrow A \approx 29.7°$

  $\sin B = \dfrac{b\sin C}{c} \approx \dfrac{8(0.9905)}{10} \approx 0.7924 \Rightarrow B \approx 52.4°$

73. Given: $A = 12°$, $B = 58°$, $a = 5$

$$C = 180° - A - B = 180° - 12° - 58° = 110°$$

$$b = \frac{a \sin B}{\sin A} = \frac{5 \sin 58°}{\sin 12°} \approx \frac{5(0.8480)}{0.2079} \approx 20.4$$

$$c = \frac{a \sin C}{\sin A} = \frac{5 \sin 110°}{\sin 12°} \approx \frac{5(0.9397)}{0.2079} \approx 22.6$$

75. Given: $B = 110°$, $a = 4$, $c = 4$

$$b^2 = a^2 + c^2 - 2ac \cos B \approx 16 + 16 - 2(4)(4)(-0.3420) \approx 42.94 \Rightarrow b \approx 6.6$$

$$\sin A = \frac{a \sin B}{b} = \frac{4 \sin 110°}{6.6} \approx \frac{4(0.9397)}{6.6} \approx 0.5736 \Rightarrow A \approx 35°$$

$$c = a \Rightarrow C = A \approx 35°$$

77. Given: $A = 75°$, $a = 2.5$, $b = 16.5$

$$\sin B = \frac{b \sin A}{a} = \frac{16.5 \sin 75°}{2.5} \approx \frac{16.5(0.9659)}{2.5} \approx 6.375 \Rightarrow \text{ no triangle formed}$$

79. Given: $B = 115°$, $a = 7$, $b = 14.5$

$$\sin A = \frac{a \sin B}{b} = \frac{7 \sin 115°}{14.5} \approx \frac{7(0.9063)}{14.5} \approx 0.4375 \Rightarrow A \approx 25.9°$$

$$C \approx 180° - 115° - 25.9° = 39.1°$$

$$c^2 = a^2 + b^2 - 2ab \cos C \approx 7^2 + 14.5^2 - 2(7)(14.5)(0.7760) \approx 101.7 \Rightarrow c \approx 10.09$$

81. Given: $A = 15°$, $a = 5$, $b = 10$

$$\sin B = \frac{b \sin A}{a} = \frac{10 \sin 15°}{5} \approx \frac{10(0.2588)}{5} \approx 0.5176 \Rightarrow B \approx 31.2° \text{ or } 148.8°$$

Case 1: $B \approx 31.2°$ $\qquad\qquad\qquad$ Case 2: $B \approx 148.8°$

$C \approx 180° - 15° - 31.2° = 133.8°$ $\qquad$ $C \approx 180° - 15° - 148.8° = 16.2°$

$c = \dfrac{a \sin C}{\sin A} \approx 13.94$ $\qquad\qquad\qquad$ $c = \dfrac{a \sin C}{\sin A} \approx 5.390$

83. Given: $B = 150°$, $a = 10$, $c = 20$

$$b^2 = a^2 + c^2 - 2ac \cos B \approx 100 + 400 - 400(-0.8660) \approx 846.4 \Rightarrow b \approx 29.09$$

$$\sin C = \frac{c \sin B}{b} \approx \frac{20(0.5)}{29.09} \approx 0.3437 \Rightarrow C \approx 20.1°$$

$$\sin A = \frac{a \sin B}{b} \approx \frac{10(0.5)}{29.09} \approx 0.1719 \Rightarrow A \approx 9.9°$$

85. Given: $B = 25°$, $a = 6.2$, $b = 4$

$$\sin A = \frac{a \sin B}{b} \approx 0.6551 \Rightarrow A \approx 40.9° \text{ or } 139.1°$$

Case 1: $A \approx 40.9°$

$C \approx 180° - 25° - 40.9° = 114.1°$

$c \approx 8.640$

Case 2: $A \approx 139.1°$

$C \approx 180° - 25° - 139.1° = 15.9°$

$c \approx 2.593$

87. $a = 4$, $b = 5$, $c = 7$

$$s = \frac{a+b+c}{2} = \frac{4+5+7}{2} = 8$$

Area $= \sqrt{s(s-a)(s-b)(s-c)} = \sqrt{8(4)(3)(1)} \approx 9.798$

89. $A = 27°$, $b = 5$, $c = 8$

Area $= \frac{1}{2}bc \sin A = \frac{1}{2}(5)(8)(0.4540) = 9.080$

91. Height of smaller triangle: $h = 75 \sin 32° \approx 39.74$ ft

Height of larger triangle: $H = b \tan 48° \approx 70.63$ ft

Height of tree: $H - h \approx 70.63 - 39.74 \approx 31$ ft

93. $\alpha = 180° - 31° = 149°$

$\phi = 180° - 149° - 17° = 14°$

$$x = \frac{50 \sin 17°}{\sin \phi} = \frac{50 \sin 17°}{\sin 14°} \approx 60.43$$

$h = x \sin 31°$

$\approx 60.43(0.5150) \approx 31.12$ meters

95. $d^2 = 850^2 + 1060^2 - 2(850)(1060) \cos 72°$

$\approx 1,289,251$

$d \approx 1135$ miles

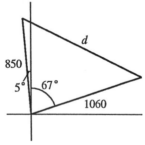

97. $r = 5\sqrt{2}$, $\theta = 315°$

$5 - 5i = 5\sqrt{2}(\cos 315° + i \sin 315°)$

99. $r = 13$, $\theta = 67.38°$

$5 + 12i = 13(\cos 67.38° + i \sin 67.38°)$

101. $100(\cos 240° + i\sin 240°) = 100\left(-\dfrac{1}{2} - \dfrac{\sqrt{3}}{2}i\right) = -50 - 50\sqrt{3}\,i$

103. $13(\cos 0 + i\sin 0) = 13(1 + 0i) = 13$

105. (a) $z_1 = 5(\cos \pi + i\sin \pi)$

$z_2 = 5\left(\cos \dfrac{\pi}{2} + i\sin \dfrac{\pi}{2}\right)$

(b) $z_1 z_2 = 25\left(\cos \dfrac{3\pi}{2} + i\sin \dfrac{3\pi}{2}\right) = -25i$

$\dfrac{z_1}{z_2} = \dfrac{5}{5}\left(\cos \dfrac{\pi}{2} + i\sin \dfrac{\pi}{2}\right) = i$

107. (a) $z_1 = -3(1 + i) = 3\sqrt{2}(\cos 225° + i\sin 225°)$

$z_2 = 2(\sqrt{3} + i) = 4(\cos 30° + i\sin 30°)$

(b) $z_1 z_2 = [3\sqrt{2}(\cos 225° + i\sin 225°)][4(\cos 30° + i\sin 30°)]$

$= 12\sqrt{2}(\cos 255° + i\sin 255°) \approx -4.392 - 16.39i$

$\dfrac{z_1}{z_2} = \dfrac{3\sqrt{2}(\cos 225° + i\sin 225°)}{4(\cos 30° + i\sin 30°)} = \dfrac{3\sqrt{2}}{4}(\cos 195° + i\sin 195°) \approx -1.025 - 0.2745i$

109. $\left[5\left(\cos \dfrac{\pi}{12} + i\sin \dfrac{\pi}{12}\right)\right]^4 = 5^4\left(\dfrac{4\pi}{12} + i\sin \dfrac{4\pi}{12}\right)$

$= 625\left(\cos \dfrac{\pi}{3} + i\sin \dfrac{\pi}{3}\right)$

$= 625\left(\dfrac{1}{2} + \dfrac{\sqrt{3}}{2}i\right) = \dfrac{625}{2} + \dfrac{625\sqrt{3}}{2}i$

111. $(2 + 3i)^6 = [\sqrt{13}(\cos 56.3° + i\sin 56.3°)]^6$

$= 13^3(\cos 337.9° + i\sin 337.9°) \approx 13^3(0.9263 - 0.3769i) \approx 2035 - 828i$

113. Sixth roots of $-729i = 729\left(\cos\dfrac{3\pi}{2} + i\sin\dfrac{3\pi}{2}\right)$:

$$\sqrt[6]{729}\left(\cos\frac{(3\pi/2) + 2k\pi}{6} + i\sin\frac{(3\pi/2) + 2k\pi}{6}\right), \quad k = 1, 2, 3, 4, 5$$

$$3\left(\cos\frac{\pi}{4} + i\sin\frac{\pi}{4}\right) \approx 2.121 + 2.121i$$

$$3\left(\cos\frac{7\pi}{12} + i\sin\frac{7\pi}{12}\right) \approx -0.7765 + 2.898i$$

$$3\left(\cos\frac{11\pi}{12} + i\sin\frac{11\pi}{12}\right) \approx -2.898 + 0.7765i$$

$$3\left(\cos\frac{5\pi}{4} + i\sin\frac{5\pi}{4}\right) \approx -2.121 - 2.121i$$

$$3\left(\cos\frac{19\pi}{12} + i\sin\frac{19\pi}{12}\right) \approx 0.7765 - 2.898i$$

$$3\left(\cos\frac{23\pi}{12} + i\sin\frac{23\pi}{12}\right) \approx 2.898 - 0.7765i$$

115. Cube roots of $-1 = \cos\pi + i\sin\pi$:

$$\cos\frac{\pi + 2k\pi}{3} + i\sin\frac{\pi + 2k\pi}{3}, \quad k = 0, 1, 2$$

$$\cos\frac{\pi}{3} + i\sin\frac{\pi}{3} = \frac{1}{2} + \frac{\sqrt{3}}{2}i$$

$$\cos\pi + i\sin\pi = -1$$

$$\cos\frac{5\pi}{3} + i\sin\frac{5\pi}{3} = \frac{1}{2} - \frac{\sqrt{3}}{2}i$$

117. $x^4 + 81 = 0$

$$x^4 = -81$$

$$-81 = 81(\cos \pi + i \sin \pi)$$

$$\sqrt[4]{-81} = \sqrt[4]{81}\left[\cos\left(\frac{\pi + 2\pi k}{4}\right) + i\sin\left(\frac{\pi + 2\pi k}{4}\right)\right], \quad k = 0,\ 1,\ 2,\ 3$$

$$3\left(\cos\frac{\pi}{4} + i\sin\frac{\pi}{4}\right) = \frac{3\sqrt{2}}{2} + \frac{3\sqrt{2}}{2}i$$

$$3\left(\cos\frac{3\pi}{4} + i\sin\frac{3\pi}{4}\right) = -\frac{3\sqrt{2}}{2} + \frac{3\sqrt{2}}{2}i$$

$$3\left(\cos\frac{5\pi}{4} + i\sin\frac{5\pi}{4}\right) = -\frac{3\sqrt{2}}{2} - \frac{3\sqrt{2}}{2}i$$

$$3\left(\cos\frac{7\pi}{4} + i\sin\frac{7\pi}{4}\right) = \frac{3\sqrt{2}}{2} - \frac{3\sqrt{2}}{2}i$$

119. $(x^3 - 1)(x^2 + 1) = 0$

$$x^3 - 1 = 0 \qquad x^2 + 1 = 0$$

$$x^3 = 1$$

$$1 = 1(\cos 0 + i\sin 0)$$

$$\sqrt[3]{1} = \sqrt[3]{1}\left[\cos\left(\frac{0 + 2\pi k}{3}\right) + i\sin\left(\frac{0 + 2\pi k}{3}\right)\right], \quad k = 0,\ 1,\ 2$$

$$1(\cos 0 + i\sin 0) = 1$$

$$1\left(\cos\frac{2\pi}{3} + i\sin\frac{2\pi}{3}\right) = -\frac{1}{2} + \frac{\sqrt{3}}{2}i$$

$$1\left(\cos\frac{4\pi}{3} + i\sin\frac{4\pi}{3}\right) = -\frac{1}{2} - \frac{\sqrt{3}}{2}i$$

$$x^2 + 1 = 0$$

$$x^2 = -1$$

$$-1 = 1(\cos \pi + i\sin \pi)$$

$$\sqrt{-1} = \sqrt{1}\left[\cos\left(\frac{\pi + 2\pi k}{2}\right) + i\sin\left(\frac{\pi + 2\pi k}{2}\right)\right], \quad k = 0,\ 1$$

$$1\left(\cos\frac{\pi}{2} + i\sin\frac{\pi}{2}\right) = i$$

$$1\left(\cos\frac{3\pi}{2} + i\sin\frac{3\pi}{2}\right) = -i$$

CHAPTER 7

Linear Models and Systems of Equations

Section 7.1 Solving Systems of Equations Algebraically and Graphically

■ You should be able to solve systems of equations by the method of substitution.
  1. Solve one of the equations for one of the variables.
  2. Substitute this expression into the other equation and solve.
  3. Back substitute into the first equation to find the value of the other variable.
  4. Check the solution in each of the original equations.

■ You should be able to find solutions graphically. (See Example 5 in the textbook.)

---

1. $2x + y = 4$ Equation 1

$-x + y = 1$ Equation 2

Graphically, the lines $y = -2x + 4$ and $y = x + 1$ intersect at $(1, 2)$. Algebraically, we do the following.

Solve for y in Equation 1: $y = 4 - 2x$

Substitute for y in Equation 2: $-x + (4 - 2x) = 1$

Solve for x: $-3x = -3$ $\Rightarrow$ $x = 1$

Backsubstitute $x = 1$: $y = 4 - 2(x) = 4 - 2 = 2$

Solution: $(1, 2)$

3. $x - y = -3$ Equation 1

$x^2 - y = -1$ Equation 2

Graphically, the line $y = x + 3$ intersects the parabola $y = x^2 + 1$ in two points, $(-1, 2)$ and $(2, 5)$. Algebraically, we do the following.

Solve for y in Equation 1: $y = x + 3$

Substitute for y in Equation 2: $x^2 - (x + 3) = -1$

Solve for x: $x^2 - x - 3 = -1$ $\Rightarrow$ $(x - 2)(x + 1) = 0$ $\Rightarrow$ $x = 2, -1$

Backsubstitute $x = 2$: $y = x + 3 = 2 + 3 = 5$

Backsubstitute $x = -1$: $y = x + 3 = -1 + 3 = 2$

Solutions: $(-1, 2)$, $(2, 5)$

5. $x + 3y = 15$ Equation 1

$x^2 + y^2 = 25$ Equation 2

Graphically, the line $y = \frac{1}{3}(-x + 15)$ intersects the circle $x^2 + y^2 = 25$ ($y_1 = \sqrt{25 - x^2}$, $y_2 = -\sqrt{25 - x^2}$) in two points $(0, 5)$ and $(3, 4)$. Algebraically, we do the following.
Solve for x in Equation 1: $x = -3y + 15$
Substitute for x in Equation 2: $(-3y + 15)^2 + y^2 = 25$
Solve for y: $10y^2 - 90y + 200 = 0$ $\Rightarrow$ $y^2 - 9y + 20 = 0$ $\Rightarrow$ $y = 5,\ 4$
Backsubstitute $y = 5$: $x = -3y + 15 = -3(5) + 15 = 0$
Backsubstitute $y = 4$: $x = -3y + 15 = -3(4) + 15 = 3$
Solutions: $(0, 5), (3, 4)$

7. $x^2 - y = 0$ Equation 1

$x^2 - 4x + y = 0$ Equation 2

Graphically, the parabolas $y = x^2$ and $y = -x^2 + 4x$ intersect in two points $(0, 0)$ and $(2, 4)$. Algebraically, we do the following.
Solve for y in Equation 1: $y = x^2$
Substitute for y in Equation 2: $x^2 - 4x + x^2 = 0$
Solve for x : $2x^2 - 4x = 0$ $\Rightarrow$ $2x(x - 2) = 0$ $\Rightarrow$ $x = 0,\ 2$
Backsubstitute $x = 0$: $y = x^2 = 0$
Backsubstitute $x = 2$: $y = x^2 = 4$
Solutions: $(0, 0), (2, 4)$

9. $x - 3y = -4$ Equation 1

$x^2 - y^3 =\ \ 0$ Equation 2

Graphically, the line $y = \frac{1}{3}(x + 4)$ intersects the curve $y = x^{2/3}$ in two points $(-1,\ 1)$ and $(8,\ 4)$. Algebraically, we do the following.
Solve for x in Equation 1: $x = 3y - 4$
Substitute for x in Equation 2: $(3y - 4)^2 - y^3 = 0$
Solve for y: $-y^3 + 9y^2 - 24y + 16 = 0$ $\Rightarrow$ $(y - 1)(y - 4)^2 = 0$ $\Rightarrow$ $y = 1,\ 4$
Backsubstitute $y = 1$: $x = 3y - 4 = 3 - 4 = -1$
Backsubstitute $y = 4$: $x = 3y - 4 = 12 - 4 = 8$
Solutions: $(-1,\ 1), (8,\ 4)$

11. $x - y = 0$ Equation 1

$5x - 3y = 10$ Equation 2

Solve for x in Equation 1: $y = x$
Substitute for y in Equation 2: $5x - 3x = 10$
Solve for x: $2x = 10$ $\Rightarrow$ $x = 5$
Backsubstitute in Equation 1: $y = x = 5$
Solution: $(5, 5)$

13. $2x - y + 2 = 0$ Equation 1

$4x + y - 5 = 0$ Equation 2

Solve for y in Equation 1: $y = 2x + 2$
Substitute for y in Equation 2 and solve for x: $4x + (2x + 2) - 5 = 0$ $\Rightarrow$ $x = \frac{1}{2}$
Backsubstitute $x = \frac{1}{2}$: $y = 2x + 2 = 2\left(\frac{1}{2}\right) + 2 = 3$
Solution: $\left(\frac{1}{2}, 3\right)$

15. $30x - 40y - 33 = 0$ Equation 1

$10x + 20y - 21 = 0$ Equation 2

Solve for x in Equation 2: $x = -2y + 2.1$
Substitute for x in Equation 1: $30(-2y + 2.1) - 40y - 33 = 0$
Solve for y: $-60y + 63 - 40y - 33 = 0$ $\Rightarrow$ $-100y + 30 = 0$ $\Rightarrow$ $y = 0.3$
Backsubstitute $y = 0.3$: $x = -2y + 2.1 = -2(0.3) + 2.1 = 1.5$
Solution: $(1.5, 0.3)$

17. $\frac{1}{5}x + \frac{1}{2}y = 8$ Equation 1

$x + y = 20$ Equation 2

Solve for x in Equation 2: $x = 20 - y$
Substitute for x in Equation 1: $\frac{1}{5}(20 - y) + \frac{1}{2}y = 8$
Solve for y: $4 - \frac{1}{5}y + \frac{1}{2}y = 8$ $\Rightarrow$ $\frac{3}{10}y = 4$ $\Rightarrow$ $y = \frac{40}{3}$
Backsubstitute $y = \frac{40}{3}$: $x = 20 - y = 20 - \frac{40}{3} = \frac{20}{3}$
Solution: $\left(\frac{20}{3}, \frac{40}{3}\right)$

19. $x - y = 0$ Equation 1

$2x + y = 0$ Equation 2

Solve for y in Equation 1: $y = x$

Substitute for y in Equation 2:

$2x + x = 0$

Solve for x: $3x = 0$ $\Rightarrow$ $x = 0$

Backsubstitute $x = 0$: $y = x = 0$

Solution: $(0, 0)$

21. $y = 2x$ Equation 1

$y = x^2 + 1$ Equation 2

Substitute for y in Equation 2:

$2x = x^2 + 1$

Solve for x:

$x^2 - 2x + 1 = (x - 1)^2 = 0 \Rightarrow x = 1$

Backsubstitute $x = 1$: $y = 2x = 2(1) = 2$

Solution: $(1, 2)$

23. $3x - 7y + 6 = 0$ Equation 1

$x^2 - y^2 = 4$ Equation 2

Solve for y in Equation 1: $y = \dfrac{3x + 6}{7}$

Solve for x in Equation 2: $x^2 - \left(\dfrac{3x + 6}{7}\right)^2 = 4$

Solve for x: $x^2 - \dfrac{9x^2}{49} - \dfrac{36x}{49} - \dfrac{36}{49} - 4 = 0 \Rightarrow 10x^2 - 9x - 58 = 0$

$$\Rightarrow x = \frac{9 \pm \sqrt{81 + 40(58)}}{20} \Rightarrow x = \frac{29}{10},\ -2$$

Backsubstitute $x = \dfrac{29}{10}$: $y = \dfrac{3x + 6}{7} = \dfrac{3(29/10) + 6}{7} = \dfrac{21}{10}$

Backsubstitute $x = -2$: $y = \dfrac{3x + 6}{7} = 0$

Solutions: $\left(\dfrac{29}{10},\ \dfrac{21}{10}\right)$, $(-2,\ 0)$

25. $y - e^{-x} = 1 \Rightarrow y = e^{-x} + 1$

$y - \ln x = 3 \Rightarrow y = \ln x + 3$

Graphing the two functions, you can use the zoom and trace features to obtain $(0.28, 1.75)$ as the only solution.

27. $y = x^4 - 2x^2 + 1$ Equation 1

$y = 1 - x^2$ Equation 2

Substitute for y in Equation 1: $1 - x^2 = x^4 - 2x^2 + 1$

Solve for x: $x^4 - x^2 = 0 \Rightarrow x^2(x^2 - 1) = 0 \Rightarrow x = 0, \pm 1$

Backsubstitute $x = 0$: $1 - x^2 = 1$

Backsubstitute $x = 1$: $1 - x^2 = 1 - 1^2 = 0$

Backsubstitute $x = -1$: $1 - x^2 = 1 - (-1)^2 = 0$

Solutions: $(0, 1), (\pm 1, 0)$

29. $xy - 1 = 0$ Equation 1

$2x - 4y + 7 = 0$ Equation 2

Solve for y in Equation 1: $y = \dfrac{1}{x}$

Substitute for y in Equation 2: $2x - 4\left(\dfrac{1}{x}\right) + 7 = 0$

Solve for x: $2x^2 - 4 + 7x = 0 \Rightarrow (2x - 1)(x + 4) = 0 \Rightarrow x = \dfrac{1}{2}, -4$

Backsubstitute $x = \dfrac{1}{2}$: $y = \dfrac{1}{x} = \dfrac{1}{1/2} = 2$

Backsubsitute $x = -4$: $y = \dfrac{1}{x} = \dfrac{1}{-4} = -\dfrac{1}{4}$

Solutions: $\left(\dfrac{1}{2}, 2\right), \left(-4, -\dfrac{1}{4}\right)$

31. $x + y = 4$

$x^2 + y^2 - 4x = 0 \Rightarrow (x - 2)^2 + y^2 = 4$

$y_1 = \sqrt{4x - x^2}$

$y_2 = -\sqrt{4x - x^2}$

Solution: $(2, 2), (4, 0)$

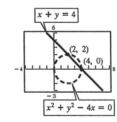

33. $2x - y + 3 = 0 \Rightarrow y = 2x + 3$

$x^2 + y^2 - 4x = 0 \Rightarrow (x - 2)^2 + y^2 = 4$

$y_1 = \sqrt{4x - x^2}$

$y_2 = -\sqrt{4x - x^2}$

No points of intersection

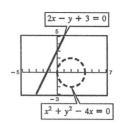

35. $x^2 + y^2 = 25,\ (y = \pm\sqrt{25 - x^2})$

$(x - 8)^2 + y^2 = 41,\ (y = \pm\sqrt{41 - (x - 8)^2})$

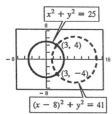

Solutions: $(3, -4),\ (3, 4)$

37. $y = e^x$

$x - y + 1 = 0 \quad \Rightarrow \quad y = x + 1$

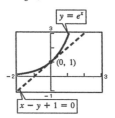

Solution: $(0, 1)$

39. $y = \sqrt{x}$

$y = x$

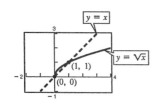

Solutions: $(0, 0),\ (1, 1)$

41. $x^2 + y^2 = 169,\ (y = \pm\sqrt{169 - x^2})$

$x^2 - 8y = 104,\ (y = \frac{1}{8}(x^2 - 104))$

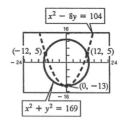

Solutions: $(0, -13),\ (\pm 12, 5)$

43. $C = 8650x + 250,000, \quad R = 9950x$

$\qquad R = C$

$\qquad 9950x = 8650x + 250,000$

$\qquad 1300x = 250,000$

$\qquad\qquad x \approx 192.3 \text{ units}$

In order for the revenue to break even with the cost, 193 units must be sold.

45. $C = 2.65x + 350,000, \quad R = 4.15x$

$\qquad R = C$

$\qquad 4.15x = 2.65x + 350,000$

$\qquad 1.5x = 350,000$

$\qquad\qquad x \approx 233,333.3$

In order for the revenue to break even with the cost, 233,334 units must be sold.

47. $C = 3.45x + 16,000, \quad R = 5.95x$

$\qquad R = C$

$\qquad 5.95x = 3.45x + 16,000$

$\qquad 2.5x = 16,000$

$\qquad\qquad x = 6400 \text{ units}$

49. $x + y = 25,000 \quad \Rightarrow \quad y = 25,000 - x$

$\qquad 0.08x + 0.085y = 2060$

$\qquad 0.08x + 0.085(25,000 - x) = 2060$

$\qquad -0.005x + 2125 = 2060$

$\qquad 0.005x = 65$

$\qquad\qquad x = \$13,000 \text{ at } 8\%$

$\qquad\qquad y = 25,000 - 13,000$

$\qquad\qquad = \$12,000 \text{ at } 8.5\%$

51. $0.06x = 0.03x + 250$

$\qquad 0.03x = 250$

$\qquad\qquad x \approx \$8,333.33$

To make the straight commission offer better, you would have to sell more than \$8,333.33 per week.

53. $V = (D-4)^2, \quad 5 \leq D \leq 40$

$V = 0.79D^2 - 2D - 4, \quad 5 \leq D \leq 40$

(a)

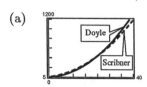

(b) The two graphs intersect at $D = 24.72$. Algebraically:

$$(D-4)^2 = 0.79D^2 - 2D - 4$$

$$D^2 - 8D + 16 = 0.79D^2 - 2D - 4$$

$$0.21D^2 - 6D + 20 = 0$$

$$D \approx 24.72, \ 3.9$$

Since $5 \leq D \leq 40$, the scales agree when $D \approx 24.72$ inches.

(c) V is larger using the Scribner Log Rule when $5 \leq D \leq 24.7$. V is larger using the Doyle Log Rule when $24.7 \leq D \leq 40$. Therefore, for large diameters, you would use the Doyle Log Rule.

55. $P = 2l + 2w = 40 \Rightarrow w = 20 - l$

$A = lw = l(20 - l) = 96$

$-l^2 + 20l - 96 = 0$

$l^2 - 20l + 96 = 0$

$(l - 8)(l - 12) = 0$

$l = 8 \quad$ or $\quad l = 12$

$w = 12 \qquad w = 8$

The dimensions are 12 miles by 8 miles.

57.

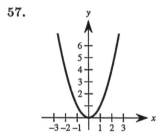

(a) The line $y = 4$ intersects the graph of $y = x^2$ at two points, $(2, 4)$ and $(-2, 4)$.

(b) The line $x = 1$ intersects the graph of $y = x^2$ at one point, $(1, 1)$.

(c) The line $y = -1$ does not intersect the graph of $y = x^2$.

Section 7.2 Systems of Linear Equations in Two Variables

- You should be able to solve a linear system by the method of elimination.
- You should know that for a system of two linear equations, one of the following is true.
  (a) There are infinitely many solutions; the lines are identical.
  (b) There is no solution; the lines are parallel.
  (c) There is one solution; the lines intersect at one point.

1.
$$2x + y = 4$$
$$\underline{x - y = 2}$$
$$3x \quad\;\; = 6$$
$$x = 2$$
$$y = 0$$
Solution: $(2, 0)$

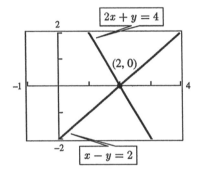

3.
$$x - y = \;\;\;0 \Rightarrow -2x + 2y = \;\;\;0$$
$$3x - 2y = -1 \Rightarrow \underline{\;\;3x - 2y = -1}$$
$$x = -1$$
$$y = -1$$
Solution: $(-1, -1)$

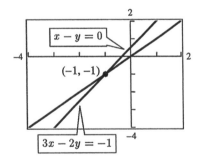

5. $\begin{aligned} x - y &= 1 \Rightarrow 2x - 2y = 2 \\ -2x + 2y &= 5 \Rightarrow \underline{-2x + 2y = 5} \\ & 0 = 7 \end{aligned}$

Inconsistent; no solution

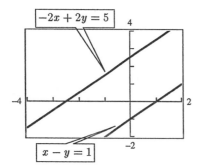

7. $\begin{aligned} 3x - 2y &= 6 \Rightarrow 6x - 4y = 12 \\ -6x + 4y &= -12 \Rightarrow \underline{-6x + 4y = -12} \\ & 0 = 0 \end{aligned}$

Solution: All points $(x,\ y)$ lying on the line $3x - 2y = 6$, or any points of the form $(2a,\ 3a - 3)$.

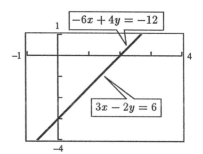

9. $\begin{aligned} 9x - 3y &= -1 \Rightarrow 18x - 6y = -2 \\ 3x + 6y &= -5 \Rightarrow \underline{3x + 6y = -5} \\ & 21x = -7 \\ & x = -\tfrac{1}{3} \\ & y = -\tfrac{2}{3} \end{aligned}$

Solution: $\left(-\tfrac{1}{3},\ -\tfrac{2}{3}\right)$

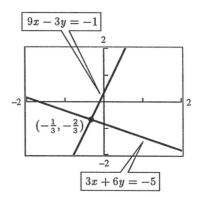

11. $\begin{aligned} x + 2y &= 4 \\ \underline{x - 2y} &= \underline{1} \\ 2x &= 5 \\ x &= \tfrac{5}{2} \\ y &= \tfrac{3}{4} \end{aligned}$

Solution: $\left(\tfrac{5}{2},\ \tfrac{3}{4}\right)$

13. $\begin{aligned} 2x + 3y &= 18 \Rightarrow 2x + 3y = 18 \\ 5x - y &= 11 \Rightarrow \underline{15x - 3y = 33} \\ & 17x = 51 \\ & x = 3 \\ & y = 4 \end{aligned}$

Solution: $(3,\ 4)$

15. $3x + 2y = 10 \Rightarrow -6x - 4y = -20$

$ 2x + 5y = 3 \Rightarrow \underline{6x + 15y = 9}$

$$11y = -11$$
$$y = -1$$
$$x = 4$$

Solution: $(4, -1)$

17. $2u + v = 120 \Rightarrow -4u - 2v = -240$

$ u + 2v = 120 \Rightarrow \underline{u + 2v = 120}$

$$-3u = -120$$
$$u = 40$$
$$v = 40$$

Solution: $(40, 40)$

19. $6r - 5s = 3 \Rightarrow 12r - 10s = 6$

$ 10s - 12r = 5 \Rightarrow \underline{-12r + 10s = 5}$

$$0 = 11$$

Inconsistent; no solution

21. $\dfrac{x}{4} + \dfrac{y}{6} = 1 \Rightarrow 6x + 4y = 24$

$ x - y = 3 \Rightarrow \underline{4x - 4y = 12}$

$$10x = 36$$
$$x = \dfrac{18}{5}$$
$$y = \dfrac{3}{5}$$

Solution: $\left(\dfrac{18}{5}, \dfrac{3}{5}\right)$

23. $\dfrac{x+3}{4} + \dfrac{y-1}{3} = 1 \Rightarrow 3(x+3) + 4(y-1) = 12 \Rightarrow 3x + 4y = 7$

$ 2x - y = 12 \Rightarrow \underline{8x - 4y = 48}$

$$11x = 55$$
$$x = 5$$
$$y = -2$$

Solution: $(5, -2)$

25. $2.5x - 3y = 1.5 \Rightarrow 25x - 30y = 15 \Rightarrow 5x - 6y = 3$

$ 10x - 12y = 6 \Rightarrow 5x - 6y = 3 \Rightarrow \underline{-5x + 6y = -3}$

$$0 = 0$$

Solution: All points (x, y) lying on the line $5x - 6y = 3$, or any points of the form $\left(a, \dfrac{5}{6}a - \dfrac{1}{2}\right)$.

27. $0.05x - 0.03y = 0.21 \Rightarrow 5x - 3y = 21 \Rightarrow 10x - 6y = \quad 42$

$\qquad 0.07x + 0.02y = 0.16 \Rightarrow 7x + 2y = 16 \Rightarrow 21x + 6y = \quad 48$

$$31x \quad\quad = \quad 90$$

$$x = \tfrac{90}{31}$$

$$y = -\tfrac{67}{31}$$

Solution: $\left(\tfrac{90}{31}, -\tfrac{67}{31}\right)$

29. $4b + \;\; 3m = \;\; 3 \Rightarrow 44b + 33m = \quad 33$

$\qquad 3b + 11m = 13 \Rightarrow -9b - 33m = -39$

$$35b \quad\quad = \quad -6$$

$$b = -\tfrac{6}{35}$$

$$m = \quad \tfrac{43}{35}$$

Solution: $\left(-\tfrac{6}{35}, \tfrac{43}{35}\right)$

31. $200y - x = \quad 200 \Rightarrow -200y + x = -200$

$\qquad 199y - x = -198 \Rightarrow \quad 199y - x = -198$

$$-y \quad\quad = -398$$

$$y = 398$$

$$x = 199y + 198 = 79{,}400$$

Solution: $(79{,}400, \;\; 398)$

Since $x = 79{,}400$ is so large, it is necessary to change the scale on the axis to see the point of intersection of the lines. Note that the slopes of the lines are nearly equal.

33. $3.6(g - w) = 1800 \Rightarrow g - w = \quad 500$

$\qquad 3(g + w) = 1800 \Rightarrow g + w = \quad 600$

$$2g \quad\quad = 1100$$

$$g = \quad 550$$

$$w = \quad 50$$

Solution: Ground speed is 550 mph and wind speed is 50 mph.

35. $\quad x + \quad y = \quad 10 \Rightarrow -2x - 2y = -20$

$\qquad 0.2x + 0.5y = 0.3(10) \Rightarrow \quad 2x + 5y = \quad 30$

$$3y = \quad 10$$

$$y = \quad \tfrac{10}{3}$$

$$x = \quad \tfrac{20}{3}$$

Solution: $\tfrac{20}{3}$ gallons of 20% solution, $\tfrac{10}{3}$ gallons of 50% solution

37.

$$x + \quad y = 12{,}000 \Rightarrow -120x - 120y = -1{,}440{,}000$$

$$0.105x + 0.12y = \quad 1380 \Rightarrow \quad \underline{105x + 120y = \quad 1{,}380{,}000}$$

$$-15x \qquad = \qquad -60{,}000$$

$$x = \qquad 4000$$

$$y = \qquad 8000$$

Solution: $4000 is invested in 10.5% fund and $8000 is invested in 12% fund.

39.

$$x + \quad y = \quad 500 \quad \Rightarrow -40x - 40y = -20{,}000$$

$$7.50x + 4.00y = 3312.50 \Rightarrow \quad \underline{75x + 40y = \quad 33{,}125}$$

$$35x \qquad = \quad 13{,}125$$

$$x = \qquad 375$$

$$y = \qquad 125$$

Solution: 375 adult tickets and 125 child tickets sold

41. Supply = Demand

$$0.125x = 50 - 0.5x$$

$$0.625x = 50$$

$$x = 80$$

$$p = 10$$

Equilibrium point: (80, 10)

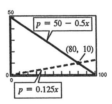

43. Supply = Demand

$$100 + x = 300 - x$$

$$2x = 200$$

$$x = 100$$

$$p = 200$$

Equilibrium point: (100, 200)

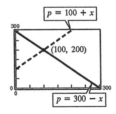

45.   Supply = Demand

$$80 + 0.00001x = 140 - 0.00002x$$

$$0.00003x = 60$$

$$x = 2{,}000{,}000$$

$$p = 100$$

Equilibrium point: $(2{,}000{,}000, \quad 100)$

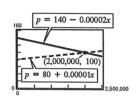

47. $x + y = 300 \Rightarrow -x - \quad y = -300$

$\quad\quad x = \ 3y \Rightarrow \quad x - 3y = \quad\quad 0$

$$- 4y = -300$$

$$y = \quad 75$$

$$x = \quad 225$$

Solution: One driver drives 75 miles and the other driver drives 225 miles.

49. $5b + 10a = 20.2 \Rightarrow -10b - 20a = -40.4$

$\quad\quad 10b + 30a = 50.1 \Rightarrow \quad 10b + 30a = \quad 50.1$

$$10a = \quad 9.7$$

$$a = \quad 0.97$$

$$b = \quad 2.10$$

$$y = ax + b$$

$$y = 0.97x + 2.10$$

51. $7b + 21a = \quad 35.1 \Rightarrow -21b - 63a = -105.3$

$\quad\quad 21b + 91a = 114.2 \Rightarrow \quad 21b + 91a = \quad 114.2$

$$28a = \quad 8.9$$

$$a = \quad \tfrac{8.9}{28} \quad \approx 0.318$$

$$b = \quad \tfrac{1137}{280} \quad \approx 4.061$$

$$y = ax + b$$

$$y = 0.318x + 4.061$$

53. $(-2, 0)$, $(0, 1)$, $(2, 3)$

$$n = 3, \quad \sum_{i=1}^{3} x_i = 0, \quad \sum_{i=1}^{3} y_i = 4,$$

$$\sum_{i=1}^{3} x_i^2 = 8, \quad \sum_{i=1}^{3} x_i y_i = 6$$

$$3b + 0 = 4$$

$$3b = 4$$

$$b = \tfrac{4}{3}$$

$$0 + 8a = 6$$

$$8a = 6$$

$$a = \tfrac{6}{8}$$

$$a = \tfrac{3}{4}$$

$$y = ax + b$$

$$y = \tfrac{3}{4}x + \tfrac{4}{3}$$

55. $(0, 4)$, $(1, 3)$, $(1, 1)$, $(2, 0)$

$$n = 4, \quad \sum_{i=1}^{4} x_i = 4, \quad \sum_{i=1}^{4} y_i = 8,$$

$$\sum_{i=1}^{4} x_i^2 = 6, \quad \sum_{i=1}^{4} x_i y_i = 4$$

$$4b + 4a = 8 \Rightarrow \quad 4b + 4a = 8$$

$$4b + 6a = 4 \Rightarrow \quad \underline{-4b - 6a = -4}$$

$$-2a = 4$$

$$a = -2$$

$$b = 4$$

$$y = ax + b$$

$$y = -2x + 4$$

57. $(1.00, 450)$, $(1.25, 375)$, $(1.50, 330)$

$$n = 3, \quad \sum_{i=1}^{3} x_i = 3.75, \quad \sum_{i=1}^{3} y_i = 1155, \quad \sum_{i=1}^{3} x_i^2 = 4.8125, \quad \sum_{i=1}^{3} x_i y_i = 1413.75$$

$$3b + 3.75a = 1155 \quad \Rightarrow \quad 11.25b + 14.0625a = 4331.25$$

$$3.75b + 4.8125a = 1413.75 \Rightarrow -11.25b - 14.4375a = -4241.25$$

$$-0.375a = 90$$

$$a = -240$$

$$b = 685$$

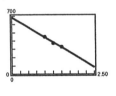

$$y = ax + b$$

$$y = -240x + 685$$

When $x = \$1.40$, $y = -240(1.40) + 685 = 349$ units.

59. Since $x = 3$ and $y = \tfrac{5}{2}$, one possible system of linear equations is

$$x + 2y = 8$$

$$x + 4y = 13.$$

Section 7.3   Systems of Linear Equations in More Than Two Variables

- You should know the operations that lead to equivalent systems of equations.
  (a) Interchange any two equations.
  (b) Multiply all terms of an equation by a nonzero constant.
  (c) Replace an equation by the sum of itself and a constant multiple of any other equation in the system.

- You should be able to use the method of Gaussian elimination.

- A linear system can have:
  (1) Exactly one solution
  (2) No solution
  (3) Infinitely many solutions.

- You should be able to graphically interpret a system of linear equations in three variables.

1.
$$\begin{aligned} x + y + z &= 6 \\ 2x - y + z &= 3 \\ 3x \quad\;\; - z &= 0 \end{aligned}$$

$$\begin{aligned} x + y + z &= 6 \\ -3y - z &= -9 \\ -3y - 4z &= -18 \end{aligned}$$

$$\begin{aligned} x + y + z &= 6 \\ - 3y - z &= -9 \\ - 3z &= -9 \end{aligned}$$

$-3z = -9 \quad \Rightarrow \quad z = 3$

$-3y - 3 = -9 \quad \Rightarrow \quad y = 2$

$x + 2 + 3 = 6 \quad \Rightarrow \quad x = 1$

Solution: $(1, 2, 3)$

3.
$$\begin{aligned} x + y + z &= -3 \\ 4x + y - 3z &= 11 \\ 2x - 3y + 2z &= 9 \end{aligned}$$

$$\begin{aligned} x + y + z &= -3 \\ -3y - 7z &= 23 \\ -5y &= 15 \end{aligned}$$

$-5y = 15 \quad \Rightarrow \quad y = -3$

$-3(-3) - 7z = 23 \quad \Rightarrow \quad z = -2$

$x - 3 - 2 = -3 \quad \Rightarrow \quad x = 2$

Solution: $(2, -3, -2)$

5.
$$3x + 3y \qquad = \ 9$$
$$2x \qquad -\ 3z = \ 10$$
$$\qquad 6y + 4z = -12$$

$$x + y \qquad = \ 3$$
$$2x \qquad -\ 3z = \ 10$$
$$\qquad 6y + 4z = -12$$

$$x + y \qquad = \ 3$$
$$-2y - 3z = \ 4$$
$$\qquad 6y + 4z = -12$$

$$x + y \qquad = \ 3$$
$$-2y - 3z = \ 4$$
$$\qquad -5z = \ 0$$

$$-5z = 0 \quad \Rightarrow \quad z = 0$$
$$-2y - 3(0) = 4 \quad \Rightarrow \quad y = -2$$
$$x - 2 = 3 \quad \Rightarrow \quad x = 5$$

Solution: $(5, -2, 0)$

7.
$$x + y - 2z = \ 3$$
$$3x - 2y + 4z = \ 1$$
$$2x - 3y + 6z = \ 8$$

$$x + y - 2z = \ 3$$
$$-5y + 10z = -8$$
$$-5y + 10z = \ 2$$

$$x + y - 2z = \ 3$$
$$-5y + 10z = -8$$
$$0 = \ 10$$

Inconsistent; no solution

9. $3x + 3y + 5z = 1$
$3x + 5y + 9z = 0$
$5x + 9y + 17z = 0$

$6x + 6y + 10z = 2$
$3x + 5y + 9z = 0$
$5x + 9y + 17z = 0$

$x - 3y - 7z = 2$
$3x + 5y + 9z = 0$
$5x + 9y + 17z = 0$

$x - 3y - 7z = 2$
$14y + 30z = -6$
$24y + 52z = -10$

$x - 3y - 7z = 2$
$84y + 180z = -36$
$84y + 182z = -35$

$x - 3y - 7z = 2$
$84y + 180z = -36$
$2z = 1$

$2z = 1 \quad \Rightarrow \quad z = \frac{1}{2}$
$84y + 180\left(\frac{1}{2}\right) = -36 \quad \Rightarrow \quad y = -\frac{3}{2}$
$x - 3\left(-\frac{3}{2}\right) - 7\left(\frac{1}{2}\right) = 2 \quad \Rightarrow \quad x = 1$
Solution: $\left(1, -\frac{3}{2}, \frac{1}{2}\right)$

11. $x + 2y - 7z = -4$
$2x + y + z = 13$
$3x + 9y - 36z = -33$

$x + 2y - 7z = -4$
$-3y + 15z = 21$
$3y - 15z = -21$

$x + 2y - 7z = -4$
$-3y + 15z = 21$

$x + 2y - 7z = -4$
$y - 5z = -7$

$x \qquad + 3z = 10$
$y - 5z = -7$

$z = a$
$y = 5a - 7$
$x = -3a + 10$
Solution: $(-3a + 10, 5a - 7, a)$

13.
$$\begin{aligned}
x \quad\quad + 4z &= 13 \\
4x - 2y + z &= 7 \\
2x - 2y - 7z &= -19
\end{aligned}$$

$$\begin{aligned}
x \quad\quad + 4z &= 13 \\
-2y - 15z &= -45 \\
-2y - 15z &= -45
\end{aligned}$$

$$\begin{aligned}
x \quad\quad + 4z &= 13 \\
-2y - 15z &= -45
\end{aligned}$$

$$\begin{aligned}
z &= a \\
y &= -\tfrac{15}{2}a + \tfrac{45}{2} \\
x &= -4a + 13
\end{aligned}$$

Solution: $\left(-4a + 13,\ -\tfrac{15}{2}a + \tfrac{45}{2},\ a\right)$

15.
$$\begin{aligned}
x - 2y + 5z &= 2 \\
3x + 2y - z &= -2
\end{aligned}$$

$$\begin{aligned}
x - 2y + 5z &= 2 \\
8y - 16z &= -8
\end{aligned}$$

$$\begin{aligned}
x - 2y + 5z &= 2 \\
y - 2z &= -1
\end{aligned}$$

$$\begin{aligned}
x \quad\quad + z &= 0 \\
y - 2z &= -1
\end{aligned}$$

$$\begin{aligned}
z &= a \\
y &= 2a - 1 \\
x &= -a
\end{aligned}$$

Solution: $(-a,\ 2a - 1,\ a)$

17.
$$\begin{aligned}
2x - 3y + z &= -2 \\
-4x + 9y \quad &= 7
\end{aligned}$$

$$\begin{aligned}
2x - 3y + z &= -2 \\
3y + 2z &= 3
\end{aligned}$$

$$\begin{aligned}
2x \quad\quad + 3z &= 1 \\
3y + 2z &= 3
\end{aligned}$$

$$\begin{aligned}
z &= a \\
y &= -\tfrac{2}{3}a + 1 \\
x &= -\tfrac{3}{2}a + \tfrac{1}{2}
\end{aligned}$$

Solution: $\left(-\tfrac{3}{2}a + \tfrac{1}{2},\ -\tfrac{2}{3}a + 1,\ a\right)$

19.

$$\begin{aligned} x \qquad\qquad + 3w &= 4 \\ 2y - \quad z - \quad w &= 0 \\ 3y \qquad - 2w &= 1 \\ 2x - \quad y + 4z \qquad &= 5 \end{aligned}$$

$$\begin{aligned} x \qquad\qquad + 3w &= 4 \\ 2y - \quad z - \quad w &= 0 \\ 3y \qquad - 2w &= 1 \\ -y + 4z - 6w &= -3 \end{aligned}$$

$$\begin{aligned} x \qquad\qquad + 3w &= 4 \\ y \quad - 4z + 6w &= 3 \\ 2y - \quad z - \quad w &= 0 \\ 3y \qquad - 2w &= 1 \end{aligned}$$

$$\begin{aligned} x \qquad\qquad + 3w &= 4 \\ y - 4z + 6w &= 3 \\ 7z - 13w &= -6 \\ 12z - 20w &= -8 \end{aligned}$$

$$\begin{aligned} x \qquad\qquad + 3w &= 4 \\ y - 4z + 6w &= 3 \\ z - \quad 3w &= -2 \\ 12z - 20w &= -8 \end{aligned}$$

$$\begin{aligned} x \qquad\qquad + 3w &= 4 \\ y - 4z + 6w &= 3 \\ z - \quad 3w &= -2 \\ 16w &= 16 \end{aligned}$$

$$\begin{aligned} 16w = 16 &\Rightarrow w = 1 \\ z - 3(1) = -2 &\Rightarrow z = 1 \\ y - 4(1) + 6(1) = 3 &\Rightarrow y = 1 \\ x + 3(1) = 4 &\Rightarrow x = 1 \end{aligned}$$

Solution: $(1, 1, 1, 1)$

21.

$$\begin{aligned} x + \qquad\quad 4z &= 1 \\ x + \quad y + 10z &= 10 \\ 2x - \quad y + \quad 2z &= -5 \end{aligned}$$

$$\begin{aligned} x + \qquad 4z &= 1 \\ y + 6z &= 9 \\ -y - 6z &= -7 \end{aligned}$$

$$\begin{aligned} x + \qquad 4z &= 1 \\ y + 6z &= 9 \\ 0 &= 2 \end{aligned}$$

Inconsistent; no solution

23.
$$5x + 4y + 22z = 0$$
$$4x + 3y + 17z = 0$$
$$4x + 2y + 19z = 0$$

$$x + y + 5z = 0$$
$$4x + 3y + 17z = 0$$
$$4x + 2y + 19z = 0$$

$$x + y + 5z = 0$$
$$-y - 3z = 0$$
$$-2y - z = 0$$

$$x + y + 5z = 0$$
$$y + \cdot 3z = 0$$
$$5z = 0$$

$$5z = 0 \quad \Rightarrow \quad z = 0$$
$$y + 3(0) = 0 \quad \Rightarrow \quad y = 0$$
$$x + 0 + 5(0) \quad \Rightarrow \quad x = 0$$
Solution: $(0, 0, 0)$

25.
$$5x + 5y - z = 0$$
$$10x + 5y + 2z = 0$$
$$5x + 15y - 9z = 0$$

$$5x + 5y - z = 0$$
$$-5y + 4z = 0$$
$$10y - 8z = 0$$

$$5x \qquad + 3z = 0$$
$$-5y + 4z = 0$$

$$z = a$$
$$y = \tfrac{4}{5}a$$
$$x = -\tfrac{3}{5}a$$
Solution: $\left(-\tfrac{3}{5}a,\ \tfrac{4}{5}a,\ a\right)$

27. $y = ax^2 + bx + c$
Passing through $(0, -4)$, $(1, 1)$, and $(2, 10)$

$$-4 = \qquad c \qquad \text{Equation 1}$$
$$1 = a + b + c \qquad \text{Equation 2}$$
$$10 = 4a + 2b + c \qquad \text{Equation 3}$$

Solution: $a = 2$, $b = 3$, $c = -4$
The equation of the parabola is
$y = 2x^2 + 3x - 4$ which can be verified
with a graphing utility.

29. $y = ax^2 + bx + c$
Passing through $(1, 0)$, $(3, 0)$, and $(2, -1)$

$$0 = a + b + c \qquad \text{Equation 1}$$
$$0 = 9a + 3b + c \qquad \text{Equation 2}$$
$$-1 = 4a + 2b + c \qquad \text{Equation 3}$$

Solution: $a = 1$, $b = -4$, $c = 3$
The equation of the parabola is
$y = x^2 - 4x + 3$, which can be verified with
a graphing utility.

31. $x^2 + y^2 + Dx + Ey + F = 0$
Passing through $(0, 0)$, $(2, -2)$, and $(4, 0)$

$$F = 0 \qquad \text{Equation 1}$$
$$8 + 2D - 2E + F = 0 \qquad \text{Equation 2}$$
$$16 + 4D \qquad + F = 0 \qquad \text{Equation 3}$$

Solution: $D = -4$, $E = 0$, $F = 0$
The equation is $x^2 + y^2 - 4x = 0$.

33. $x^2 + y^2 + Dx + Ey + F = 0$
Passing through $(3, -1)$, $(-2, 4)$, and $(6, 8)$

$$10 + 3D - E + F = 0 \qquad \text{Equation 1}$$
$$20 - 2D + 4E + F = 0 \qquad \text{Equation 2}$$
$$100 + 6D + 8E + F = 0 \qquad \text{Equation 3}$$

Solution: $D = -6$, $E = -8$, $F = 0$
The equation is $x^2 + y^2 - 6x - 8y = 0$.

35. $s = \frac{1}{2}at^2 + v_0 t + s_0$
$(t, s) = (1, 128)$, $(2, 80)$, $(3, 0)$

$$128 = \tfrac{1}{2}a + v_0 + s_0 \qquad \text{Equation 1}$$
$$80 = 2a + 2v_0 + s_0 \qquad \text{Equation 2}$$
$$0 = \tfrac{9}{2}a + 3v_0 + s_0 \qquad \text{Equation 3}$$

$$s = \tfrac{1}{2}(-32)t^2 + 0t + 144$$
$$s = -16t^2 + 144$$

37. $s = \frac{1}{2}at^2 + v_0 t + s_0$
$(t, s) = (1, 452)$, $(3, 260)$, $(4, 116)$

$$452 = \tfrac{1}{2}a + v_0 + s_0 \qquad \text{Equation 1}$$
$$260 = \tfrac{9}{2}a + 3v_0 + s_0 \qquad \text{Equation 2}$$
$$116 = 8a + 4v_0 + s_0 \qquad \text{Equation 3}$$

$$s = \tfrac{1}{2}(-32)t^2 - 32t + 500$$
$$s = -16t^2 - 32t + 500$$

39.
$$x + y + z = 16{,}000$$
$$0.05x + 0.06y + 0.07z = 990$$
$$x = z - 3000$$
$$y = z - 2000$$

$$(z - 3000) + (z - 2000) + z = 16{,}000$$
$$3z = 21{,}000$$
$$z = 7000$$

$x = 4000$, $y = 5000$

Solution: $x = \$4000$ at 5%, $y = \$5000$ at 6%, $z = \$7000$ at 7%

41.
$$x + y + z = 775,000$$
$$0.08x + 0.09y + 0.10z = 67,500$$
$$x = 4z$$

$$y + 5z = 775,000 \Rightarrow -9y - 45z = -6,975,000$$
$$0.09y + 0.42z = 67,500 \Rightarrow \underline{\quad 9y + 42z = 6,750,000}$$
$$-3z = -225,000$$
$$z = 75,000$$

$y = 775,000 - 5z = 400,000, \quad x = 4z = 300,000$

Solution: $x = \$300,000$ at 8%, $y = \$400,000$ at 9%, $z = \$75,000$ at 10%

43.
$$C + M + B + G = 500,000$$
$$0.10C + 0.08M + 0.12B + 0.13G = 0.10(500,000)$$
$$B + G = \tfrac{1}{4}(500,000)$$

This system has infinitely many solutions.

Let $G = s$, then $B = 125,000 - s$, $M = 125,000 + \tfrac{1}{2}s$, and $C = 250,000 - \tfrac{1}{2}s$.

Solution: $250,000 - \tfrac{1}{2}s$ in certificates of deposit, $125,000 + \tfrac{1}{2}s$ in municipal bonds, $125,000 - s$ in blue-chip stocks, and s in growth stocks

45. $\tfrac{1}{5}x + \tfrac{1}{2}z = 12$

$\tfrac{2}{5}x + \tfrac{1}{2}z = 16$

$\tfrac{2}{5}x + y = 26$

$\tfrac{1}{5}x + \tfrac{1}{2}z = 12$

$\tfrac{1}{5}x = 4$

$\tfrac{2}{5}x + y = 26$

$\tfrac{1}{5}x = 4 \quad \Rightarrow \quad x = 20$

$\tfrac{2}{5}(20) + y = 26 \quad \Rightarrow \quad 18$

$\tfrac{1}{5}(20) + \tfrac{1}{2}z = 12 \quad \Rightarrow \quad z = 16$

Solution: 20 gallons of spray x
18 gallons of spray y
16 gallons of spray z

47. To haul 15 units of A and 16 units of B, some of the possible ways to use the trucks are:

(1) 4 medium trucks

(2) 2 large trucks, 1 medium truck, 2 small trucks.

49.
$$t_1 - 2t_2 \qquad = \quad 0$$
$$t_1 \qquad\quad - 2a = \; 128$$
$$t_2 + \quad a = \quad 32$$

$$t_1 - 2t_2 \qquad = \quad 0$$
$$2t^2 - 2a = \; 128$$
$$t_2 + \quad a = \quad 32$$

$$t_1 - 2t_2 \qquad = \quad 0$$
$$2t_2 - 2a = \; 128$$
$$2a = -32$$

$$2a = -32 \quad \Rightarrow \quad a = -16$$
$$2t_2 - 2(-16) = 128 \quad \Rightarrow \quad t_2 = 48$$
$$t_1 - 2(48) = 0 \quad \Rightarrow \quad t_1 = 96$$
Solution: $a = -16 \text{ ft/sec}^2$
$$t_1 = 96 \text{ lb}$$
$$t_2 = 48 \text{ lb}$$

51.
$$4c + \qquad 40a = \quad 19$$
$$40b \qquad\;\; = -12$$
$$40c + \quad 544a = \; 160$$

$$4c + \qquad 40a = \quad 19$$
$$40b \qquad\;\; = -12$$
$$144a = -30$$

$$144a = -30 \quad \Rightarrow \quad a = -\tfrac{5}{24}$$
$$40b = -12 \quad \Rightarrow \quad b = -\tfrac{3}{10}$$
$$4c + 40\left(-\tfrac{5}{24}\right) = 19 \quad \Rightarrow \quad c = \tfrac{41}{6}$$
$$y = ax^2 + bx + c$$
$$y = -\tfrac{5}{24}x^2 - \tfrac{3}{10}x + \tfrac{41}{6}$$

53.
$$4c + \qquad 9b + \qquad 29a = \quad 20$$
$$9c + \quad 29b + \qquad 99a = \quad 70$$
$$29c + \quad 99b + \quad 353a = \; 254$$

$$1044c + 2349b + \quad 7569a = 5220$$
$$1044c + 3364b + 11{,}484a = 8120$$
$$1044c + 3564b + 12{,}708a = 9144$$

$$1044c + 2349b + \quad 7569a = 5220$$
$$1015b + \quad 3915a = 2900$$
$$1215b + \quad 5139a = 3924$$

$$1044c + 2349b + \quad 7569a = 5220$$
$$7b + \qquad 27a = \quad 20$$
$$135b + \quad 571a = \quad 436$$

$$1044c + 2349b + \quad 7569a = 5220$$
$$945b + \quad 3645a = 2700$$
$$945b + \quad 3997a = 3052$$

$$1044c + 2349b + \quad 7569a = 5220$$
$$945b + \quad 3645a = 2700$$
$$352a = \quad 352$$

$$352a = 352 \Rightarrow a = 1$$
$$945b + 3645(1) = 2700 \Rightarrow b = -1$$
$$1044c + 2349(-1) + 7569(1) = 5220 \Rightarrow c = 0$$
$$y = ax^2 + bx + c$$
$$y = x^2 - x$$

55. (a) and (b)

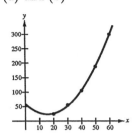

(b) $(20, 25)$, $(30, 55)$, $(40, 105)$, $(50, 188)$, $(60, 300)$

$n = 5$

$$\sum_{i=1}^{5} x_i = 200 \qquad \sum_{i=1}^{5} y_i = 673$$

$$\sum_{i=1}^{5} x_i^{2} = 9000 \qquad \sum_{i=1}^{5} x_i y_i = 33{,}750$$

$$\sum_{i=1}^{5} x_i^{3} = 440{,}000 \qquad \sum_{i=1}^{5} x_i^{2} y_i = 1{,}777{,}500$$

$$\sum_{i=1}^{5} x_i^{4} = 22{,}740{,}000$$

$$5c + \quad 200b + \quad 9000a = \quad 673$$
$$200c + \quad 9000b + \quad 440{,}000a = \quad 33{,}750$$
$$9000c + 440{,}000b + 22{,}740{,}000a = 1{,}777{,}500$$

Solving this system, we get $a \approx 0.141$, $b \approx -4.427$, and $c \approx 58.400$.

$$y = ax^2 + bx + c$$
$$y = 0.141x^2 - 4.427x + 58.400$$

57. Since $x = 4$, $y = -1$, and $z = 2$, one possible system of linear equations is

$$2x + 3y + \quad z = \quad 7$$
$$x - 2y + 4z = 14$$
$$x - 2y + 2z = 10.$$

Section 7.4   Partial Fractions

■ You should know how to decompose a rational function $N(x)/D(x)$ into partial fractions.

(a) If the fraction is improper, divide to obtain
$$\frac{N(x)}{D(x)} = p(x) + \frac{N_1(x)}{D(x)}$$
where $p(x)$ is a polynomial.

(b) Factor the denominator completely into linear and irreducible (over the reals) quadratic factors.

(c) For each factor of the form $(px+q)^m$, the partial fraction decomposition includes the terms
$$\frac{A_1}{(px+q)} + \frac{A_2}{(px+q)^2} + \cdots + \frac{A_m}{(px+q)^m}.$$

(d) For each irreducible factor of the form $(ax^2+bx+c)^n$, the partial fraction decomposition includes the terms
$$\frac{B_1x + C_1}{ax^2+bx+c} + \frac{B_2x + C_2}{(ax^2+bx+c)^2} + \cdots + \frac{B_nx + C_n}{(ax^2+bx+c)^n}.$$

■ You should know how to determine the values of the constants in the numerators.

(a) Set $\dfrac{N_1(x)}{D(x)}$ = partial fraction decomposition.

(b) Multiply both sides by $D(x)$. This is called the basic equation.

(c) For distinct linear factors, substitute the roots of the distinct linear factors into the basic equation.

(d) For repeated linear factors, use the coefficients found in part (c) to rewrite the basic equation. Then use other values of x to solve for the remaining coefficients.

(e) For quadratic factors, expand the basic equation, collect like terms, and then equate the coefficients of like powers.

■ You should know how to verify a partial fraction decomposition using a graphing utility.

1. $\dfrac{1}{x^2-1} = \dfrac{A}{x+1} + \dfrac{B}{x-1}$

$1 = A(x-1) + B(x+1)$

Let $x = -1$: $1 = -2A \Rightarrow A = -\frac{1}{2}$.

Let $x = 1$: $1 = 2B \Rightarrow B = \frac{1}{2}$.

$$\dfrac{1}{x^2-1} = \dfrac{1}{2}\left[\dfrac{1}{x-1} - \dfrac{1}{x+1}\right]$$

3. $\dfrac{1}{x^2+x} = \dfrac{A}{x} + \dfrac{B}{x+1}$

$1 = A(x+1) + Bx$

Let $x = 0$: $1 = A$.

Let $x = -1$: $1 = -B \Rightarrow B = -1$.

$$\dfrac{1}{x^2+x} = \dfrac{1}{x} - \dfrac{1}{x+1}$$

5. $\dfrac{1}{2x^2+x} = \dfrac{A}{2x+1} + \dfrac{B}{x}$

$1 = Ax + B(2x+1)$

Let $x = -\frac{1}{2}$: $1 = -\frac{1}{2}A \Rightarrow A = -2$.

Let $x = 0$: $1 = B$.

$$\dfrac{1}{2x^2+x} = \dfrac{1}{x} - \dfrac{2}{2x+1}$$

7. $\dfrac{3}{x^2+x-2} = \dfrac{A}{x-1} + \dfrac{B}{x+2}$

$3 = A(x+2) + B(x-1)$

Let $x = 1$: $3 = 3A \Rightarrow A = 1$.

Let $x = -2$: $3 = -3B \Rightarrow B = -1$.

$$\dfrac{3}{x^2+x-2} = \dfrac{1}{x-1} - \dfrac{1}{x+2}$$

9. $\dfrac{5-x}{2x^2+x-1} = \dfrac{A}{2x-1} + \dfrac{B}{x+1}$

$-x+5 = A(x+1) + B(2x-1)$

Let $x = \frac{1}{2}$: $\frac{9}{2} = \frac{3}{2}A \Rightarrow A = 3$.

Let $x = -1$: $6 = -3B \Rightarrow B = -2$.

$$\dfrac{5-x}{2x^2+x-1} = \dfrac{3}{2x-1} - \dfrac{2}{x+1}$$

11. $\dfrac{x^2+12x+12}{x^3-4x} = \dfrac{A}{x} + \dfrac{B}{x+2} + \dfrac{C}{x-2}$

$x^2+12x+12 = A(x+2)(x-2) + Bx(x-2) + Cx(x+2)$

Let $x = 0$: $12 = -4A \Rightarrow A = -3$.

Let $x = -2$: $-8 = 8B \Rightarrow B = -1$.

Let $x = 2$: $40 = 8C \Rightarrow C = 5$.

$$\dfrac{x^2+12x+12}{x^3-4x} = -\dfrac{3}{x} - \dfrac{1}{x+2} + \dfrac{5}{x-2}$$

13. $\dfrac{4x^2 + 2x - 1}{x^2(x + 1)} = \dfrac{A}{x} + \dfrac{B}{x^2} + \dfrac{C}{x + 1}$

$4x^2 + 2x - 1 = Ax(x + 1) + B(x + 1) + Cx^2$

Let $x = 0$: $-1 = B$.

Let $x = -1$: $1 = C$.

Let $x = 1$: $5 = 2A + 2B + C$

$$5 = 2A - 2 + 1$$

$$6 = 2A$$

$$3 = A$$

$\dfrac{4x^2 + 2x - 1}{x^2(x + 1)} = \dfrac{3}{x} - \dfrac{1}{x^2} + \dfrac{1}{x + 1}$

15. $\dfrac{x - 1}{x^3 + x^2} = \dfrac{A}{x} + \dfrac{B}{x^2} + \dfrac{C}{x + 1}$

$x - 1 = Ax(x + 1) + B(x + 1) + Cx^2$

Let $x = -1$: $-2 = C$.

Let $x = 0$: $-1 = B$.

Let $x = 1$: $0 = 2A + 2B + C$

$$0 = 2A - 2 - 2$$

$$2 = A$$

$\dfrac{x - 1}{x^3 + x^2} = \dfrac{2}{x} - \dfrac{1}{x^2} - \dfrac{2}{x + 1}$

17. $\dfrac{3x}{(x - 3)^2} = \dfrac{A}{x - 3} + \dfrac{B}{(x - 3)^2}$

$3x = A(x - 3) + B$

Let $x = 3$: $9 = B$.

Let $x = 0$: $0 = -3A + B$

$$0 = -3A + 9$$

$$3 = A$$

$\dfrac{3x}{(x - 3)^2} = \dfrac{3}{x - 3} + \dfrac{9}{(x - 3)^2}$

19. $\dfrac{x^2 - 1}{x(x^2 + 1)} = \dfrac{A}{x} + \dfrac{Bx + C}{x^2 + 1}$

$x^2 - 1 = A(x^2 + 1) + (Bx + C)x$

Let $x = 0$: $-1 = A$.

$$x^2 - 1 = Ax^2 + A + Bx^2 + Cx$$

$$= -x^2 - 1 + Bx^2 + Cx$$

$$= x^2(B - 1) + Cx - 1$$

Equating coefficients of like powers:

$$1 = B - 1$$

$$2 = B \quad \text{and} \quad 0 = C$$

$\dfrac{x^2 - 1}{x(x^2 + 1)} = -\dfrac{1}{x} + \dfrac{2x}{x^2 + 1}$

21. $\dfrac{x^2}{x^4 - 2x^2 - 8} = \dfrac{x^2}{(x^2 - 4)(x^2 + 2)} = \dfrac{A}{x + 2} + \dfrac{B}{x - 2} + \dfrac{Cx + D}{x^2 + 2}$

$x^2 = A(x - 2)(x^2 + 2) + B(x + 2)(x^2 + 2) + (Cx + D)(x^2 - 4)$

Let $x = -2$: $4 = -24A \Rightarrow A = -\frac{1}{6}$.

Let $x = 2$: $4 = 24B \Rightarrow B = \frac{1}{6}$.

$$x^2 = -\frac{1}{6}(x - 2)(x^2 + 2) + \frac{1}{6}(x + 2)(x^2 + 2) + (Cx + D)(x^2 - 4)$$

$$x^2 = -\frac{1}{6}x^3 + \frac{1}{3}x^2 - \frac{1}{3}x + \frac{2}{3} + \frac{1}{6}x^3 + \frac{1}{3}x^2 + \frac{1}{3}x + \frac{2}{3} + Cx^3 + Dx^2 - 4Cx - 4D$$

$$x^2 = Cx^3 + \left(\frac{2}{3} + D\right)x^2 - 4Cx + \left(\frac{4}{3} - 4D\right)$$

Equating coefficients of like powers:

$C \Rightarrow 0$

$1 = \dfrac{2}{3} + D \Rightarrow D = \dfrac{1}{3}$

$\dfrac{x^2}{x^4 - 2x^2 - 8} = \dfrac{1}{6(x - 2)} - \dfrac{1}{6(x + 2)} + \dfrac{1}{3(x^2 + 2)}$

23. $\dfrac{x}{16x^4 - 1} = \dfrac{A}{2x + 1} + \dfrac{B}{2x - 1} + \dfrac{Cx + D}{4x^2 + 1}$

$x = A(2x - 1)(4x^2 + 1) + B(2x + 1)(4x^2 + 1) + (Cx + D)(2x + 1)(2x - 1)$

Let $x = -\frac{1}{2}$: $-\frac{1}{2} = -4A \Rightarrow A = \frac{1}{8}$.

Let $x = \frac{1}{2}$: $\frac{1}{2} = 4B \Rightarrow B = \frac{1}{8}$.

Let $x = 0$: $0 = -A + B - D$

$0 = -\frac{1}{8} + \frac{1}{8} - D$

$0 = D$

Let $x = 1$: $1 = 5A + 15B + 3C + 3D$

$1 = \frac{5}{8} + \frac{15}{8} + 3C + 0$

$-\frac{1}{2} = C$

$\dfrac{x}{16x^4 - 1} = \dfrac{1/8}{2x + 1} + \dfrac{1/8}{2x - 1} - \dfrac{x/2}{4x^2 + 1} = \dfrac{1}{8}\left[\dfrac{1}{2x + 1} + \dfrac{1}{2x - 1} - \dfrac{4x}{4x^2 + 1}\right]$

25.
$$\frac{x^2 + x + 2}{(x^2 + 2)^2} = \frac{Ax + B}{x^2 + 2} + \frac{Cx + D}{(x^2 + 2)^2}$$

$$x^2 + x + 2 = (Ax + B)(x^2 + 2) + Cx + D$$

$$x^2 + x + 2 = Ax^3 + Bx^2 + (2A + C)x + (2B + D)$$

Equating coefficient of like powers:

$$0 = A$$

$$1 = B$$

$$1 = 2A + C \Rightarrow C = 1$$

$$2 = 2B + D \Rightarrow D = 0$$

$$\frac{x^2 + x + 2}{(x^2 + 2)^2} = \frac{1}{x^2 + 2} + \frac{x}{(x^2 + 2)^2}$$

27.
$$\frac{x^2 + 5}{(x + 1)(x^2 - 2x + 3)} = \frac{A}{x + 1} + \frac{Bx + C}{x^2 - 2x + 3}$$

$$x^2 + 5 = A(x^2 - 2x + 3) + (Bx + C)(x + 1)$$

Let $x = -1$: $6 = 6A \Rightarrow A = 1$.

$$x^2 + 5 = x^2 - 2x + 3 + Bx^2 + Bx + Cx + C = x^2(1 + B) + x(-2 + B + C) + (3 + C)$$

Equating coefficients of like powers:

$$1 = 1 + B, \quad 0 = -2 + B + C, \quad \text{and } 5 = 3 + C$$

$$0 = B \qquad\qquad 0 = -2 + 0 + C \qquad\qquad 2 = C$$

$$2 = C$$

$$\frac{x^2 + 5}{(x + 1)(x^2 - 2x + 3)} = \frac{1}{x + 1} + \frac{2}{x^2 - 2x + 3}$$

29.
$$\frac{2x^3 - 4x^2 - 15x + 5}{x^2 - 2x - 8} = 2x + \frac{x + 5}{(x + 2)(x - 4)}$$

$$\frac{x + 5}{(x + 2)(x - 4)} = \frac{A}{x + 2} + \frac{B}{x - 4}$$

$$x + 5 = A(x - 4) + B(x + 2)$$

Let $x = -2$: $3 = -6A \Rightarrow A = -\frac{1}{2}$.

Let $x = 4$: $9 = 6B \Rightarrow B = \frac{3}{2}$.

$$\frac{2x^3 - 4x^2 - 15x + 5}{x^2 - 2x - 8} = 2x + \frac{1}{2}\left[\frac{3}{x - 4} - \frac{1}{x + 2}\right]$$

31.
$$\frac{x^4}{(x-1)^3} = \frac{x^4}{x^3 - 3x^2 + 3x - 1} = x + 3 + \frac{6x^2 - 8x + 3}{(x-1)^3}$$

$$\frac{6x^2 - 8x + 3}{(x-1)^3} = \frac{A}{x-1} + \frac{B}{(x-1)^2} + \frac{C}{(x-1)^3}$$

$$6x^2 - 8x + 3 = A(x-1)^2 + B(x-1) + C$$

Let $x = 1$: $1 = C$. $6x^2 - 8x + 3 = Ax^2 - 2Ax + A + Bx - B + 1$

$$6x^2 - 8x + 3 = Ax^2 + (-2A + B)x + (A - B + 1)$$

Equating coefficients of like powers:

$6 = A, \quad -8 = -2A + B$ and $3 = A - B + 1$

$\qquad\qquad -8 = -12 + B \qquad\quad 3 = 6 - B + 1$

$\qquad\qquad\quad 4 = \qquad B \qquad\quad 4 = \qquad B$

$$\frac{x^4}{(x-1)^3} = x + 3 + \frac{6}{x-1} + \frac{4}{(x-1)^2} + \frac{1}{(x-1)^3}$$

33. $\dfrac{1}{a^2 - x^2} = \dfrac{A}{a+x} + \dfrac{B}{a-x}$, a is a constant.

$1 = A(a - x) + B(a + x)$

Let $x = -a$: $1 = 2aA \Rightarrow A = \dfrac{1}{2a}$.

Let $x = a$: $1 = 2aB \Rightarrow B = \dfrac{1}{2a}$.

$$\frac{1}{a^2 - x^2} = \frac{1}{2a}\left[\frac{1}{a+x} + \frac{1}{a-x}\right]$$

To check this result graphically, let $a = 1$ and graph

$$y_1 = \frac{1}{1 - x^2}$$

$$y_2 = \frac{1}{2}\left[\frac{1}{1+x} + \frac{1}{1-x}\right]$$

on the same viewing rectangle.

35. $\dfrac{1}{x(a - x)} = \dfrac{A}{x} + \dfrac{B}{a-x}$

$1 = A(a - x) + Bx$

Let $x = 0$: $1 = aA \Rightarrow A = \dfrac{1}{a}$.

Let $x = a$: $1 = aB \Rightarrow B = \dfrac{1}{a}$.

$$\frac{1}{x(a-x)} = \frac{1}{a}\left(\frac{1}{x} + \frac{1}{a-x}\right)$$

To check this result graphically, let $a = 1$ and graph

$$y_1 = \frac{1}{x(1-x)}$$

$$y_2 = \left(\frac{1}{x} + \frac{1}{1-x}\right)$$

on the same viewing rectangle.

Section 7.5   Systems of Inequalities

■ You should be able to sketch the graph of an inequality in two variables:
   (a) Replace the inequality with an equal sign and graph the equation. Use a dashed line
       for $<$ or $>$, a solid line for $\leq$ or $\geq$.
   (b) Test a point in each region formed by the graph. If the point satisfies the inequality,
       shade the whole region.

■ You should be able to sketch the solution set of a system of inequalities.

---

1. The graph of $x > 3$ is the half-plane to the right of the line $x = 3$. Graph (f)

3. The graph of $2x + 3y \leq 6$ is the half-plane below the line $2x + 3y = 6$ together with the line.
Graph (e)

5. The graph of $x^2 + y^2 < 4$ is the interior of the circle centered at the origin with radius 2.
Graph (a)

7. The graph of $xy = 2$ is a hyperbola with the axes as asymptotes. The graph of $xy > 2$ is
graph (b).

9. $x \geq 2$ **11.** $y \geq -1$ **13.** $y < 2 - x$

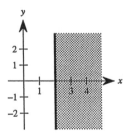 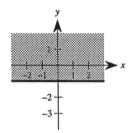 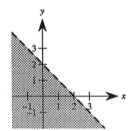

15. $2y - x \geq 4$

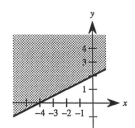

17. $(x+1)^2 + (y-2)^2 < 9$

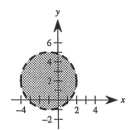

19. $y \leq \dfrac{1}{1+x^2}$

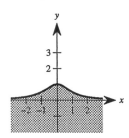

21. $x + y \leq 1$

$\quad\quad -x + y \leq 1$

$\quad\quad y \geq 0$

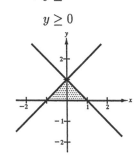

23. $x + y \leq 5$

$\quad\quad x \geq 2$

$\quad\quad y \geq 0$

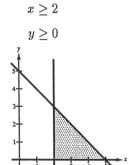

25. $-3x + 2y < 6$

$\quad\quad x + 4y > -2$

$\quad\quad 2x + y < 3$

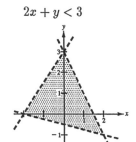

27. $2x + y > 2$

$\quad\quad 6x + 3y < 2$

$\quad\quad$ No solution

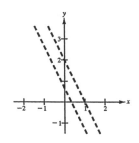

29. $x \geq 1$

$\quad\quad x - 2y \leq 3$

$\quad\quad 3x + 2y \geq 9$

$\quad\quad x + y \leq 6$

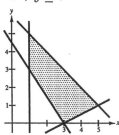

31. $x^2 + y^2 \leq 9$

$\quad\quad x^2 + y^2 \geq 1$

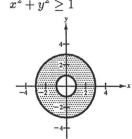

33. $x > y^2$

$x < y + 2$

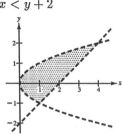

35. $y \leq \sqrt{3x} + 1$

$y \geq x + 1$

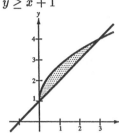

37. $y < x^3 - 2x + 1$

$y > -2x$

$x \leq 1$

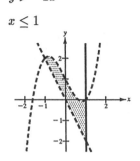

39. $x^2 y \geq 1$

$0 < x \leq 4$

$y \leq 4$

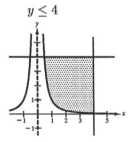

41. $2 \leq x \leq 5$

$1 \leq y \leq 7$

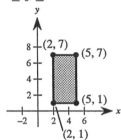

43. $y \geq 0$

$y \leq \frac{3}{2}x$

$y \leq -x + 5$

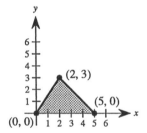

45. $x^2 + y^2 \leq 16$

$x \geq 0$

$y \geq 0$

47. $x =$ number of tables

$y =$ number of chairs

$x + \frac{3}{2}y \leq 12$

$\frac{4}{3}x + \frac{3}{2}y \leq 15$

$x \geq 0$

$y \geq 0$

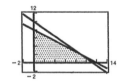

49. $x =$ amount in one account

$y =$ amount in other account

$x + y \leq 20,000$

$x \geq 5,000$

$y \geq 5,000$

$2x \leq y$

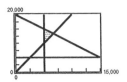

51. $x =$ ounces of food X

$y =$ ounces of food Y

Calcium: $20x + 10y \geq 280$

Iron: $15x + 10y \geq 160$

Vitamin B: $10x + 20y \geq 180$

$x \geq \quad 0$

$y \geq \quad 0$

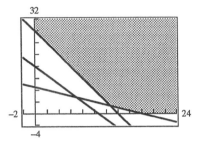

53. Demand $=$ Supply

$50 - 0.5x = 0.125x$

$50 = 0.625x$

$80 = x$

$10 = p$

Point of equilibrium: $(80, \ 10)$

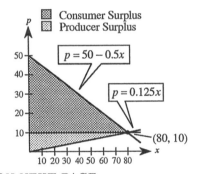

-CONTINUED ON NEXT PAGE-

53. –CONTINUED–

The consumer surplus is the area of the triangle bounded by

$$p \leq 50 - 0.5x$$

$$p \geq 10$$

$$x \geq 0.$$

Consumer surplus $= \frac{1}{2}$(base)(height) $= \frac{1}{2}(80)(40) = \$1600$

The producer surplus is the area of the triangle bounded by

$$p \geq 0.125x$$

$$p \leq 10$$

$$x \geq 0.$$

Producer surplus $= \frac{1}{2}$(base)(height) $= \frac{1}{2}(80)(10) = \$400$

55. Demand $=$ Supply

$$300 - x = 100 + x$$

$$200 = 2x$$

$$100 = x$$

$$200 = p$$

Point of equilibrium: $(100, 200)$

The consumer surplus is the area of the triangle bounded by

$$p \leq 300 - x$$

$$p \geq 200$$

$$x \geq 0.$$

Consumer surplus $= \frac{1}{2}$(base)(height) $= \frac{1}{2}(100)(100) = 5000$

The producer surplus is the area of the triangle bounded by

$$p \geq 100 + x$$

$$p \leq 200$$

$$x \geq 0.$$

Producer surplus $= \frac{1}{2}$(base)(height) $= \frac{1}{2}(100)(100) = 5000$

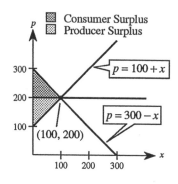

57.   Demand = Supply

$$140 - 0.00002x = 80 + 0.00001x$$

$$60 = 0.00003x$$

$$2{,}000{,}000 = x$$

$$100 = p$$

Point of equilibrium: $(2{,}000{,}000, \quad 100)$

The consumer surplus is the area of the triangle bounded by

$$p \le 140 - 0.00002x$$

$$p \ge 100$$

$$x \ge 0.$$

Consumer surplus = $\frac{1}{2}$(base)(height) = $\frac{1}{2}$(2,000,000)(40) = \$40,000,000 or \$40 million

The producer surplus is the area of the triangle bounded by

$$p \ge 80 + 0.00001x$$

$$p \le 100$$

$$x \ge 0.$$

Producer surplus = $\frac{1}{2}$(base)(height) = $\frac{1}{2}$(2,000,000)(20) = \$20,000,000 or \$20 million

59. Inside track: $2x + \pi y \ge 125$

Body-building area: $xy \ge 500$

$$x \ge 0$$

$$y \ge 0$$

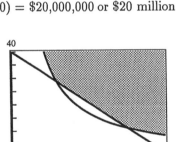

Section 7.6   Linear Programming

- If a linear programming problem has a solution, it must occur at a vertex of the set of feasible solutions.

- You should be able to solve a linear programming problem graphically.

- You should be able to solve linear programming problems that arise in real life business applications.

1. $z = 4x + 5y$

At $(0, 6)$: $z = 4(0) + 5(6) = 30$
At $(0, 0)$: $z = 4(0) + 5(0) = 0$
At $(6, 0)$: $z = 4(6) + 5(0) = 24$
The maximum value is 30 at $(0, 6)$.
The minimum value is 0 at $(0, 0)$.

3. $z = 10x + 6y$

At $(0, 6)$: $z = 10(0) + 6(6) = 36$
At $(0, 0)$: $z = 10(0) + 6(0) = 0$
At $(6, 0)$: $z = 10(6) + 6(0) = 60$
The maximum value is 60 at $(6, 0)$.
The minimum value is 0 at $(0, 0)$.

5. $z = 3x + 2y$

At $(0, 5)$: $z = 3(0) + 2(5) = 10$
At $(4, 0)$: $z = 3(4) + 2(0) = 12$
At $(3, 4)$: $z = 3(3) + 2(4) = 17$
At $(0, 0)$: $z = 3(0) + 2(0) = 0$
The maximum value is 17 at $(3, 4)$.
The minimum value is 0 at $(0, 0)$.

7. $z = 5x + \dfrac{y}{2}$

At $(0, 5)$: $z = 5(0) + \frac{5}{2} = \frac{5}{2}$
At $(4, 0)$: $z = 5(4) + \frac{0}{2} = 20$
At $(3, 4)$: $z = 5(3) + \frac{4}{2} = 17$
At $(0, 0)$: $z = 5(0) + \frac{0}{2} = 0$
The maximum value is 20 at $(4, 0)$.
The minimum value is 0 at $(0, 0)$.

9. $z = 10x + 7y$

At $(0, 45)$: $z = 10(0) + 7(45) = 315$
At $(30, 45)$: $z = 10(30) + 7(45) = 615$
At $(60, 20)$: $z = 10(60) + 7(20) = 740$
At $(60, 0)$: $z = 10(60) + 7(0) = 600$
At $(0, 0)$: $z = 10(0) + 7(0) = 0$
The maximum value is 740 at $(60, 20)$.
The minimum value is 0 at $(0, 0)$.

11. $z = 25x + 30y$

At $(0, 45)$: $z = 25(0) + 30(45) = 1,350$
At $(30, 45)$: $z = 25(30) + 30(45) = 2,100$
At $(60, 20)$: $z = 25(60) + 30(20) = 2,100$
At $(60, 0)$: $z = 25(60) + 30(0) = 1,500$
At $(0, 0)$: $z = 25(0) + 30(0) = 0$
The maximum value is 2,100 at any point along the line segment connecting $(30, 45)$ and $(60, 20)$.
The minimum value is 0 at $(0, 0)$.

13. $z = 6x + 10y$

At $(0, 2)$: $z = 6(0) + 10(2) = 20$

At $(5, 0)$: $z = 6(5) + 10(0) = 30$

At $(0, 0)$: $z = 6(0) + 10(0) = 0$

The maximum value is 30 at $(5, 0)$.

The minimum value is 0 at $(0, 0)$.

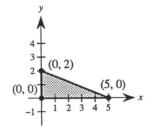

15. $z = 9x + 24y$

At $(0, 2)$: $z = 9(0) + 24(2) = 48$

At $(5, 0)$: $z = 9(5) + 24(0) = 45$

At $(0, 0)$: $z = 9(0) + 24(0) = 0$

The maximum value is 48 at $(0, 2)$.

The minimum value is 0 at $(0, 0)$.

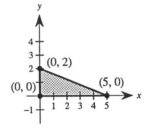

17. $z = 4x + 5y$

At $(10, 0)$: $z = 4(10) + 5(0) = 40$

At $(5, 3)$: $z = 4(5) + 5(3) = 35$

At $(3, 5)$: $z = 4(3) + 5(5) = 37$

At $(0, 9)$: $z = 4(0) + 5(9) = 45$

C is unbounded.

Therefore, there is no maximum.

The minimum value is 35 at $(5, 3)$.

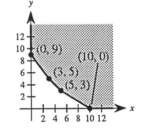

19. $z = 2x + 7y$

At $(10, 0)$: $z = 2(10) + 7(0) = 20$

At $(5, 3)$: $z = 2(5) + 7(3) = 31$

At $(3, 5)$: $z = 2(3) + 7(5) = 41$

At $(0, 9)$: $z = 2(0) + 7(9) = 63$

C is unbounded.

Therefore, there is no maximum.

The minimum value is 20 at $(10, 0)$.

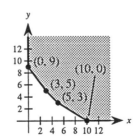

21. $z = 4x + y$

At $(36, 0)$: $z = 4(36) + 0 = 144$
At $(40, 0)$: $z = 4(40) + 0 = 160$
At $(24, 8)$: $z = 4(24) + 8 = 104$
The maximum value is 160 at $(40, 0)$.
The minimum value is 104 at $(24, 8)$.

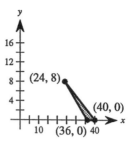

23. $z = x + 4y$

At $(36, 0)$: $z = 36 + 4(0) = 36$
At $(40, 0)$: $z = 40 + 4(0) = 40$
At $(24, 8)$: $z = 24 + 4(8) = 56$
The maximum value is 56 at $(24, 8)$.
The minimum value is 36 at $(36, 0)$.

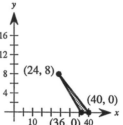

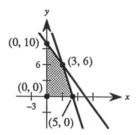

Figure for Exercises 25 and 27

25. $z = 2x + y$

At $(0, 10)$: $z = 2(0) + (10) = 10$
At $(3, 6)$: $z = 2(3) + (6) = 12$
At $(5, 0)$: $z = 2(5) + (0) = 10$
At $(0, 0)$: $z = 2(0) + (0) = 0$
The maximum value is 12 at $(3, 6)$.

27. $z = x + y$

At $(0, 10)$: $z = (0) + (10) = 10$
At $(3, 6)$: $z = (3) + (6) = 9$
At $(5, 0)$: $z = (5) + (0) = 5$
At $(0, 0)$: $z = (0) + (0) = 0$
The maximum value is 10 at $(0, 10)$.

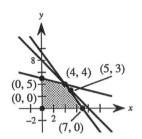

Figure for Exercises 29 and 31

29. $z = x + 5y$

At $(0, 5)$: $z = (0) + 5(5) = 25$

At $(4, 4)$: $z = (4) + 5(4) = 24$

At $(5, 3)$: $z = (5) + 5(3) = 20$

At $(7, 0)$: $z = (7) + 5(0) = 7$

At $(0, 0)$: $z = (0) + 5(0) = 0$

The maximum value is 25 at $(0, \ 5)$.

31. $z = 4x + 5y$

At $(0, 5)$: $z = 4(0) + 5(5) = 25$

At $(4, 4)$: $z = 4(4) + 5(4) = 36$

At $(5, 3)$: $z = 4(5) + 5(3) = 35$

At $(7, 0)$: $z = 4(7) + 5(0) = 28$

At $(0, 0)$: $z = 4(0) + 5(0) = 0$

The maximum value is 36 at $(4, \ 4)$.

33. $x = $ number of \$250 models

$y = $ number of \$400 models

Constraints: $250x + 400y \le 70,000$

$$x + y \le 250$$

$$x \ge 0$$

$$y \ge 0$$

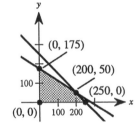

Objective function: $P = 45x + 50y$

Vertices: $(0, 175), (200, 50), (250, 0), (0, 0)$

At $(0, 175)$: $P = 45(0) + 50(175) = 8,750$

At $(200, 50)$: $P = 45(200) + 50(50) = 11,500$

At $(250, 0)$: $P = 45(250) + 50(0) = 11,250$

At $(0, 0)$: $P = 45(0) + 50(0) = 0$

To maximize the profit, the merchant should stock 200 units of the model costing \$250 and 50 units of the model costing \$400.

35. $x =$ number of bags of Brand X

$y =$ number of bags of Brand Y

Constraints: $2x + y \geq 12$

$2x + 9y \geq 36$

$2x + 3y \geq 24$

$x \geq 0$

$y \geq 0$

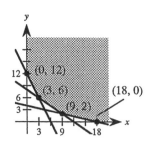

Objective function: $C = 25x + 20y$

Vertices: $(0, 12), (3, 6), (9, 2), (18, 0)$

At $(0, 12)$: $C = 25(0) + 20(12) = 240$

At $(3, 6)$: $C = 25(3) + 20(6) = 195$

At $(9, 2)$: $C = 25(9) + 20(2) = 265$

At $(18, 0)$: $C = 25(18) + 20(0) = 450$

To minimize cost, use three bags of Brand X and six bags of Brand Y for a total cost of $195.

37. $x =$ number of Model A

$y =$ number of Model B

Constraints: $2x + 2.5y \leq 4000$

$4x + y \leq 4800$

$x + 0.75y \leq 1500$

$x \geq 0$

$y \geq 0$

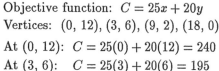

Objective function: $P = 45x + 50y$

Vertices: $(0, 0), (0, 1600), (750,\ 1000), (1050,\ 600), (1200,\ 0)$

At $(0, 0)$: $P = 45(0) + 50(0) = 0$

At $(0, 1600)$: $P = 45(0) + 50(1600) = 80{,}000$

At $(750,\ 1000)$: $P = 45(750) + 50(1000) = 83{,}750$

At $(1050,\ 600)$: $P = 45(1050) + 50(600) = 77{,}250$

At $(1200,\ 0)$: $P = 45(1200) + 50(0) = 54{,}000$

The maximum profit occurs when 750 units of Model A and 1000 units of Model B are produced.

39. Let x = number of audits.

Let y = number of tax returns.

Constraints: $100x + 12.5y \leq 900$

$$10x + 2.5y \leq 100$$

$$x \geq 0$$

$$y \geq 0$$

Objective function: $R = 2000x + 300y$

Vertices: $(0, 0)$, $(0, 40)$, $(8, 8)$, $(9, 0)$

At $(0, 0)$: $R = 2000(0) + 300(0) = 0$

At $(0, 40)$: $R = 2000(0) + 300(40) = 12{,}000$

At $(8, 8)$: $R = 2000(8) + 300(8) = 18{,}400$

At $(9, 0)$: $R = 2000(9) + 300(0) = 18{,}000$

The revenue will be maximum if the firm does 8 audits and 8 tax returns each week.

41. At $(0, 0)$: $z = 2.5(0) + 0 = 0$

At $(2, 0)$: $z = 2.5(2) + 0 = 5$

At $\left(\frac{20}{19}, \frac{45}{19}\right)$: $z = 2.5\left(\frac{20}{19}\right) + \frac{25}{19} = 5$

At $(0, 3)$: $z = 2.5(0) + 3 = 3$

z is maximum at any point along the line segment connecting $(2, 0)$ and $\left(\frac{20}{19}, \frac{45}{19}\right)$.

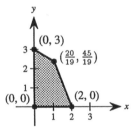

43. At $(0, 0)$: $z = -(0) + 2(0) = 0$

At $(0, 7)$: $z = -(0) + 2(7) = 14$

At $(7, 0)$: $z = -(7) + 2(0) = -7$

The constraint $x \leq 10$ is extraneous.

The maximum value is 14 at $(0, 7)$.

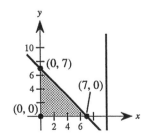

45. At $(0, 0)$: $z = 3(0) + 4(0) = 0$
At $(0, 1)$: $z = 3(0) + 4(1) = 4$
At $(1, 0)$: $z = 3(1) + 4(0) = 3$
The constraint $2x + y \leq 4$ is extraneous.
The maximum value is 4 at $(0, 1)$.

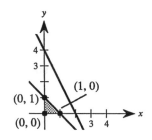

47. $z = 3x + ty$
At $(0, 0)$: $z = 3(0) + t(0) = 0$
At $(0, 5)$: $z = 3(0) + t(5) = 5t$
At $(3, 4)$: $z = 3(3) + t(4) = 9 + 4t$
At $(4, 0)$: $z = 3(4) + t(0) = 12$

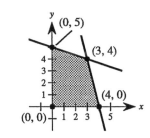

(a) For the maximum value to be at $(0, 5)$,
$z = 5t$ must be greater than $z = 9 + 4t$
and $z = 12$.

$$5t > 9 + 4t \quad \text{and} \quad 5t > 12$$

$$t > 9 \qquad\qquad t > \tfrac{12}{5}$$

Thus, $t > 9$.

(b) For the maximum value to be at $(3, 4)$,
$z = 9 + 4t$ must be greater than $z = 5t$
and $z = 12$.

$$9 + 4t > 5t \quad \text{and} \quad 9 + 4t > 12$$

$$9 > t \qquad\qquad 4t > 3$$

$$t > \tfrac{3}{4}$$

Thus, $\tfrac{3}{4} < t < 9$.

Chapter 7   Review Exercises

1. $x + y = 2$ Equation 1

   $x - y = 0$ Equation 2

   Solve for y in Equation 2: $y = x$
   Substitute in Equation 1: $x + x = 2$ $\Rightarrow$ $x = 1$
   Backsubstitute $x = 1$: $y = x$ $\Rightarrow$ $y = 1$
   Solution: $(1, 1)$

3. $x^2 - y^2 = 9$ Equation 1

   $x - y = 1$ Equation 2

   Solve for x in Equation 2: $x = y + 1$
   Substitute for x in Equation 1:
   $$(y + 1)^2 - y^2 = 9 \quad \Rightarrow \quad 2y + 1 = 9 \quad \Rightarrow \quad y = 4$$
   Backsubstitute $y = 4$: $x = y + 1 = 4 + 1 = 5$
   Solution: $(5, 4)$

5. $y = 2x^2$ Equation 1

   $y = x^4 - 2x^2$ Equation 2

   Substitute for y in Equation 2:
   $$2x^2 = x^4 - 2x^2 \Rightarrow 0 = x^2(x^2 - 4)$$
   $$x = 0, \pm 2$$
   Backsubstitute $x = 0$: $y = 2(0)^2 = 0$
   Backsubstitute $x = 2$: $y = 2(2)^2 = 8$
   Backsubstitute $x = -2$: $y = 2(-2)^2 = 8$
   Solutions: $(0, 0)$, $(2, 8)$, $(-2, 8)$

7. $2x - y = 2 \Rightarrow 16x - 8y = 16$

   $6x + 8y = 39 \Rightarrow \underline{6x + 8y = 39}$

   $ 22x = 55$

   $ x = \tfrac{5}{2}$

   $ y = \phantom{\tfrac{5}{}} 3$

   Solution: $\left(\tfrac{5}{2}, 3\right)$

9. $ 3x - 2y = 0 \Rightarrow -3x + 2y = 0$

   $3x + 2(y + 5) = 10 \Rightarrow \underline{3x + 2y = 0}$

   $ 4y = 0$

   $ y = 0$

   $ x = 0$

   Solution: $(0, 0)$

11. $1.25x - 2y = 3.5 \Rightarrow 5x - 8y = 14$

   $5x - 8y = 14 \Rightarrow \underline{-5x + 8y = -14}$

   $ 0 = 0$

   Solution: All points (x, y) lying on the
   line $5x - 8y = 14$, or any points of the
   form $\left(\tfrac{14}{5} + \tfrac{8}{5}a, a\right)$.

13. $y^2 - 2y + x = 0$

$\qquad x + y = 0$

One way to solve this problem is to reverse the roles of x and y. That is, let $x = Y$ and $y = X$, and graph

$\qquad Y = 2X - X^2$

$\qquad Y = -X.$

We see that there are two points of intersection, $(X, Y) = (0, 0)$ and $(X, Y) = (3, -3)$. Thus, the solutions to the original equations are $(x, y) = (0, 0)$ and $(x, y) = (-3, 3)$.

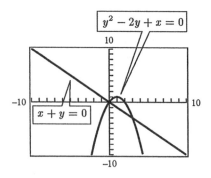

15. $y = 2(6 - x)$

$\qquad y = 2^{x-2}$

The unique solution is $(x, y) = (4, 4)$.

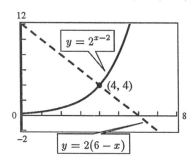

17. $C = 2.85x + 10{,}000$

$\qquad R = 4.95x$

Break-even:

$\qquad R = C$

$\qquad 4.95x = 2.85x + 10{,}000$

$\qquad 2.10x = 10{,}000$

$\qquad x \approx 4762$ units

19. $x =$ amount of 75% solution

$\qquad y =$ amount of 50% solution

$$
\begin{array}{rcll}
x + \quad y = & 100 & \Rightarrow & -0.5x - 0.5y = -50 \\
0.75x + 0.50y = 0.60(100) & & \Rightarrow & \underline{0.75x + 0.5y = \quad 60} \\
& & & 0.25x \qquad\quad = \quad 10 \\
& & & x = \quad 40 \\
& & & y = \quad 60
\end{array}
$$

Solution: 40 gallons of 75% solution and 60 gallons of 50% solution

21. $x =$ ground speed of Pittsburgh to Philadelphia flight

$y =$ ground speed of Philadelphia to Pittsburgh flight

$$x = y + 25$$

$$\tfrac{2}{3}x + \tfrac{2}{3}y = 275$$

$$\tfrac{2}{3}(y + 25) + \tfrac{2}{3}y = 275$$

$$\tfrac{4}{3}y + \tfrac{50}{3} = 275$$

$$\tfrac{4}{3}y = \tfrac{775}{3}$$

$$y = 193.75$$

$$x = 218.75$$

Solution: 218.75 mph for the Pittsburgh to Philadelphia flight and 193.75 mph for the Philadelphia to Pittsburgh flight

23. Supply $=$ Demand

$$22 + 0.00001x = 37 - 0.0002x$$

$$0.00021x = 15$$

$$x = \tfrac{500{,}000}{7}$$

$$y = \tfrac{159}{7}$$

Point of equilibrium: $\left(\tfrac{500{,}000}{7}, \tfrac{159}{7}\right)$

25.
$$\begin{aligned} x + 2y + 6z &= 4 \\ -3x + 2y - z &= -4 \\ 4x + 2z &= 16 \end{aligned}$$

$$\begin{aligned} x + 2y + 6z &= 4 \\ 8y + 17z &= 8 \\ -8y - 22z &= 0 \end{aligned}$$

$$\begin{aligned} x + 2y + 6z &= 4 \\ 8y + 17z &= 8 \\ -5z &= 8 \end{aligned}$$

$$-5z = 8 \Rightarrow z = -\tfrac{8}{5}$$
$$8y + 17\left(-\tfrac{8}{5}\right) = 8 \Rightarrow y = \tfrac{22}{5}$$
$$x + 2\left(\tfrac{22}{5}\right) + 6\left(-\tfrac{8}{5}\right) = 4 \Rightarrow x = \tfrac{24}{5}$$

Solution: $\left(\tfrac{24}{5}, \tfrac{22}{5}, -\tfrac{8}{5}\right)$

27.
$$\begin{aligned} x - 2y + z &= -6 \\ 2x - 3y &= -7 \\ -x + 3y - 3z &= 11 \end{aligned}$$

$$\begin{aligned} x - 2y + z &= -6 \\ y - 2z &= 5 \\ y - 2z &= 5 \end{aligned}$$

$$\begin{aligned} x \quad - 3z &= 4 \\ y - 2z &= 5 \\ z &= a \end{aligned}$$

$$y - 2a = 5 \Rightarrow y = 2a + 5$$
$$x - 3a = 4 \Rightarrow x = 3a + 4$$

Solution: $(3a + 4, 2a + 5, a)$

29. $2x + 5y - 19z = 34$

$3x + 8y - 31z = 54$

$6x + 15y - 57z = 102$

$6x + 16y - 62z = 108$

$6x + 15y - 57z = 102$

$y - 5z = 6$

$6x \qquad + 18z = 12$

$y - 5z = 6$

$z = a$

$y - 5a = 6 \quad \Rightarrow \quad y = 5a + 6$

$6x + 18a = 12 \quad \Rightarrow \quad x = -3a + 2$

Solution: $(-3a + 2, \ 5a + 6, \ a)$

31. $\begin{bmatrix} -1 & 1 & 2 & \vdots & 1 \\ 2 & 3 & 1 & \vdots & -2 \\ 5 & 4 & 2 & \vdots & 4 \end{bmatrix} \Rightarrow \begin{bmatrix} 1 & -1 & -2 & \vdots & -1 \\ 0 & 5 & 5 & \vdots & 0 \\ 0 & 9 & 12 & \vdots & 9 \end{bmatrix} \Rightarrow \begin{bmatrix} 1 & 0 & -1 & \vdots & -1 \\ 0 & 1 & 1 & \vdots & 0 \\ 0 & 0 & 3 & \vdots & 9 \end{bmatrix}$

$\Rightarrow \begin{bmatrix} 1 & 0 & 0 & \vdots & 2 \\ 0 & 1 & 0 & \vdots & -3 \\ 0 & 0 & 1 & \vdots & 3 \end{bmatrix}$

$x = 2$

$y = -3$

$z = 3$

Answer: $(2, \ -3, \ 3)$

33. $\begin{bmatrix} 2 & 1 & 2 & \vdots & 4 \\ 2 & 2 & 0 & \vdots & 5 \\ 2 & -1 & 6 & \vdots & 2 \end{bmatrix} \Rightarrow \begin{bmatrix} 2 & 1 & 2 & \vdots & 4 \\ 0 & 1 & -2 & \vdots & 1 \\ 0 & -2 & 4 & \vdots & -2 \end{bmatrix} \Rightarrow \begin{bmatrix} 2 & 0 & 4 & \vdots & 3 \\ 0 & 1 & -2 & \vdots & 1 \\ 0 & 0 & 0 & \vdots & 0 \end{bmatrix}$

Let $z = a$.

$y - 2a = 1 \Rightarrow y = 2a + 1$

$2x + 4a = 3 \Rightarrow x = -2a + \frac{3}{2}$

Answer: $(-2a + \frac{3}{2}, \ 2a + 1, \ a)$

35. $y = ax^2 + bx + c$

     At $(0, -6)$: $-6 = \; c$

     At $(1, -3)$: $-3 = \; a + \; b + c \Rightarrow \; a + \; b = \; 3 \Rightarrow -2a - 2b = -6$

     At $(2, 4)$: $4 = 4a + 2b + c \Rightarrow 4a + 2b = 10 \Rightarrow \;\underline{\; 4a + 2b = \; 10 \;}$

$$2a \;\;\;\;\;\; = \;\; 4$$

$$a = \;\; 2$$

$$b = \;\; 1$$

     Solution: $y = 2x^2 + x - 6$

37. $x^2 + y^2 + Dx + Ey + F = 0$

     At $(2, 2)$: $4 + 4 + 2D + 2E + F = 0 \Rightarrow 2D + 2E + F = -8$

     At $(5, -1)$: $25 + 1 + 5D - \;\; E + F = 0 \Rightarrow 5D - \;\; E - F = -26$

     At $(-1, -1)$: $1 + 1 - \;\; D - \;\; E + F = 0 \Rightarrow -D - \;\; E + F = -2$

$$D + \;\; E - \;\; F = \;\;\; 2$$

$$5D - \;\; E + \;\; F = -26$$

$$2D + 2E + \;\; F = \;\; -8$$

$$D + \;\; E - \;\; F = \;\;\; 2$$

$$-\, 6E + 6F = -36$$

$$3F = -12$$

$$3F = -12 \;\;\; \Rightarrow \;\;\; F = -4$$

$$-6E + 6(-4) = -36 \;\;\; \Rightarrow \;\;\; E = 2$$

$$D + 2 + 4 = 2 \;\;\; \Rightarrow \;\;\; D = -4$$

     Solution: $y = x^2 + y^2 - 4x + 2y - 4 = 0$

39. x = fraction of A to total

y = fraction of B to total

z = fraction of C to total

$\frac{1}{5}x \quad\; + \frac{1}{3}z = \frac{6}{27}$

$\frac{2}{5}x \quad\; + \frac{1}{3}z = \frac{8}{27}$

$\frac{2}{5}x + y + \frac{1}{3}z = \frac{13}{27}$

Solution: $x = \frac{10}{27}$, $y = \frac{5}{27}$, $z = \frac{12}{27}$

Thus, the ratio is $(10, 5, 12)$.

41. $\dfrac{4-x}{x^2+6x+8} = \dfrac{A}{x+2} + \dfrac{B}{x+4}$

$4 - x = A(x+4) + B(x+2)$

Let $x = -2$: $6 = 2A \;\Rightarrow\; A = 3$.

Let $x = -4$: $8 = -2B \;\Rightarrow\; B = -4$.

$\dfrac{4-x}{x^2+6x+8} = \dfrac{3}{x+2} - \dfrac{4}{x+4}$

43. $\dfrac{x^2}{x^2+2x-15} = 1 - \dfrac{2x-15}{x^2+2x-15} = 1 + \dfrac{A}{x+5} + \dfrac{B}{x-3}$

$-2x + 15 = A(x-3) + B(x+5)$

Let $x = -5$: $25 = -8A \;\Rightarrow\; A = -\frac{25}{8}$.

Let $x = 3$: $9 = 8B \;\Rightarrow\; B = \frac{9}{8}$.

$\dfrac{x^2}{x^2+2x-15} = 1 + \dfrac{9}{8(x-3)} - \dfrac{25}{8(x+5)}$

45. $\dfrac{x^2+2x}{x^3-x^2+x-1} = \dfrac{A}{x-1} + \dfrac{Bx+C}{x^2+1}$

$x^2 + 2x = A(x^2+1) + (Bx+C)(x-1)$

Let $x = 1$: $3 = 2A \;\Rightarrow\; A = \frac{3}{2}$.

Let $x = 0$: $0 = A - C \;\Rightarrow\; C = \frac{3}{2}$.

Let $x = 2$: $8 = 5A + 2B + C$

$\qquad 8 = \left(\frac{15}{2}\right) + 2B + \left(\frac{3}{2}\right) \;\Rightarrow\; B = -\frac{1}{2}$.

$\dfrac{x^2+2x}{x^3-x^2+x-1} = \dfrac{3/2}{x-1} + \dfrac{-(1/2)x+3/2}{x^2+1} = \dfrac{1}{2}\left(\dfrac{3}{x-1} - \dfrac{x-3}{x^2+1}\right)$

47. $\dfrac{3x^3 + 4x}{(x^2+1)^2} = \dfrac{Ax+B}{x^2+1} + \dfrac{Cx+D}{(x^2+1)^2}$

$3x^3 + 4x = (Ax+B)(x^2+1) + Cx + D = Ax^3 + Bx^2 + (A+C)x + B + D$

Equating coefficients of like powers:

$3 = A$

$0 = B$

$4 = 3 + C \;\Rightarrow\; C = 1$

$0 = B + D \;\Rightarrow\; D = 0$

$\dfrac{3x^3 + 4x}{(x^2+1)^2} = \dfrac{3x}{x^2+1} + \dfrac{x}{(x^2+1)^2}$

49. $x + 2y \le 160$

$3x + y \le 180$

$x \ge 0$

$y \ge 0$

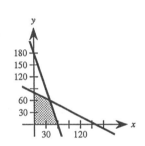

51. $3x + 2y \ge 24$

$x + 2y \ge 12$

$2 \le x \le 15$

$y \le 15$

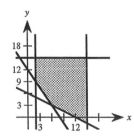

53. $y < x + 1$

$y > x^2 - 1$

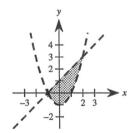

55. $2x - 3y \ge 0$

$2x - y \le 8$

$y \ge 0$

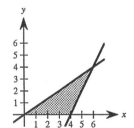

57. $-x + y \leq 4$

$2x + y \leq 22$

$-x + y \geq -2$

$2x + y \geq 7$

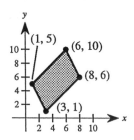

59. $x = $ Harrisburg market

$y = $ Philadelphia market

$x + y \leq 1500$

$x \geq 400$

$y \geq 600$

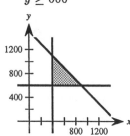

61.   Demand $=$ Supply

$160 - 0.0001x = 70 + 0.0002x$

$90 = 0.0003x$

$x = 300,000$ units

$p = \$130$

Point of equilibrium: $(300,000,\ 130)$

Consumer surplus: $\frac{1}{2}(300,000)(30) = \$4,500,000$

Producer surplus: $\frac{1}{2}(300,000)(60) = \$9,000,000$

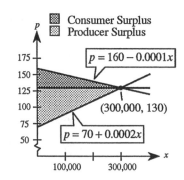

63. $z = 3x + 4y$

At $(0, 0)$: $z = 3(0) + 4(0) = 0$

At $(7, 0)$: $z = 3(7) + 4(0) = 21$

At $(5, 8)$: $z = 3(5) + 4(8) = 47$

At $(0, 10)$: $z = 3(0) + 4(10) = 40$

The maximum value is 47 at $(5, 8)$.

65. $z = 1.75x + 2.25x$

At (0, 25): $z = 1.75(0) + 2.25(25) = 56.25$

At (5, 15): $z = 1.75(5) + 2.25(15) = 42.5$

At (15, 0): $z = 1.75(15) + 2.25(0) = 26.25$

The minimum value is 26.25 at (15, 0).

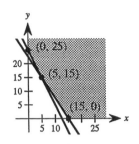

67. $x =$ number of product A

$y =$ number of product B

Constraints: $4x + 2y \le 24$

$$x + 2y \le 9$$

$$x + y \le 8$$

Objective function: $P = 18x + 24y$

At (0, 0): $P = 18(0) + 24(0) = 0$

At (6, 0): $P = 18(6) + 24(0) = 108$

At (5, 2): $P = 18(5) + 24(2) = 138$

At $\left(0, \frac{9}{2}\right)$: $P = 18(0) + 24\left(\frac{9}{2}\right) = 108$

The maximum value is \$138 at (5, 2).

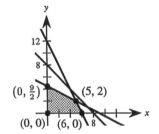

69. x = number of bags of Brand X
y = number of bags of Brand Y
Constraints: $8x + 2y \geq 16$

$$x + y \geq 5$$

$$2x + 7y \geq 20$$

$$x \geq 0, \ y \geq 0$$

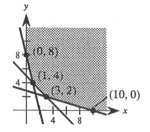

Objective function: $C = 15x + 30y$
At $(0, 8)$: $C = 15(0) + 30(8) = 240$

At $(1, 4)$: $C = 15(1) + 30(4) = 135$

At $(3, 2)$: $C = 15(3) + 30(2) = 105$

At $(10, 0)$: $C = 15(10) + 30(0) = 150$
The minimum is 105 when three bags of
Brand X and two bags of Brand Y are
mixed.

CHAPTER 8

Matrices and Determinants

Section 8.1   Matrices and Systems of Linear Equations

- You should know the definition of a matrix.
- You should know the three elementary row operations.
  (a) Interchange two rows.
  (b) Multiply a row by a nonzero constant.
  (c) Add a multiple of one row to another row.
- You should be able to determine if a matrix is in row-echelon or reduced row-echelon form.
- You should be able to solve a system of linear equations by Gaussian elimination with back substitution.
- You should be able to solve a system of linear equations by Gauss-Jordan elimination.

1. 3×2 **3.** 5×1 **5.** 2×2

7. Reduced row-echelon form   **9.** Not in row-echelon form

11. $\begin{bmatrix} 1 & 4 & 3 \\ 2 & 10 & 5 \end{bmatrix}$ $-2R_1 + R_2 \rightarrow \begin{bmatrix} 1 & 4 & 3 \\ 0 & 2 & -1 \end{bmatrix}$

13. $\begin{bmatrix} 1 & 1 & 4 & -1 \\ 3 & 8 & 10 & 3 \\ -2 & 1 & 12 & 6 \end{bmatrix}$ $\begin{matrix} -3R_1 + R_2 \rightarrow \\ 2R_1 + R_3 \rightarrow \end{matrix} \begin{bmatrix} 1 & 1 & 4 & -1 \\ 0 & 5 & -2 & 6 \\ 0 & 3 & 20 & 4 \end{bmatrix}$

$\frac{1}{5}R_2 \rightarrow \begin{bmatrix} 1 & 1 & 4 & -1 \\ 0 & 1 & -\frac{2}{5} & \frac{6}{5} \\ 0 & 3 & 20 & 4 \end{bmatrix}$

15. $\begin{bmatrix} 1 & 2 & 3 \\ 2 & -1 & -4 \\ 3 & 1 & -1 \end{bmatrix}$

(a) $\begin{bmatrix} 1 & 2 & 3 \\ 0 & -5 & -10 \\ 3 & 1 & -1 \end{bmatrix}$ (b) $\begin{bmatrix} 1 & 2 & 3 \\ 0 & -5 & -10 \\ 0 & -5 & -10 \end{bmatrix}$ (c) $\begin{bmatrix} 1 & 2 & 3 \\ 0 & -5 & -10 \\ 0 & 0 & 0 \end{bmatrix}$

(d) $\begin{bmatrix} 1 & 2 & 3 \\ 0 & 1 & 2 \\ 0 & 0 & 0 \end{bmatrix}$ (e) $\begin{bmatrix} 1 & 0 & -1 \\ 0 & 1 & 2 \\ 0 & 0 & 0 \end{bmatrix}$

17. $\begin{bmatrix} 1 & 1 & 0 & 5 \\ -2 & -1 & 2 & -10 \\ 3 & 6 & 7 & 14 \end{bmatrix} \Rightarrow \begin{bmatrix} 1 & 1 & 0 & 5 \\ 0 & 1 & 2 & 0 \\ 0 & 3 & 7 & -1 \end{bmatrix} \Rightarrow \begin{bmatrix} 1 & 1 & 0 & 5 \\ 0 & 1 & 2 & 0 \\ 0 & 0 & 1 & -1 \end{bmatrix}$

19. $\begin{bmatrix} 1 & -1 & -1 & 1 \\ 5 & -4 & 1 & 8 \\ -6 & 8 & 18 & 0 \end{bmatrix} \Rightarrow \begin{bmatrix} 1 & -1 & -1 & 1 \\ 0 & 1 & 6 & 3 \\ 0 & 2 & 12 & 6 \end{bmatrix} \Rightarrow \begin{bmatrix} 1 & -1 & -1 & 1 \\ 0 & 1 & 6 & 3 \\ 0 & 0 & 0 & 0 \end{bmatrix}$

21. $\begin{bmatrix} 3 & 3 & 3 \\ -1 & 0 & -4 \\ 2 & 4 & -2 \end{bmatrix} \Rightarrow \begin{bmatrix} 1 & 1 & 1 \\ -1 & 0 & -4 \\ 2 & 4 & -2 \end{bmatrix} \Rightarrow \begin{bmatrix} 1 & 1 & 1 \\ 0 & 1 & -3 \\ 0 & 2 & -4 \end{bmatrix} \Rightarrow \begin{bmatrix} 1 & 0 & 4 \\ 0 & 1 & -3 \\ 0 & 0 & 2 \end{bmatrix}$

$\Rightarrow \begin{bmatrix} 1 & 0 & 4 \\ 0 & 1 & -3 \\ 0 & 0 & 1 \end{bmatrix} \Rightarrow \begin{bmatrix} 1 & 0 & 0 \\ 0 & 1 & 0 \\ 0 & 0 & 1 \end{bmatrix}$

23. $\begin{bmatrix} 1 & 2 & 3 & -5 \\ 1 & 2 & 4 & -9 \\ -2 & -4 & -4 & 3 \\ 4 & 8 & 11 & -14 \end{bmatrix} \Rightarrow \begin{bmatrix} 1 & 2 & 3 & -5 \\ 0 & 0 & 1 & -4 \\ 0 & 0 & 2 & -7 \\ 0 & 0 & -1 & 6 \end{bmatrix} \Rightarrow \begin{bmatrix} 1 & 2 & 0 & 7 \\ 0 & 0 & 1 & -4 \\ 0 & 0 & 0 & 1 \\ 0 & 0 & 0 & 2 \end{bmatrix}$

$\Rightarrow \begin{bmatrix} 1 & 2 & 0 & 0 \\ 0 & 0 & 1 & 0 \\ 0 & 0 & 0 & 1 \\ 0 & 0 & 0 & 0 \end{bmatrix}$

25. $4x + 3y = 8$

$x - 2y = 3$

27. $x \quad\quad + 2z = -10$

$3y - z = 5$

$4x + 2y \quad\quad = 3$

29. $x - 2y = 4$

$y = -3$

$x = 4 + 2y$

$= 4 + 2(-3)$

$= -2$

$(-2, \ -3)$

31. $x - y + 2z = 4$

$y - z = 2$

$z = -2$

$y = 2 + z$

$= 2 + (-2)$

$= 0$

$x = 4 + y - 2z$

$= 4 + 0 - 2(-2)$

$= 8$

$(8, \ 0, \ -2)$

33. Row 1: $x = 7$

Row 2: $y = -5$

$(7, \ -5)$

35. Row 1: $x = -4$

Row 2: $y = -8$

Row 3: $z = 2$

$(-4, \ -8, \ 2)$

37. $x + 2y = 7$

$2x + y = 8$

$$\begin{bmatrix} 1 & 2 & \vdots & 7 \\ 2 & 1 & \vdots & 8 \end{bmatrix} \Rightarrow \begin{bmatrix} 1 & 2 & \vdots & 7 \\ 0 & -3 & \vdots & -6 \end{bmatrix} \Rightarrow \begin{bmatrix} 1 & 2 & \vdots & 7 \\ 0 & 1 & \vdots & 2 \end{bmatrix}$$

$y = 2$

$x + 2(2) = 7 \quad \Rightarrow \quad x = 3$

Solution: $(3, 2)$

39. $-3x + 5y = -22$

$3x + 4y = 4$

$4x - 8y = 32$

$$\begin{bmatrix} -3 & 5 & \vdots & -22 \\ 3 & 4 & \vdots & 4 \\ 4 & -8 & \vdots & 32 \end{bmatrix} \Rightarrow \begin{bmatrix} 1 & -3 & \vdots & 10 \\ 3 & 4 & \vdots & 4 \\ 4 & -8 & \vdots & 32 \end{bmatrix} \Rightarrow \begin{bmatrix} 1 & -3 & \vdots & 10 \\ 0 & 13 & \vdots & -26 \\ 0 & 4 & \vdots & -8 \end{bmatrix}$$

$$\Rightarrow \begin{bmatrix} 1 & -3 & \vdots & 10 \\ 0 & 1 & \vdots & -2 \\ 0 & 0 & \vdots & 0 \end{bmatrix}$$

$y = -2$

$x - 3(-2) = 10 \quad \Rightarrow \quad x = 4$

Solution: $(4, -2)$

41. $8x - 4y = 7$

$5x + 2y = 1$

$$\begin{bmatrix} 8 & -4 & \vdots & 7 \\ 5 & 2 & \vdots & 1 \end{bmatrix} \Rightarrow \begin{bmatrix} 24 & -12 & \vdots & 21 \\ 25 & 10 & \vdots & 5 \end{bmatrix} \Rightarrow \begin{bmatrix} -1 & -22 & \vdots & 16 \\ 25 & 10 & \vdots & 5 \end{bmatrix}$$

$$\Rightarrow \begin{bmatrix} -1 & -22 & \vdots & 16 \\ 0 & -540 & \vdots & 405 \end{bmatrix} \Rightarrow \begin{bmatrix} 1 & 22 & \vdots & -16 \\ 0 & 1 & \vdots & -\frac{3}{4} \end{bmatrix}$$

$y = -\frac{3}{4}$

$x + 22\left(-\frac{3}{4}\right) = -16 \quad \Rightarrow \quad x = \frac{1}{2}$

Solution: $\left(\frac{1}{2}, -\frac{3}{4}\right)$

43. $-x + 2y = 1.5$

$2x - 4y = 3$

$$\begin{bmatrix} -1 & 2 & \vdots & 1.5 \\ 2 & -4 & \vdots & 3 \end{bmatrix} \Rightarrow \begin{bmatrix} -1 & 2 & \vdots & 1.5 \\ 0 & 0 & \vdots & 6 \end{bmatrix}$$

The system is inconsistent and there is no solution.

45. $x \qquad - 3z = -2$

$3x + y - 2z = 5$

$2x + 2y + z = 4$

$$\begin{bmatrix} 1 & 0 & -3 & \vdots & -2 \\ 3 & 1 & -2 & \vdots & 5 \\ 2 & 2 & 1 & \vdots & 4 \end{bmatrix} \Rightarrow \begin{bmatrix} 1 & 0 & -3 & \vdots & -2 \\ 0 & 1 & 7 & \vdots & 11 \\ 0 & 2 & 7 & \vdots & 8 \end{bmatrix} \Rightarrow \begin{bmatrix} 1 & 0 & -3 & \vdots & -2 \\ 0 & 1 & 7 & \vdots & 11 \\ 0 & 0 & -7 & \vdots & -14 \end{bmatrix}$$

$$\Rightarrow \begin{bmatrix} 1 & 0 & -3 & \vdots & -2 \\ 0 & 1 & 7 & \vdots & 11 \\ 0 & 0 & 1 & \vdots & 2 \end{bmatrix}$$

$z = 2$

$y + 7(2) = 11 \quad \Rightarrow \quad y = -3$

$x - 3(2) = -2 \quad \Rightarrow \quad x = 4$

Solution: $(4, -3, 2)$

47. $x + y - 5z = 3$

$x \qquad - 2z = 1$

$2x - y - z = 0$

$$\begin{bmatrix} 1 & 1 & -5 & \vdots & 3 \\ 1 & 0 & -2 & \vdots & 1 \\ 2 & -1 & -1 & \vdots & 0 \end{bmatrix} \Rightarrow \begin{bmatrix} 1 & 1 & -5 & \vdots & 3 \\ 0 & -1 & 3 & \vdots & -2 \\ 0 & -3 & 9 & \vdots & -6 \end{bmatrix} \Rightarrow \begin{bmatrix} 1 & 1 & -5 & \vdots & 3 \\ 0 & -1 & 3 & \vdots & -2 \\ 0 & 0 & 0 & \vdots & 0 \end{bmatrix}$$

$$\Rightarrow \begin{bmatrix} 1 & 0 & -2 & \vdots & 1 \\ 0 & 1 & -3 & \vdots & 2 \\ 0 & 0 & 0 & \vdots & 0 \end{bmatrix}$$

$z = a$

$y = 3a + 2$

$x = 2a + 1$

Solution: $(2a + 1, \ 3a + 2, \ a)$

49. $x + 2y + z = 8$

$3x + 7y + 6z = 26$

$$\begin{bmatrix} 1 & 2 & 1 & \vdots & 8 \\ 3 & 7 & 6 & \vdots & 26 \end{bmatrix} \Rightarrow \begin{bmatrix} 1 & 2 & 1 & \vdots & 8 \\ 0 & 1 & 3 & \vdots & 2 \end{bmatrix} \Rightarrow \begin{bmatrix} 1 & 0 & -5 & \vdots & 4 \\ 0 & 1 & 3 & \vdots & 2 \end{bmatrix}$$

$z = a$

$y = -3a + 2$

$x = 5a + 4$

Solution: $(5a + 4, \ -3a + 2, \ a)$

51. $3x + 3y + 12z = 6$

$\quad x + y + 4z = 2$

$\quad 2x + 5y + 20z = 10$

$\quad -x + 2y + 8z = 4$

$$\begin{bmatrix} 3 & 3 & 12 & \vdots & 6 \\ 1 & 1 & 4 & \vdots & 2 \\ 2 & 5 & 20 & \vdots & 10 \\ -1 & 2 & 8 & \vdots & 4 \end{bmatrix} \Rightarrow \begin{bmatrix} 1 & 1 & 4 & \vdots & 2 \\ 1 & 1 & 4 & \vdots & 2 \\ 2 & 5 & 20 & \vdots & 10 \\ -1 & 2 & 8 & \vdots & 4 \end{bmatrix}$$

$$\Rightarrow \begin{bmatrix} 1 & 1 & 4 & \vdots & 2 \\ 0 & 0 & 0 & \vdots & 0 \\ 0 & 3 & 12 & \vdots & 6 \\ 0 & 3 & 12 & \vdots & 6 \end{bmatrix}$$

$$\Rightarrow \begin{bmatrix} 1 & 1 & 4 & \vdots & 2 \\ 0 & 0 & 0 & \vdots & 0 \\ 0 & 3 & 12 & \vdots & 6 \\ 0 & 0 & 0 & \vdots & 0 \end{bmatrix}$$

$$\Rightarrow \begin{bmatrix} 1 & 1 & 4 & \vdots & 2 \\ 0 & 0 & 0 & \vdots & 0 \\ 0 & 1 & 4 & \vdots & 2 \\ 0 & 0 & 0 & \vdots & 0 \end{bmatrix}$$

$$\Rightarrow \begin{bmatrix} 1 & 0 & 0 & \vdots & 0 \\ 0 & 0 & 0 & \vdots & 0 \\ 0 & 1 & 4 & \vdots & 2 \\ 0 & 0 & 0 & \vdots & 0 \end{bmatrix}$$

$z = a$

$y = -4a + 2$

$x = 0$

Solution: $(0, -4a + 2, a)$

53. $2x + y - z + 2w = -6$

    $3x + 4y \qquad + w = 1$

    $x + 5y + 2z + 6w = -3$

    $5x + 2y - z - w = 3$

$$\begin{bmatrix} 2 & 1 & -1 & 2 & \vdots & -6 \\ 3 & 4 & 0 & 1 & \vdots & 1 \\ 1 & 5 & 2 & 6 & \vdots & -3 \\ 5 & 2 & -1 & -1 & \vdots & 3 \end{bmatrix} \Rightarrow \begin{bmatrix} 1 & 5 & 2 & 6 & \vdots & -3 \\ 3 & 4 & 0 & 1 & \vdots & 1 \\ 2 & 1 & -1 & 2 & \vdots & -6 \\ 5 & 2 & -1 & -1 & \vdots & 3 \end{bmatrix}$$

$$\Rightarrow \begin{bmatrix} 1 & 5 & 2 & 6 & \vdots & -3 \\ 0 & -11 & -6 & -17 & \vdots & 10 \\ 0 & -9 & -5 & -10 & \vdots & 0 \\ 0 & -23 & -11 & -31 & \vdots & 18 \end{bmatrix}$$

$$\Rightarrow \begin{bmatrix} 1 & 5 & 2 & 6 & \vdots & -3 \\ 0 & -1 & 1 & 3 & \vdots & -2 \\ 0 & -9 & -5 & -10 & \vdots & 0 \\ 0 & -23 & -11 & -31 & \vdots & 18 \end{bmatrix}$$

$$\Rightarrow \begin{bmatrix} 1 & 5 & 2 & 6 & \vdots & -3 \\ 0 & 1 & -1 & -3 & \vdots & 2 \\ 0 & -9 & -5 & -10 & \vdots & 0 \\ 0 & -23 & -11 & -31 & \vdots & 18 \end{bmatrix}$$

$$\Rightarrow \begin{bmatrix} 1 & 5 & 2 & 6 & \vdots & -3 \\ 0 & 1 & -1 & -3 & \vdots & 2 \\ 0 & 0 & -14 & -37 & \vdots & 18 \\ 0 & 0 & -34 & -100 & \vdots & 64 \end{bmatrix}$$

$$\Rightarrow \begin{bmatrix} 1 & 5 & 2 & 6 & \vdots & -3 \\ 0 & 1 & -1 & -3 & \vdots & 2 \\ 0 & 0 & 238 & 629 & \vdots & -306 \\ 0 & 0 & -238 & -700 & \vdots & 448 \end{bmatrix}$$

$$\Rightarrow \begin{bmatrix} 1 & 5 & 2 & 6 & \vdots & -3 \\ 0 & 1 & -1 & -3 & \vdots & 2 \\ 0 & 0 & 238 & 629 & \vdots & -306 \\ 0 & 0 & 0 & -71 & \vdots & 142 \end{bmatrix}$$

$$\Rightarrow \begin{bmatrix} 1 & 5 & 2 & 6 & \vdots & -3 \\ 0 & 1 & -1 & -3 & \vdots & 2 \\ 0 & 0 & 1 & \frac{37}{14} & \vdots & -\frac{9}{7} \\ 0 & 0 & 0 & 1 & \vdots & -2 \end{bmatrix}$$

$$w = -2$$

$$1 + \tfrac{37}{14}(-2) = -\tfrac{9}{7} \quad \Rightarrow \quad z = 4$$

$$y - 4 - 3(-2) = 2 \quad \Rightarrow \quad y = 0$$

$$x + 5(0) + 2(4) + 6(-2) = -3 \quad \Rightarrow \quad x = 1$$

Solution: $(1,\ 0,\ 4,\ -2)$

55. $x + 2y = 0$

$-x - y = 0$

$$\begin{bmatrix} 1 & 2 & \vdots & 0 \\ -1 & -1 & \vdots & 0 \end{bmatrix} \Rightarrow \begin{bmatrix} 1 & 2 & \vdots & 0 \\ 0 & 1 & \vdots & 0 \end{bmatrix} \Rightarrow \begin{bmatrix} 1 & 0 & \vdots & 0 \\ 0 & 1 & \vdots & 0 \end{bmatrix}$$

$x = 0$

$y = 0$

Solution: $(0, 0)$

57. $x + y + z = 0$

$2x + 3y + z = 0$

$3x + 5y + z = 0$

$$\begin{bmatrix} 1 & 1 & 1 & \vdots & 0 \\ 2 & 3 & 1 & \vdots & 0 \\ 3 & 5 & 1 & \vdots & 0 \end{bmatrix} \Rightarrow \begin{bmatrix} 1 & 1 & 1 & \vdots & 0 \\ 0 & 1 & -1 & \vdots & 0 \\ 0 & 2 & -2 & \vdots & 0 \end{bmatrix} \Rightarrow \begin{bmatrix} 1 & 0 & 2 & \vdots & 0 \\ 0 & 1 & -1 & \vdots & 0 \\ 0 & 0 & 0 & \vdots & 0 \end{bmatrix}$$

$z = a$

$y = a$

$x = -2a$

Solution: $(-2a, \ a, \ a)$

59. $x =$ amount at 8% $\qquad\qquad\qquad x + \quad y + \quad z = 1{,}500{,}000$

$y =$ amount at 9% $\qquad\qquad\quad 0.08x + 0.09y + 0.12z = \quad 133{,}000$

$z =$ amount at 12% $\qquad\qquad\qquad x - \qquad\qquad 4z = \qquad\quad 0$

$$\begin{bmatrix} 1 & 1 & 1 & \vdots & 1{,}500{,}000 \\ 0.08 & 0.09 & 0.12 & \vdots & 133{,}000 \\ 1 & 0 & -4 & \vdots & 0 \end{bmatrix} \Rightarrow \begin{bmatrix} 1 & 1 & 1 & \vdots & 1{,}500{,}000 \\ 0 & 0.01 & 0.04 & \vdots & 13{,}000 \\ 0 & -1 & -5 & \vdots & -1{,}500{,}000 \end{bmatrix}$$

$$\Rightarrow \begin{bmatrix} 1 & 1 & 1 & \vdots & 1{,}500{,}000 \\ 0 & 1 & 4 & \vdots & 1{,}300{,}000 \\ 0 & -1 & -5 & \vdots & -1{,}500{,}000 \end{bmatrix}$$

$$\Rightarrow \begin{bmatrix} 1 & 0 & -3 & \vdots & 200{,}000 \\ 0 & 1 & 4 & \vdots & 1{,}300{,}000 \\ 0 & 0 & -1 & \vdots & -200{,}000 \end{bmatrix}$$

$$\Rightarrow \begin{bmatrix} 1 & 0 & -3 & \vdots & 200{,}000 \\ 0 & 1 & 4 & \vdots & 1{,}300{,}000 \\ 0 & 0 & 1 & \vdots & 200{,}000 \end{bmatrix}$$

$z = 200{,}000, \quad y = 500{,}000, \quad x = 800{,}000$

Solution: \$800,000 at 8%, \$500,000 at 9%, \$200,000 at 12%

61.

$$\frac{4x^2}{(x+1)^2(x-1)} = \frac{A}{x-1} + \frac{B}{x+1} + \frac{C}{(x+1)^2}$$

$$4x^2 = A(x+1)^2 + B(x-1)(x+1) + C(x-1)$$

$$4x^2 = Ax^2 + 2Ax + A + Bx^2 - B + Cx - C$$

Equating coefficients of like powers of x:

$$A + B \qquad = 4$$
$$2A \qquad + C = 0$$
$$A - B - C = 0$$

The solution to this system is $A = 1$, $B = 3$, and $C = -2$. Thus,

$$\frac{4x^2}{(x+1)^2(x-1)} = \frac{1}{x-1} + \frac{3}{x+1} + \frac{-2}{(x+1)^2}.$$

63. At $(1, 7)$: $\quad 7 = a(1)^2 + b(1) + c \quad \Rightarrow \quad a + b + c = 7$

At $(2, 12)$: $\quad 12 = a(2)^2 + b(2) + c \quad \Rightarrow \quad 4a + 2b + c = 12$

At $(3, 19)$: $\quad 19 = a(3)^2 + b(3) + c \quad \Rightarrow \quad 9a + 3b + c = 19$

$$\begin{bmatrix} 1 & 1 & 1 & \vdots & 7 \\ 4 & 2 & 1 & \vdots & 12 \\ 9 & 3 & 1 & \vdots & 19 \end{bmatrix} \Rightarrow \begin{bmatrix} 1 & 1 & 1 & \vdots & 7 \\ 0 & -2 & -3 & \vdots & -16 \\ 0 & -6 & -8 & \vdots & -44 \end{bmatrix} \Rightarrow \begin{bmatrix} 1 & 1 & 1 & \vdots & 7 \\ 0 & 1 & \frac{3}{2} & \vdots & 8 \\ 0 & 0 & 1 & \vdots & 4 \end{bmatrix}$$

$$c = 4$$

$$b + \tfrac{3}{2}(4) = 8 \quad \Rightarrow \quad b = 2$$

$$a + 2 + 4 = 7 \quad \Rightarrow \quad a = 1$$

Solution: $y = x^2 + 2x + 4$

65. At $(1, 1)$: $\quad (1)^2 + (1)^2 + D(1) + E(1) + F = 0 \quad \Rightarrow \quad D + D + F = -2$

At $(3, 3)$: $\quad (3)^2 + (3)^2 + D(3) + E(3) + F = 0 \quad \Rightarrow \quad 3D + 3E + F = -18$

At $(4, 2)$: $\quad (4)^2 + (2)^2 + D(4) + E(2) + F = 0 \quad \Rightarrow \quad 4D + 2E + F = -20$

$$\begin{bmatrix} 1 & 1 & 1 & \vdots & -2 \\ 3 & 3 & 1 & \vdots & -18 \\ 4 & 2 & 1 & \vdots & -20 \end{bmatrix} \Rightarrow \begin{bmatrix} 1 & 1 & 1 & \vdots & -2 \\ 0 & 0 & -2 & \vdots & -12 \\ 0 & -2 & -3 & \vdots & -12 \end{bmatrix} \Rightarrow \begin{bmatrix} 1 & 1 & 1 & \vdots & -2 \\ 0 & 1 & \frac{3}{2} & \vdots & 6 \\ 0 & 0 & 1 & \vdots & 6 \end{bmatrix}$$

$$F = 6$$

$$E + (\tfrac{3}{2})6 = 6 \quad \Rightarrow \quad E = -3$$

$$D + (-3) + 6 = -2 \quad \Rightarrow \quad D = -5$$

Solution: $x^2 + y^2 - 5x - 3y + 6 = 0$

Section 8.2 Operations with Matrices

- $A = B$ if and only if they have the same order and $a_{ij} = b_{ij}$.

- You should be able to perform the operations of matrix addition, scalar multiplication, and matrix multiplication.

- Some properties of matrix addition, scalar multiplication, and matrix multiplication are:
  (a) $A + B = B + A$ (b) $A + (B + C) = (A + B) + C$
  (c) $(cd)A = c(dA)$ (d) $1A = A$
  (e) $c(A + B) = cA + cB$ (f) $(c + d)A = cA + dA$
  (g) $A(BC) = (AB)C$ (h) $A(B + C) = AB + AC$
  (i) $(A + B)C = AC + BC$ (j) $c(AB) = (cA)B = A(cB)$

- You should remember that $AB \neq BA$ in general.

- The zero matrix is the additive identity, and the identity matrix I_n is the multiplicative identity.

1. $x = -4$, $y = 22$

3. $\left.\begin{array}{l} 5 = 2x + 1 \\ 6 = 3x \end{array}\right\} \Rightarrow x = 2$

$4 = 3y + 5 \quad \Rightarrow y = 3$

$x = 2$, $y = 3$

5. (a) $A + B = \begin{bmatrix} 1 & -1 \\ 2 & -1 \end{bmatrix} + \begin{bmatrix} 2 & -1 \\ -1 & 8 \end{bmatrix} = \begin{bmatrix} 1+2 & -1-1 \\ 2-1 & -1+8 \end{bmatrix} = \begin{bmatrix} 3 & -2 \\ 1 & 7 \end{bmatrix}$

(b) $A - B = \begin{bmatrix} 1 & -1 \\ 2 & -1 \end{bmatrix} - \begin{bmatrix} 2 & -1 \\ -1 & 8 \end{bmatrix} = \begin{bmatrix} 1-2 & -1+1 \\ 2+1 & -1-8 \end{bmatrix} = \begin{bmatrix} -1 & 0 \\ 3 & -9 \end{bmatrix}$

(c) $3A = 3\begin{bmatrix} 1 & -1 \\ 2 & -1 \end{bmatrix} = \begin{bmatrix} 3(1) & 3(-1) \\ 3(2) & 3(-1) \end{bmatrix} = \begin{bmatrix} 3 & -3 \\ 6 & -3 \end{bmatrix}$

(d) $3A - 2B = \begin{bmatrix} 3 & -3 \\ 6 & -3 \end{bmatrix} - 2\begin{bmatrix} 2 & -1 \\ -1 & 8 \end{bmatrix} = \begin{bmatrix} 3 & -3 \\ 6 & -3 \end{bmatrix} + \begin{bmatrix} -4 & 2 \\ 2 & -16 \end{bmatrix} = \begin{bmatrix} -1 & -1 \\ 8 & -19 \end{bmatrix}$

7. (a) $A + B = \begin{bmatrix} 6 & -1 \\ 2 & 4 \\ -3 & 5 \end{bmatrix} + \begin{bmatrix} 1 & 4 \\ -1 & 5 \\ 1 & 10 \end{bmatrix} = \begin{bmatrix} 6+1 & -1+4 \\ 2-1 & 4+5 \\ -3+1 & 5+10 \end{bmatrix} = \begin{bmatrix} 7 & 3 \\ 1 & 9 \\ -2 & 15 \end{bmatrix}$

(b) $A - B = \begin{bmatrix} 6 & -1 \\ 2 & 4 \\ -3 & 5 \end{bmatrix} - \begin{bmatrix} 1 & 4 \\ -1 & 5 \\ 1 & 10 \end{bmatrix} = \begin{bmatrix} 6-1 & -1-4 \\ 2+1 & 4-5 \\ -3-1 & 5-10 \end{bmatrix} = \begin{bmatrix} 5 & -5 \\ 3 & -1 \\ -4 & -5 \end{bmatrix}$

(c) $3A = 3 \begin{bmatrix} 6 & -1 \\ 2 & 4 \\ -3 & 5 \end{bmatrix} = \begin{bmatrix} 3(6) & 3(-1) \\ 3(2) & 3(4) \\ 3(-3) & 3(5) \end{bmatrix} = \begin{bmatrix} 18 & -3 \\ 6 & 12 \\ -9 & 15 \end{bmatrix}$

(d) $3A - 2B = \begin{bmatrix} 18 & -3 \\ 6 & 12 \\ -9 & 15 \end{bmatrix} - 2 \begin{bmatrix} 1 & 4 \\ -1 & 5 \\ 1 & 10 \end{bmatrix} = \begin{bmatrix} 18 & -3 \\ 6 & 12 \\ -9 & 15 \end{bmatrix} + \begin{bmatrix} -2 & -8 \\ 2 & -10 \\ -2 & -20 \end{bmatrix} = \begin{bmatrix} 16 & -11 \\ 8 & 2 \\ -11 & -5 \end{bmatrix}$

9. (a) $A + B = \begin{bmatrix} 2+1 & 2+1 & -1+(-1) & 0+1 & 1+0 \\ 1+(-3) & 1+4 & -2+9 & 0+(-6) & -1+(-7) \end{bmatrix}$

$= \begin{bmatrix} 3 & 3 & -2 & 1 & 1 \\ -2 & 5 & 7 & -6 & -8 \end{bmatrix}$

(b) $A - B = \begin{bmatrix} 2-1 & 2-1 & -1-(-1) & 0-1 & 1-0 \\ 1-(-3) & 1-4 & -2-9 & 0-(-6) & -1-(-7) \end{bmatrix}$

$= \begin{bmatrix} 1 & 1 & 0 & -1 & 1 \\ 4 & -3 & -11 & 6 & 6 \end{bmatrix}$

(c) $3A = \begin{bmatrix} 3(2) & 3(2) & 3(-1) & 3(0) & 3(1) \\ 3(1) & 3(1) & 3(-2) & 3(0) & 3(-1) \end{bmatrix} = \begin{bmatrix} 6 & 6 & -3 & 0 & 3 \\ 3 & 3 & -6 & 0 & -3 \end{bmatrix}$

(d) $3A - 2B = \begin{bmatrix} 6 & 6 & -3 & 0 & 3 \\ 3 & 3 & -6 & 0 & -3 \end{bmatrix} - \begin{bmatrix} 2 & 2 & -2 & 2 & 0 \\ -6 & 8 & 18 & -12 & -14 \end{bmatrix}$

$= \begin{bmatrix} 4 & 4 & -1 & -2 & 3 \\ 9 & -5 & -24 & 12 & 11 \end{bmatrix}$

11. (a) $AB = \begin{bmatrix} 1 & 2 \\ 4 & 2 \end{bmatrix} \begin{bmatrix} 2 & -1 \\ -1 & 8 \end{bmatrix} = \begin{bmatrix} 1(2)+2(-1) & 1(-1)+2(8) \\ 4(2)+2(-1) & 4(-1)+2(8) \end{bmatrix} = \begin{bmatrix} 0 & 15 \\ 6 & 12 \end{bmatrix}$

(b) $BA = \begin{bmatrix} 2 & -1 \\ -1 & 8 \end{bmatrix} \begin{bmatrix} 1 & 2 \\ 4 & 2 \end{bmatrix} = \begin{bmatrix} 2(1)+(-1)4 & 2(2)+(-1)2 \\ -1(1)+8(4) & -1(2)+8(2) \end{bmatrix} = \begin{bmatrix} -2 & 2 \\ 31 & 14 \end{bmatrix}$

(c) $A^2 = \begin{bmatrix} 1 & 2 \\ 4 & 2 \end{bmatrix} \begin{bmatrix} 1 & 2 \\ 4 & 2 \end{bmatrix} = \begin{bmatrix} 1(1)+2(4) & 1(2)+2(2) \\ 4(1)+2(4) & 4(2)+2(2) \end{bmatrix} = \begin{bmatrix} 9 & 6 \\ 12 & 12 \end{bmatrix}$

13. (a) $AB = \begin{bmatrix} 3 & -1 \\ 1 & 3 \end{bmatrix} \begin{bmatrix} 1 & -3 \\ 3 & 1 \end{bmatrix} = \begin{bmatrix} 3(1) + (-1)(3) & 3(-3) + (-1)(1) \\ 1(1) + 3(3) & 1(-3) + 3(1) \end{bmatrix} = \begin{bmatrix} 0 & -10 \\ 10 & 0 \end{bmatrix}$

(b) $BA = \begin{bmatrix} 1 & -3 \\ 3 & 1 \end{bmatrix} \begin{bmatrix} 3 & -1 \\ 1 & 3 \end{bmatrix} = \begin{bmatrix} 1(3) + (-3)(1) & 1(-1) + (-3)(3) \\ 3(3) + 1(1) & 3(-1) + 1(3) \end{bmatrix} = \begin{bmatrix} 0 & -10 \\ 10 & 0 \end{bmatrix}$

(c) $A^2 = \begin{bmatrix} 3 & -1 \\ 1 & 3 \end{bmatrix} \begin{bmatrix} 3 & -1 \\ 1 & 3 \end{bmatrix} = \begin{bmatrix} 3(3) + (-1)(1) & 3(-1) + (-1)(3) \\ 1(3) + 3(1) & 1(-1) + 3(3) \end{bmatrix} = \begin{bmatrix} 8 & -6 \\ 6 & 8 \end{bmatrix}$

15. (a) $AB = \begin{bmatrix} 1 & -1 & 7 \\ 2 & -1 & 8 \\ 3 & 1 & -1 \end{bmatrix} \begin{bmatrix} 1 & 1 & 2 \\ 2 & 1 & 1 \\ 1 & -3 & 2 \end{bmatrix}$

$= \begin{bmatrix} 1(1) + (-1)2 + 7(1) & 1(1) + (-1)(1) + 7(-3) & 1(2) + (-1)1 + 7(2) \\ 2(1) + (-1)2 + 8(1) & 2(1) + (-1)(1) + 8(-3) & 2(2) + (-1)(1) + 8(2) \\ 3(1) + 1(2) + (-1)1 & 3(1) + 1(1) + (-1)(-3) & 3(2) + 1(1) + (-1)(2) \end{bmatrix}$

$= \begin{bmatrix} 6 & -21 & 15 \\ 8 & -23 & 19 \\ 4 & 7 & 5 \end{bmatrix}$

(b) $BA = \begin{bmatrix} 1 & 1 & 2 \\ 2 & 1 & 1 \\ 1 & -3 & 2 \end{bmatrix} \begin{bmatrix} 1 & -1 & 7 \\ 2 & -1 & 8 \\ 3 & 1 & -1 \end{bmatrix}$

$= \begin{bmatrix} 1(1) + 1(2) + 2(3) & 1(-1) + 1(-1) + 2(1) & 1(7) + 1(8) + 2(-1) \\ 2(1) + 1(2) + 1(3) & 2(-1) + 1(-1) + 1(1) & 2(7) + 1(8) + 1(-1) \\ 1(1) + (-3)(2) + 2(3) & 1(-1) + (-3)(-1) + 2(1) & 1(7) + (-3)(8) + 2(-1) \end{bmatrix}$

$= \begin{bmatrix} 9 & 0 & 13 \\ 7 & -2 & 21 \\ 1 & 5 & -19 \end{bmatrix}$

(c) $A^2 = \begin{bmatrix} 1 & -1 & 7 \\ 2 & -1 & 8 \\ 3 & 1 & -1 \end{bmatrix} \begin{bmatrix} 1 & -1 & 7 \\ 2 & -1 & 8 \\ 3 & 1 & -1 \end{bmatrix}$

$= \begin{bmatrix} 1(1) + (-1)(2) + 7(3) & 1(-1) + (-1)(-1) + 7(1) & 1(7) + (-1)8 + 7(-1) \\ 2(1) + (-1)(2) + 8(3) & 2(-1) + (-1)(-1) + 8(1) & 2(7) + (-1)8 + 8(-1) \\ 3(1) + 1(2) + (-1)(3) & 3(-1) + 1(-1) + (-1)(1) & 3(7) + 1(8) + (-1)(-1) \end{bmatrix}$

$= \begin{bmatrix} 20 & 7 & -8 \\ 24 & 7 & -2 \\ 2 & -5 & 30 \end{bmatrix}$

17. A is 3×2 and B is 3×3. Since the number of columns of A does not equal the number of rows of B, the multiplication is not possible.

19. A is 3×2 and B is $2 \times 2 \Rightarrow AB$ is 3×2.

$$AB = \begin{bmatrix} -1 & 3 \\ 4 & -5 \\ 0 & 2 \end{bmatrix} \begin{bmatrix} 1 & 2 \\ 0 & 7 \end{bmatrix}$$

$$= \begin{bmatrix} -1 & 19 \\ 4 & -27 \\ 0 & 14 \end{bmatrix}$$

21. A is 3×3 and B is $3 \times 3 \Rightarrow AB$ is 3×3.

$$AB = \begin{bmatrix} 5 & 0 & 0 \\ 0 & -8 & 0 \\ 0 & 0 & 7 \end{bmatrix} \begin{bmatrix} \frac{1}{5} & 0 & 0 \\ 0 & -\frac{1}{8} & 0 \\ 0 & 0 & \frac{1}{2} \end{bmatrix}$$

$$= \begin{bmatrix} 1 & 0 & 0 \\ 0 & 1 & 0 \\ 0 & 0 & \frac{7}{2} \end{bmatrix}$$

23. A is 4×1 and B is $1 \times 2 \Rightarrow AB$ is 4×2.

$$AB = \begin{bmatrix} 6 \\ -2 \\ 1 \\ 6 \end{bmatrix} \begin{bmatrix} 10 & 12 \end{bmatrix}$$

$$= \begin{bmatrix} 60 & 72 \\ -20 & -24 \\ 10 & 12 \\ 60 & 72 \end{bmatrix}$$

25. $X = 3A - 2B = 3 \begin{bmatrix} -2 & -1 \\ 1 & 0 \\ 3 & -4 \end{bmatrix} - 2 \begin{bmatrix} 0 & 3 \\ 2 & 0 \\ -4 & -1 \end{bmatrix}$

$$= \begin{bmatrix} -6 & -3 \\ 3 & 0 \\ 9 & -12 \end{bmatrix} - \begin{bmatrix} 0 & 6 \\ 4 & 0 \\ -8 & -2 \end{bmatrix} = \begin{bmatrix} -6 & -9 \\ -1 & 0 \\ 17 & -10 \end{bmatrix}$$

27. $X = -\frac{3}{2}A + \frac{1}{2}B = -\frac{3}{2} \begin{bmatrix} -2 & -1 \\ 1 & 0 \\ 3 & -4 \end{bmatrix} + \frac{1}{2} \begin{bmatrix} 0 & 3 \\ 2 & 0 \\ -4 & -1 \end{bmatrix}$

$$= \begin{bmatrix} 3 & \frac{3}{2} \\ -\frac{3}{2} & 0 \\ -\frac{9}{2} & 6 \end{bmatrix} + \begin{bmatrix} 0 & \frac{3}{2} \\ 1 & 0 \\ -2 & -\frac{1}{2} \end{bmatrix} = \begin{bmatrix} 3 & 3 \\ -\frac{1}{2} & 0 \\ -\frac{13}{2} & \frac{11}{2} \end{bmatrix}$$

29. $A = \begin{bmatrix} -1 & 1 \\ -2 & 1 \end{bmatrix}$, $X = \begin{bmatrix} x \\ y \end{bmatrix}$, $B = \begin{bmatrix} 4 \\ 0 \end{bmatrix}$

$$\begin{bmatrix} -1 & 1 & \vdots & 4 \\ -2 & 1 & \vdots & 0 \end{bmatrix} \Rightarrow \begin{bmatrix} 1 & -1 & \vdots & -4 \\ 0 & -1 & \vdots & -8 \end{bmatrix} \Rightarrow \begin{bmatrix} 1 & 0 & \vdots & 4 \\ 0 & 1 & \vdots & 8 \end{bmatrix}$$

$x = 4$, $y = 8$

31. $A = \begin{bmatrix} 1 & -2 & 3 \\ -1 & 3 & -1 \\ 2 & -5 & 5 \end{bmatrix}$, $X = \begin{bmatrix} x \\ y \\ z \end{bmatrix}$, $B = \begin{bmatrix} 9 \\ -6 \\ 17 \end{bmatrix}$

$\begin{bmatrix} 1 & -2 & 3 & \vdots & 9 \\ -1 & 3 & -1 & \vdots & -6 \\ 2 & -5 & 5 & \vdots & 17 \end{bmatrix} \Rightarrow \begin{bmatrix} 1 & -2 & 3 & \vdots & 9 \\ 0 & 1 & 2 & \vdots & 3 \\ 0 & -1 & -1 & \vdots & -1 \end{bmatrix}$

$\Rightarrow \begin{bmatrix} 1 & 0 & 7 & \vdots & 15 \\ 0 & 1 & 2 & \vdots & 3 \\ 0 & 0 & 1 & \vdots & 2 \end{bmatrix}$

$\Rightarrow \begin{bmatrix} 1 & 0 & 0 & \vdots & 1 \\ 0 & 1 & 0 & \vdots & -1 \\ 0 & 0 & 1 & \vdots & 2 \end{bmatrix}$

$x = 1, \ y = -1, \ z = 2$

33. $AC = \begin{bmatrix} 1 & 2 & 3 \\ 0 & 5 & 4 \\ 3 & -2 & 1 \end{bmatrix} \begin{bmatrix} 0 & 0 & 0 \\ 0 & 0 & 0 \\ 4 & -2 & 3 \end{bmatrix} = \begin{bmatrix} 12 & -6 & 9 \\ 16 & -8 & 12 \\ 4 & -2 & 3 \end{bmatrix}$

$BC = \begin{bmatrix} 4 & -6 & 3 \\ 5 & 4 & 4 \\ -1 & 0 & 1 \end{bmatrix} \begin{bmatrix} 0 & 0 & 0 \\ 0 & 0 & 0 \\ 4 & -2 & 3 \end{bmatrix} = \begin{bmatrix} 12 & -6 & 9 \\ 16 & -8 & 12 \\ 4 & -2 & 3 \end{bmatrix}$

Thus, $AC = BC$ even though $A \neq B$.

35. $1.20 \begin{bmatrix} 60 & 40 & 20 \\ 30 & 90 & 60 \end{bmatrix} = \begin{bmatrix} 72 & 48 & 24 \\ 36 & 108 & 72 \end{bmatrix}$

37. $BA = [3.75 \quad 7.00] \begin{bmatrix} 100 & 75 & 75 \\ 125 & 150 & 100 \end{bmatrix}$

$= [\$1250.00 \quad \$1331.25 \quad \$981.25]$

The entries in the last matrix represent the profit for both crops at each of the three outlets.

39. (a) We multiply the entries in the first row of S by those of the second column of T.

$$3(1100) + 2(1350) + 2(1650) + 3(3000) + 0(3200) = \$18,300$$

(b) We multiply the entries in the third row of S by those in the first column of T.

$$4(840) + 2(1200) + 1(1450) + 3(2650) + 2(3050) = \$21,260$$

(c) $ST = \begin{bmatrix} 3 & 2 & 2 & 3 & 0 \\ 0 & 2 & 3 & 4 & 3 \\ 4 & 2 & 1 & 3 & 2 \end{bmatrix} \begin{bmatrix} 840 & 1100 \\ 1200 & 1350 \\ 1450 & 1650 \\ 2650 & 3000 \\ 3050 & 3200 \end{bmatrix} = \begin{matrix} \text{Wholesale} \quad \text{Retail} \\ \begin{bmatrix} \$15,770 & \$18,300 \\ \$26,500 & \$29,250 \\ \$21,260 & \$24,150 \end{bmatrix} \begin{matrix} 1 \\ 2 \\ 3 \end{matrix} \left.\begin{matrix} \\ \\ \end{matrix}\right\} \text{Outlet} \end{matrix}$

This represents the wholesale and retail price of the inventory at each outlet. Note that the answers to parts (a) and (b) are in ST.

41. $P^2 = \begin{bmatrix} 0.6 & 0.1 & 0.1 \\ 0.2 & 0.7 & 0.1 \\ 0.2 & 0.2 & 0.8 \end{bmatrix} \begin{bmatrix} 0.6 & 0.1 & 0.1 \\ 0.2 & 0.7 & 0.1 \\ 0.2 & 0.2 & 0.8 \end{bmatrix} = \begin{bmatrix} 0.40 & 0.15 & 0.15 \\ 0.28 & 0.53 & 0.17 \\ 0.32 & 0.32 & 0.68 \end{bmatrix}$

Section 8.3   Inverse Matrices and Systems of Linear Equations

■ The inverse of a square matrix A is a matrix A^{-1} satisfying $AA^{-1} = I_n = A^{-1}A$.

■ You should be able to find the inverse, if it exists, of a 2×2 matrix.

■ You should be able to find inverses using your graphing utility.

■ You should be able to use inverse matrices to solve systems of equations.

1. $AB = \begin{bmatrix} 2 & 1 \\ 5 & 3 \end{bmatrix} \begin{bmatrix} 3 & -1 \\ -5 & 2 \end{bmatrix} = \begin{bmatrix} 6-5 & -2+2 \\ 15-15 & -5+6 \end{bmatrix} = \begin{bmatrix} 1 & 0 \\ 0 & 1 \end{bmatrix}$

   $BA = \begin{bmatrix} 3 & -1 \\ -5 & 2 \end{bmatrix} \begin{bmatrix} 2 & 1 \\ 5 & 3 \end{bmatrix} = \begin{bmatrix} 6-5 & 3-3 \\ -10+10 & -5+6 \end{bmatrix} = \begin{bmatrix} 1 & 0 \\ 0 & 1 \end{bmatrix}$

3. $AB = \begin{bmatrix} 1 & 2 \\ 3 & 4 \end{bmatrix} \begin{bmatrix} -2 & 1 \\ \frac{3}{2} & -\frac{1}{2} \end{bmatrix} = \begin{bmatrix} -2+3 & 1-1 \\ -6+6 & 3-2 \end{bmatrix} = \begin{bmatrix} 1 & 0 \\ 0 & 1 \end{bmatrix}$

   $BA = \begin{bmatrix} -2 & 1 \\ \frac{3}{2} & -\frac{1}{2} \end{bmatrix} \begin{bmatrix} 1 & 2 \\ 3 & 4 \end{bmatrix} = \begin{bmatrix} -2+3 & -4+4 \\ \frac{3}{2}-\frac{3}{2} & 3-2 \end{bmatrix} = \begin{bmatrix} 1 & 0 \\ 0 & 1 \end{bmatrix}$

5. $AB = \frac{1}{3} \begin{bmatrix} -2 & 2 & 3 \\ 1 & -1 & 0 \\ 0 & 1 & 4 \end{bmatrix} \begin{bmatrix} -4 & -5 & 3 \\ -4 & -8 & 3 \\ 1 & 2 & 0 \end{bmatrix}$

   $= \frac{1}{3} \begin{bmatrix} -8+8+3 & 10-16+6 & -6+6 \\ -4+4 & -5+8 & 3-3 \\ -4+4 & -8+8 & 3 \end{bmatrix} = \frac{1}{3} \begin{bmatrix} 3 & 0 & 0 \\ 0 & 3 & 0 \\ 0 & 0 & 3 \end{bmatrix} = I_3$

   $BA = \frac{1}{3} \begin{bmatrix} -4 & -5 & 3 \\ -4 & -8 & 3 \\ 1 & 2 & 0 \end{bmatrix} \begin{bmatrix} -2 & 2 & 3 \\ 1 & -1 & 0 \\ 0 & 1 & 4 \end{bmatrix} = \frac{1}{3} \begin{bmatrix} 8-5 & -8+5+3 & -12+12 \\ 8-8 & -8+8+3 & -12+12 \\ -2+2 & 2-2 & 3 \end{bmatrix} = I_3$

7. $AB = \begin{bmatrix} 2 & 0 & 1 & 1 \\ 3 & 0 & 0 & 1 \\ -1 & 1 & -2 & 1 \\ 4 & -1 & 1 & 0 \end{bmatrix} \begin{bmatrix} -1 & 2 & -1 & -1 \\ -4 & 9 & -5 & -6 \\ 0 & 1 & -1 & -1 \\ 3 & -5 & 3 & 3 \end{bmatrix}$

$= \begin{bmatrix} -2+0+0+3 & 4+0+1+(-5) & -2+0+(-1)+3 & -2+0+(-1)+3 \\ -3+0+0+3 & 6+0+0+(-5) & -3+0+0+3 & -3+0+0+3 \\ 1+(-4)+0+3 & -2+9+(-2)+(-5) & 1+(-5)+2+3 & 1+(-6)+2+3 \\ -4+4+0+0 & 8+(-9)+1+0 & -4+5+(-1)+0 & -4+6+(-1)+0 \end{bmatrix}$

$= \begin{bmatrix} 1 & 0 & 0 & 0 \\ 0 & 1 & 0 & 0 \\ 0 & 0 & 1 & 0 \\ 0 & 0 & 0 & 1 \end{bmatrix}$

$BA = \begin{bmatrix} -1 & 2 & -1 & -1 \\ -4 & 9 & -5 & -6 \\ 0 & 1 & -1 & -1 \\ 3 & -5 & 3 & 3 \end{bmatrix} \begin{bmatrix} 2 & 0 & 1 & 1 \\ 3 & 0 & 0 & 1 \\ -1 & 1 & -2 & 1 \\ 4 & -1 & 1 & 0 \end{bmatrix}$

$= \begin{bmatrix} -2+6+1+(-4) & 0+0+(-1)+1 & -1+0+2+(-1) & -1+2+(-1)+0 \\ -8+27+5+(-24) & 0+0+(-5)+6 & -4+0+10+(-6) & -4+9+(-5)+0 \\ 0+3+1+(-4) & 0+0+(-1)+1 & 0+0+2+(-1) & 0+1+(-1)+0 \\ 6+(-15)+(-3)+12 & 0+0+3+(-3) & 3+0+(-6)+3 & 3+(-5)+3+0 \end{bmatrix}$

$= \begin{bmatrix} 1 & 0 & 0 & 0 \\ 0 & 1 & 0 & 0 \\ 0 & 0 & 1 & 0 \\ 0 & 0 & 0 & 1 \end{bmatrix}$

9. $A^{-1} = \dfrac{1}{ad-bc}\begin{bmatrix} d & -b \\ -c & a \end{bmatrix} = \dfrac{1}{6}\begin{bmatrix} 3 & 0 \\ 0 & 2 \end{bmatrix} = \begin{bmatrix} \frac{1}{2} & 0 \\ 0 & \frac{1}{3} \end{bmatrix}$

11. $A^{-1} = \dfrac{1}{ad-bc}\begin{bmatrix} d & -b \\ -c & a \end{bmatrix} = \dfrac{1}{-3+4}\begin{bmatrix} -3 & 2 \\ -2 & 1 \end{bmatrix} = \begin{bmatrix} -3 & 2 \\ -2 & 1 \end{bmatrix}$

13. $A^{-1} = \dfrac{1}{ad-bc}\begin{bmatrix} d & -b \\ -c & a \end{bmatrix} = \dfrac{1}{-1+2}\begin{bmatrix} 1 & -1 \\ 2 & -1 \end{bmatrix} = \begin{bmatrix} 1 & -1 \\ 2 & -1 \end{bmatrix}$

15. Since $ad-bc = 16-16 = 0$, the inverse does not exist.

17. $A = \begin{bmatrix} 2 & 7 & 1 \\ -3 & -9 & 2 \end{bmatrix}$

A has no inverse because it is not square.

19. Using a graphing utility:

$$A^{-1} = \begin{bmatrix} 1 & 1 & -1 \\ -3 & 2 & -1 \\ 3 & -3 & 2 \end{bmatrix}$$

21. Using a graphing utility:

$$A^{-1} = \begin{bmatrix} -175 & 37 & -13 \\ 95 & -20 & 7 \\ 14 & -3 & 1 \end{bmatrix}$$

23. Using a graphing utility:

$$A^{-1} = \frac{1}{2} \begin{bmatrix} -3 & 3 & 2 \\ 9 & -7 & -6 \\ -2 & 2 & 2 \end{bmatrix}$$

25. Using a graphing utility:

$$A^{-1} = \frac{5}{11} \begin{bmatrix} 0 & -4 & 2 \\ -22 & 11 & 11 \\ 22 & -6 & -8 \end{bmatrix}$$

27. Using a graphing utility:

$$A^{-1} = \begin{bmatrix} 1 & 0 & 0 \\ -0.75 & 0.25 & 0 \\ 0.35 & -0.25 & 0.2 \end{bmatrix}$$

29. Using a graphing utility, we see that the inverse of A does not exist.

31. Using a graphing utility:

$$A^{-1} = \begin{bmatrix} -\frac{1}{8} & 0 & 0 & 0 \\ 0 & 1 & 0 & 0 \\ 0 & 0 & \frac{1}{4} & 0 \\ 0 & 0 & 0 & -\frac{1}{5} \end{bmatrix}$$

33. Using a graphing utility:

$$A^{-1} = \begin{bmatrix} -24 & 7 & 1 & -2 \\ -10 & 3 & 0 & -1 \\ -29 & 7 & 3 & -2 \\ 12 & -3 & -1 & 1 \end{bmatrix}$$

35. Using a graphing utility, the solution is $(2, -2)$.

37. Using a graphing utility, we find that the system is inconsistent.

39. Using a graphing utility, the solution is $\left(\frac{2}{3}, \frac{1}{2}\right)$.

41. Using a graphing utility, the solution is $(-1, 3, 2)$.

43. Using a graphing utility, we see that the coefficient matrix is not invertible. However, using row reduction, we find that there is an infinite number of solutions.

$$\left(\frac{5}{16}a + \frac{13}{16}, \frac{19}{16}a + \frac{11}{16}, a\right)$$

45. Using a graphing utility, the solution is $(5, 0, -2, 3)$.

For Exercises 47 and 49 we have: $A = \begin{bmatrix} 1 & 1 & 1 \\ 0.065 & 0.07 & 0.09 \\ 0 & 2 & -1 \end{bmatrix}$. **Using a graphing utility,**

we obtain: $A^{-1} = \frac{1}{11}\begin{bmatrix} 50 & -600 & -4 \\ -13 & 200 & 5 \\ -26 & 400 & -1 \end{bmatrix}$.

47. $B = \begin{bmatrix} 25,000 \\ 1,900 \\ 0 \end{bmatrix}$

$X = A^{-1}B = \frac{1}{11}\begin{bmatrix} 50 & -600 & -4 \\ -13 & 200 & 5 \\ -265 & 400 & -1 \end{bmatrix}\begin{bmatrix} 25,000 \\ 1,900 \\ 0 \end{bmatrix} = \begin{bmatrix} 10,000 \\ 5,000 \\ 10,000 \end{bmatrix}$

Answer: $10,000 in AAA-rated bonds, $5,000 in A-rated bonds, $10,000 in B-rated bonds

49. $B = \begin{bmatrix} 12,000 \\ 835 \\ 0 \end{bmatrix}$

$X = A^{-1}B = \frac{1}{11}\begin{bmatrix} 50 & -600 & -4 \\ -13 & 200 & 5 \\ -26 & 400 & -1 \end{bmatrix}\begin{bmatrix} 12,000 \\ 835 \\ 0 \end{bmatrix} = \begin{bmatrix} 9000 \\ 1000 \\ 2000 \end{bmatrix}$

Answer: $9,000 in AAA-rated bonds, $1,000 in A-rated bonds, $2,000 in B-rated bonds

For Exercise 51 we have: $A = \begin{bmatrix} 2 & 0 & 4 \\ 0 & 1 & 4 \\ 1 & 1 & -1 \end{bmatrix}$. **Using a graphing utility, we obtain:**

$A^{-1} = \frac{1}{14}\begin{bmatrix} 5 & -4 & 4 \\ -4 & 6 & 8 \\ 1 & 2 & -2 \end{bmatrix}$.

51. $B = \begin{bmatrix} 14 \\ 28 \\ 0 \end{bmatrix}$

$X = A^{-1}B = \frac{1}{14}\begin{bmatrix} 5 & -4 & 4 \\ -4 & 6 & 8 \\ 1 & 2 & -2 \end{bmatrix}\begin{bmatrix} 14 \\ 28 \\ 0 \end{bmatrix} = \begin{bmatrix} -3 \\ 8 \\ 5 \end{bmatrix}$

Answer: $I_1 = -3$ amps, $I_2 = 8$ amps, $I_3 = 5$ amps

Section 8.4   The Determinant of a Square Matrix

■ The determinant of the 2×2 matrix $A = \begin{bmatrix} a_1 & b_1 \\ a_2 & b_2 \end{bmatrix}$ is given by

$$\det A = \begin{vmatrix} a_1 & b_1 \\ a_2 & b_2 \end{vmatrix} = a_1 b_2 - a_2 b_1$$

■ You should be able to calculate the minors and cofactors of a matrix.

■ You should be able to calculate the determinant of an $n \times n$ matrix.

■ The determinant of a triangular matrix is the product of the diagonal entries.

1. 5

3. $\begin{vmatrix} 2 & 1 \\ 3 & 4 \end{vmatrix} = 2(4) - 1(3) = 8 - 3 = 5$

5. $\begin{vmatrix} 5 & 2 \\ -6 & 3 \end{vmatrix} = 5(3) - 2(-6) = 15 + 12 = 27$

7. $\begin{vmatrix} -7 & 6 \\ \frac{1}{2} & 3 \end{vmatrix} = -7(3) - 6\left(\frac{1}{2}\right) = -21 - 3 = -24$

9. $\begin{vmatrix} 2 & 6 \\ 0 & 3 \end{vmatrix} = 2(3) - 6(0) = 6$

11. $\begin{vmatrix} 2 & -1 & 0 \\ 4 & 2 & 1 \\ 4 & 2 & 1 \end{vmatrix} \begin{matrix} 2 & -1 \\ 4 & 2 \\ 4 & 2 \end{matrix} = 4 + (-4) + 0 - 0 - 4 - (-4) = 0$

13. $\begin{vmatrix} 0.3 & 0.2 & 0.2 \\ 0.2 & 0.2 & 0.2 \\ -0.4 & 0.4 & 0.3 \end{vmatrix} \begin{matrix} 0.3 & 0.2 \\ 0.2 & 0.2 \\ -0.4 & 0.4 \end{matrix} = 0.018 + (-0.016) + 0.016 - (-0.016) - 0.024 - 0.012 = -0.002$

15. $\begin{vmatrix} 1 & 4 & -2 \\ 3 & 6 & -6 \\ -2 & 1 & 4 \end{vmatrix} \begin{matrix} 1 & 4 \\ 3 & 6 \\ -2 & 1 \end{matrix} = 24 + 48 + (-6) - 24 - (-6) - 48 = 0$

17. $\begin{vmatrix} 6 & 3 & -7 \\ 0 & 0 & 0 \\ 4 & 6 & 3 \end{vmatrix} = 0(C_{21}) + 0(C_{22}) + 0(C_{23})$
$= 0$

19. $\begin{vmatrix} -1 & 2 & -5 \\ 0 & 3 & 4 \\ 0 & 0 & 3 \end{vmatrix} = (-1)(3)(3) = -9$

(Upper Triangular Matrix)

21. $\begin{vmatrix} -1 & 0 & 0 & 0 \\ 2 & 3 & 0 & 0 \\ -4 & 5 & 3 & 0 \\ 1 & 0 & 2 & 2 \end{vmatrix} = (-1)(3)(3)(2) = -18$

(Lower Triangular Matrix)

23. $\begin{vmatrix} x & y & 1 \\ -2 & -2 & 1 \\ 1 & 5 & 1 \end{vmatrix} \begin{matrix} x & y \\ -2 & -2 \\ 1 & 5 \end{matrix} = -2x + y + (-10) - (-2) - 5x - (-2y) = -7x + 3y - 8$

25. (a) $M_{11} = -5$

       $M_{12} = 2$

       $M_{21} = 4$

       $M_{22} = 3$

(b) $C_{11} = M_{11} = -5$

       $C_{12} = -M_{12} = -2$

       $C_{21} = -M_{21} = -4$

       $C_{22} = M_{22} = 3$

27. (a) $M_{11} = \begin{vmatrix} 2 & -6 \\ 3 & 6 \end{vmatrix} = 12 + 18 = 30$

       $M_{12} = \begin{vmatrix} 3 & -6 \\ -1 & 6 \end{vmatrix} = 18 - 6 = 12$

       $M_{13} = \begin{vmatrix} 3 & 2 \\ -1 & 3 \end{vmatrix} = 9 + 2 = 11$

       $M_{21} = \begin{vmatrix} -2 & 8 \\ 3 & 6 \end{vmatrix} = -12 - 24 = -36$

       $M_{22} = \begin{vmatrix} 3 & 8 \\ -1 & 6 \end{vmatrix} = 18 + 8 = 26$

       $M_{23} = \begin{vmatrix} 3 & -2 \\ -1 & 3 \end{vmatrix} = 9 - 2 = 7$

       $M_{31} = \begin{vmatrix} -2 & 8 \\ 2 & -6 \end{vmatrix} = 12 - 16 = -4$

       $M_{32} = \begin{vmatrix} 3 & 8 \\ 3 & -6 \end{vmatrix} = -18 - 24 = -42$

       $M_{33} = \begin{vmatrix} 3 & -2 \\ 3 & 2 \end{vmatrix} = 6 + 6 = 12$

(b) $C_{11} = (-1)^2 M_{11} = 30$

       $C_{12} = (-1)^3 M_{12} = -12$

       $C_{13} = (-1)^4 M_{13} = 11$

       $C_{21} = (-1)^3 M_{21} = 36$

       $C_{22} = (-1)^4 M_{22} = 26$

       $C_{23} = (-1)^5 M_{23} = -7$

       $C_{31} = (-1)^4 M_{31} = -4$

       $C_{32} = (-1)^5 M_{32} = 42$

       $C_{33} = (-1)^6 M_{33} = 12$

29. (a)
$$\begin{vmatrix} -3 & 2 & 1 \\ 4 & 5 & 6 \\ 2 & -3 & 1 \end{vmatrix} = -3C_{11} + 2C_{12} + 1C_{13}$$
$$= -3(23) + 2(8) + 1(-22)$$
$$= -75$$

31. (a)
$$\begin{vmatrix} 5 & 0 & -3 \\ 0 & 12 & 4 \\ 1 & 6 & 3 \end{vmatrix} = 0C_{21} + 12C_{22} + 4C_{23}$$
$$= 0 + 12(18) + 4(-30)$$
$$= 96$$

(b)
$$\begin{vmatrix} -3 & 2 & 1 \\ 4 & 5 & 6 \\ 2 & -3 & 1 \end{vmatrix} = 2C_{12} + 5C_{22} - 3C_{32}$$
$$= 2(8) + 5(-5) - 3(22)$$
$$= -75$$

(b)
$$\begin{vmatrix} 5 & 0 & -3 \\ 0 & 12 & 4 \\ 1 & 6 & 3 \end{vmatrix} = 0C_{12} + 12C_{22} + 6C_{32}$$
$$= 0 + 12(18) + 6(-20)$$
$$= 96$$

33. (a)
$$\begin{vmatrix} 6 & 0 & -3 & 5 \\ 4 & 13 & 6 & -8 \\ -1 & 0 & 7 & 4 \\ 8 & 6 & 0 & 2 \end{vmatrix} = 4C_{21} + 13C_{22} + 6C_{23} - 8C_{24}$$
$$= 4(282) + 13(-298) + 6(174) - 8(-234) = 170$$

(b)
$$\begin{vmatrix} 6 & 0 & -3 & 5 \\ 4 & 13 & 6 & -8 \\ -1 & 0 & 7 & 4 \\ 8 & 6 & 0 & 2 \end{vmatrix} = 0C_{12} + 13C_{22} + 0C_{32} + 6C_{42}$$
$$= 0 + 13(-298) + 0 + 6(674) = 170$$

35. Expansion along the third column:
$$\begin{vmatrix} 1 & 4 & -2 \\ 3 & 2 & 0 \\ -1 & 4 & 3 \end{vmatrix} = -2\begin{vmatrix} 3 & 2 \\ -1 & 4 \end{vmatrix} + 0 + 3\begin{vmatrix} 1 & 4 \\ 3 & 2 \end{vmatrix}$$
$$= -2(14) + 3(-10)$$
$$= -28 - 30 = -58$$

37. Expansion along the first column:
$$\begin{vmatrix} 2 & 4 & 6 \\ 0 & 3 & 1 \\ 0 & 0 & -5 \end{vmatrix} = 2\begin{vmatrix} 3 & 1 \\ 0 & -5 \end{vmatrix} + 0 + 0$$
$$= 2(-15) = -30$$

39. Expansion along the second row:
$$\begin{vmatrix} 3 & 6 & -5 & 4 \\ -2 & 0 & 6 & 0 \\ 1 & 1 & 2 & 2 \\ 0 & 3 & -1 & -1 \end{vmatrix} = -(-2)\begin{vmatrix} 6 & -5 & 4 \\ 1 & 2 & 2 \\ 3 & -1 & -1 \end{vmatrix} - 6\begin{vmatrix} 3 & 6 & 4 \\ 1 & 1 & 2 \\ 0 & 3 & -1 \end{vmatrix}$$
$$= 2[6(0) - 1(9) + 3(-18)] - 6[3(-7) - (-18)]$$
$$= 2[-9 - 54] - 6[-21 + 18]$$
$$= -126 + 18 = -108$$

41. Expansion along the first column:

$$\begin{vmatrix} 5 & 3 & 0 & 6 \\ 4 & 6 & 4 & 12 \\ 0 & 2 & -3 & 4 \\ 0 & 1 & -2 & 2 \end{vmatrix} = 5 \begin{vmatrix} 6 & 4 & 12 \\ 2 & -3 & 4 \\ 1 & -2 & 2 \end{vmatrix} - 4 \begin{vmatrix} 3 & 0 & 6 \\ 2 & -3 & 4 \\ 1 & -2 & 2 \end{vmatrix}$$

$$= 5\,[\,6(2) - 2(32) + 1(52)\,] - 4\,[\,3(2) - 0 + 6(-1)\,]$$

$$= 5\,[\,12 - 64 + 52\,] - 4\,[\,6 - 6\,] = 5(0) - 4(0) = 0$$

43. Expansion along the second column:

$$\begin{vmatrix} 3 & 2 & 4 & -1 & 5 \\ -2 & 0 & 1 & 3 & 2 \\ 1 & 0 & 0 & 4 & 0 \\ 6 & 0 & 2 & -1 & 0 \\ 3 & 0 & 5 & 1 & 0 \end{vmatrix} = -2 \begin{vmatrix} -2 & 1 & 3 & 2 \\ 1 & 0 & 4 & 0 \\ 6 & 2 & -1 & 0 \\ 3 & 5 & 1 & 0 \end{vmatrix}$$

$$= -2(-2) \begin{vmatrix} 1 & 0 & 4 \\ 6 & 2 & -1 \\ 3 & 5 & 1 \end{vmatrix} \qquad \text{Expansion along the fourth column}$$

$$= 4[1(7) - 0 + 4(24)] = 4[7 + 96] = 412$$

45. $\begin{vmatrix} 1 & 2 & 5 \\ 1 & 4 & 2 \\ 0 & 3 & -4 \end{vmatrix} = \begin{vmatrix} 1 & 2 & 5 \\ 0 & 2 & -3 \\ 0 & 3 & -4 \end{vmatrix}$

$$= 1(-1)^2 \begin{vmatrix} 2 & -3 \\ 3 & -4 \end{vmatrix} = 1$$

47. $\begin{vmatrix} 3 & -1 & -3 \\ -1 & -4 & -2 \\ 3 & -1 & -1 \end{vmatrix} = \begin{vmatrix} 0 & -13 & -9 \\ -1 & -4 & -2 \\ 0 & -13 & -7 \end{vmatrix}$

$$= - \begin{vmatrix} 0 & -13 & -9 \\ 1 & 4 & 2 \\ 0 & -13 & -7 \end{vmatrix}$$

$$= (-1)(-1)^3 \begin{vmatrix} -13 & -9 \\ -13 & -7 \end{vmatrix} = -26$$

49. $\begin{vmatrix} 3 & 8 & -7 \\ 0 & -5 & 4 \\ 8 & 1 & 6 \end{vmatrix} = 3 \begin{vmatrix} -5 & 4 \\ 1 & 6 \end{vmatrix} + 8 \begin{vmatrix} 8 & -7 \\ -5 & 4 \end{vmatrix}$

$$= 3(-34) + 8(-3) = -126$$

51. $\begin{vmatrix} 2 & -1 & 3 \\ 1 & 2 & -1 \\ 3 & -4 & 7 \end{vmatrix} = \begin{vmatrix} 0 & -5 & 5 \\ 1 & 2 & -1 \\ 0 & -10 & 10 \end{vmatrix} = 0$

(Row 3 is a multiple of Row 1.)

53. $\begin{vmatrix} 7 & 0 & -14 \\ -2 & 5 & 4 \\ -6 & 2 & 12 \end{vmatrix} = \begin{vmatrix} 7 & 0 & 0 \\ -2 & 5 & 0 \\ -6 & 2 & 0 \end{vmatrix} = 0$

55. $\begin{vmatrix} 4 & -8 & 5 & 0 \\ 8 & -5 & 3 & 0 \\ 8 & 5 & 2 & 0 \\ 1 & 7 & -5 & 1 \end{vmatrix} = (-1)^8 \begin{vmatrix} 4 & -8 & 5 \\ 8 & -5 & 3 \\ 8 & 5 & 2 \end{vmatrix}$

$$= 4 \begin{vmatrix} 1 & -8 & 5 \\ 2 & -5 & 3 \\ 2 & 5 & 2 \end{vmatrix}$$

$$= 4 \begin{vmatrix} 1 & -8 & 5 \\ 0 & 11 & -7 \\ 0 & 21 & -8 \end{vmatrix}$$

$$= 4(-1)^2 \begin{vmatrix} 11 & -7 \\ 21 & -8 \end{vmatrix}$$

$$= 4(-88 + 147) = 236$$

57. $\begin{vmatrix} 0 & -3 & 8 & 2 \\ 8 & 1 & -1 & 6 \\ -4 & 6 & 0 & 9 \\ -7 & 0 & 0 & 14 \end{vmatrix} = \begin{vmatrix} 64 & 5 & 0 & 50 \\ 8 & 1 & -1 & 6 \\ -4 & 6 & 0 & 9 \\ -7 & 0 & 0 & 14 \end{vmatrix}$

$$= -1(-1)^5 \begin{vmatrix} 64 & 5 & 50 \\ -4 & 6 & 9 \\ -7 & 0 & 14 \end{vmatrix}$$

$$= \begin{vmatrix} 64 & 5 & 178 \\ -4 & 6 & 1 \\ -7 & 0 & 0 \end{vmatrix}$$

$$= -7(-1)^4 \begin{vmatrix} 5 & 178 \\ 6 & 1 \end{vmatrix}$$

$$= -7(-1063) = 7441$$

59.
$$\begin{vmatrix} 3 & -2 & 4 & 3 & 1 \\ -1 & 0 & 2 & 1 & 0 \\ 5 & -1 & 0 & 3 & 2 \\ 4 & 7 & -8 & 0 & 0 \\ 1 & 2 & 3 & 0 & 2 \end{vmatrix} = \begin{vmatrix} 3 & -2 & 4 & 3 & 1 \\ -1 & 0 & 2 & 1 & 0 \\ -1 & 3 & -8 & -3 & 0 \\ 4 & 7 & -8 & 0 & 0 \\ -5 & 6 & -5 & -6 & 0 \end{vmatrix}$$

$$= 1(-1)^6 \begin{vmatrix} -1 & 0 & 2 & 1 \\ -1 & 3 & -8 & -3 \\ 4 & 7 & -8 & 0 \\ -5 & 6 & -5 & -6 \end{vmatrix} = \begin{vmatrix} -1 & 0 & 2 & 1 \\ -4 & 3 & -2 & 0 \\ 4 & 7 & -8 & 0 \\ -11 & 6 & 7 & 0 \end{vmatrix}$$

$$= 1(-1)^5 \begin{vmatrix} -4 & 3 & -2 \\ 4 & 7 & -8 \\ -11 & 6 & 7 \end{vmatrix} = -1 \begin{vmatrix} -4 & 3 & -2 \\ -7 & 13 & -1 \\ -11 & 6 & 7 \end{vmatrix}$$

$$= -1 \begin{vmatrix} 10 & -23 & 0 \\ -7 & 13 & -1 \\ -60 & 97 & 0 \end{vmatrix} = -1(-1)(-1)^5 \begin{vmatrix} 10 & -23 \\ -60 & 97 \end{vmatrix}$$

$$= -1(970 - 1380) = 410$$

61. $\begin{vmatrix} x-1 & 2 \\ 3 & x-2 \end{vmatrix} = 0$

$(x-1)(x-2) - 6 = 0$

$x^2 - 3x - 4 = 0$

$(x+1)(x-4) = 0$

$x = -1 \text{ or } x = 4$

63. $\begin{vmatrix} 4u & -1 \\ -1 & 2v \end{vmatrix} = 8uv - 1$

65. $\begin{vmatrix} e^{2x} & e^{3x} \\ 2e^{2x} & 3e^{3x} \end{vmatrix} = 3e^{5x} - 2e^{5x} = e^{5x}$

67. $\begin{vmatrix} x & \ln x \\ 1 & 1/x \end{vmatrix} = 1 - \ln x$

69. (a) $\begin{vmatrix} -1 & 0 \\ 0 & 3 \end{vmatrix} = -3 - 0 = -3$

(b) $\begin{vmatrix} 2 & 0 \\ 0 & -1 \end{vmatrix} = -2 - 0 = -2$

(c) $\begin{bmatrix} -1 & 0 \\ 0 & 3 \end{bmatrix} \begin{bmatrix} 2 & 0 \\ 0 & -1 \end{bmatrix} = \begin{bmatrix} -2+0 & 0+0 \\ 0+0 & 0-3 \end{bmatrix}$

$= \begin{bmatrix} -2 & 0 \\ 0 & -3 \end{bmatrix}$

(d) $\begin{vmatrix} -2 & 0 \\ 0 & -3 \end{vmatrix} = 6 - 0 = 6$

71. (a) $\begin{vmatrix} -1 & 2 & 1 \\ 1 & 0 & 1 \\ 0 & 1 & 0 \end{vmatrix} = \begin{vmatrix} -1 & 2 & 1 \\ 0 & 2 & 2 \\ 0 & 1 & 0 \end{vmatrix} = -1 \begin{vmatrix} 2 & 2 \\ 1 & 0 \end{vmatrix} = (-1)(-2) = 2$

(b) $\begin{vmatrix} -1 & 0 & 0 \\ 0 & 2 & 0 \\ 0 & 0 & 3 \end{vmatrix} = (-1)(2)(3) = -6$

(c) $\begin{bmatrix} -1 & 2 & 1 \\ 1 & 0 & 1 \\ 0 & 1 & 0 \end{bmatrix} \begin{bmatrix} -1 & 0 & 0 \\ 0 & 2 & 0 \\ 0 & 0 & 3 \end{bmatrix} = \begin{bmatrix} 1+0+0 & 0+4+0 & 0+0+3 \\ -1+0+0 & 0+0+0 & 0+0+3 \\ 0+0+0 & 0+2+0 & 0+0+0 \end{bmatrix} = \begin{bmatrix} 1 & 4 & 3 \\ -1 & 0 & 3 \\ 0 & 2 & 0 \end{bmatrix}$

(d) $\begin{vmatrix} 1 & 4 & 3 \\ -1 & 0 & 3 \\ 0 & 2 & 0 \end{vmatrix} = \begin{vmatrix} 1 & 4 & 3 \\ 0 & 4 & 6 \\ 0 & 2 & 0 \end{vmatrix} = 1 \begin{vmatrix} 4 & 6 \\ 2 & 0 \end{vmatrix} = 0 - 12 = -12$

73. Let $A = \begin{bmatrix} 1 & 0 \\ 0 & 1 \end{bmatrix}$ and $B = \begin{bmatrix} -1 & 0 \\ 0 & -1 \end{bmatrix}$. Then $A + B = \begin{bmatrix} 0 & 0 \\ 0 & 0 \end{bmatrix}$.

$|A + B| = 0$ and $|A| + |B| = 1 + 1 = 2$

Thus, $|A + B| \neq |A| + |B|$.

Section 8.5   Applications of Matrices and Determinants

> ■ You should be able to use Cramer's Rule to solve a system of n linear equations in n variables.
>
> ■ The area of a triangle with vertices $(x_1,\ y_1)$, $(x_2,\ y_2)$, and $(x_3,\ y_3)$ is
>
> $$\text{Area} = \pm\frac{1}{2}\begin{vmatrix} x_1 & y_1 & 1 \\ x_2 & y_2 & 1 \\ x_3 & y_3 & 1 \end{vmatrix}$$
>
> ■ Three points $(x_1,\ y_1)$, $(x_2,\ y_2)$, and $(x_3,\ y_3)$ are collinear if and only if
>
> $$\begin{vmatrix} x_1 & y_1 & 1 \\ x_2 & y_2 & 1 \\ x_3 & y_3 & 1 \end{vmatrix} = 0$$
>
> ■ An equation of the line passing through the distinct points $(x_1,\ y_1)$ and $(x_2,\ y_2)$ is given by
>
> $$\begin{vmatrix} x & y & 1 \\ x_1 & y_1 & 1 \\ x_2 & y_2 & 1 \end{vmatrix} = 0$$
>
> ■ Cryptography: You should know how to use matrices to encode and decode messages.

1. $D = \begin{vmatrix} 1 & 2 \\ -1 & 1 \end{vmatrix} = 3$

$$x = \frac{D_x}{D} = \frac{\begin{vmatrix} 5 & 2 \\ 1 & 1 \end{vmatrix}}{3} = \frac{3}{3} = 1$$

$$y = \frac{D_y}{D} = \frac{\begin{vmatrix} 1 & 5 \\ -1 & 1 \end{vmatrix}}{3} = \frac{6}{3} = 2$$

Answer: $(1,\ 2)$

3. $D = \begin{vmatrix} 3 & 4 \\ 5 & 3 \end{vmatrix} = -11$

$$x = \frac{D_x}{D} = \frac{\begin{vmatrix} -2 & 4 \\ 4 & 3 \end{vmatrix}}{-11}$$

$$= \frac{-22}{-11} = 2$$

$$y = \frac{D_y}{D} = \frac{\begin{vmatrix} 3 & -2 \\ 5 & 4 \end{vmatrix}}{-11}$$

$$= \frac{22}{-11} = -2$$

Answer: $(2,\ -2)$

5. $D = \begin{vmatrix} 20 & 8 \\ 12 & -24 \end{vmatrix} = -576$

$x = \dfrac{D_x}{D} = \dfrac{\begin{vmatrix} 11 & 8 \\ 21 & -24 \end{vmatrix}}{-576} = \dfrac{-432}{-576} = \dfrac{3}{4}$

$y = \dfrac{D_y}{D} = \dfrac{\begin{vmatrix} 20 & 11 \\ 12 & 21 \end{vmatrix}}{-576} = \dfrac{288}{-576} = -\dfrac{1}{2}$

Answer: $\left(\dfrac{3}{4},\ -\dfrac{1}{2}\right)$

7. $D = \begin{vmatrix} -0.4 & 0.8 \\ 2 & -4 \end{vmatrix} = 0$

Since the determinant of the coefficient matrix is zero, Cramer's Rule does not apply.

9. $D = \begin{vmatrix} 3 & 6 \\ 6 & 14 \end{vmatrix} = 6$

$x = \dfrac{D_x}{D} = \dfrac{\begin{vmatrix} 5 & 6 \\ 11 & 14 \end{vmatrix}}{6} = \dfrac{4}{6} = \dfrac{2}{3}$

$y = \dfrac{D_y}{D} = \dfrac{\begin{vmatrix} 3 & 5 \\ 6 & 11 \end{vmatrix}}{6} = \dfrac{3}{6} = \dfrac{1}{2}$

Answer: $\left(\dfrac{2}{3},\ \dfrac{1}{2}\right)$

11. $D = \begin{vmatrix} 4 & -1 & 1 \\ 2 & 2 & 3 \\ 5 & -2 & 6 \end{vmatrix} = 55$

$x = \dfrac{D_x}{D} = \dfrac{\begin{vmatrix} -5 & -1 & 1 \\ 10 & 2 & 3 \\ 1 & -2 & 6 \end{vmatrix}}{55} = \dfrac{-55}{55} = -1$

13. $D = \begin{vmatrix} 3 & 4 & 4 \\ 4 & -4 & 6 \\ 6 & -6 & 0 \end{vmatrix} = 252$

$x = \dfrac{D_x}{D} = \dfrac{\begin{vmatrix} 11 & 4 & 4 \\ 11 & -4 & 6 \\ 3 & -6 & 0 \end{vmatrix}}{252} = \dfrac{252}{252} = 1$

15. $D = \begin{vmatrix} 3 & 3 & 5 \\ 3 & 5 & 9 \\ 5 & 9 & 17 \end{vmatrix} = 4$

$x = \dfrac{D_x}{D} = \dfrac{\begin{vmatrix} 1 & 3 & 5 \\ 2 & 5 & 9 \\ 4 & 9 & 17 \end{vmatrix}}{4} = \dfrac{0}{4} = 0$

17. $D = \begin{vmatrix} 5 & -3 & 2 \\ 2 & 2 & -3 \\ 1 & -7 & 8 \end{vmatrix} = 0$

Since the determinant of the coefficient matrix is zero, Cramer's Rule does not apply.

19. $D = \begin{vmatrix} 7 & -3 & 0 & 2 \\ -2 & 1 & 0 & -1 \\ 4 & 0 & 1 & -2 \\ -1 & 1 & 0 & -1 \end{vmatrix} = \begin{vmatrix} 7 & -3 & 2 \\ -2 & 1 & -1 \\ -1 & 1 & -1 \end{vmatrix} = 1$

$x = \dfrac{D_x}{D} = \dfrac{\begin{vmatrix} 41 & -3 & 0 & 2 \\ -13 & 1 & 0 & -1 \\ 12 & 0 & 1 & -2 \\ -8 & 1 & 0 & -1 \end{vmatrix}}{1}$

$= \dfrac{\begin{vmatrix} 41 & -3 & 2 \\ -13 & 1 & -1 \\ -8 & 1 & -1 \end{vmatrix}}{1} = \dfrac{5}{1} = 5$

21. $D = \begin{vmatrix} -4 & 0 & 10 \\ 0 & 5 & 10 \\ 1 & -1 & 1 \end{vmatrix} = -110$

$I_1 = \dfrac{\begin{vmatrix} 5 & 0 & 10 \\ 70 & 5 & 10 \\ 0 & -1 & 1 \end{vmatrix}}{-110} = \dfrac{-625}{-110} = \dfrac{125}{22}$

$I_2 = \dfrac{\begin{vmatrix} -4 & 5 & 10 \\ 0 & 70 & 10 \\ 1 & 0 & 1 \end{vmatrix}}{-110} = \dfrac{-930}{-110} = \dfrac{93}{11}$

$I_3 = \dfrac{\begin{vmatrix} -4 & 0 & 5 \\ 0 & 5 & 70 \\ 1 & -1 & 0 \end{vmatrix}}{-110} = \dfrac{-305}{-110} = \dfrac{61}{22}$

Answer:

$I_1 = \frac{125}{22}$ amps, $I_2 = \frac{93}{11}$ amps, $I_3 = \frac{61}{22}$ amps

23. $D = \begin{vmatrix} 9 & 45 \\ 45 & 285 \end{vmatrix} = 540$

$a = \dfrac{\begin{vmatrix} 24.983 & 45 \\ 137.012 & 285 \end{vmatrix}}{540} = \dfrac{954.615}{540} \approx 1.768$

$b = \dfrac{\begin{vmatrix} 9 & 24.983 \\ 45 & 137.012 \end{vmatrix}}{540} = \dfrac{108.873}{540} \approx 0.202$

$y \approx 1.768 + 0.202t$

When $t = 12$, $y \approx 1.768 + 0.202(12) \approx 4.2$ or $4200

25. $A = \pm\frac{1}{2}\begin{vmatrix} 1 & 5 & 1 \\ 3 & 1 & 1 \\ 0 & 0 & 1 \end{vmatrix} = \pm\frac{1}{2}(-14)$
$= 7$ square units

27. $A = \pm\frac{1}{2}\begin{vmatrix} -2 & -3 & 1 \\ 2 & -3 & 1 \\ 0 & 4 & 1 \end{vmatrix} = \pm\frac{1}{2}(28)$
$= 14$ square units

29. $A = \pm\frac{1}{2}\begin{vmatrix} 0 & \frac{1}{2} & 1 \\ \frac{5}{2} & 0 & 1 \\ 4 & 3 & 1 \end{vmatrix} = \pm\frac{1}{2}(\frac{33}{4})$
$= \frac{33}{8}$ square units

31. $A = \pm\frac{1}{2}\begin{vmatrix} -2 & 4 & 1 \\ 2 & 3 & 1 \\ -1 & 5 & 1 \end{vmatrix} = \pm\frac{1}{2}(5)$
$= \frac{5}{2}$ square units

33. $A = \pm\frac{1}{2}\begin{vmatrix} -3 & 5 & 1 \\ 2 & 6 & 1 \\ 3 & -5 & 1 \end{vmatrix} = \pm\frac{1}{2}(-56)$
$= 28$ square units

35. Vertex $A : (0, 25)$
Vertex $B : (10, 0)$
Vertex $C : (28, 5)$

$A = \pm\frac{1}{2}\begin{vmatrix} 0 & 25 & 1 \\ 10 & 0 & 1 \\ 28 & 5 & 1 \end{vmatrix} = \pm\frac{1}{2}(500)$
$= 250$ square miles

37. $\begin{vmatrix} 3 & -1 & 1 \\ 0 & -3 & 1 \\ 12 & 5 & 1 \end{vmatrix} = 0$

The points are collinear.

39. $\begin{vmatrix} 2 & -\frac{1}{2} & 1 \\ -4 & 4 & 1 \\ 6 & -3 & 1 \end{vmatrix} = -3 \neq 0$

The points are not collinear.

41. $\begin{vmatrix} 0 & 2 & 1 \\ 1 & 2.4 & 1 \\ -1 & 1.6 & 1 \end{vmatrix} = 0$

The points are collinear.

43. $\begin{vmatrix} x & y & 1 \\ 0 & 0 & 1 \\ 5 & 3 & 1 \end{vmatrix} = 0$

$x \begin{vmatrix} 0 & 1 \\ 3 & 1 \end{vmatrix} - y \begin{vmatrix} 0 & 1 \\ 5 & 1 \end{vmatrix} + 1 \begin{vmatrix} 0 & 0 \\ 5 & 3 \end{vmatrix} = 0$

$-3x + 5y + 0 = 0$

$3x - 5y = 0$

45. $\begin{vmatrix} x & y & 1 \\ -4 & 3 & 1 \\ 2 & 1 & 1 \end{vmatrix} = 0$

$x \begin{vmatrix} 3 & 1 \\ 1 & 1 \end{vmatrix} - y \begin{vmatrix} -4 & 1 \\ 2 & 1 \end{vmatrix} + 1 \begin{vmatrix} -4 & 3 \\ 2 & 1 \end{vmatrix} = 0$

$2x + 6y - 10 = 0$

$x + 3y - 5 = 0$

47. $\begin{vmatrix} x & y & 1 \\ -\frac{1}{2} & 3 & 1 \\ \frac{5}{2} & 1 & 1 \end{vmatrix} = 0$

$x \begin{vmatrix} 3 & 1 \\ 1 & 1 \end{vmatrix} - y \begin{vmatrix} -\frac{1}{2} & 1 \\ \frac{5}{2} & 1 \end{vmatrix} + 1 \begin{vmatrix} -\frac{1}{2} & 3 \\ \frac{5}{2} & 1 \end{vmatrix} = 0$

$2x + 3y - 8 = 0$

49. L A N D I N G — S U C C E S S F U L
[12 1 14] [4 9 14] [7 0 19] [21 3 3] [5 19 19] [6 21 12]

$[12 \quad 1 \quad 14] A = [1 \quad -25 \quad -65]$

$[4 \quad 9 \quad 14] A = [17 \quad 15 \quad -9]$

$[7 \quad 0 \quad 19] A = [-12 \quad -62 \quad -119]$

$[21 \quad 3 \quad 3] A = [27 \quad 51 \quad 48]$

$[5 \quad 19 \quad 19] A = [43 \quad 67 \quad 48]$

$[6 \quad 21 \quad 12] A = [57 \quad 111 \quad 117]$

Cryptogram: 1 −25 −65 17 15 −9 −12 −62 −119 27 51 48 43 67 48 57 111 117

51. H A P P Y — B I R T H D A Y —
[8 1 16] [16 25 0] [2 9 18] [20 8 4] [1 25 0]

$[8 \quad 1 \quad 16] A = [-5 \quad -41 \quad -87]$

$[16 \quad 25 \quad 0] A = [91 \quad 207 \quad 257]$

$[2 \quad 9 \quad 18] A = [11 \quad -5 \quad -41]$

$[20 \quad 8 \quad 4] A = [40 \quad 80 \quad 84]$

$[1 \quad 25 \quad 0] A = [76 \quad 177 \quad 227]$

Cryptogram: −5 −41 −87 91 207 257 11 −5 −41 40 80 84 76 177 227

53. To find A^{-1}, use Gauss-Jordan elimination.

$$\begin{bmatrix} 1 & 2 & 2 & \vdots & 1 & 0 & 0 \\ 3 & 7 & 9 & \vdots & 0 & 1 & 0 \\ -1 & -4 & -7 & \vdots & 0 & 0 & 1 \end{bmatrix} \rightarrow \begin{bmatrix} 1 & 0 & 0 & \vdots & -13 & 6 & 4 \\ 0 & 1 & 0 & \vdots & 12 & -5 & -3 \\ 0 & 0 & 1 & \vdots & -5 & 2 & 1 \end{bmatrix}$$

$$A^{-1} = \begin{bmatrix} -13 & 6 & 4 \\ 12 & -5 & -3 \\ -5 & 2 & 1 \end{bmatrix}$$

$$\begin{bmatrix} 20 & 17 & -15 \end{bmatrix} A^{-1} = \begin{bmatrix} 19 & 5 & 14 \end{bmatrix}$$

$$\begin{bmatrix} -12 & -56 & -104 \end{bmatrix} A^{-1} = \begin{bmatrix} 4 & 0 & 16 \end{bmatrix}$$

$$\begin{bmatrix} 1 & -25 & -65 \end{bmatrix} A^{-1} = \begin{bmatrix} 12 & 1 & 14 \end{bmatrix}$$

$$\begin{bmatrix} 62 & 143 & 181 \end{bmatrix} A^{-1} = \begin{bmatrix} 5 & 19 & 0 \end{bmatrix}$$

19 5 14 4 0 16 12 1 14 5 19 0

S E N D ⎯ P L A N E S ⎯

Chapter 8   Review Exercises

1. $\begin{bmatrix} 5 & 4 & \vdots & 2 \\ -1 & 1 & \vdots & -22 \end{bmatrix} \Rightarrow \begin{bmatrix} 1 & -1 & \vdots & 22 \\ 5 & 4 & \vdots & 2 \end{bmatrix}$

$\Rightarrow \begin{bmatrix} 1 & -1 & \vdots & 22 \\ 0 & 9 & \vdots & -108 \end{bmatrix}$

$\Rightarrow \begin{bmatrix} 1 & -1 & \vdots & 22 \\ 0 & 1 & \vdots & -12 \end{bmatrix}$

$\Rightarrow \begin{bmatrix} 1 & 0 & \vdots & 10 \\ 0 & 1 & \vdots & -12 \end{bmatrix}$

$x = 10$

$y = -12$

Answer: $(10, -12)$

3. $\begin{bmatrix} 0.2 & -0.1 & \vdots & 0.07 \\ 0.4 & -0.5 & \vdots & -0.01 \end{bmatrix} \Rightarrow \begin{bmatrix} 1 & -0.5 & \vdots & 0.35 \\ 0 & -0.3 & \vdots & -0.15 \end{bmatrix} \Rightarrow \begin{bmatrix} 1 & 0 & \vdots & 0.6 \\ 0 & 1 & \vdots & 0.5 \end{bmatrix}$

$x = 0.6$

$y = 0.5$

Answer: $(0.6, 0.5)$

5. $\begin{bmatrix} 2 & 3 & 3 & \vdots & 3 \\ 6 & 6 & 12 & \vdots & 13 \\ 12 & 9 & -1 & \vdots & 2 \end{bmatrix} \Rightarrow \begin{bmatrix} 2 & 3 & 3 & \vdots & 3 \\ 0 & -3 & 3 & \vdots & 4 \\ 0 & -3 & -25 & \vdots & -24 \end{bmatrix}$

$\Rightarrow \begin{bmatrix} 2 & 0 & 6 & \vdots & 7 \\ 0 & -3 & 3 & \vdots & 4 \\ 0 & 0 & -28 & \vdots & -28 \end{bmatrix} \Rightarrow \begin{bmatrix} 1 & 0 & 3 & \vdots & \frac{7}{2} \\ 0 & 1 & -1 & \vdots & -\frac{4}{3} \\ 0 & 0 & 1 & \vdots & 1 \end{bmatrix}$

$z = 1$

$y - 1 = -\frac{4}{3} \Rightarrow y = \frac{1}{3}$

$x + 3(1) = \frac{7}{2} \Rightarrow x = \frac{1}{2}$

Answer: $\left(\frac{1}{2}, \frac{1}{3}, 1\right)$

7.
$$\left[\begin{array}{cccc:c} 1 & 2 & 0 & 1 & 3 \\ 0 & -3 & 3 & 0 & 0 \\ 4 & 4 & 1 & 2 & 0 \\ 2 & 0 & 1 & 0 & 3 \end{array}\right] \Rightarrow \left[\begin{array}{cccc:c} 1 & 2 & 0 & 1 & 3 \\ 0 & 1 & -1 & 0 & 0 \\ 0 & -4 & 1 & -2 & -12 \\ 0 & -4 & 1 & -2 & -3 \end{array}\right] \Rightarrow \left[\begin{array}{cccc:c} 1 & 2 & 0 & 1 & 3 \\ 0 & 1 & -1 & 0 & 0 \\ 0 & -4 & 1 & -2 & -12 \\ 0 & 0 & 0 & 0 & 9 \end{array}\right]$$

$$x + 2y \quad + w = 3$$
$$y - z \quad = 0$$
$$-4y + z - 2w = -12$$
$$0 = 9$$

Inconsistent, no solution

9.
$$\left[\begin{array}{ccc} 2 & 1 & 0 \\ 0 & 5 & -4 \end{array}\right] - 3\left[\begin{array}{ccc} 5 & 3 & -6 \\ 0 & -2 & 5 \end{array}\right] = \left[\begin{array}{ccc} 2 & 1 & 0 \\ 0 & 5 & -4 \end{array}\right] + \left[\begin{array}{ccc} -15 & -9 & 18 \\ 0 & 6 & -15 \end{array}\right] =$$
$$\left[\begin{array}{ccc} -13 & -8 & 18 \\ 0 & 11 & -19 \end{array}\right]$$

11.
$$\left[\begin{array}{cc} 1 & 2 \\ 5 & -4 \\ 6 & 0 \end{array}\right]\left[\begin{array}{ccc} 6 & -2 & 8 \\ 4 & 0 & 0 \end{array}\right] = \left[\begin{array}{ccc} 14 & -2 & 8 \\ 14 & -10 & 40 \\ 36 & -12 & 48 \end{array}\right]$$

13.
$$\left[\begin{array}{ccc} 1 & 5 & 6 \\ 2 & -4 & 0 \end{array}\right]\left[\begin{array}{cc} 6 & 4 \\ -2 & 0 \\ 8 & 0 \end{array}\right] = \left[\begin{array}{cc} 6-10+48 & 4 \\ 12+8 & 8 \end{array}\right] = \left[\begin{array}{cc} 44 & 4 \\ 20 & 8 \end{array}\right]$$

15.
$$\left[\begin{array}{ccc} 1 & 3 & 2 \\ 0 & 2 & -4 \\ 0 & 0 & 3 \end{array}\right]\left[\begin{array}{ccc} 4 & -3 & 2 \\ 0 & 3 & -1 \\ 0 & 0 & 2 \end{array}\right] = \left[\begin{array}{ccc} 4 & 6 & 3 \\ 0 & 6 & -10 \\ 0 & 0 & 6 \end{array}\right]$$

17. $X = 3\left[\begin{array}{cc} -4 & 0 \\ 1 & -5 \\ -3 & 2 \end{array}\right] - 2\left[\begin{array}{cc} 1 & 2 \\ -2 & 1 \\ 4 & 4 \end{array}\right]$

$$= \left[\begin{array}{cc} -14 & -4 \\ 7 & -17 \\ -17 & -2 \end{array}\right]$$

19. $X = \frac{1}{3}\left(\left[\begin{array}{cc} 1 & 2 \\ -2 & 1 \\ 4 & 4 \end{array}\right] - 2\left[\begin{array}{cc} -4 & 0 \\ 1 & -5 \\ -3 & 2 \end{array}\right]\right)$

$$= \frac{1}{3}\left[\begin{array}{cc} 9 & 2 \\ -4 & 11 \\ 10 & 0 \end{array}\right]$$

21. $5x + 4y = 2$
$$-x + y = -22$$

23. $\begin{bmatrix} 2 & 6 & \vdots & 1 & 0 \\ 3 & -6 & \vdots & 0 & 1 \end{bmatrix} \Rightarrow \begin{bmatrix} 1 & -12 & \vdots & -1 & 1 \\ 3 & -6 & \vdots & 0 & 1 \end{bmatrix}$

$\Rightarrow \begin{bmatrix} 1 & -12 & \vdots & -1 & 1 \\ 0 & 30 & \vdots & 3 & -2 \end{bmatrix}$

$\Rightarrow \begin{bmatrix} 1 & -12 & \vdots & -1 & 1 \\ 0 & 1 & \vdots & \frac{1}{10} & -\frac{1}{15} \end{bmatrix}$

$\Rightarrow \begin{bmatrix} 1 & 0 & \vdots & \frac{1}{5} & \frac{1}{5} \\ 0 & 1 & \vdots & \frac{1}{10} & -\frac{1}{15} \end{bmatrix}$

$A^{-1} = \begin{bmatrix} \frac{1}{5} & \frac{1}{5} \\ \frac{1}{10} & -\frac{1}{15} \end{bmatrix}$

25. $\begin{bmatrix} 2 & 0 & 3 & \vdots & 1 & 0 & 0 \\ -1 & 1 & 1 & \vdots & 0 & 1 & 0 \\ 2 & -2 & 1 & \vdots & 0 & 0 & 1 \end{bmatrix} \Rightarrow \begin{bmatrix} 1 & 1 & 4 & \vdots & 1 & 1 & 0 \\ 0 & 2 & 5 & \vdots & 1 & 2 & 0 \\ 0 & -4 & -7 & \vdots & -2 & -2 & 1 \end{bmatrix}$

$\Rightarrow \begin{bmatrix} 1 & 0 & \frac{3}{2} & \vdots & \frac{1}{2} & 0 & 0 \\ 0 & 1 & \frac{5}{2} & \vdots & \frac{1}{2} & 1 & 0 \\ 0 & 0 & 3 & \vdots & 0 & 2 & 1 \end{bmatrix}$

$\Rightarrow \begin{bmatrix} 1 & 0 & 0 & \vdots & \frac{1}{2} & -1 & -\frac{1}{2} \\ 0 & 1 & 0 & \vdots & \frac{1}{2} & -\frac{2}{3} & -\frac{5}{6} \\ 0 & 0 & 1 & \vdots & 0 & \frac{2}{3} & \frac{1}{3} \end{bmatrix}$

$A^{-1} = \begin{bmatrix} \frac{1}{2} & -1 & -\frac{1}{2} \\ \frac{1}{2} & -\frac{2}{3} & -\frac{5}{6} \\ 0 & \frac{2}{3} & \frac{1}{3} \end{bmatrix}$

27. $\begin{vmatrix} 50 & -30 \\ 10 & 5 \end{vmatrix} = 250 - (-300) = 550$

29. $\begin{vmatrix} 3 & 0 & -4 & 0 \\ 0 & 8 & 1 & 2 \\ 6 & 1 & 8 & 2 \\ 0 & 3 & -4 & 1 \end{vmatrix} = 3\begin{vmatrix} 8 & 1 & 2 \\ 1 & 8 & 2 \\ 3 & -4 & 1 \end{vmatrix} + (-4)\begin{vmatrix} 0 & 8 & 2 \\ 6 & 1 & 2 \\ 0 & 3 & 1 \end{vmatrix}$ (Expansion along Row 1)

$= 3[8(8 - (-8)) - 1(1 - 6) + 2(-4 - 24)] - 4[0 - 6(8 - 6) + 0]$

$= 3[128 + 5 - 56] - 4[-12] = 279$

31. (a) $\begin{bmatrix} x \\ y \end{bmatrix} = A^{-1}B = \begin{bmatrix} -2 & 1 \\ \frac{3}{2} & -\frac{1}{2} \end{bmatrix} \begin{bmatrix} -1 \\ -5 \end{bmatrix} = \begin{bmatrix} -3 \\ 1 \end{bmatrix}$

(b) $D = \begin{vmatrix} 1 & 2 \\ 3 & 4 \end{vmatrix} = -2$

$$x = \frac{D_x}{D} = \frac{\begin{vmatrix} -1 & 2 \\ -5 & 4 \end{vmatrix}}{-2} = \frac{6}{-2} = -3$$

$$y = \frac{D_y}{D} = \frac{\begin{vmatrix} 1 & -1 \\ 3 & -5 \end{vmatrix}}{-2} = \frac{-2}{-2} = 1$$

Answer: $(-3, 1)$

33. (a) $\begin{bmatrix} x \\ y \\ z \end{bmatrix} = \begin{bmatrix} 1 & 0 & 1 \\ 4 & 4 & 3 \\ -4 & -3 & -3 \end{bmatrix} \begin{bmatrix} 2 \\ -1 \\ -1 \end{bmatrix} = \begin{bmatrix} 1 \\ 1 \\ -2 \end{bmatrix}$

(b) $D = \begin{vmatrix} -3 & -3 & -4 \\ 0 & 1 & 1 \\ 4 & 3 & 4 \end{vmatrix} = 1$

$$x = \frac{D_x}{D} = \frac{\begin{vmatrix} 2 & -3 & -4 \\ -1 & 1 & 1 \\ -1 & 3 & 4 \end{vmatrix}}{1} = \frac{1}{1} = 1$$

$$y = \frac{D_y}{D} = \frac{\begin{vmatrix} -3 & 2 & -4 \\ 0 & -1 & 1 \\ 4 & -1 & 4 \end{vmatrix}}{1} = \frac{1}{1} = 1$$

$$z = \frac{D_z}{D} = \frac{\begin{vmatrix} -3 & -3 & 2 \\ 0 & 1 & -1 \\ 4 & 3 & -1 \end{vmatrix}}{1} = \frac{-2}{1} = -2$$

Answer: $(1, 1, -2)$

35. (a) $\begin{bmatrix} x \\ y \\ z \end{bmatrix} = \begin{bmatrix} 2 & 4 & \frac{7}{2} \\ -1 & -2 & -\frac{3}{2} \\ 1 & 1 & \frac{1}{2} \end{bmatrix} \begin{bmatrix} 2 \\ 10 \\ -12 \end{bmatrix} = \begin{bmatrix} 2 \\ -4 \\ 6 \end{bmatrix}$

(b) $D = \begin{vmatrix} 1 & 3 & 2 \\ -2 & -5 & -1 \\ 2 & 4 & 0 \end{vmatrix} = 2$

$$x = \frac{D_x}{D} = \frac{\begin{vmatrix} 2 & 3 & 2 \\ 10 & -5 & -1 \\ -12 & 4 & 0 \end{vmatrix}}{2} = \frac{4}{2} = 2$$

$$y = \frac{D_y}{D} = \frac{\begin{vmatrix} 1 & 2 & 2 \\ -2 & 10 & -1 \\ 2 & -12 & 0 \end{vmatrix}}{2} = \frac{-8}{2} = -4$$

$$z = \frac{D_z}{D} = \frac{\begin{vmatrix} 1 & 3 & 2 \\ -2 & -5 & 10 \\ 2 & 4 & -12 \end{vmatrix}}{2} = \frac{12}{2} = 6$$

Answer: $(2, -4, 6)$

37. (a) $\begin{bmatrix} 2 & 3 & -4 & \vdots & 1 & 0 & 0 \\ 1 & -1 & 2 & \vdots & 0 & 1 & 0 \\ 3 & 7 & -10 & \vdots & 0 & 0 & 1 \end{bmatrix} \Rightarrow \begin{bmatrix} 1 & -1 & 2 & \vdots & 0 & 1 & 0 \\ 0 & 5 & -8 & \vdots & 1 & -2 & 0 \\ 0 & 10 & -16 & \vdots & 0 & -3 & 1 \end{bmatrix}$

$$\Rightarrow \begin{bmatrix} 1 & -1 & 2 & \vdots & 0 & 1 & 0 \\ 0 & 5 & -8 & \vdots & 1 & -2 & 0 \\ 0 & 0 & 0 & \vdots & -2 & 1 & 1 \end{bmatrix}$$

(b) $D = \begin{vmatrix} 2 & 3 & -4 \\ 1 & -1 & 2 \\ 3 & 7 & -10 \end{vmatrix} = 0$

Answer: A has no inverse. The system is inconsistent.

39. Area $= \pm\frac{1}{2} \begin{vmatrix} 1 & 0 & 1 \\ 5 & 0 & 1 \\ 0 & 8 & 1 \end{vmatrix} = \pm\frac{1}{2}(32)$
$= 16$ square units

41. Area $= \pm\frac{1}{2} \begin{vmatrix} 1 & 2 & 1 \\ 4 & -5 & 1 \\ 3 & 2 & 1 \end{vmatrix} = \pm\frac{1}{2}(14)$
$= 7$ square units

43.
$$\begin{vmatrix} x & y & 1 \\ -4 & 0 & 1 \\ 4 & 4 & 1 \end{vmatrix} = 0$$

$$x\begin{vmatrix} 0 & 1 \\ 4 & 1 \end{vmatrix} - y\begin{vmatrix} -4 & 1 \\ 4 & 1 \end{vmatrix} + 1\begin{vmatrix} -4 & 0 \\ 4 & 4 \end{vmatrix} = 0$$

$$-4x + 8y - 16 = 0$$

$$x - 2y + 4 = 0$$

45.
$$\begin{vmatrix} x & y & 1 \\ -\frac{5}{2} & 3 & 1 \\ \frac{7}{2} & 1 & 1 \end{vmatrix} = 0$$

$$x\begin{vmatrix} 3 & 1 \\ 1 & 1 \end{vmatrix} - y\begin{vmatrix} -\frac{5}{2} & 1 \\ \frac{7}{2} & 1 \end{vmatrix} + 1\begin{vmatrix} -\frac{5}{2} & 3 \\ \frac{7}{2} & 1 \end{vmatrix} = 0$$

$$2x + 6y - 13 = 0$$

47. Let x = the number of carnations, and y = the number of roses. Then,

$$x + y = 12$$

$$0.75x + 1.50y = \$12.00.$$

By Cramer's Rule we have

$$x = \frac{\begin{vmatrix} 12 & 1 \\ 12 & 1.50 \end{vmatrix}}{\begin{vmatrix} 1 & 1 \\ 0.75 & 1.50 \end{vmatrix}} = \frac{6}{0.75} = 8.$$

Using back-substitution in the first equation yields $y = 4$. The florist should use 8 carnations and 4 roses.

49.
$$5b + 10a = 17.8 \Rightarrow -10b - 20a = -35.6$$
$$10b + 30a = 45.7 \Rightarrow \underline{10b + 30a = 45.7}$$
$$10a = 10.1$$
$$a = 1.01$$
$$b = 1.54$$

Least squares regression line:
$$y = 1.01x + 1.54$$

51. $2 = a(-1)^2 + b(-1) + c \Rightarrow a - b + c = 2$

$3 = a(0) + b(0) + c \Rightarrow c = 3$

$6 = a(1)^2 + b(1) + c \Rightarrow a + b + c = 6$

$$\begin{bmatrix} 1 & -1 & 1 & \vdots & 2 \\ 0 & 0 & 1 & \vdots & 3 \\ 1 & 1 & 1 & \vdots & 6 \end{bmatrix} \Rightarrow \begin{bmatrix} 1 & -1 & 1 & \vdots & 2 \\ 0 & 2 & 0 & \vdots & 4 \\ 0 & 0 & 1 & \vdots & 3 \end{bmatrix}$$

$$\Rightarrow \begin{bmatrix} 1 & 0 & 0 & \vdots & 1 \\ 0 & 1 & 0 & \vdots & 2 \\ 0 & 0 & 1 & \vdots & 3 \end{bmatrix}$$

$c = 3$

$b = 2$

$a = 1$

Answer: $y = x^2 + 2x + 3$

53. $|4A| = 4^3(2) = 128$, since $4A$ means that each of the three rows of A was multiplied by 4.

CHAPTER 9

Sequences, Probability, and Statistics

Section 9.1   Sequences and Summations Notation

- Given the general nth term in a sequence, you should be able to find, or list, some of the terms.
- You should be able to find an expression for the nth term of a sequence.
- You should be able to use and evaluate factorials.
- You should be able to use sigma notation for a sum.

1. $a_n = 2n + 1$

$a_1 = 2(1) + 1 = 3$

$a_2 = 2(2) + 1 = 5$

$a_3 = 2(3) + 1 = 7$

$a_4 = 2(4) + 1 = 9$

$a_5 = 2(5) + 1 = 10$

3. $a_n = 2^n$

$a_1 = 2^1 = 2$

$a_2 = 2^2 = 4$

$a_3 = 2^3 = 8$

$a_4 = 2^4 = 16$

$a_5 = 2^5 = 32$

5. $a_n = (-2)^n$

$a_1 = (-2)^1 = -2$

$a_2 = (-2)^2 = 4$

$a_3 = (-2)^3 = -8$

$a_4 = (-2)^4 = 16$

$a_5 = (-2)^5 = -32$

7. $a_n = \dfrac{1 + (-1)^n}{n}$

$a_1 = \dfrac{1 + (-1)}{1} = \dfrac{0}{1} = 0$

$a_2 = \dfrac{1 + (-1)^2}{2} = \dfrac{2}{2} = 1$

$a_3 = \dfrac{1 + (-1)^3}{3} = \dfrac{0}{3} = 0$

$a_4 = \dfrac{1 + (-1)^4}{4} = \dfrac{2}{4} = \dfrac{1}{2}$

$a_5 = \dfrac{1 + (-1)^5}{5} = \dfrac{0}{5} = 0$

9. $a_n = 3 - \dfrac{1}{2^n}$

$a_1 = 3 - \dfrac{1}{2^1} = \dfrac{5}{2}$

$a_2 = 3 - \dfrac{1}{2^2} = \dfrac{11}{4}$

$a_3 = 3 - \dfrac{1}{2^3} = \dfrac{23}{8}$

$a_4 = 3 - \dfrac{1}{2^4} = \dfrac{47}{16}$

$a_5 = 3 - \dfrac{1}{2^5} = \dfrac{95}{32}$

11. $a_n = \dfrac{1}{n^{3/2}}$

$a_1 = \dfrac{1}{1^{3/2}} = 1$

$a_2 = \dfrac{1}{2^{3/2}}$

$a_3 = \dfrac{1}{3^{3/2}}$

$a_4 = \dfrac{1}{4^{3/2}}$

$a_5 = \dfrac{1}{5^{3/2}}$

13. $a_n = \dfrac{3^n}{n!}$

$a_1 = \dfrac{3^1}{1!} = 3$

$a_2 = \dfrac{3^2}{2!} = \dfrac{9}{2}$

$a_3 = \dfrac{3^3}{3!} = \dfrac{9}{2}$

$a_4 = \dfrac{3^4}{4!} = \dfrac{27}{8}$

$a_5 = \dfrac{3^5}{5!} = \dfrac{81}{40}$

15. $a_n = \dfrac{(-1)^n}{n^2}$

$a_1 = \dfrac{(-1)^1}{1^2} = -1$

$a_2 = \dfrac{(-1)^2}{2^2} = \dfrac{1}{4}$

$a_3 = \dfrac{(-1)^3}{3^2} = -\dfrac{1}{9}$

$a_4 = \dfrac{(-1)^4}{4^2} = \dfrac{1}{16}$

$a_5 = \dfrac{(-1)^5}{5^2} = -\dfrac{1}{25}$

17. $a_1 = 3$

$a_{k+1} = 2(a_k - 1)$

$a_1 = 3$

$a_2 = 2(3-1) = 4$

$a_3 = 2(4-1) = 6$

$a_4 = 2(6-1) = 10$

$a_5 = 2(10-1) = 18$

19. $\dfrac{4!}{6!} = \dfrac{4!}{6 \cdot 5 \cdot 4!} = \dfrac{1}{30}$

21. $\dfrac{(n+1)!}{n!} = \dfrac{(n+1)n!}{n!} = n+1$

23. $\dfrac{(2n-1)!}{(2n+1)!} = \dfrac{(2n-1)!}{(2n+1)(2n)(2n-1)!}$

$= \dfrac{1}{2n(2n+1)}$

25. $a_1 = 1 = 3(1) - 2$

$a_2 = 4 = 3(2) - 2$

$a_3 = 7 = 3(3) - 2$

$a_4 = 10 = 3(4) - 2$

$a_5 = 13 = 3(5) - 2$

$a_n = 3n - 2$

27. $a_1 = 0 = (1)^2 - 1$

$a_2 = 3 = (2)^2 - 1$

$a_3 = 8 = (3)^2 - 1$

$a_4 = 15 = (4)^2 - 1$

$a_5 = 24 = (5)^2 - 1$

$a_n = n^2 - 1$

29. $a_1 = \dfrac{1}{2} = \dfrac{(-1)^{1+1}}{2^1}$

$a_2 = -\dfrac{1}{4} = \dfrac{(-1)^{2+1}}{2^2}$

$a_3 = \dfrac{1}{8} = \dfrac{(-1)^{3+1}}{2^3}$

$a_4 = -\dfrac{1}{16} = \dfrac{(-1)^{4+1}}{2^4}$

$a_n = \dfrac{(-1)^{n+1}}{2^n}$

31. $a_1 = 1 + \dfrac{1}{1}$

$a_2 = 1 + \dfrac{1}{2}$

$a_3 = 1 + \dfrac{1}{3}$

$a_4 = 1 + \dfrac{1}{4}$

$a_5 = 1 + \dfrac{1}{5}$

$a_n = 1 + \dfrac{1}{n}$

33. $a_1 = 1 = \dfrac{1}{1!}$

$a_2 = \dfrac{1}{2} = \dfrac{1}{2!}$

$a_3 = \dfrac{1}{6} = \dfrac{1}{3!}$

$a_4 = \dfrac{1}{24} = \dfrac{1}{4!}$

$a_5 = \dfrac{1}{120} = \dfrac{1}{5!}$

$a_n = \dfrac{1}{n!}$

35. $a_1 = 1 = (-1)^{1+1}$

$a_2 = -1 = (-1)^{2+1}$

$a_3 = 1 = (-1)^{3+1}$

$a_4 = -1 = (-1)^{4+1}$

$a_5 = 1 = (-1)^{5+1}$

$a_n = (-1)^{n+1}$

37. $\displaystyle\sum_{i=1}^{5}(2i+1) = (2\cdot 1+1)+(2\cdot 2+1)+(2\cdot 3+1)+(2\cdot 4+1)+(2\cdot 5+1) = 35$

39. $\displaystyle\sum_{k=1}^{4}10 = 10+10+10+10 = 40$

41. $\displaystyle\sum_{i=0}^{4}i^2 = 0^2+1^2+2^2+3^2+4^2 = 30$

43. $\displaystyle\sum_{k=0}^{3}\dfrac{1}{k^2+1} = \dfrac{1}{0^2+1}+\dfrac{1}{1^2+1}+\dfrac{1}{2^2+1}+\dfrac{1}{3^2+1} = \dfrac{9}{5}$

45. $\displaystyle\sum_{i=1}^{4}[(i-1)^2+(i+1)^3] = [(1-1)^2+(1+1)^3+(2-1)^2+(2+1)^3+(3-1)^2$

$+(3+1)^3+(4-1)^2+(4+1)^3] = 238$

47. $\displaystyle\sum_{i=1}^{4}(9+2i) = (9+2\cdot 1)+(9+2\cdot 2)+(9+2\cdot 3)+(9+2\cdot 4) = 56$

49. $\displaystyle\sum_{k=0}^{4}\dfrac{(-1)^k}{k+1} = \dfrac{(-1)^0}{0+1}+\dfrac{(-1)^1}{1+1}+\dfrac{(-1)^2}{2+1}+\dfrac{(-1)^3}{3+1}+\dfrac{(-1)^4}{4+1} = \dfrac{47}{60}$

51. $\dfrac{1}{3(1)}+\dfrac{1}{3(2)}+\dfrac{1}{3(3)}+\cdots+\dfrac{1}{3(9)} = \displaystyle\sum_{i=1}^{9}\dfrac{1}{3i}$

53. $\left[2\left(\dfrac{1}{8}\right)+3\right]+\left[2\left(\dfrac{2}{8}\right)+3\right]+\cdots+\left[2\left(\dfrac{8}{8}\right)+3\right] = \displaystyle\sum_{i=1}^{8}\left[2\left(\dfrac{i}{8}\right)+3\right]$

55. $3-9+27-81+243-729 = 3^1-3^2+3^3-3^4+3^5-3^6 = \displaystyle\sum_{i=1}^{6}(-1)^{i+1}3^i$

57. $\dfrac{1}{1^2} - \dfrac{1}{2^2} + \dfrac{1}{3^2} - \dfrac{1}{4^2} + \cdots - \dfrac{1}{20^2} = \displaystyle\sum_{i=1}^{20} \dfrac{(-1)^{i+1}}{i^2}$ **59.** $\dfrac{1}{4} + \dfrac{3}{8} + \dfrac{7}{16} + \dfrac{15}{32} + \dfrac{31}{64} = \displaystyle\sum_{i=1}^{5} \dfrac{2^i - 1}{2^{i+1}}$

61. (a) $A_1 = 5000 \left(1 + \dfrac{0.08}{4}\right)^1 = \$5100.00$ $A_5 = 5000 \left(1 + \dfrac{0.08}{4}\right)^5 \approx \$5520.40$

$A_2 = 5000 \left(1 + \dfrac{0.08}{4}\right)^2 = \$5202.00$ $A_6 = 5000 \left(1 + \dfrac{0.08}{4}\right)^6 \approx \$5630.81$

$A_3 = 5000 \left(1 + \dfrac{0.08}{4}\right)^3 = \$5306.04$ $A_7 = 5000 \left(1 + \dfrac{0.08}{4}\right)^7 \approx \$5743.43$

$A_4 = 5000 \left(1 + \dfrac{0.08}{4}\right)^4 \approx \$5412.16$ $A_8 = 5000 \left(1 + \dfrac{0.08}{4}\right)^8 \approx \$5858.30$

(b) $A_{40} = 5000 \left(1 + \dfrac{0.08}{4}\right)^{40} \approx \$11{,}040.20$

63. $a_0 = 242.67 + 42.67 \cdot 0 = 242.67$

$a_1 = 242.67 + 42.67 \cdot 1 = 285.34$

$a_2 = 242.67 + 42.67 \cdot 2 = 328.01$

$a_3 = 242.67 + 42.67 \cdot 3 = 370.68$

$a_4 = 242.67 + 42.67 \cdot 4 = 413.35$

$a_5 = 242.67 + 42.67 \cdot 5 = 456.02$

$a_6 = 242.67 + 42.67 \cdot 6 = 498.69$

$a_7 = 242.67 + 42.67 \cdot 7 = 541.36$

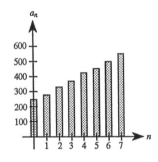

65. $\displaystyle\sum_{n=5}^{10}(0.20n + 1.17) = [0.20(5) + 1.17] + [0.20(6) + 1.17] + [0.20(7) + 1.17] + [0.20(8) + 1.17]$

$+ [0.20(9) + 1.17] + [0.20(10) + 1.17] = \$16.02$

$2.20 + 2.40 + 2.55 + 2.76 + 2.98 + 3.22 = \$16.11$

67. $\displaystyle\sum_{i=1}^{n}(x_i - \bar{x}) = \sum_{i=1}^{n} x_i - \sum_{i=1}^{n} \bar{x} = \sum_{i=1}^{n} x_i - n\bar{x} = \sum_{i=1}^{n} x_i - n\left(\dfrac{1}{n}\sum_{i=1}^{n} x_i\right) = 0$

69. $a_{n+2} = a_n + a_{n+1}, \quad a_1 = a_2 = 1$

(a) $a_1 = 1$ $\qquad\qquad$ $a_7 = 5 + 8 = 13$

$\quad a_2 = 1$ $\qquad\qquad$ $a_8 = 8 + 13 = 21$

$\quad a_3 = 1 + 1 = 2$ $\qquad$ $a_9 = 13 + 21 = 34$

$\quad a_4 = 1 + 2 = 3$ $\qquad$ $a_{10} = 21 + 34 = 55$

$\quad a_5 = 2 + 3 = 5$ $\qquad$ $a_{11} = 34 + 55 = 89$

$\quad a_6 = 3 + 5 = 8$ $\qquad$ $a_{12} = 55 + 89 = 144$

(b) $b_n = \dfrac{a_{n+1}}{a_n}$

$\quad b_2 = \dfrac{a_3}{a_2} = \dfrac{2}{1} = 2$ $\qquad\qquad$ $b_7 = \dfrac{a_8}{a_7} = \dfrac{21}{13} = 1.615$

$\quad b_3 = \dfrac{a_4}{a_3} = \dfrac{3}{2} = 1.5$ $\qquad\qquad$ $b_8 = \dfrac{a_9}{a_8} = \dfrac{34}{21} = 1.619$

$\quad b_4 = \dfrac{a_5}{a_4} = \dfrac{5}{3} = 1.6\overline{6}$ $\qquad\qquad$ $b_9 = \dfrac{a_{10}}{a_9} = \dfrac{55}{34} = 1.618$

$\quad b_5 = \dfrac{a_6}{a_5} = \dfrac{8}{5} = 1.6$ $\qquad\qquad$ $b_{10} = \dfrac{a_{11}}{a_{10}} = \dfrac{89}{55} = 1.618$

$\quad b_6 = \dfrac{a_7}{a_6} = \dfrac{13}{8} = 1.625$ $\qquad\qquad$ $b_{11} = \dfrac{a_{12}}{a_{11}} = \dfrac{144}{89} = 1.618$

(c) $b_n = \dfrac{a_{n+1}}{a_n} = \dfrac{a_n + a_{n-1}}{a_n} = 1 + \dfrac{a_{n-1}}{a_n} = 1 + \dfrac{1}{a_n/a_{n-1}} = 1 + \dfrac{1}{b_{n-1}}$

Section 9.2 Arithmetic Sequences

■ You should be able to recognize an arithmetic sequence, find its common difference, d, and find its nth term, $a_n = dn + c$.

■ You should be able to find the sum of an arithmetic sequence with n terms using the formula
$$S = \frac{n}{2}(a_1 + a_n).$$

■ You should know that the arithmetic mean of a and b is $(a + b)/2$.

---

1. 4, 7, 10, 13, 16, ...

Arithmetic sequence, $d = 3$

3. 1, 2, 4, 8, 16, ...

Not an arithmetic sequence

5. $\frac{9}{4}$, 2, $\frac{7}{4}$, $\frac{3}{2}$, $\frac{5}{4}$, ...

Arithmetic sequence, $d = -\frac{1}{4}$

7. $\frac{1}{3}$, $\frac{2}{3}$, $\frac{4}{3}$, $\frac{8}{3}$, $\frac{16}{3}$, ...

Not an arithmetic sequence

9. 5.3, 5.7, 6.1, 6.5, 6.9, ...

Arithmetic sequence, $d = 0.4$

11. $a_n = 5 + 3n$

8, 11, 14, 17, 20

Arithmetic sequence, $d = 3$

13. $a_n = \dfrac{1}{n + 1}$

$\dfrac{1}{2}, \dfrac{1}{3}, \dfrac{1}{4}, \dfrac{1}{5}, \dfrac{1}{6}$

Not an arithmetic sequence

15. $a_n = 100 - 3n$

97, 94, 91, 88, 85

Arithmetic sequence, $d = -3$

17. $a_n = 3 + \dfrac{(-1)^n 2}{n}$

1, 4, $\dfrac{7}{3}$, $\dfrac{7}{2}$, $\dfrac{13}{5}$

Not an arithmetic sequence

19. $a_1 = 1$, $d = 3$

$a_n = dn + c$

$a_1 = 1 = 3(1) + c \Rightarrow c = -2$

$a_n = 3n - 2$

21. $a_1 = 100$, $d = -8$
$a_n = dn + c$
$a_1 = 100 = -8(1) + c \Rightarrow c = 108$
$a_n = -8n + 108$

23. $a_1 = x$, $d = 2x$
$a_n = dn + c$
$a_1 = x = (2x)(1) + c \Rightarrow c = -x$
$a_n = 2xn - x$

25. $4, \frac{3}{2}, -1, -\frac{7}{2}, \ldots \Rightarrow d = -\frac{5}{2}$
$a_n = dn + c$
$a_1 = 4 = -\frac{5}{2}(1) + c \Rightarrow c = \frac{13}{2}$
$a_n = -\frac{5}{2}n + \frac{13}{2}$

27. $a_1 = 5$, $a_4 = 15$
$a_n = dn + c$
$a_1 = 5 = d(1) + c$, $a_4 = 15 = d(4) + c$
$d + c = 5$
$4d + c = 15$
Solving this system of equations yields
$d = \frac{10}{3}$ and $c = \frac{5}{3}$.
$a_n = \frac{10}{3}n + \frac{5}{3}$

29. $a_3 = 94$, $a_6 = 85$
$a_n = dn + c$
$a_3 = 94 = d(3) + c$, $a_6 = 85 = d(6) + c$
$3d + c = 94$
$6d + c = 85$
Solving this system of equalities yields
$d = -3$ and $c = 103$.
$a_n = -3n + 103$

31. $a_1 = 5$, $d = 6$
$a_1 = 5$
$a_2 = 5 + 6 = 11$
$a_3 = 11 + 6 = 17$
$a_4 = 17 + 6 = 23$
$a_5 = 23 + 6 = 29$

33. $a_1 = -2.6$, $d = -0.4$
$a_1 = -2.6$
$a_2 = -2.6 - 0.4 = -3.0$
$a_3 = -3.0 - 0.4 = -3.4$
$a_4 = -3.4 - 0.4 = -3.8$
$a_5 = -4.2$

35. $a_1 = \frac{3}{2}$, $a_{k+1} = a_k - \frac{1}{4} \Rightarrow d = -\frac{1}{4}$
$a_1 = \frac{3}{2}$
$a_2 = \frac{3}{2} - \frac{1}{4} = \frac{5}{4}$
$a_3 = \frac{5}{4} - \frac{1}{4} = 1$
$a_4 = 1 - \frac{1}{4} = \frac{3}{4}$
$a_5 = \frac{3}{4} - \frac{1}{4} = \frac{1}{2}$

37. $a_1 = 2$, $a_{12} = 46$

$a_1 = 2 = d(1) + c$, $a_{12} = 46 = d(12) + c$

$d + c = 2$

$12d + c = 46$

Solving this system yields $d = 4$ and $c = -2$.

$a_n = 4n - 2$

$a_1 = 2$

$a_2 = 6$

$a_3 = 10$

$a_4 = 14$

$a_5 = 18$

39. $a_8 = 26$, $a_{12} = 42$

$a_8 = 26 = d(8) + c$, $a_{12} = 42 = d(12) + c$

$8d + c = 26$

$12d + c = 42$

Solving this system yields $d = 4$ and $c = -6$.

$a_n = 4n - 6$

$a_1 = -2$

$a_2 = 2$

$a_3 = 6$

$a_4 = 10$

$a_5 = 14$

41. 8, 20, 32, 44, $\ldots$, $n = 10$

$a_n = 12n - 4$

$a_1 = 8$ and $a_{10} = 116$

$S_{10} = \frac{10}{2}(8 + 116) = 620$

43. -6, -2, 2, 6, $\ldots$, $n = 50$

$a_n = 4n - 10$

$a_1 = -6$ and $a_{50} = 190$

$S_{50} = \frac{50}{2}(-6 + 190) = 4600$

45. 40, 37, 34, 31, $\ldots$, $n = 10$

$a_n = -3n + 43$

$a_1 = 40$ and $a_{10} = 13$

$S_{10} = \frac{10}{2}(40 + 13) = 265$

47. $a_1 = 100$, $a_{25} = 220$, $n = 25$

$S_{25} = \frac{25}{2}(100 + 220) = 4000$

49. $a_n = n$

$a_1 = 1$, $a_{50} = 50$

$S_{50} = \frac{50}{2}(1 + 50) = 1275$

51. $a_n = 5n$

$a_1 = 5$, $a_{100} = 500$

$S_{100} = \frac{100}{2}(5 + 500) = 25{,}250$

53. $\displaystyle\sum_{n=11}^{30} n - \sum_{n=1}^{10} n = \frac{20}{2}(11 + 30) - \frac{10}{2}(1 + 10) = 410 - 55 = 355$

55. $a_n = n + 3$

$a_1 = 4$, $a_{500} = 503$

$S_{500} = \frac{500}{2}(4 + 503) = 126{,}750$

57. $a_n = 2n + 5$

$a_1 = 7$, $a_{20} = 45$

$S_{20} = \frac{20}{2}(7 + 45) = 520$

59. $\displaystyle\sum_{n=0}^{50}(1000 - 5n) = 1000 + \sum_{n=1}^{50}(1000 - 5n) = 1000 + \frac{50}{2}(995 + 750) = 44{,}625$

61. $5, m_1, m_2, 17$

$a_4 = 17 = 5 + 3d$

$d = 4$

$m_1 = 5 + 4 = 9$

$m_2 = 9 + 4 = 13$

63. $3, m_1, m_2, m_3, 6$

$a_5 = 6 = 3 + 4d$

$d = \frac{3}{4}$

$m_1 = 3 + \frac{3}{4} = \frac{15}{4}$

$m_2 = \frac{15}{4} + \frac{3}{4} = \frac{9}{2}$

$m_3 = \frac{9}{2} + \frac{3}{4} = \frac{21}{4}$

65. $a_1 = 1$, $a_{100} = 199$, $n = 100$

$S_{100} = \frac{100}{2}(1 + 199) = 10{,}000$

67. (a) $a_n = a_1 + (n - 1)d$

$= 27{,}500 + (n - 1)1500$

$= 1500n + 26{,}000$

$a_6 = 1500(6) + 26{,}000 = \$35{,}000$

(b) $S_6 = \frac{6}{2}(27{,}500 + 35{,}000) = \$187{,}500$

69. $a_n = 16 + 4n$

$a_1 = 20$, $a_{30} = 136$

$S_{30} = \frac{30}{2}(20 + 136) = 2340$ seats

71. $a_1 = 14$, $a_{20} = 33$

$S_{20} = \frac{20}{2}(14 + 33)$

$= 470$ bricks

73. Let $S = 1 + 2 + 3 + \cdots + (n - 1) + n$ and $S = n + (n - 1) + \cdots + 2 + 1$. Adding these two expressions for S:

$$2S = (n + 1) + (n + 1) + \cdots + (n + 1) + (n + 1) \qquad (n \text{ times})$$

$$2S = n(n + 1) \Rightarrow S = \frac{n(n + 1)}{2}$$

Section 9.3 Geometric Sequences

- You should be able to identify a geometric sequence, find its common ratio, r, and find the nth term, $a_n = a_1 r^{n-1}$.

- You should be able to find the sum of a geometric sequence with common ratio r using the formula
$$S = \frac{a_1(1 - r^n)}{1 - r}, \quad r \neq 1.$$

- You should know that if $|r| < 1$, then
$$\sum_{n=0}^{\infty} a_1 r^n = \sum_{n=1}^{\infty} a_1 r^{n-1} = \frac{a_1}{1 - r}.$$

---

1. 5, 15, 45, 135, ...

Geometric sequence

$r = 3$

3. 3, 12, 21, 30, ...

Not a geometric sequence

5. 1, $-\frac{1}{2}$, $\frac{1}{4}$, $-\frac{1}{8}$, ...

Geometric sequence

$r = -\frac{1}{2}$

7. $\frac{1}{2}$, $\frac{2}{3}$, $\frac{3}{4}$, $\frac{4}{5}$, ...

Not a geometric sequence

9. 1, $\frac{1}{2}$, $\frac{1}{3}$, $\frac{1}{4}$, ...

Not a geometric sequence

11. $a_1 = 2$, $r = 3$

$a_1 = 2$

$a_2 = 2(3)^1 = 6$

$a_3 = 2(3)^2 = 18$

$a_4 = 2(3)^3 = 54$

$a_5 = 2(3)^4 = 162$

13. $a_1 = 1$, $r = \dfrac{1}{2}$

$a_1 = 1$

$a_2 = 1\left(\dfrac{1}{2}\right)^1 = \dfrac{1}{2}$

$a_3 = 1\left(\dfrac{1}{2}\right)^2 = \dfrac{1}{4}$

$a_4 = 1\left(\dfrac{1}{2}\right)^3 = \dfrac{1}{8}$

$a_5 = 1\left(\dfrac{1}{2}\right)^4 = \dfrac{1}{16}$

15. $a_1 = 5$, $r = -\dfrac{1}{10}$

$a_1 = 5$

$a_2 = 5\left(-\dfrac{1}{10}\right)^1 = -\dfrac{1}{2}$

$a_3 = 5\left(-\dfrac{1}{10}\right)^2 = \dfrac{1}{20}$

$a_4 = 5\left(-\dfrac{1}{10}\right)^3 = -\dfrac{1}{200}$

$a_5 = 5\left(-\dfrac{1}{10}\right)^4 = \dfrac{1}{2000}$

17. $a_1 = 1$, $r = e$

$a_1 = 1$

$a_2 = 1e^1 = e$

$a_3 = 1e^2 = e^2$

$a_4 = 1e^3 = e^3$

$a_5 = 1e^4 = e^4$

19. $a_1 = 3$, $r = \dfrac{x}{2}$

$a_1 = 3$

$a_2 = 3\left(\dfrac{x}{2}\right)^1 = \dfrac{3x}{2}$

$a_3 = 3\left(\dfrac{x}{2}\right)^2 = \dfrac{3x^2}{4}$

$a_4 = 3\left(\dfrac{x}{2}\right)^3 = \dfrac{3x^3}{8}$

$a_5 = 3\left(\dfrac{x}{2}\right)^4 = \dfrac{3x^4}{16}$

21. $a_1 = 4$, $r = \dfrac{1}{2}$, $n = 10$

$a_{10} = 4\left(\dfrac{1}{2}\right)^9$

$= \dfrac{1}{128} = \left(\dfrac{1}{2}\right)^7$

23. $a_1 = 6$, $r = -\dfrac{1}{3}$, $n = 12$

$a_{12} = 6\left(-\dfrac{1}{3}\right)^{11}$

$= -\dfrac{2}{3^{10}}$

25. $a_1 = 100$, $r = e^x$, $n = 9$

$a_9 = 100(e^x)^8 = 100e^{8x}$

27. $a_1 = 500$, $r = 1.02$, $n = 40$

$a_{40} = 500(1.02)^{39}$

29. $a_1 = 16$, $a_4 = \dfrac{27}{4}$, $n = 3$

$a_4 = 16r^3 = \dfrac{27}{4}$

$r^3 = \dfrac{27}{64}$

$r = \dfrac{3}{4}$

$a_3 = 16\left(\dfrac{3}{4}\right)^2 = 9$

31. $a_2 = -18$, $a_5 = \dfrac{2}{3}$, $n = 6$

$a_2 r^3 = a_5$

$-18r^3 = \dfrac{2}{3}$

$r^3 = -\dfrac{1}{27}$

$r = -\dfrac{1}{3}$

$a_6 = a_5 r$

$a_6 = \dfrac{2}{3}\left(-\dfrac{1}{3}\right) = -\dfrac{2}{9}$

33. $A = P\left(1+\dfrac{r}{n}\right)^{nt} = 1000\left(1+\dfrac{0.10}{n}\right)^{n(10)}$

(a) $n = 1,$ $A = 1000(1+0.10)^{10} \approx \$2593.74$

(b) $n = 2,$ $A = 1000\left(1+\dfrac{0.10}{2}\right)^{2(10)} \approx \$2653.30$

(c) $n = 4,$ $A = 1000\left(1+\dfrac{0.10}{4}\right)^{4(10)} \approx \$2685.06$

(d) $n = 12,$ $A = 1000\left(1+\dfrac{0.10}{12}\right)^{12(10)} \approx \$2707.04$

(e) $n = 365,$ $A = 1000\left(1+\dfrac{0.10}{365}\right)^{365(10)} \approx \$2717.91$

35. $V = $ value after n years

$P = $ initial price $= \$135,000$

$r = $ remaining value rate

$= 100\% - 30\% = 70\%$

$n = $ number of years $= 5$

$V = Pr^n = 135,000(0.7)^5 = \$22,689.45$

37. $\displaystyle\sum_{n=1}^{9} 2^{n-1} = \dfrac{1(1-2^9)}{1-2} = 511$

39. $\displaystyle\sum_{i=1}^{7} 64\left(-\dfrac{1}{2}\right)^{i-1} = \dfrac{64\left(1-(-1/2)^7\right)}{1-(-1/2)} = 43$

41. $\displaystyle\sum_{i=1}^{10} 8\left(-\dfrac{1}{4}\right)^{i-1} = \dfrac{8\left(1-(-1/4)^{10}\right)}{1-(-1/4)} = \dfrac{32(1-(-0.25)^{10})}{5} \approx 6.40$

43. $\displaystyle\sum_{n=0}^{20} 3\left(\dfrac{3}{2}\right)^{n} = \dfrac{3\left(1-(3/2)^{21}\right)}{1-(3/2)} = -6\left(1-\left(\dfrac{3}{2}\right)^{21}\right) \approx 29{,}921.31$

45. $\displaystyle\sum_{n=0}^{5} 300(1.06)^{n} = \dfrac{300(1-1.06^6)}{1-1.06} \approx 2092.60$

47. $A = \displaystyle\sum_{n=1}^{60} 100\left(1+\dfrac{0.10}{12}\right)^{n} = 100\left(1+\dfrac{0.10}{12}\right) \cdot \dfrac{\left[1-\left(1+\dfrac{0.10}{12}\right)^{60}\right]}{\left[1-\left(1+\dfrac{0.10}{12}\right)\right]} \approx \$7808.24$

49. Let $N = 12t$ be the total number of deposits.

$$A = P\left(1+\frac{r}{12}\right) + P\left(1+\frac{r}{12}\right)^2 + \cdots + P\left(1+\frac{r}{12}\right)^N$$

$$= \left(1+\frac{r}{12}\right)\left[P + P\left(1+\frac{r}{12}\right) + \cdots + P\left(1+\frac{r}{12}\right)^{N-1}\right]$$

$$= P\left(1+\frac{r}{12}\right)\sum_{n=1}^{N}\left(1+\frac{r}{12}\right)^{n-1}$$

$$= P\left(1+\frac{r}{12}\right)\frac{1-\left(1+\frac{r}{12}\right)^N}{1-\left(1+\frac{r}{12}\right)}$$

$$= P\left(1+\frac{r}{12}\right)\left(-\frac{12}{r}\right)\left[1-\left(1+\frac{r}{12}\right)^N\right]$$

$$= P\left(\frac{12}{r}+1\right)\left[-1+\left(1+\frac{r}{12}\right)^N\right]$$

$$= P\left[\left(1+\frac{r}{12}\right)^N - 1\right]\left(1+\frac{12}{r}\right)$$

$$= P\left[\left(1+\frac{r}{12}\right)^{12t} - 1\right]\left(1+\frac{12}{r}\right)$$

51. (a) $A = 50\left[\left(1+\dfrac{0.07}{12}\right)^{12(20)} - 1\right]\left(1+\dfrac{12}{0.07}\right) \approx \$26{,}198.27$

(b) $A = \dfrac{50e^{0.07/12}(e^{0.07(20)} - 1)}{e^{0.07/12} - 1} \approx \$26{,}263.88$

53. (a) $A = 100\left[\left(1+\dfrac{0.10}{12}\right)^{12(40)} - 1\right]\left(1+\dfrac{12}{0.10}\right) \approx \$637{,}678.02$

(b) $A = \dfrac{100e^{0.10/12}\left(e^{0.10(40)} - 1\right)}{e^{0.10/12} - 1} \approx \$645{,}861.43$

55. $P = W\left(1+\frac{r}{12}\right)^{-1} + W\left(1+\frac{r}{12}\right)^{-2} + \cdots + W\left(1+\frac{r}{12}\right)^{-12t}$

$= W\left(1+\frac{r}{12}\right)^{-1}\left[1+\left(1+\frac{r}{12}\right)^{-1}+\cdots+\left[\left(1+\frac{r}{12}\right)^{-1}\right]^{12t-1}\right]$

$= W\left(1+\frac{r}{12}\right)^{-1}\left[\dfrac{1-\left(1+\frac{r}{12}\right)^{-12t}}{1-\left(1+\frac{r}{12}\right)^{-1}}\right]$

$= \dfrac{W\left(\frac{12+r}{12}\right)^{-1}}{1-\left(\frac{12+r}{12}\right)^{-1}}\left[1-\left(1+\frac{r}{12}\right)^{-12t}\right]$

$= \dfrac{W\left(\frac{12}{12+r}\right)}{1-\frac{12}{12+r}}\left[1-\left(1+\frac{r}{12}\right)^{-12t}\right]$

$= \dfrac{W\left(\frac{12}{12+r}\right)}{\frac{12+r-12}{12+r}}\left[1-\left(1+\frac{r}{12}\right)^{-12t}\right]$

$= W\left(\frac{12}{r}\right)\left[1-\left(1+\frac{r}{12}\right)^{-12t}\right]$

57. $\sum_{n=0}^{9} 167.5e^{0.12n} = 167.5\dfrac{\left[1-\left(e^{0.12}\right)^{10}\right]}{1-e^{0.12}} \approx \$3048.1$ million

59. $a_n = 30{,}000(1.05)^{n-1}$

$T = \sum_{n=1}^{40} 30{,}000(1.05)^{n-1} = 30{,}000\dfrac{(1-1.05^{40})}{(1-1.05)} \approx \$3{,}623{,}993.23$

61. $\sum_{n=0}^{\infty}\left(\frac{1}{2}\right)^n = 1+\frac{1}{2}+\frac{1}{4}+\frac{1}{8}+\cdots = \dfrac{1}{1-\frac{1}{2}} = 2$

63. $\sum_{n=0}^{\infty}\left(-\frac{1}{2}\right)^n = 1-\frac{1}{2}+\frac{1}{4}-\frac{1}{8}+\cdots = \dfrac{1}{1-\left(-\frac{1}{2}\right)} = \frac{2}{3}$

65. $\sum_{n=0}^{\infty}4\left(\frac{1}{4}\right)^n = 4+1+\frac{1}{4}+\frac{1}{16}+\cdots = \dfrac{4}{1-\frac{1}{4}} = \frac{16}{3}$

67. $8 + 6 + \dfrac{9}{2} + \dfrac{27}{8} + \cdots = \displaystyle\sum_{n=0}^{\infty} 8\left(\dfrac{3}{4}\right)^{n} = \dfrac{8}{1 - \frac{3}{4}} = 32$

69. $4 - 2 + 1 - \dfrac{1}{2} + \cdots = \displaystyle\sum_{n=0}^{\infty} 4\left(-\dfrac{1}{2}\right)^{n} = \dfrac{4}{1 - \left(-\frac{1}{2}\right)} = \dfrac{8}{3}$

71. The horizontal asymptote of f is the sum of the series.

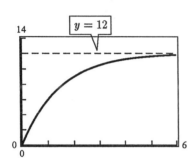

73. Total distance $= \left[\displaystyle\sum_{n=0}^{\infty} 32(0.81)^{n}\right] - 16$

$= \dfrac{32}{1 - 0.81} - 16$

≈ 152.42 feet

Section 9.4   Mathematical Induction

- You should be sure that you understand the principle of mathematical induction. If P_n is a statement involving the positive integer n, where P_1 is true and the truth of P_k implies the truth of P_{k+1}, then P_n is true for all positive integers n.

- You should be able to verify (by induction) the formulas for the sums of powers of integers and be able to use these formulas.

- You should be able to calculate finite differences of a sequence.

1. $P_{k+1} = \dfrac{5}{(k+1)[(k+1)+1]}$

$= \dfrac{5}{(k+1)(k+2)}$

3. $P_{k+1} = \dfrac{(k+1)^2[(k+1)+1]^2}{4}$

$= \dfrac{(k+1)^2(k+2)^2}{4}$

5. 1. When $n = 1$, $S_1 = 2 = 1(1+1)$.

   2. Assume that $S_k = 2 + 4 + 6 + 8 + \cdots + 2k = k(k+1)$. Then,

   $S_{k+1} = 2 + 4 + 6 + 8 + \cdots + 2k + 2(k+1)$

   $= S_k + 2(k+1) = k(k+1) + 2(k+1) = (k+1)(k+2) = (k+1[(k+1)+1].$

   We conclude by mathematical induction that the formula is valid for all positive integer values of n.

7. 1. When $n = 1$, $S_1 = 2 = \frac{1}{2}(5(1) - 1)$.

   2. Assume that $S_k = 2 + 7 + 12 + 17 + \cdots + (5k - 3) = (k/2)(5k - 1)$. Then,

   $S_{k+1} = 2 + 7 + 12 + 17 + \cdots + (5k - 3) + [5(k+1) - 3]$

   $= S_k + (5k + 5 - 3) = \dfrac{k}{2}(5k - 1) + 5k + 2$

   $= \dfrac{5k^2 - k + 10k + 4}{2} = \dfrac{5k^2 + 9k + 4}{2}$

   $= \dfrac{(k+1)(5k+4)}{2} = \dfrac{(k+1)}{2}[5(k+1) - 1].$

   We conclude by mathematical induction that the formula is valid for all positive integer values of n.

9. 1. When $n = 1$, $S_1 = 1 = 2^1 - 1$.

2. Assume that $S_k = 1 + 2 + 2^2 + 2^3 + \cdots + 2^{k-1} = 2^k - 1$. Then,

$$S_{k+1} = 1 + 2 + 2^2 + 2^3 + \cdots + 2^{k-1} + 2^{k+1-1}$$

$$= S_k + 2^k = 2^k - 1 + 2^k = 2 \cdot 2^k - 1 = 2^{k+1} - 1.$$

Therefore, we conclude that this formula holds for all positive integer values of n.

11. 1. When $n = 1$, $S_1 = 1 = \dfrac{1(1+1)}{2}$.

2. Assume that $S_k = 1 + 2 + 3 + 4 + \cdots + k = \dfrac{k(k+1)}{2}$. Then,

$$S_{k+1} = 1 + 2 + 3 + 4 + \cdots + k + (k+1)$$

$$= S_k + (k+1) = \frac{k(k+1)}{2} + \frac{2(k+1)}{2} = \frac{(k+1)(k+2)}{2}.$$

Therefore, we conclude that this formula holds for all positive integer values of n.

13. 1. When $n = 1$, $S_1 = 1^3 = 1 = \dfrac{1(1+1)^2}{4}$.

2. Assume that $S_k = 1^3 + 2^3 + 3^3 + 4^3 + \cdots + k^3 = \dfrac{k^2(k+1)^2}{4}$. Then,

$$S_{k+1} = 1^3 + 2^3 + 3^3 + 4^3 + \cdots + k^3 + (k+1)^3$$

$$= S_k + (k+1)^3 = \frac{k^2(k+1)^2}{4} + (k+1)^3$$

$$= \frac{k^2(k+1)^2 + 4(k+1)^3}{4} = \frac{(k+1)^2[k^2 + 4(k+1)]}{4}$$

$$= \frac{(k+1)^2(k^2 + 4k + 4)}{4} = \frac{(k+1)^2(k+2)^2}{4}.$$

Therefore, we conclude that this formula holds for all positive integer values of n.

15. 1. When $n = 1$, $S_1 = 1^5 = \dfrac{1^2(1+1)^2(2 \cdot 1^2 + 2 \cdot 1 - 1)}{12}$.

2. Assume that $S_k = \displaystyle\sum_{i=1}^{k} i^5 = \dfrac{k^2(k+1)^2(2k^2 + 2k - 1)}{12}$. Then,

$S_{k+1} = S_k + (k+1)^5$

$= \dfrac{k^2(k+1)^2(2k^2 + 2k - 1)}{12} + (k+1)^5$

$= \dfrac{k^2(k+1)^2(2k^2 + 2k - 1) + 12(k+1)^5}{12}$

$= \dfrac{(k+1)^2[k^2(2k^2 + 2k - 1) + 12(k+1)^3]}{12}$

$= \dfrac{(k+1)^2(k+2)^2(2k^2 + 6k + 3)}{12}$

$= \dfrac{(k+1)^2(k+2)^2(2(k+1)^2 + 2(k+1) - 1)}{12}$.

Therefore, we conclude that this formula holds for all positive integer values of n.

17. 1. When $n = 1$, $S_1 = 2 = \dfrac{1(2)(3)}{3}$.

2. Assume that $S_k = 1(2) + 2(3) + 3(4) + \cdots + k(k+1) = \dfrac{k(k+1)(k+2)}{3}$. Then,

$S_{k+1} = 1(2) + 2(3) + 3(4) + \cdots + k(k+1) + (k+1)(k+2)$

$= S_k + (k+1)(k+2)$

$= \dfrac{k(k+1)(k+2)}{3} + \dfrac{3(k+1)(k+2)}{3}$

$= \dfrac{(k+1)(k+2)(k+3)}{3}$.

Thus, this formula is valid for all positive integer values of n.

19. $\displaystyle\sum_{n=1}^{20} n = \dfrac{20(20+1)}{2} = 210$ **21.** $\displaystyle\sum_{n=1}^{6} n^2 = \dfrac{6(6+1)(2 \cdot 6 + 1)}{6}$ **23.** $\displaystyle\sum_{n=1}^{5} n^3 = \dfrac{5^2(5+1)^2}{4} = 225$

$= 91$

25. $\displaystyle\sum_{n=1}^{6} n^4 = \dfrac{6(6+1)(2 \cdot 6 + 1)(3 \cdot 6^2 + 3 \cdot 6 - 1)}{30} = 2275$

27. $\displaystyle\sum_{n=1}^{6}(n^2 - n) = \sum_{n=1}^{6}n^2 - \sum_{n=1}^{6}n = \frac{6(6+1)(2\cdot 6+1)}{6} - \frac{6(6+1)}{2} = 91 - 21 = 70$

29. 3, 7, 11, 15, ... is an arithmetic sequence with $a_1 = 3$, common difference $d = 4$, and $a_n = a_1 + (n-1)d = 3 + (n-1)4 = 4n - 1$. Hence, the sum of the first n terms is

$$S = \frac{n}{2}(a_1 + a_n) = \frac{n}{2}(3 + (4n - 1)) = \frac{n}{2}(4n + 2) = n(2n + 1).$$

31. 1, $\frac{9}{10}$, $\frac{81}{100}$, $\frac{729}{1000}$, ... is a geometric sequence with $a_1 = 1$ and common ratio $r = \frac{9}{10}$. Hence, the sum of the first n terms is

$$S = a_1\left(\frac{1 - r^n}{1 - r}\right) = 1\left(\frac{1 - (9/10)^n}{1 - (9/10)}\right) = 10(1 - (0.9)^n).$$

33. $\frac{1}{4}$, $\frac{1}{12}$, $\frac{1}{24}$, $\frac{1}{40}$, ..., $\frac{1}{2n(n-1)}$, ... The sum of the first n terms is

$$\sum_{i=1}^{n}\frac{1}{2i(i-1)} = \frac{1}{2}\sum_{i=1}^{n}\frac{1}{i(i-1)} = \frac{1}{2}\left[\left(\frac{1}{1} - \frac{1}{2}\right) + \left(\frac{1}{2} - \frac{1}{3}\right) + \cdots + \left(\frac{1}{n} - \frac{1}{n+1}\right)\right]$$

$$= \frac{1}{2}\left(1 - \frac{1}{n+1}\right) = \frac{n}{2(n+1)}.$$

35. 1. When $n = 7$, $\left(\dfrac{4}{3}\right)^7 \approx 7.4915 > 7.$

2. Assume that $\left(\dfrac{4}{3}\right)^k > k$, $k > 7$. Then,

$$\left(\frac{4}{3}\right)^{k+1} = \left(\frac{4}{3}\right)^k\left(\frac{4}{3}\right) > k\left(\frac{4}{3}\right) = k + \frac{k}{3} > k + 1 \text{ for } k > 7.$$

Thus, $\left(\dfrac{4}{3}\right)^{k+1} > k + 1.$ Therefore, $\left(\dfrac{4}{3}\right)^n > n.$

37. 1. When $n = 4$, $4! = 24 > 2^4 = 16.$

2. Assume that $k! > 2^k$, $k > 4$.
$$(k + 1)! = (k + 1)k! > (k + 1)2^k > 2 \cdot 2^k = 2^{k+1}.$$

Therefore, $n! \geq 2^n$ for all integers $n \geq 4$.

39. 1. When $n = 1$, $(ab)^1 = a^1 b^1$.

2. Assume that $(ab)^k = a^k b^k$. Then,

$$(ab)^{k+1} = (ab)^k (ab) = a^k b^k ab = a^{k+1} b^{k+1}.$$

Thus, $(ab)^n = a^n b^n$.

41. 1. When $n = 1$, $(x_1)^{-1} = x_1^{-1}$.

2. Assume that $(x_1 x_2 x_3 \ldots x_k)^{-1} = x_1^{-1} x_2^{-1} x_3^{-1} \ldots x_k^{-1}$.

$$(x_1 x_2 x_3 \ldots x_k x_{k+1})^{-1} = (x_1 x_2 x_3 \ldots x_k)^{-1} (x_{k+1})^{-1} = x_1^{-1} x_2^{-1} x_3^{-1} \ldots x_k^{-1} x_{k+1}^{-1}.$$

Thus, $(x_1 x_2 x_3 \ldots x_n)^{-1} = x_1^{-1} x_2^{-1} x_3^{-1} \ldots x_n^{-1}$.

43. 1. When $n = 1$, $x(y_1) = xy_1$.

2. Assume that $x(y_1 + y_2 + \cdots + y_k) = xy_1 + xy_2 + \cdots + xy_k$. Then,

$$xy_1 + xy_2 + \cdots + xy_k + xy_{k+1} = x(y_1 + y_2 + \cdots + y_k) + xy_{k+1}$$
$$= x[(y_1 + y_2 + \cdots + y_k) + y_{k+1}]$$
$$= x(y_1 + y_2 + \cdots + y_k + y_{k+1}).$$

Hence, the formula holds.

45. 1. When $n = 1$, 3 is a factor of $(1^3 + 3 \cdot 1^2 + 2 \cdot 1) = 6$.

2. Assume that 3 is a factor of $k^3 + 3k^2 + 2k$. Then,

$$(k+1)^3 + 3(k+1)^2 + 2(k+1) = k^3 + 6k^2 + 11k + 6$$
$$= (k^3 + 3k^2 + 2k) + (3k^2 + 9k + 6)$$
$$= (k^3 + 3k^2 + 2k) + 3(k^2 + 3k + 2)$$

Since 3 is a factor of each of the two terms, it follows that 3 is a factor of $(n^3 + 3n^2 + 2n)$ for all positive integers n.

47. $a_0 = 1, \quad a_n = a_{n-1} + 2$

$a_1 = a_0 + 2 = 1 + 2 = 3$

$a_2 = a_1 + 2 = 3 + 2 = 5$

$a_3 = a_2 + 2 = 5 + 2 = 7$

$a_4 = a_3 + 2 = 7 + 2 = 9$

49. $a_0 = 4, \quad a_1 = 2, \quad a_n = a_{n-1} - a_{n-2}$

$a_2 = a_1 - a_0 = 2 - 4 = -2$

$a_3 = a_2 - a_1 = -2 - 2 = -4$

$a_4 = a_3 - a_2 = -4 - (-2) = -2$

51. $f(1) = 0, \quad a_n = a_{n-1} + 3$

$$
\begin{array}{ccccc}
0 & 3 & 6 & 9 & 12 \\
& 3 & 3 & 3 & 3 \\
& & 0 & 0 & 0 \\
\end{array}
$$

Linear

53. $f(1) = 3, \quad a_n = a_{n-1} - n$

$$
\begin{array}{ccccc}
3 & 1 & -2 & -6 & -11 \\
& -2 & -3 & -4 & -5 \\
& & -1 & -1 & -1 \\
\end{array}
$$

Quadratic

55. $a_0, \quad a_n = a_{n-1} + n$

$$
\begin{array}{ccccc}
0 & 1 & 3 & 6 & 10 \\
& 1 & 2 & 3 & 4 \\
& & 1 & 1 & 1 \\
\end{array}
$$

Quadratic

57. $f(1) = 2, \quad a_n = a_{n-1} + 2$

$$
\begin{array}{ccccc}
2 & 4 & 6 & 8 & 10 \\
& 2 & 2 & 2 & 2 \\
& & 0 & 0 & 0 \\
\end{array}
$$

Linear

59. $a_0 = 1, \quad a_n = a_{n-1} + n^2$

$$
\begin{array}{ccccc}
1 & 2 & 6 & 15 & 31 \\
& 1 & 4 & 9 & 16 \\
& & 3 & 5 & 7 \\
\end{array}
$$

Neither linear nor quadratic

61. $a_0 = 3, \ a_1 = 3, \ a_4 = 15$

$f(n) = an^2 + bn + c$

$f(0) = a(0)^2 + b(0) + c = 3$

$f(1) = a(1)^2 + b(1) + c = 3$

$f(4) = a(4)^2 + b(4) + c = 15$

The system of three equations is:

$$
\begin{aligned}
c &= 3 \\
a + b + c &= 3 \\
16a + 4b + c &= 15
\end{aligned}
$$

The solution is

$a = 1, \ b = -1, \ c = 3 \Rightarrow f(n) = n^2 - n + 3.$

63. $a_0 = -3, \ a_2 = 1, \ a_4 = 9$

$f(n) = an^2 + bn + c$

$f(0) = a(0)^2 + b(0) + c = -3$

$f(2) = a(2)^2 + b(2) + c = 1$

$f(4) = a(4)^2 + b(4) + c = 9$

The system of three equations is:

$$
\begin{aligned}
c &= -3 \\
4a + 2b + c &= 1 \\
16a + 4b + c &= 9
\end{aligned}
$$

The solution is $a = \frac{1}{2}, \ b = 1, \ c = -3 \Rightarrow$
$f(n) = \frac{1}{2}n^2 + n - 3.$

Section 9.5   The Binomial Theorem

- You should be able to use the Binomial Theorem

$$(x+y)^n = x^n + nx^{n-1}y + \frac{n(n-1)}{2!}x^{n-2}y^2 + \cdots + {}_nC_m{}^n x^{n-m}y^m + \cdots + y^n$$

  where ${}_nC_m = \dfrac{n!}{(n-m)!m!}$, to expand $(x+y)^n$.

- You should be able to use Pascal's Triangle in binomial expansion.

---

1. ${}_5C_3 = \dfrac{5!}{3!2!} = \dfrac{5 \cdot 4}{2 \cdot 1} = 10$

3. ${}_{12}C_0 = \dfrac{12!}{0!12!} = 1$

5. ${}_{20}C_{15} = \dfrac{20!}{15!5!}$
$= \dfrac{20 \cdot 19 \cdot 18 \cdot 17 \cdot 16}{5 \cdot 4 \cdot 3 \cdot 2 \cdot 1}$
$= 15{,}504$

7. ${}_{100}C_{98} = \dfrac{100!}{98!2!}$
$= \dfrac{100 \cdot 99}{2 \cdot 1}$
$= 4950$

9. ${}_{100}C_2 = \dfrac{100!}{2!98!} = \dfrac{100 \cdot 99}{2 \cdot 1} = 4950$

11. $(x+1)^4 = {}_4C_0x^4 + {}_4C_1x^3(1) + {}_4C_2x^2(1)^2 + {}_4C_3x(1)^3 + {}_4C_4(1)^4$
$= x^4 + 4x^3 + 6x^2 + 4x + 1$

13. $(a+2)^3 = {}_3C_0a^3 + {}_3C_1a^2(2) + {}_3C_2a(2)^2 + {}_3C_3(2)^3$
$= a^3 + 6a^2 + 12a + 8$

15. $(y-2)^4 = {}_4C_0y^4 - {}_4C_1y^3(2) + {}_4C_2y^2(2)^2 - {}_4C_3y(2)^3 + {}_4C_4(2)^4$
$= y^4 - 8y^3 + 24y^2 - 32y + 16$

17. $(x+y)^5 = {}_5C_0x^5 + {}_5C_1x^4y + {}_5C_2x^3y^2 + {}_5C_3x^2y^3 + {}_5C_4xy^4 + {}_5C_5y^5$
$= x^5 + 5x^4y + 10x^3y^2 + 10x^2y^3 + 5xy^4 + y^5$

19. $(r+3s)^6 = {}_6C_0r^6 + {}_6C_1r^5(3s) + {}_6C_2r^4(3s)^2 + {}_6C_3r^3(3s)^3 + {}_6C_4r^2(3s)^4 + {}_6C_5r(3s)^5 + {}_6C_6(3s)^6$
$= r^6 + 6(3s)r^5 + 15(9s^2)r^4 + 20(27s^3)r^3 + 15(81s^4)r^2 + 6(243s^5)r + 729s^6$
$= r^6 + 18r^5s + 135r^4s^2 + 540r^3s^3 + 1215r^2s^4 + 1458rs^5 + 729s^6$

21. $(x-y)^5 = {}_5C_0x^5 - {}_5C_1x^4y + {}_5C_2x^3y^2 - {}_5C_3x^2y^3 + {}_5C_4xy^4 - {}_5C_5y^5$

$\qquad = x^5 - 5x^4y + 10x^3y^2 - 10x^2y^3 + 5xy^4 - y^5$

23. $(1-2x)^3 = {}_3C_01^3 - {}_3C_11^2(2x) + {}_3C_21(2x)^2 - {}_3C_3(2x)^3$

$\qquad\qquad = 1 - 3(2x) + 3(2x)^2 - (2x)^3$

$\qquad\qquad = 1 - 6x + 12x^2 - 8x^3$

25. $(x^2+5)^4 = {}_4C_0(x^2)^4 + {}_4C_1(x^2)^3(5) + {}_4C_2(x^2)^2(5)^2 + {}_4C_3(x^2)(5)^3 + {}_4C_4(5)^4$

$\qquad\qquad = x^8 + 4x^6(5) + 6x^4(25) + 4x^2(125) + 625$

$\qquad\qquad = x^8 + 20x^6 + 150x^4 + 500x^2 + 625$

27. $\left(\dfrac{1}{x}+y\right)^5 = {}_5C_0\left(\dfrac{1}{x}\right)^5 + {}_5C_1\left(\dfrac{1}{x}\right)^4 y + {}_5C_2\left(\dfrac{1}{x}\right)^3 y^2 + {}_5C_3\left(\dfrac{1}{x}\right)^2 y^3 + {}_5C_4\left(\dfrac{1}{x}\right)y^4 + {}_5C_5y^5$

$\qquad\qquad = \dfrac{1}{x^5} + \dfrac{5y}{x^4} + \dfrac{10y^2}{x^3} + \dfrac{10y^3}{x^2} + \dfrac{5y^4}{x} + y^5$

29. $2(x-3)^4 + 5(x-3)^2 = 2[{}_4C_0x^4 - {}_4C_1x^3(3) + {}_4C_2x^2(3)^2 - {}_4C_3x(3)^3 + {}_4C_4(3)^4]$

$\qquad\qquad\qquad\qquad\quad + 5[{}_2C_0x^2 - {}_2C_1x(3) + {}_2C_2(3)^2]$

$\qquad\qquad\qquad\quad = 2[(1)x^4 - 4(3)x^3 + 6(9)x^2 - 4(27)x + 1(81)] + 5[(1)x^2 - 2(3)x + (1)9]$

$\qquad\qquad\qquad\quad = 2x^4 - 24x^3 + 113x^2 - 246x + 207$

31. $(1+i)^4 = {}_4C_01^4 + {}_4C_1(1)^3i + {}_4C_2(1)^2i^2 + {}_4C_31 \cdot i^3 + {}_4C_4i^4$

$\qquad\quad = 1 + 4i - 6 - 4i + 1$

$\qquad\quad = -4$

33. $(2-3i)^6 = {}_6C_02^6 - {}_6C_12^5(3i) + {}_6C_22^4(3i)^2 - {}_6C_32^3(3i)^3 + {}_6C_42^2(3i)^4 - {}_6C_52(3i)^5 + {}_6C_6(3i)^6$

$\qquad\qquad = 64 - 576i - 2160 + 4320i + 4860 - 2916i - 729$

$\qquad\qquad = 2035 + 828i$

35. $\left(-\dfrac{1}{2} + \dfrac{\sqrt{3}}{2}i\right)^3 = \dfrac{1}{8}(-1+\sqrt{3}\,i)^3$

$\qquad\qquad\qquad\qquad = \dfrac{1}{8}[(-1)^3 + 3(-1)^2(\sqrt{3}\,i) + 3(-1)(\sqrt{3}\,i)^2 + (\sqrt{3}\,i)^3]$

$\qquad\qquad\qquad\qquad = \dfrac{1}{8}[-1 + 3\sqrt{3}\,i + 9 - 3\sqrt{3}\,i]$

$\qquad\qquad\qquad\qquad = 1$

37. 5th Row of Pascal's Triangle: 1 5 10 10 5 1

$$(2t - s)^5 = 1(2t)^5 + 5(2t)^4(-s) + 10(2t)^3(-s)^2 + 10(2t)^2(-s)^3 + 5(2t)(-s)^4 + 1(-s)^5$$
$$= 32t^5 - 80t^4 s + 80t^3 s^2 - 40t^2 s^3 + 10ts^4 - s^5$$

39. 4th Row of Pascal's Triangle: 1 4 6 4 1

$$(3 - 2z)^4 = 3^4 - 4(3)^3(2z) + 6(3)^2(2z)^2 - 4(3)(2z)^3 + (2z)^4$$
$$= 81 - 216z + 216z^2 - 96z^3 + 16z^4$$

41. $_{12}C_7 x^5 (3)^7 = \dfrac{12!}{(12-7)!7!} \cdot 3^7 x^5$

$= 1{,}732{,}104 x^5$

$a = -326{,}592$

43. $_{10}C_2 x^8 (-2y)^2 = \dfrac{10!}{(10-2)!2!} \cdot 4x^8 y^2$

$= 180 x^8 y^2$

$a = 180$

45. $_9 C_5 (3x)^4 (-2y)^5 = \dfrac{9!}{(9-5)!4!}(81x^4)(-32y^5)$

$= -326{,}592 x^4 y^5$

$a = -326{,}592$

47. $_{10}C_6 (x^2)^4 (1)^6 = \dfrac{10!}{(10-6)!6!} x^8$

$= 210 x^8$

$a = 210$

49. $_7 C_4 \left(\dfrac{1}{2}\right)^4 \left(\dfrac{1}{2}\right)^3 = \dfrac{7 \cdot 6 \cdot 5}{3 \cdot 2}\left(\dfrac{1}{2}\right)^7$

$= \dfrac{35}{128} \approx 0.273$

51. $_8 C_4 \left(\dfrac{1}{3}\right)^4 \left(\dfrac{2}{3}\right)^4 = \dfrac{8 \cdot 7 \cdot 6 \cdot 5}{4 \cdot 3 \cdot 2} \cdot \dfrac{2^4}{3^8}$

≈ 0.171

53. $(1.02)^8 = (1 + 0.02)^8 = 1 + 8(0.02) + 28(0.02)^2 + 56(0.02)^3 + 70(0.02)^4 + 56(0.02)^5$
$$+ 28(0.02)^6 + 8(0.02)^7 + (0.02)^8$$
$$= 1 + 0.16 + 0.0112 + 0.000448 + \cdots \approx 1.172$$

55. $(2.99)^{12} = (3 - 0.01)^{12} = 3^{12} - 12(3)^{11}(0.01) + 66(3)^{10}(0.01)^2 - 220(3)^9(0.01)^3 + 495(3)^8(0.01)^4$
$$- 792(3)^7(0.01)^5 + 924(3)^6(0.01)^6 - 792(3)^5(0.01)^7 + 495(3)^4(0.01)^8$$
$$- 220(3)^3(0.01)^9 + 66(3)^2(0.01)^{10} - 12(3)(0.01)^{11} + (0.01)^{12}$$
$$= 531{,}441 - 21{,}257.64 + 389.7234 - 4.33026 + 0.03247695$$
$$- 0.0001732104 + \cdots$$
$$\approx 510{,}568.785$$

57. $f(x) = -x^2 + 3x + 2$

$\quad g(x) = f(x - 2)$

$\qquad = -(x - 2)^2 + 3(x - 2) + 2$

$\qquad = -(x^2 - 4x + 4) + 3x - 6 + 2$

$\qquad = -x^2 + 7x - 8$

$\quad g$ is f shifted 2 units to the right.

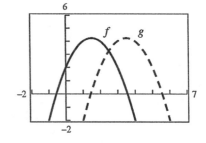

59. $f(x) = x^3 - 4x$

$\quad g(x) = f(x + 4)$

$\qquad = (x + 4)^3 - 4(x + 4)$

$\qquad = x^3 + 12x^2 + 48x + 64 - 4x - 16$

$\qquad = x^3 + 12x^2 + 44x + 48$

$\quad g$ is f shifted 4 units to the left.

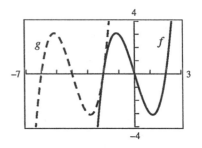

61. $f(t) = 0.2187t^2 + 0.6715t + 26.67$

$\quad g(t) = f(t + 10)$

$\qquad = 0.2187(t + 10)^2 + 0.6715(t + 10) + 26.67$

$\qquad = 0.2187(t^2 + 20t + 100) + 0.6715t + 6.715 + 26.67$

$\qquad = 0.2187t^2 + 5.0455t + 55.255$

63. $_nC_m = \dfrac{n!}{(n - m)!m!} = \dfrac{n!}{m!(n - m)!} = {_nC_{n-m}}$

65. $_nC_m + {_nC_{m-1}} = \dfrac{n!}{(n-m)!m!} + \dfrac{n!}{(n-m+1)!(m-1)!}$

$$= \frac{n!(n-m+1)!(m-1)! + n!(n-m)!m!}{(n-m)!m!(n-m+1)!(m-1)!}$$

$$= \frac{n![(n-m+1)!(m-1)! + m!(n-m)!]}{(n-m)!m!(n-m+1)!(m-1)!}$$

$$= \frac{n!(m-1)![(n-m+1)! + m(n-m)!]}{(n-m)!m!(n-m+1)!(m-1)!}$$

$$= \frac{n!(n-m)![(n-m+1)+m]}{(n-m)!m!(n-m+1)!}$$

$$= \frac{n![n+1]}{m!(n-m+1)!}$$

$$= \frac{(n+1)!}{[(n+1)-m]!m!}$$

$$= {_{n+1}C_m}$$

67. $_nC_0 + {_nC_1} + {_nC_2} + {_nC_3} + \cdots + {_nC_n} = (1+1)^n = 2^n$

Section 9.6   Counting Principles, Permutations, and Combinations

■ You should know The Fundamental Principle of Counting.

■ $_nP_m = \dfrac{n!}{(n-m)!}$ is the number of permutations of n elements taken m at a time.

■ Given a set of n objects that has n_1 of one kind, n_2 of a second kind, and so on, the number of distinguishable permutations is

$$\frac{n!}{n_1!n_2!\ldots n_k!}.$$

■ $_nC_m = \dfrac{n!}{(n-m)!m!}$ is the number of combinations of n elements taken m at a time.

1.

First Number	*Second Number*
1	7
2	6
3	5
4	4
5	3
6	2
7	1

A total of 8 may be obtained 7 different ways.

3. $3 \cdot 4 = 12$ ways to fill the positions

5. $2 \cdot 3 \cdot 2 \cdot 1 = 12$ ways to be seated

7. $26 \cdot 26 \cdot 10 \cdot 10 \cdot 10 \cdot 10 = 6{,}760{,}000$ distinct license plate numbers

9. $2 \cdot 2 \cdot 2 \cdot 2 \cdot 2 \cdot 2 = 2^6 = 64$ different ways

11. (a) $9 \cdot 10 \cdot 10 = 900$ ways
    (b) $9 \cdot 9 \cdot 8 = 648$ ways
    (c) $9 \cdot 10 \cdot 2 = 180$ ways (The last digit must be 0 or 5.)
    (d) $6 \cdot 10 \cdot 10 = 600$ ways (The first digit must be greater than or equal to 4.)

13. $40 \cdot 40 \cdot 40 = 64{,}000$ different lock combinations

15. (a) $6 \cdot 5 \cdot 4 \cdot 3 \cdot 2 \cdot 1 = 720$ different ways

(b) $6 \cdot 4 \cdot 2 = 48$ different ways

17. $_4P_4 = \dfrac{4!}{(4-4)!} = \dfrac{4!}{0!} = 24$

19. $_8P_3 = \dfrac{8!}{(8-3)!} = \dfrac{8!}{5!} = 336$

21. $_{20}P_5 = \dfrac{20!}{(20-5)!}$

$= \dfrac{20!}{15!}$

$= 1,860,480$

23. $_{100}P_2 = \dfrac{100!}{(100-2)!}$

$= \dfrac{100!}{98!}$

$= 9900$

25. $_5P_4 = \dfrac{5!}{(5-4)!}$

$= \dfrac{5!}{1!}$

$= 120$

27.

ABCD	BACD	CABD	DABC
ABDC	BADC	CADB	DACB
ACBD	BCAD	CBAD	DBAC
ACDB	BCDA	CBDA	DBCA
ADBC	BDAC	CDAB	DCAB
ADCB	BDCA	CDBA	DCBA

29. $5! = 120$ ways

31. $_{12}P_4 = 12 \cdot 11 \cdot 10 \cdot 9 = 11,880$ ways

33. $\dfrac{7!}{2!1!3!1!} = 420$

35. $\dfrac{9!}{2!4!3!} = 1260$

37. $\dfrac{7!}{2!1!1!1!1!} = 2520$

39. AB, AC, AD, AE, AF, BC, BD, BE, BF, DC, CE, CF, DE, DF, EF

41. $_{20}C_4 = \dfrac{20!}{(20-4)!4!}$

$= \dfrac{20!}{16!4!}$

$= 4845$

43. $_{40}C_6 = \dfrac{40!}{(40-6)!6!}$

$= \dfrac{40!}{34!6!}$

$= 3,838,380$

45. $_{100}C_4 = \dfrac{100!}{(100-4)!4!}$

$= \dfrac{100!}{96!4!}$

$= 3,921,225$

47. $_8C_3 \, _5C_2 = \dfrac{8!}{(8-3)!3!} \cdot \dfrac{5!}{(5-2)!2!}$

$= 560$

49. (a) $_8C_4 = \dfrac{8!}{(8-4)!4!} = \dfrac{8!}{4!4!} = 70$

(b) $_3C_2\,_5C_2 = \dfrac{3!}{(3-2)!2!} \cdot \dfrac{5!}{(5-2)!2!} = \dfrac{3!}{1!2!} \cdot \dfrac{5!}{3!2!} = 30$

51. (a) $_8C_4 = \dfrac{8!}{(8-4)!4!} = \dfrac{8!}{4!4!} = 70$

(b) Number of ways to obtain no couples: $2^4 = 16$
Number of ways to obtain at least one couple: $_8C_4 - 2^4 = 70 - 16 = 54$

(c) $2^4 = 16$

53. $_5C_2 - 5 = \dfrac{5!}{(5-2)!2!} - 5$

$= 10 - 5 = 5$

55. $_8C_2 - 8 = \dfrac{8!}{(8-2)!2!} - 8$

$= 28 - 8 = 20$

57. $14 \cdot {}_nP_3 = {}_{n+2}P_4$

$14n(n-1)(n-2) = (n+2)(n+1)(n)(n-1)$

$0 = (n+2)(n+1)(n)(n-1) - 14n(n-1)(n-2)$

$0 = n(n-1)[n^2 + 3n + 2 - 14n + 28]$

$0 = n(n-1)(n^2 - 11n + 30)$

$0 = n(n-1)(n-5)(n-6)$

Since $n \geq 3$, $n = 5$ or $n = 6$.

59. $_nP_{n-1} = n(n-1)(n-2)\cdots 3 \cdot 2 = n(n-1)(n-2)\cdots 3 \cdot 2 \cdot 1 = {}_nP_n$

61. $_nC_{n-1} = \dfrac{n!}{(n-(n-1))!(n-1)!} = \dfrac{n!}{1!(n-1)!} = \dfrac{n!}{(n-1)!1!} = {}_nC_1$

63. $_nC_m = \dfrac{n!}{(n-m)!m!}$

$= \dfrac{n(n-1)(n-2)\cdots(n-m+1)(n-m)!}{(n-m)!m!}$

$= \dfrac{n(n-1)(n-2)\cdots(n-m+1)}{m!} = \dfrac{{}_nP_m}{m!}$

Section 9.7 Probability

You should know the following basic principles of probability.

- If an event E has $n(E)$ equally likely outcomes and its sample space has $n(S)$ equally likely outcomes, then the probability of event E is

$$P(E) = \frac{n(E)}{n(S)}, \text{ where } 0 \le P(E) \le 1.$$

- If A and B are mutually exclusive events, then $P(A \cup B) = P(A) + P(B)$. If A and B are not mutually exclusive events, then $P(A \cup B) = P(A) + P(B) - P(A \cap B)$.

- If A and B are independent events, then the probability that both A and B will occur is $P(A)P(B)$.

- The probability of the complement of an event A is $P(A') = 1 - P(A)$.

1. $\{(h,\ 1),\ (h,\ 2),\ (h,\ 3),\ (h,\ 4),\ (h,\ 5),\ (h,\ 6),(t,\ 1),\ (t,\ 2),\ (t,\ 3),\ (t,\ 4),\ (t,\ 5),\ (t,\ 6)\}$

3. $\{ABC,\ ACB,\ BAC,\ BCA,\ CAB,\ CBA\}$

5. $\{AB,\ AC,\ AD,\ AE,\ BC,\ BD,\ BE,\ CD,\ CE,\ DE\}$

7. $n(E) = \{HHT, HTH, THH\}$

   $P(E) = \dfrac{n(E)}{n(S)} = \dfrac{3}{8}$

9. $P(TTT) = \frac{1}{8}$

   $P(\text{at least one head}) = 1 - \frac{1}{8} = \frac{7}{8}$

11. There are three face cards (K, Q, and J) in each of the four suits. Therefore, there are 12 face cards in a deck.

    $$P(E) = \tfrac{12}{52} = \tfrac{3}{13}$$

13. Twenty-six of the cards are black. Six of these are face cards (J, Q, K of clubs and spades). Therefore, there are 20 black cards that are not face cards.

    $$P(E) = \tfrac{20}{52} = \tfrac{5}{13}$$

15. $n(S) = 6 \cdot 6 = 36$

    $E = \{(1,3),\ (2,2),\ (3,1)\}$

    $P(E) = \tfrac{3}{36} = \tfrac{1}{12}$

17. $n(S) = 6 \cdot 6 = 36$

$E = \{(1,6),\ (2,5),\ (3,4),\ (4,3),\ (5,2),\ (6,1),\ (2,6),\ (3,5),\ (4,\ 4),\ (5,3),\ (6,2),$

$\quad (3,6),\ (4,5),\ (5,4),\ (6,3),\ (4,6),\ (5,5),\ (6,4),\ (5,6),\ (6,6),\ (6,5)\}$

$P(E) = \frac{21}{36} = \frac{7}{12}$

19. $n(S) = 6 \cdot 6 = 36$

$E = \{(1,2),\ (1,4),\ (1,6),\ (2,1),\ (2,3),\ (2,5),(3,2),\ (3,4),\ (4,1),\ (4,3),\ (5,2),\ (6,1)\}$

$P(E) = \frac{12}{36} = \frac{1}{3}$

21. $n(S) = {}_6C_2 = 15$
$n(E) = {}_3C_2 = 3$
$P(E) = \frac{3}{15} = \frac{1}{5}$

23. $n(S) = {}_6C_2 = 15$
$n(E) = {}_4C_2 = 6$
$P(E) = \frac{6}{15} = \frac{2}{5}$

25. $1 - p = 1 - 0.7 = 0.3$

27. $1 - p = 1 - 0.15 = 0.85$

29. $n(S) = 1254$

(a) $n(E) = 672$

$P(E) = \frac{672}{1254} = \frac{112}{209}$

(b) $n(E) = 582$

$P(E) = \frac{582}{1254} = \frac{97}{209}$

(c) $n(E) = 672 - 124$

$= 548$

$P(E) = \frac{548}{1254} = \frac{274}{627}$

31. $p + p + 2p = 1$

$p = 0.25$

Taylor: 0.50
Moore: 0.25
Jenkins: 0.25

33. $n(S) = {}_{20}C_{10} = 184{,}756$

(a) $n(E) = {}_{15}C_{10} = 3003$

$P(E) = \frac{3003}{184{,}756} = \frac{21}{1292} \approx 0.016$

(b) $n(E) = {}_{15}C_8\ {}_5C_2 = 64{,}350$

$P(E) = \frac{64{,}350}{184{,}756} = \frac{225}{646} \approx 0.348$

(c) $n(E) = {}_{15}C_9\ {}_5C_1 + {}_{15}C_{10}$

$= 25{,}025 + 3003 = 28{,}028$

$P(E) = \frac{28{,}028}{184{,}756} = \frac{49}{323} \approx 0.152$

35. Total ways to insert 4 letters:
$4! = 24$ ways

4 correct: 1 way
3 correct: not possible
2 correct: 6 ways
1 correct: 8 ways
0 correct: 9 ways

(a) $\dfrac{8}{24} = \dfrac{1}{3}$

(b) $\dfrac{8 + 6 + 1}{24} = \dfrac{15}{24} = \dfrac{5}{8}$

37. (a) $n(S) = 5! = 120$

$n(E) = 1$

$P(E) = \frac{1}{120}$

(b) $n(S) = 4! = 24$

$n(E) = 1$

$P(E) = \frac{1}{24}$

39. (a) $\left(\frac{4}{52}\right)\left(\frac{4}{52}\right) = \frac{1}{169}$

(b) $\left(\frac{4}{52}\right)\left(\frac{3}{51}\right) = \frac{1}{221}$

41. $n(S) = {}_{12}C_4 = 495$

(a) $n(E) = {}_9C_4 = 126$

$P(E) = \frac{126}{495} = \frac{14}{55}$

(b) $n(E) = {}_9C_2 \, {}_3C_2 = 108$

$P(E) = \frac{108}{495} = \frac{12}{55}$

(c) $n(E) = {}_9C_2 \, {}_3C_2 + {}_9C_3 \, {}_3C_1 + {}_9C_4 \, {}_3C_0 = 486$

$P(E) = \frac{486}{495} = \frac{54}{55}$

43. (a) $P(EE) = \frac{15}{30} \cdot \frac{15}{30} = \frac{1}{4}$

(b) $P(EO \text{ or } OE) = 2\left(\frac{15}{30}\right)\left(\frac{15}{30}\right) = \frac{1}{2}$

(c) $P(N_1 < 10, \ N_2 < 10) = \frac{9}{30} \cdot \frac{9}{30} = \frac{9}{100}$

(d) $P(N_1 N_1) = \frac{30}{30} \cdot \frac{1}{30} = \frac{1}{30}$

45. (a) $P(SS) = (0.985)^2 \approx 0.9702$

(b) $P(S) = 1 - P(FF)$

$= 1 - (0.015)^2 \approx 0.9998$

(c) $P(FF) = (0.015)^2 \approx 0.0002$

47. (a) $P(SSSSS) = \left(\frac{1}{4}\right)^5 = \frac{1}{1024}$

(b) $P(NNNNN) = \left(\frac{3}{4}\right)^5 = \frac{243}{1024}$

(c) $P(\text{at least one contract})$

$= 1 - P(NNNNN)$

$= 1 - \frac{243}{1024} = \frac{781}{1024}$

49. (a) $P(BBBB) = \left(\frac{1}{2}\right)\left(\frac{1}{2}\right)\left(\frac{1}{2}\right)\left(\frac{1}{2}\right) = \frac{1}{16}$

(b) $P(BBBB) + P(GGGG) = \frac{1}{16} + \frac{1}{16} = \frac{1}{8}$

(c) $1 - P(GGGG) = 1 - \frac{1}{16} = \frac{15}{16}$

51. $P(CC) = (0.32)(0.32) = 0.1024$

Section 9.8   Exploring Data: Measures of Central Tendency

■ You should be able to compute the following three measures of central tendency.

(a) The mean or average of n numbers is the sum of the numbers divided by n.

(b) The median of n numbers is the middle number when the numbers are written in order. If n is even, the median is the average of the two middle numbers.

(c) The mode of n numbers is the number that occurs most frequently. If two numbers tie for most frequent occurrence, the collection has two modes and is called bimodal.

■ You should be able to work with data that is already organized in a frequency distribution of histogram.

■ You should be able to select the best measure of central tendency in order to describe a set of data.

1. mean $= \dfrac{5 + 7 + 7 + 8 + 9 + 12 + 14}{7} = \dfrac{62}{7} \approx 8.86$

   median $= 8$

   mode $= 7$

3. mean $= \dfrac{5 + 7 + 7 + 8 + 9 + 12 + 24}{7} = \dfrac{72}{7} \approx 10.29$

   median $= 8$

   mode $= 7$

5. mean $= \dfrac{5 + 7 + 7 + 9 + 12 + 14}{6} = \dfrac{54}{6} = 9$

   median $= \dfrac{7 + 9}{2} = 8$

   mode $= 7$

7. The mean is sensitive to extreme values.

9. mean $= \dfrac{52.00 + 52.50 + 57.00 + 57.99 + 59.84 + 65.35 + 65.35 + 67.92 + 74.98 + 81.76 + 83.18 + 87.82}{12}$

$= \dfrac{805.69}{12} \approx 67.14$

median $= 65.35$

11. mean $= \dfrac{1(0) + 24(1) + 45(2) + 54(3) + 50(4) + 19(5) + 7(6)}{200} = \dfrac{613}{200} = 3.065 \approx 3.07$

median $= 3$

mode $= 3$

13. average $= \dfrac{27(1) + 29(7) + 31(5) + 33(11) + 35(19) + 37(25) + 39(12) + 41(11) + 43(5) + 45(3) + 47(1)}{100}$

$= \dfrac{3654}{100} = 36.54 = 36,540 \text{miles}$

15. mean $= 76.6$

median $= 82$

mode$=42$

The median gives the most representative description.

17. Since $\dfrac{254}{2} = 127$, it is true that at least 127 employees earn at least \$9.18 per hour.

Section 9.9   Exploring Data: Measures of Dispersion

■ Consider the numbers x_1, x_2, $\cdots$, x_n with a mean of $\overline{x}$. The variance of the set is

$$v = \frac{(x_1 - \overline{x})^2 + (x_2 - \overline{x})^2 + \cdots + (x_n - \overline{x})^2}{n}$$

and the standard deviation of the set is

$$\sigma = \sqrt{v}$$

■ You should be able to calculate the variance and standard deviation by hand.

■ You should be able to use the alternate formula for standard deviation:

$$\sigma = \sqrt{\frac{x_1^2 + x_2^2 + \cdots + x_n^2}{n} - \overline{x}^2}$$

■ You should be able to sketch box-and-whisker plots.

1. $\overline{x} = \dfrac{2 + 4 + 8 + 10}{4} = \dfrac{24}{4} = 6$

$v = \dfrac{(2 - 6)^2 + (4 - 6)^2 + (8 - 6)^2 + (10 - 6)^2}{4} = \dfrac{40}{4} = 10$

$\sigma = \sqrt{v} = \sqrt{10} \approx 3.16$

3. $\overline{x} = \dfrac{0 + 1 + 1 + 2 + 2 + 2 + 3 + 3 + 4}{9} = \dfrac{18}{9} = 2$

$v = \dfrac{(0 - 2)^2 + (1 - 2)^2 + (1 - 2)^2 + (2 - 2)^2 + (2 - 2)^2 + (2 - 2)^2 + (3 - 2)^2 + (3 - 2)^2 + (4 - 2)^2}{9}$

$= \dfrac{12}{9} = \dfrac{4}{3}$

$\sigma = \sqrt{v} = \sqrt{\dfrac{4}{3}} \approx 1.54$

5. $\overline{x} = \dfrac{1 + 2 + 3 + 4 + 5 + 6 + 7}{7} = 4$

$v = \dfrac{(1 - 4)^2 + (2 - 4)^2 + (3 - 4)^2 + (4 - 4)^2 + (5 - 4)^2 + (6 - 4)^2 + (7 - 4)^2}{7} = \dfrac{28}{7} = 4$

$\sigma = \sqrt{v} = \sqrt{4} = 2$

7. $\overline{x} = \dfrac{49 + 62 + 40 + 29 + 32 + 70}{6} = \dfrac{282}{6} = 47$

$v = \dfrac{(49 - 47)^2 + (62 - 47)^2 + (40 - 47)^2 + (29 - 47)^2 + (32 - 47)^2 + (70 - 47)^2}{6}$

$= \dfrac{1356}{6} = 226$

$\sigma = \sqrt{v} = \sqrt{226} \approx 15.03$

9. The mean is $\overline{x} = 6$. Then,

$\sigma = \sqrt{\dfrac{2^2 + 4^2 + 6^2 + 6^2 + 13^2 + 5^2}{6} - 6^2} = \sqrt{\dfrac{286}{6} - 36} = \sqrt{\dfrac{35}{3}} \approx 3.41$

11. The mean is $\overline{x} = \dfrac{1800}{6} = 300$. Then,

$\sigma = \sqrt{\dfrac{246^2 + 336^2 + 473^2 + 167^2 + 219^2 + 359^2}{6} - 300^2}$

$= \sqrt{\dfrac{601872}{6} - 300^2} = \sqrt{10,312} \approx 101.55$

13. The mean is $\overline{x} = \dfrac{29}{5} = 5.8$. Then,

$\sigma = \sqrt{\dfrac{8.1^2 + 6.9^2 + 3.7^2 + 4.2^2 + 6.1^2}{5} - 5.8^2}$

$= \sqrt{\dfrac{181.76}{5} - 5.8^2} = \sqrt{2.712} \approx 1.65$

15. The mean is $\overline{x} = 12$. Furthermore $|x_i - 12| = 8$ for all x_i.

17. (a) $\bar{x} = \dfrac{8 + 2(10) + 2(14) + 16}{6} = \dfrac{72}{6} = 12$

$\sigma = \sqrt{\dfrac{8^2 + 2(10)^2 + 2(14)^2 + 16^2}{6} - 12^2}$

$ = \sqrt{\dfrac{912}{6} - 12^2} = \sqrt{8} \approx 2.83$

(b) $\bar{x} = \dfrac{16 + 2(18) + 2(22) + 24}{6} = \dfrac{120}{6} = 20$

$\sigma = \sqrt{\dfrac{16^2 + 2(18)^2 + 2(22)^2 + 24^2}{6} - 20^2} = \sqrt{\dfrac{2448}{6} - 20^2}$

$ = \sqrt{8} \approx 2.83$

(c) $\bar{x} = \dfrac{10 + 2(11) + 2(13) + 14}{6} = \dfrac{72}{6} = 12$

$\sigma = \sqrt{\dfrac{10^2 + 2(11)^2 + 2(13)^2 + 14^2}{6} - 12^2} = \sqrt{\dfrac{876}{6} - 12^2}$

$ = \sqrt{2} \approx 1.41$

(d) $\bar{x} = \dfrac{7 + 2(8) + 2(10) + 11}{6} = \dfrac{54}{6} = 9$

$\sigma = \sqrt{\dfrac{7^2 + 2(8)^2 + 2(10)^2 + 11^2}{6} - 9^2} = \sqrt{\dfrac{498}{6} - 9^2} = \sqrt{2} \approx 1.41$

19. It will increase the mean by 5, but the standard deviation will not change.

21. $\bar{x} = 235$ mean

$\sigma = 28$ standard deviation

$n = 600$ scores

By Chebychev's Theorem, $1 - \dfrac{1}{k^2} = 1 - \dfrac{1}{2^2} = \dfrac{3}{4}$ $(k = 2)$

of the scores lie between 2 standard deviations:

$[235 - 2(28),\ 235 + 2(28)] = [179,\ 291]$

Similarly, $1 - \dfrac{1}{3^2} = \dfrac{8}{9}$ $(k = 3)$ of the scores lie between 3 standard deviations:

$[235 - 3(28),\ 235 + 3(28)] = [151,\ 319]$

If the standard deviations were 16, the intervals would be:

$[235 - 2(16),\ 235 + 2(16)] = [203,\ 267]$ $\left(\tfrac{3}{4}\text{ of scores}\right)$

$[235 - 3(16),\ 235 + 3(16)] = [187,\ 283]$ $\left(\tfrac{8}{9}\text{ of scores}\right)$

23. 12, 13, 13, 14, 14, 15, 20, 23, 23
median = 14

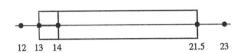

    12 13 14   21.5   23

25. 46, 47, 47, 48, 48, 49, 50, 51, 52, 53

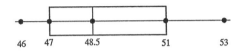

   46   47   48.5   51   53

27. 10.0, 10.8, 11.0, 12.5, 12.6, 13.5, 15.1, 18.4, 20.2, 27.2, 30.6, 38.3, 42.7, 53.0, 56.3, 68.9, 72.7, 78.3, 85.1, 85.2

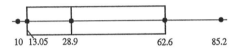

  10 13.05   28.9   62.6   85.2

New design:
18.9, 19.0, 23.1, 23.2, 23.5, 24.8, 25.6, 31.1, 35.3, 37.2, 45.5, 46.7, 54.0, 55.8, 60.0, 67.9, 71.5, 80.5, 87.8, 99.5

  18.9 24.15 41.35   63.95   99.5

From the plots, you can see that the lifetime of the product increased overall.

Chapter 9 Review Exercises

1. $\dfrac{1}{2(1)} + \dfrac{1}{2(2)} + \dfrac{1}{2(3)} + \cdots + \dfrac{1}{2(20)} = \displaystyle\sum_{k=1}^{20} \dfrac{1}{2k}$

3. $\dfrac{1}{2} + \dfrac{2}{3} + \dfrac{3}{4} + \cdots + \dfrac{9}{10} = \displaystyle\sum_{k=1}^{9} \dfrac{k}{k+1}$

5. $\displaystyle\sum_{i=1}^{6} 5 = 5 + 5 + 5 + 5 + 5 + 5 = 30$

7. $\displaystyle\sum_{j=3}^{10} (2j - 3) = 3 + 5 + 7 + 9 + \cdots + 17$
$= 80$

9. Geometric, $a_0 = 1$, $r = 2$, $n = 7$

$\displaystyle\sum_{i=0}^{6} 2^i = 1\left(\dfrac{1 - 2^7}{1 - 2}\right) = 127$

11. $\displaystyle\sum_{i=0}^{\infty} \left(\dfrac{7}{8}\right)^i = \dfrac{1}{1 - r} = \dfrac{1}{1 - \frac{7}{8}} = 8$

(Sum of infinite geometric sequence)

13. Geometric, $a_0 = 4$, $r = \dfrac{2}{3}$

$\displaystyle\sum_{k=0}^{\infty} 4\left(\dfrac{2}{3}\right)^k = \dfrac{4}{1 - \frac{2}{3}} = 12$

15. Arithmetic

$a_1 = \frac{14}{3}$, $a_{11} = \frac{34}{3}$, $n = 11$

$\displaystyle\sum_{k=1}^{11} \left(\tfrac{2}{3}k + 4\right) = \tfrac{11}{2}\left(\tfrac{14}{3} + \tfrac{34}{3}\right) = 88$

17. $\displaystyle\sum_{n=0}^{10} (n^2 + 3) = \sum_{n=0}^{10} n^2 + \sum_{n=0}^{10} 3 = \dfrac{10(10 + 1)(2 \cdot 10 + 1)}{6} + 3(11) = 418$

19. $a_1 = 3$

$a_2 = 3 + 4 = 7$

$a_3 = 7 + 4 = 11$

$a_4 = 11 + 4 = 15$

$a_5 = 15 + 4 = 19$

21. $a_4 = 10 = d(4) + c$

$a_{10} = 28 = d(10) + c$

$4d + c = 10$

$10d + c = 28$

Solving this system yields $d = 3$ and $c = -2$.

Thus, $a_n = 3n - 2$

$a_1 = 1$

$a_2 = 4$

$a_3 = 7$

$a_4 = 10$

$a_5 = 13.$

23. $a_1 = 100 = 1(-3) + c \Rightarrow c = 103$

$a_n = -3n + 103$

$a_{20} = 43, \ n = 20$

$\displaystyle\sum_{n=1}^{20} (-3n + 103) = \frac{20}{2}(100 + 43)$

$= 1430$

25. $\displaystyle\sum_{i=1}^{100} 5i = 5\sum_{i=1}^{100} i$

$= 5\left(\dfrac{100(101)}{2}\right)$

$= 25{,}250$

27. $a_1 = 4$

$a_2 = 4\left(-\dfrac{1}{4}\right) = -1$

$a_3 = 4\left(-\dfrac{1}{4}\right)^2 = \dfrac{1}{4}$

$a_4 = 4\left(-\dfrac{1}{4}\right)^3 = -\dfrac{1}{16}$

$a_5 = 4\left(-\dfrac{1}{4}\right)^4 = \dfrac{1}{64}$

29. $a_3 = 4 = (9)r^2, \ r^2 = \dfrac{4}{9}, \ r = \pm\dfrac{2}{3}$

$a_1 = 9 \qquad\qquad$ or $a_1 = 9$

$a_2 = 9\left(\dfrac{2}{3}\right) = 6 \qquad a_2 = 9\left(-\dfrac{2}{3}\right) = -6$

$a_3 = 9\left(\dfrac{2}{3}\right)^2 = 4 \qquad a_3 = 9\left(-\dfrac{2}{3}\right)^2 = 4$

$a_4 = 9\left(\dfrac{2}{3}\right)^3 = \dfrac{8}{3} \qquad a_4 = 9\left(-\dfrac{2}{3}\right)^3 = -\dfrac{8}{3}$

$a_5 = 9\left(\dfrac{2}{3}\right)^4 = \dfrac{16}{9} \qquad a_5 = 9\left(-\dfrac{2}{3}\right)^4 = \dfrac{16}{9}$

31. $r = \dfrac{a_2}{a_1} = \dfrac{-8}{16} = -\dfrac{1}{2}$

$a_n = 16\left(-\dfrac{1}{2}\right)^{n-1}$

$\displaystyle\sum_{n=1}^{20} 16\left(-\dfrac{1}{2}\right)^{n-1} = 16\left(\dfrac{1 - \left(-\dfrac{1}{2}\right)^{20}}{1 - \left(-\dfrac{1}{2}\right)}\right)$

≈ 10.667

33. (a) $a_t = 120{,}000(0.70)^t$

(b) $a_5 = 120{,}000(0.70)^5 = \$20{,}168.40$

35. $A = \displaystyle\sum_{i=1}^{24} 200\left(1 + \dfrac{0.06}{12}\right)^i = \sum_{i=1}^{24} 200(1.005)^i = 200(1.005)\left[\dfrac{1 - (1.005)^{24}}{1 - 1.005}\right] \approx \$5111.82$

37. 1. When $n = 1$, $1 = \frac{1}{2}[3(1) - 1] = 1$.

2. Assume that $1 + 4 + 7 + \cdots + (3k - 2) = (k/2)(3k - 1)$. Then,

$$1 + 4 + 7 + \cdots + (3k - 2) + [3(k + 1) - 2] = [1 + 4 + 7 + \cdots + (3k - 2)] + (3k + 1)$$

$$= \frac{k}{2}(3k - 1) + (3k + 1)$$

$$= \frac{k(3k - 1)}{2} + \frac{2(3k + 1)}{2}$$

$$= \frac{3k^2 + 5k + 2}{2}$$

$$= \frac{(k + 1)(3k + 2)}{2}$$

$$= \frac{(k + 1)}{2}[3(k + 1) - 1].$$

Thus, the formula holds for all positive intergers n.

39. 1. When $n = 1$, $ar^0 = a = \frac{a(1 - r^1)}{1 - r} = a$.

2. Assume that $\sum_{i=0}^{k-1} ar^i = \frac{a(1 - r^k)}{1 - r}$. Then,

$$\sum_{i=0}^{k+1-1} ar^i = \frac{a(1 - r^k)}{1 - r} + ar^k$$

$$= \frac{a(1 - r^k) + ar^k(1 - r)}{1 - r} = \frac{a(1 - r^k + r^k - r^{k+1})}{1 - r} = \frac{a(1 - r^{k+1})}{1 - r}.$$

Thus, the formula holds for all positive integers n.

41. $_6C_4 = \frac{6!}{(6 - 4)!4!} = 15$ **43.** $_{25}C_5 = \frac{25 \cdot 24 \cdot 23 \cdot 22 \cdot 21}{5 \cdot 4 \cdot 3 \cdot 2 \cdot 1} = 53{,}130$

45. $\left(\frac{x}{2} + y\right)^4 = \left(\frac{x}{2}\right)^4 + 4\left(\frac{x}{2}\right)^3 y + 6\left(\frac{x}{2}\right)^2 y^2 + 4\left(\frac{x}{2}\right) y^3 + y^4 = \frac{x^4}{16} + \frac{x^3 y}{2} + \frac{3x^2 y^2}{2} + 2xy^3 + y^4$

47. $\left(\frac{2}{x} - 3x\right)^6 = \left(\frac{2}{x}\right)^6 - 6\left(\frac{2}{x}\right)^5 (3x) + 15\left(\frac{2}{x}\right)^4 (3x)^2 - 20\left(\frac{2}{x}\right)^3 (3x)^3$

$$+ 15\left(\frac{2}{x}\right)^2 (3x)^4 - 6\left(\frac{2}{x}\right) (3x)^5 + (3x)^6$$

$$= \frac{64}{x^6} - \frac{576}{x^4} + \frac{2160}{x^2} - 4320 + 4860x^2 - 2916x^4 + 729x^6$$

49. $(5 + 2i)^4 = (5)^4 + 4(5)^3(2i) + 6(5)^2(2i)^2 + 4(5)(2i)^3 + (2i)^4$

$$= 625 + 1000i - 600 - 160i + 16$$

$$= 41 - 840i$$

51. (a) $_2C_2 = 1$

(b) $_4C_2 = 6$

(c) $_6C_2 = 15$

53. $26 \cdot 26 \cdot 10 \cdot 26 \cdot 26 \cdot 26$

$$= 118{,}813{,}760$$

55. $P(\text{pair}) = \frac{10}{10} \cdot \frac{1}{9} = \frac{1}{9}$

57. $E_3 = \{3\}, \ P(E_3) = \frac{1}{6}$

$E_6 = \{(1,5), \ (2,4), \ (3,3), \ (4,2), \ (5,1)\}, \ \ P(E_6) = \frac{5}{36}$

The probability of rolling a 3 with a single die is greater than the probability of obtaining a total of 6 with two dice.

59. $1 - P(HHHHH) = 1 - \left(\frac{1}{2}\right)^5 = \frac{31}{32}$

61. $n(S) =_{52}C_5 = 2{,}598{,}960$

$n(E) =_{13}C_2 \ _4C_2 \ _4C_2 \ _{44}C_1 = 123{,}552$

$$P(E) = \frac{123{,}552}{2{,}598{,}960} \approx 0.0475$$

63. (a) $\bar{x} = \dfrac{2(2) + 4 + 2(6)}{5} = \dfrac{20}{5} = 4$

$\sigma = \sqrt{\dfrac{2(2)^2 + 4^2 + 2(6)^2}{5} - 4^2}$

$= \sqrt{\dfrac{96}{5} - 4^2} = \sqrt{3.2} \approx 1.79$

(b) $\bar{x} = \dfrac{2(8) + 10 + 2(12)}{5} = \dfrac{50}{5} = 10$

$\sigma = \sqrt{\dfrac{2(8)^2 + 10^2 + 2(12)^2}{5} - 10^2}$

$= \sqrt{\dfrac{516}{5} - 10^2} = \sqrt{3.2} \approx 1.79$

(c) $\bar{x} = \dfrac{2(7) + 8 + 2(9)}{5} = \dfrac{40}{5} = 8$

$\sigma = \sqrt{\dfrac{2(7)^2 + 8^2 + 2(9)^2}{5} - 8^2}$

$= \sqrt{\dfrac{324}{5} - 8^2} = \sqrt{0.8} \approx 0.89$

(d) $\bar{x} = \dfrac{2(19) + 20 + 2(21)}{5} = \dfrac{100}{5} = 20$

$\sigma = \sqrt{\dfrac{2(19)^2 + 20^2 + 2(21)^2}{5} - 20^2}$

$= \sqrt{\dfrac{2004}{5} - 20^2} = \sqrt{0.8} = \approx 0.89$

65. 4, 6, 6, 6, 11, 12, 14, 14, 16, 18

mean $= 10.7$
median $= 11.5$
variance $= 21.61$
standard deviation $= 4.65$

67. 104.0, 143.9, 167.1, 182.4, 194.3, 206.0

mean $= 166.28$
median $= 174.75$
variance $= 1167.2$
standard deviation $= 34.16$

69. 35, 36, 37, 38, 40, 41, 42, 42, 44, 44, 46,
46, 46, 46, 47, 47, 47, 48, 48, 48, 50, 51,
51, 52, 52, 52, 53, 53, 54, 55, 55, 56, 56,
56, 56, 56, 56, 57, 58, 59, 59, 62, 62, 63, 64

mean $= 50.356$
median $= 51$
variance $= 54.54$
standard deviation $= 7.39$

CHAPTER 10

Conics, Parametric Equations, and Polar Coordinates

Section 10.1   Introduction to Conics: Parabolas

- A parabola is the set of all points (x, y) that are equidistant from a fixed line (directrix) and a fixed point (focus) not on the line.

- The standard form of the equation of a parabola with vertex (h, k) is
$$(x - h)^2 = 4p(y - k)$$
$$(y - k)^2 = 4p(x - h)$$

- You should be able to sketch the graph of a parabola.

- You should be able to use parabolas in real life situations.

---

1. $y^2 = 4x$
Vertex: $(0, 0)$
$p = 1 > 0$
Opens to the right
Matches graph (e)

3. $x^2 = 8y$
Vertex: $(0, 0)$
$p = 2 > 0$
Opens upward
Matches graph (a)

5. $(y - 1)^2 = 4(x - 2)$
Vertex: $(2, 1)$
$p = 1 > 0$
Opens to the right
Matches graph (d)

7. $y = 4x^2$, $x^2 = \frac{1}{4}y = 4\left(\frac{1}{16}\right)y$
Vertex: $(0, 0)$
Focus: $\left(0, \frac{1}{16}\right)$
Directrix: $y = -\frac{1}{16}$

9. $y^2 = -6x = 4\left(-\frac{3}{2}\right)x$
Vertex: $(0, 0)$
Focus: $\left(-\frac{3}{2}, 0\right)$
Directrix: $x = \frac{3}{2}$

11. $x^2 + 8y = 0$, $x^2 = 4(-2)y$
Vertex: $(0, 0)$
Focus: $(0, -2)$
Directrix: $y = 2$

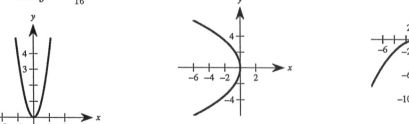

13. $(x-1)^2 + 8(y+2) = 0$
$(x-1)^2 = 4(-2)(y+2)$
Vertex: $(1, -2)$
Focus: $(1, -4)$
Directrix: $y = 0$

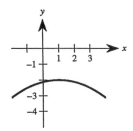

15. $\left(y + \frac{1}{2}\right)^2 = 2(x-5)$
$\qquad = 4\left(\frac{1}{2}\right)(x-5)$
Vertex: $\left(5, -\frac{1}{2}\right)$
Focus: $\left(\frac{11}{2}, -\frac{1}{2}\right)$
Directrix: $x = \frac{9}{2}$

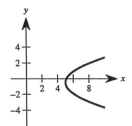

17. $y = \frac{1}{4}(x^2 - 2x + 5)$
$4y - 4 = (x-1)^2$
$(x-1)^2 = 4(1)(y-1)$
Vertex: $(1, 1)$
Focus: $(1, 2)$
Directrix: $y = 0$

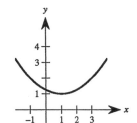

19. $y^2 - 4y - 4x = 0$
$y^2 - 4y + 4 = 4x + 4$
$(y-2)^2 = 4(1)(x+1)$
Vertex: $(-1, 2)$
Focus: $(0, 2)$
Directrix: $x = -2$

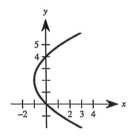

21. $y^2 + 4y + 8x - 12 = 0$
$y^2 + 4y + 4 = -8x + 12 + 4$
$(y+2)^2 = -4(2)(x-2)$
Vertex: $(2, -2)$
Focus: $(0, -2)$
Directrix: $x = 4$

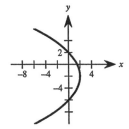

23.
$$y = -\tfrac{1}{6}(x^2 + 4x - 2)$$
$$-6y + 6 = (x + 2)^2$$
$$(x + 2)^2 = 4(-\tfrac{3}{2})(y - 1)$$
Vertex: $(-2,\ 1)$
Focus: $\left(-2,\ -\tfrac{1}{2}\right)$
Directrix: $y = \tfrac{5}{2}$

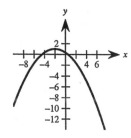

25.
$$y^2 + x + y = 0$$
$$y^2 + y + \tfrac{1}{4} = -x + \tfrac{1}{4}$$
$$\left(y + \tfrac{1}{2}\right)^2 = 4\left(-\tfrac{1}{4}\right)\left(x - \tfrac{1}{4}\right)$$
Vertex: $\left(\tfrac{1}{4},\ -\tfrac{1}{2}\right)$
Focus: $\left(0,\ -\tfrac{1}{2}\right)$
Directrix: $x = \tfrac{1}{2}$

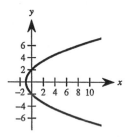

27. Vertex: $(0,\ 0) \Rightarrow h = 0,\ \ k = 0$
Focus: $\left(0,\ -\tfrac{3}{2}\right) \Rightarrow p = -\tfrac{3}{2}$
$$(x - h)^2 = 4p(y - k)$$
$$x^2 = 4\left(-\tfrac{3}{2}\right)y$$
$$x^2 = -6y$$

29. Vertex: $(0,\ 0) \Rightarrow h = 0,\ \ k = 0$
Directrix: $x = 3 \Rightarrow p = -3$
$$(y - k)^2 = 4p(x - h)$$
$$y^2 = 4(-3)x$$
$$y^2 = -12x$$

31. Vertex: $(0,\ 4) \Rightarrow h = 0,\ \ k = 4$
Directrix: $y = 2 \Rightarrow p = 2$
$$(x - h)^2 = 4p(y - k)$$
$$x^2 = 8(y - 4)$$
$$x^2 - 8y + 32 = 0$$

33. $(0, \ 3)$: $(0-h)^2 = 4p(3-k) \Rightarrow h^2 = 12p - 4pk$

$(3, \ 4)$: $(3-h)^2 = 4p(4-k) \Rightarrow (3-h)^2 = 16p - 4pk$

$(4, 11)$: $(4-h)^2 = 4p(11-k) \Rightarrow (4-h)^2 = 44p - 4pk$

By subtraction:

$$h^2 - (3-h)^2 = 12p - 4pk - (16p - 4pk) \Rightarrow 6h - 9 = -4p$$

$$h^2 - (4-h)^2 = 12p - 4pk - (44p - 4pk) \Rightarrow 8h - 16 = -32p$$

By elimination:

$$6h - 9 = -4p$$

$$\underline{-h + 2 = \quad 4p}$$

$$5h - 7 = \quad 0 \Rightarrow h = \tfrac{7}{5}$$

$$6\left(\frac{7}{5}\right) - 9 = -4p \Rightarrow p = \frac{3}{20}$$

$$\left(\frac{7}{5}\right)^2 = 12\left(\frac{3}{20}\right) - 4\left(\frac{3}{20}\right)k \Rightarrow k = -\frac{4}{15}$$

$$\left(x - \frac{7}{5}\right)^2 = 4\left(\frac{3}{20}\right)\left(y - \left(-\frac{4}{15}\right)\right)$$

$$x^2 - \frac{14}{5}x + \frac{49}{25} = \frac{3}{5}y + \frac{12}{75}$$

$$25x^2 - 70x + 49 = 15y + 4$$

$$5x^2 - 14x - 3y + 9 = 0$$

35. The x-intercepts occur at $(\pm 2, \ 0)$ and the parabola opens downward.

$$y = -(x+2)(x-2)$$

$$y = -(x^2 - 4)$$

$$x^2 + y - 4 = 0$$

37. Vertex: $(0, \ 0) \Rightarrow h = 0, \quad k = 0$

Focus: $(0, \ 3) \Rightarrow p = 3$

$$(x - h)^2 = 4p(y - k)$$

$$x^2 = 12y$$

39. (a) $(x - 0)^2 = 4p(y - 0)$

$$x^2 = 4py$$

At $(200, 50)$: $200^2 = 4p(50) \Rightarrow p = 200.$

$$x^2 = 4(200)y$$

$$x^2 = 800y$$

$$y = \tfrac{1}{800}x^2$$

(b) $y = \tfrac{1}{800}(100)^2$

$$y = \tfrac{25}{2} \text{ feet}$$

41. (a) $17{,}500\sqrt{2} \approx 24{,}749$ mph

(b) Vertex: $(0, 4100)$

Focus: $(0, 0)$

$$(x - 0) = 4(-4100)(y - 4100)$$

$$x^2 = -16{,}400(y - 4100)$$

43. (a) $y = -\dfrac{16}{32^2}x^2 + 75$

$$y = -\dfrac{1}{64}x^2 + 75$$

(b) $\quad 0 = -\dfrac{1}{64}x^2 + 75$

$$x^2 = 4800$$

$$x = 40\sqrt{3} \approx 69.3 \text{ feet}$$

45. $550(5280)\left(\dfrac{1}{3600}\right) = \dfrac{2420}{3}$ feet per second

$$0 = -\dfrac{16}{(2420/3)^2}x^2 + 42{,}000$$

$$x^2 = 42{,}000\left(\dfrac{2420^2}{144}\right) = \dfrac{5{,}124{,}350{,}000}{3}$$

$$x \approx 41{,}329 \text{ feet}$$

47.

$$y = \dfrac{1}{2}x^2$$

$$2y = x^2$$

$$4\left(\dfrac{1}{2}\right)y = x^2$$

$$p = \dfrac{1}{2}$$

Focus: $\left(0, \dfrac{1}{2}\right)$

$$d_1 = \dfrac{1}{2} - b$$

$$d_2 = \sqrt{(4 - 0)^2 + \left(8 - \tfrac{1}{2}\right)^2} = \dfrac{17}{2}$$

$$\dfrac{1}{2} - b = \dfrac{17}{2}$$

$$b = -8$$

$$m = \dfrac{8 - (-8)}{4 - 0} = 4$$

Tangent line: $y = 4x - 8$

x-intercept: $(2, 0)$

49.

$$y = -2x^2$$

$$-\dfrac{1}{2}y = x^2$$

$$4\left(-\dfrac{1}{8}\right)y = x^2$$

$$p = -\dfrac{1}{8}$$

Focus: $\left(-\tfrac{1}{8}, 0\right)$

$$d_1 = \dfrac{1}{8} + b$$

$$d_2 = \sqrt{(-1 - 0)^2 + \left(-2 + \tfrac{1}{8}\right)^2} = \dfrac{17}{8}$$

$$\dfrac{1}{8} + b = \dfrac{17}{8}$$

$$b = 2$$

$$m = \dfrac{-2 - 2}{-1 - 0} = 4$$

Tangent line: $y = 4x + 2$

x-intercept: $\left(-\tfrac{1}{2}, 0\right)$

Section 10.2   Ellipses

- An ellipse is the set of all points (x, y) the sum of whose distances from two distinct points (foci) is constant.

- The standard form of the equation of an ellipse, with center (h, k) and major and minor axes of lengths $2a$ and $2b(0 < b < a)$, is

$$\frac{(x - h)^2}{a^2} + \frac{(y - k)^2}{b^2} = 1$$

$$\frac{(x - h)^2}{b^2} + \frac{(y - k)^2}{a^2} = 1$$

- You should be able to sketch the graph of an ellipse.

- You should be able to use ellipses in real life situations.

- The eccentricity of an ellipse is $e = \dfrac{c}{a}$.

1. $\dfrac{x^2}{1} + \dfrac{y^2}{9} = 1$

Center: $(0, 0)$

$a = 3, \quad b = 1$

Vertical major axis

Matches graph (e)

3. $\dfrac{x^2}{9} + \dfrac{y^2}{4} = 1$

Center: $(0, 0)$

$a = 3, \quad b = 2$

Horizontal major axis

Matches graph (c)

5. $\dfrac{(x - 2)^2}{16} + \dfrac{(y + 1)^2}{4} = 1$

Center: $(2, -1)$

$a = 4, \quad b = 2$

Horizontal major axis

Matches graph (f)

7. $\dfrac{x^2}{25} + \dfrac{y^2}{16} = 1$

$a^2 = 25, \quad b^2 = 16,$

$c^2 = 9$

Center: $(0, 0)$

Foci: $(\pm 3, 0)$

Vertices: $(\pm 5, 0), \quad e = \dfrac{3}{5}$

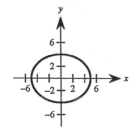

9. $\dfrac{x^2}{16} + \dfrac{y^2}{25} = 1$

$a^2 = 25, \quad b^2 = 16,$

$c^2 = 9$

Center: $(0, 0)$

Foci: $(0, \pm 3)$

Vertices: $(0, \pm 5), \quad e = \dfrac{3}{5}$

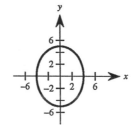

11. $\dfrac{x^2}{9} + \dfrac{y^2}{5} = 1$

$a^2 = 9, \quad b^2 = 5,$

$c^2 = 4$

Center: $(0, 0)$

Foci: $(\pm 2, 0)$

Vertices: $(\pm 3, 0)$

$e = \dfrac{2}{3}$

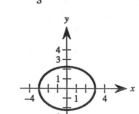

13. $x^2 + 4y^2 = 4, \quad \dfrac{x^2}{4} + \dfrac{y^2}{1} = 1$

$a^2 = 4, \quad b^2 = 1, \quad c^2 = 3$

Center: $(0, 0)$

Foci: $(\pm\sqrt{3}, 0)$

Vertices: $(\pm 2, 0), \quad e = \dfrac{\sqrt{3}}{2}$

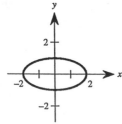

15. $3x^2 + 2y^2 = 6, \quad \dfrac{x^2}{2} + \dfrac{y^2}{3} = 1$

$a^2 = 3, \quad b^2 = 2, \quad c^2 = 1$

Center: $(0, 0)$

Foci: $(0, \pm 1)$

Vertices: $(0, \pm\sqrt{3})$

$e = \dfrac{1}{\sqrt{3}} = \dfrac{\sqrt{3}}{3}$

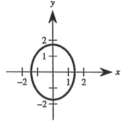

17. $\dfrac{(x-1)^2}{9} + \dfrac{(y-5)^2}{25} = 1$

$a^2 = 25, \quad b^2 = 9, \quad c^2 = 16$

Center: $(1, 5)$

Foci: $(1, 9), (1, 1)$

Vertices: $(1, 10), (1, 0), \quad e = \frac{4}{5}$

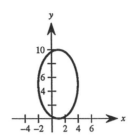

19. $9x^2 + 4y^2 + 36x - 24y + 36 = 0$

$9(x^2 + 4x + 4) + 4(y^2 - 6y + 9) = -36 + 36 + 36$

$$\dfrac{(x+2)^2}{4} + \dfrac{(y-3)^2}{9} = 1$$

$a^2 = 9, \quad b^2 = 4, \quad c^2 = 5$

Center: $(-2, 3)$

Foci: $(-2, 3 \pm \sqrt{5})$

Vertices: $(-2, 6), (-2, 0), \quad e = \dfrac{\sqrt{5}}{3}$

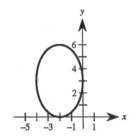

21. $16x^2 + 25y^2 - 32x + 50y + 16 = 0$

$16(x^2 - 2x + 1) + 25(y^2 + 2y + 1) = -16 + 16 + 25$

$$\dfrac{(x-1)^2}{25/16} + (y+1)^2 = 1$$

$a^2 = \dfrac{25}{16}, \quad b^2 = 1, \quad c^2 = \dfrac{9}{16}$

Center: $(1, -1)$

Foci: $\left(\dfrac{7}{4}, -1\right), \left(\dfrac{1}{4}, -1\right)$

Vertices: $\left(\dfrac{9}{4}, -1\right), \left(-\dfrac{1}{4}, -1\right), \quad e = \dfrac{3}{5}$

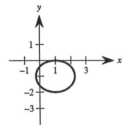

23. $4x^2 + y^2 = 1$

$$\frac{x^2}{1/4} + \frac{y^2}{1} = 1$$

$a^2 = 1, \ b^2 = \frac{1}{4}, \ c^2 = \frac{3}{4}$

Center: $(0, 0)$

Foci: $(0, \pm\sqrt{3}/2)$

Vertices: $(0, \pm 1)$

$e = \sqrt{3}/2$

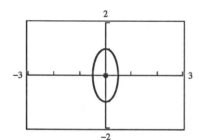

25. $12x^2 + 20y^2 - 12x + 40y - 37 = 0$

$$12\left(x^2 - x + \frac{1}{4}\right) + 20(y^2 + 2y + 1) = 37 + 3 + 20$$

$$\frac{[x - (1/2)]^2}{5} + \frac{(y+1)^2}{3} = 1$$

$a^2 = 5, \ b^2 = 3, \ c^2 = 2$

Center: $\left(\dfrac{1}{2}, \ -1\right)$

Foci: $\left(\dfrac{1}{2} \pm \sqrt{2}, \ -1\right)$

Vertices: $\left(\dfrac{1}{2} \pm \sqrt{5}, \ -1\right)$

$e = \sqrt{10}/5$

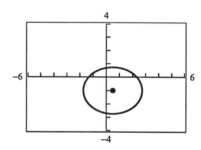

27.
$$x^2 + 2y^2 - 3x + 4y + 0.25 = 0$$

$$\left(x^2 - 3x + \frac{9}{4}\right) + 2(y^2 + 2y + 1) = -\frac{1}{4} + \frac{9}{4} + 2 = 4$$

$$\left(x - \frac{3}{2}\right)^2 + 2(y+1)^2 = 4$$

$$\frac{\left(x - \frac{3}{2}\right)^2}{2^2} + \frac{(y+1)^2}{(\sqrt{2})^2} = 1$$

Center: $\left(\frac{3}{2}, -1\right)$

$a = 2,\ b = \sqrt{2}, \Rightarrow c^2 = a^2 - b^2 = 2$

$$c = \sqrt{2}.$$

Foci: $\left(\frac{3}{2} + \sqrt{2},\ -1\right)$ and $\left(\frac{3}{2} - \sqrt{2},\ -1\right)$

Vertices: $\left(\frac{3}{2} + 2,\ -1\right) = \left(\frac{7}{2},\ -1\right)$ and $\left(\frac{3}{2} - 2,\ -1\right) = \left(-\frac{1}{2},\ -1\right).$

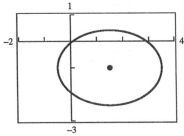

29. Vertices: $(\pm 6,\ 0) \Rightarrow a = 6$
Foci: $(\pm 5,\ 0) \Rightarrow c = 5$
$b^2 = a^2 - c^2 = 36 - 25 = 11$
Center: $(0,\ 0) = (h,\ k)$
$$\frac{(x-h)^2}{a^2} + \frac{(y-k)^2}{b^2} = 1$$
$$\frac{x^2}{36} + \frac{y^2}{11} = 1$$

31. Vertices: $(0,\ \pm 2) \Rightarrow a = 2$
Minor axis of length $2 \Rightarrow b = 1$
Center: $(0,\ 0) = (h,\ k)$
$$\frac{(y-k)^2}{a^2} + \frac{(x-h)^2}{b^2} = 1$$
$$\frac{y^2}{4} + x^2 = 1$$

33. Foci: $(0, 0)$, $(0, 8) \Rightarrow c = 4$

Major axis of length $16 \Rightarrow a = 8$

$b^2 = a^2 - c^2 = 64 - 16 = 48$

Center: $(0, 4) = (h, k)$

$$\frac{(y - k)^2}{a^2} + \frac{(k - h)^2}{b^2} = 1$$

$$\frac{(y - 4)^2}{64} + \frac{x^2}{48} = 1$$

35. Center: $(3, 2) = (h, k)$

$a = 3c$

Foci: $(1, 2)$, $(5, 2) \Rightarrow c = 2, \quad a = 6$

$b^2 = a^2 - c^2 = 36 - 4 = 32$

$$\frac{(x - h)^2}{a^2} + \frac{(y - k)^2}{b^2} = 1$$

$$\frac{(x - 3)^2}{36} + \frac{(y - 2)^2}{32} = 1$$

37. Vertices: $\left(\pm\frac{5}{2}, 0\right) \Rightarrow a = \frac{5}{2}$

Minor axis of length $2 \Rightarrow b = 2$

$c^2 = a^2 - b^2 = \frac{25}{4} - 4 = \frac{9}{4} \Rightarrow c = \frac{3}{2}$

Place tacks 1.5 feet from center.

Length of string: $2a = 5$ feet

39.

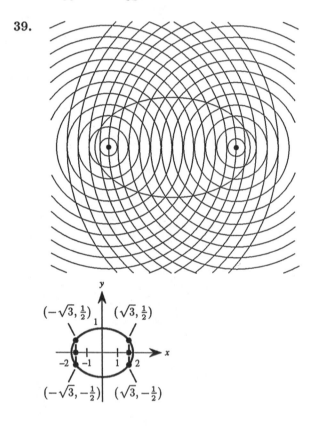

41. $\dfrac{x^2}{4} + \dfrac{y^2}{1} = 1$

$a = 2, \ b = 1, \ c = \sqrt{3}$

Points on the ellipse: $(\pm 2, 0)$, $(0, \pm 1)$

Length of latus recta: $\dfrac{2b^2}{a} = \dfrac{2(1)^2}{2} = 1$

Additional points:

$$\left(-\sqrt{3}, \ \pm\frac{1}{2}\right), \ \left(\sqrt{3}, \ \pm\frac{1}{2}\right)$$

43. $9x^2 + 4y^2 = 36$

$$\frac{x^2}{4} + \frac{y^2}{9} = 1$$

$a = 3$, $b = 2$, $c = \sqrt{5}$

Points on the ellipse: $(\pm 2,\ 0)$, $(0,\ \pm 3)$

Length of latus recta: $\dfrac{2b^2}{a} = \dfrac{2 \cdot 2^2}{3} = \dfrac{8}{3}$

Additional points:

$$\left(\pm \frac{4}{3},\ -\sqrt{5}\right),\ \left(\pm \frac{4}{3},\ \sqrt{5}\right)$$

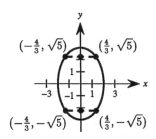

45. $a = 92.957 \times 10^6$, $e = 0.017$

$$e = \frac{c}{a}$$

$$0.017 = \frac{c}{92.957 \times 10^6}$$

$$c \approx 1.580 \times 10^6$$

Least distance:

$a - c = 92.957 \times 10^6 - 1.580 \times 10^6 = 91.377 \times 10^6$

Greatest distance:

$a + c = 92.957 \times 10^6 + 1.580 \times 10^6 = 94.537 \times 10^6$

47. Least distance: $a - c = 1.3495 \times 10^9$

Greatest distance:

$$a + c = 1.5045 \times 10^9$$

$$a = 1.3495 \times 10^9 + c$$

$$(1.3495 \times 10^9 + c) + c = 1.5045 \times 10^9$$

$$2c = 1.55 \times 10^8$$

$$c = 7.75 \times 10^7$$

$$a = 1.3495 \times 10^9 + 7.75 \times 10^7$$

$$a = 1.427 \times 10^9$$

$$e = \frac{c}{a} = \frac{7.75 \times 10^7}{1.427 \times 10^9} \approx 0.0543$$

49. $A = 583 + 4000 = 4583$, $P = 132 + 4000 = 4132$

$$e = \frac{4583 - 4132}{4583 + 4132} = \frac{451}{8715} = 0.052$$

51. $b^2 = a^2 - c^2 = a^2 - a^2 \left(\dfrac{c^2}{a^2} \right)$

$$= a^2 \left(1 - \dfrac{c^2}{a^2} \right) = a^2(1 - e^2)$$

$$\dfrac{(x-h)^2}{a^2} + \dfrac{(y-k)^2}{b^2} = 1$$

$$\dfrac{(x-h)^2}{a^2} + \dfrac{(y-k)^2}{a^2(1-e^2)} = 1$$

As $e \Rightarrow 0$, $1 - e^2 \Rightarrow 1$ and we have $\dfrac{x^2}{a^2} + \dfrac{y^2}{a^2} = 1$ or the circle $x^2 + y^2 = a^2$.

Section 10.3 Hyperbolas

- A hyperbola is the set of all points (x, y) the difference of whose distances from two distinct points (foci) is constant.

- The standard form of the equation of a hyperbola with center (h, k) is

$$\frac{(x - h)^2}{a^2} - \frac{(y - k)^2}{b^2} = 1$$

$$\frac{(x - k)^2}{a^2} - \frac{(x - h)^2}{b^2} = 1$$

- You should be able to sketch the graph of a hyperbola.

- The asymptotes of a hyperbola are

$$y = k \pm \frac{b}{a}(x - h) \qquad \text{horizontal transverse axis}$$

$$y = k \pm \frac{a}{b}(x - h) \qquad \text{vertical transverse axis}$$

- You should be able to use hyperbolas in real life situations.

- You should be able to classify a conic $Ax^2 + Cy^2 + Dx + Ey + F = 0$.
  - (a) Circle: $A = C$
  - (b) Parabola: $AC = 0$
  - (c) Ellipse: $AC > 0$
  - (d) Hyperbola: $AC < 0$

1. $\dfrac{x^2}{9} - \dfrac{y^2}{4} = 1$

   Center: $(0, 0)$
   $a = 3, \quad b = 2$
   Horizontal transverse axis
   Matches graph (e)

3. $\dfrac{y^2}{1} - \dfrac{x^2}{16} = 1$

   Center: $(0, 0)$
   $a = 1, \quad b = 4$
   Vertical transverse axis
   Matches graph (f)

5. $\dfrac{(x - 2)^2}{9} - \dfrac{y^2}{4} = 1$

   Center: $(2, 0)$
   $a = 3, \quad b = 2$
   Horizontal transverse axis
   Matches graph (d)

7. $x^2 - y^2 = 1$
$a = 1, \quad b = 1, \quad c = \sqrt{2}$
Center: $(0, 0)$
Vertices: $(\pm 1, 0)$
Foci: $(\pm\sqrt{2}, 0)$
Asymptotes: $y = \pm x$

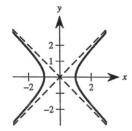

9. $\dfrac{y^2}{1} - \dfrac{x^2}{4} = 1$
$a = 1, \quad b = 2, \quad c = \sqrt{5}$
Center: $(0, 0)$
Vertices: $(0, \pm 1)$
Foci: $(0, \pm\sqrt{5})$
Asymptotes: $y = \pm\frac{1}{2}x$

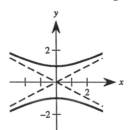

11. $\dfrac{y^2}{25} - \dfrac{x^2}{144} = 1$
$a = 5, \quad b = 12, \quad c = 13$
Center: $(0, 0)$
Vertices: $(0, \pm 5)$
Foci: $(0, \pm 13)$
Asymptotes: $y = \pm\frac{5}{12}x$

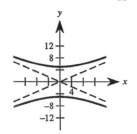

13. $5y^2 - 4x^2 = 20$
$\dfrac{y^2}{4} - \dfrac{x^2}{5} = 1$
$a = 2, \quad b = \sqrt{5}, \quad c = 3$
Center: $(0, 0)$
Vertices: $(0, \pm 2)$
Foci: $(0, \pm 3)$

Asymptotes: $y = \pm\dfrac{2}{\sqrt{5}}\, x$

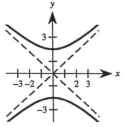

15. $\dfrac{(x-1)^2}{4} - \dfrac{(y+2)^2}{1} = 1$
$a = 2, \quad b = 1, \quad c = \sqrt{5}$
Center: $(1, -2)$
Vertices:
  $(-1, -2), \ (3, -2)$
Foci: $(1 \pm \sqrt{5}, -2)$
Asymptotes:
  $y = -2 \pm \frac{1}{2}(x - 1)$

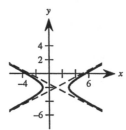

17. $(y+6)^2 - (x-2)^2 = 1$
$a = 1, \quad b = 1, \quad c = \sqrt{2}$
Center: $(2, -6)$
Vertices:
  $(2, -5), \ (2, -7)$
Foci: $(2, -6 \pm \sqrt{2})$
Asymptotes:
  $y = -6 \pm (x - 2)$

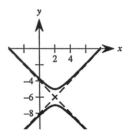

19. $9x^2 - y^2 - 36x - 6y + 18 = 0$

$9(x^2 - 4x + 4) - (y^2 + 6y + 9) = -18 + 36 - 9$

$$\frac{(x-2)^2}{1} - \frac{(y+3)^2}{9} = 1$$

$a = 1, \quad b = 3, \quad c = \sqrt{10}$

Center: $(2, -3)$

Vertices: $(1, -3), (3, -3)$

Foci: $(2 \pm \sqrt{10}, -3)$

Asymptotes: $y = -3 \pm 3(x - 2)$

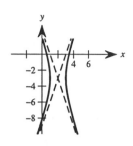

21. $x^2 - 9y^2 + 2x - 54y - 80 = 0$

$(x^2 + 2x + 1) - 9(y^2 + 6y + 9) = 80 + 1 - 81$

$(x + 1)^2 - 9(y + 3)^2 = 0$

$y + 3 = \pm\frac{1}{3}(x + 1)$

Degenerate hyperbola is two intersecting
lines

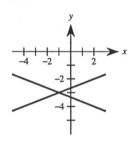

23. $2x^2 - 3y^2 = 6$

$$\frac{x^2}{3} - \frac{y^2}{2} = 1$$

$a = \sqrt{3}, \quad b = \sqrt{2}, \quad c = \sqrt{5}$

Center: $(0, 0)$

Vertices: $(\pm\sqrt{3}, 0)$

Foci: $(\pm\sqrt{5}, 0)$

Asymptotes: $y = \pm\sqrt{\frac{2}{3}}\, x$

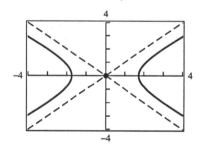

25. $9y^2 - x^2 + 2x + 54y + 62 = 0$

$9(y^2 + 6y + 9) - (x^2 - 2x + 1) = -62 - 1 + 81$

$$\frac{(y+3)^2}{2} - \frac{(x-1)^2}{18} = 1$$

$a = \sqrt{2}, \quad b = 3\sqrt{2}, \quad c = 2\sqrt{5}$

Center: $(1, -3)$

Vertices: $(1, -3 \pm \sqrt{2})$

Foci: $(1, -3 \pm 2\sqrt{5})$

Asymptotes: $y = -3 \pm \frac{1}{3}(x - 1)$

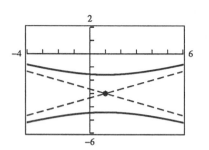

27. $3x^2 - 2y^2 - 6x - 12y - 27 = 0$

$3(x^2 - 2x + 1) - 2(y^2 + 6y + 9) = 27 + 3 - 18$

$3(x - 1)^2 - 2(y + 3)^2 = 12$

$$\frac{(x-1)^2}{2^2} - \frac{(y+3)^2}{(\sqrt{6})^2} = 1$$

Center: $(1, -3)$

$a = 2, \ b = \sqrt{6}, \ c^2 = a^2 + b^2 = 10$

$$c = \sqrt{10}$$

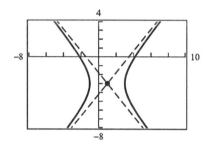

Foci: $(1 \pm \sqrt{10}, -3)$

Vertices: $(1 \pm 2, -3) = (3, -3)$ and $(-1, -3)$

Asymptotes: $y + 3 = \pm \dfrac{\sqrt{6}}{2}(x - 1)$

$$y = -3 \pm \frac{\sqrt{6}}{2}(x - 1)$$

29. Vertices: $(0, \pm 2) \quad \Rightarrow \quad a = 2$

Foci: $(0, \pm 4) \quad \Rightarrow \quad c = 4$

$b^2 = c^2 - a^2 = 16 - 4 = 12$

Center: $(0, 0) = (h, k)$

$$\frac{(y-k)^2}{a^2} - \frac{(x-h)^2}{b^2} = 1$$

$$\frac{y^2}{4} - \frac{x^2}{12} = 1$$

31. Vertices: $(\pm 1, 0) \quad \Rightarrow \quad a = 1$

Asymptotes: $y = \pm 3x \quad \Rightarrow \quad \dfrac{b}{a} = 3, \ b = 3$

Center: $(0, 0) = (h, k)$

$$\frac{(x-k)^2}{a^2} - \frac{(y-h)^2}{b^2} = 1$$

$$x^2 - \frac{y^2}{9} = 1$$

33. Vertices: $(2, 0), (6, 0)$ $\Rightarrow$ $a = 2$

Foci: $(0, 0), (8, 0)$ $\Rightarrow$ $c = 4$

$b^2 = c^2 - a^2 = 16 - 4 = 12$

Center: $(4, 0) = (h, k)$

$$\frac{(x - h)^2}{a^2} - \frac{(y - k)^2}{b^2} = 1$$

$$\frac{(x - 4)^2}{4} - \frac{y^2}{12} = 1$$

35. Vertices: $(2, 3), (2, -3)$ $\Rightarrow$ $a = 3$

Solution point: $(0, 5)$

Center: $(2, 0) = (h, k)$

$$\frac{(y - k)^2}{a^2} - \frac{(x - h)^2}{b^2} = 1$$

$$\frac{y^2}{9} - \frac{(x - 2)^2}{b^2} = 1 \quad \Rightarrow \quad b^2 = \frac{9(x - 2)^2}{y^2 - 9} = \frac{9(-2)^2}{25 - 9} = \frac{36}{16} = \frac{9}{4}$$

$$\frac{y^2}{9} - \frac{(x - 2)^2}{9/4} = 1$$

37. Vertices: $(0, 2), (6, 2)$ $\Rightarrow$ $a = 3$

Asymptotes: $y = \frac{2}{3}x, \quad y = 4 - \frac{2}{3}x$

$\frac{b}{a} = \frac{2}{3}$ $\Rightarrow$ $b = 2$

Center: $(3, 2) = (h, k)$

$$\frac{(x - h)^2}{a^2} - \frac{(y - k)^2}{b^2} = 1$$

$$\frac{(x - 3)^2}{9} - \frac{(y - 2)^2}{4} = 1$$

39. Since $\overline{AB} = 1100$ feet and the sound takes one second longer to reach B than A, the explosion must occur on the vertical line through A and B below A.

Foci: $(\pm 4400, 0)$ $\Rightarrow$ $c = 4400$

Center: $(0, 0) = (h, k)$

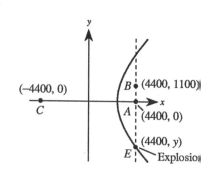

$$\frac{\overline{CE}}{1100} - \frac{\overline{AE}}{1100} = 5 \quad \Rightarrow \quad 2a = 5500, \quad a = \frac{5500}{2} = 2750$$

$$b^2 = c^2 - a^2 = (4400)^2 - (2750)^2 = 11{,}797{,}500$$

$$\frac{x^2}{(2750)^2} - \frac{y^2}{11{,}797{,}500} = 1$$

$$y^2 = 11{,}797{,}500\left(\frac{x^2}{(2750)^2} - 1\right)$$

$$y^2 = 11{,}797{,}500\left(\frac{(4400)^2}{(2750)^2} - 1\right) = 18{,}404{,}100$$

$$y = -4290$$

The explosion occurs at $(4400, -4290)$.

41. Center: $(0, 0)$

Vertex: $(a, 0)$

Focus: $(c, 0) = (12, 0)$

$b^2 = c^2 - a^2 = 12^2 - a^2$

$$\frac{(x - 0)^2}{a^2} - \frac{(y - 0)^2}{b^2} = 1$$

$$\frac{(12 - 0)^2}{a^2} - \frac{(12 - 0)^2}{12^2 - a^2} = 1$$

$$\frac{144}{a^2} - \frac{144}{144 - a^2} = 1$$

$$144(144 - a^2) - 144a^2 = a^2(144 - a^2)$$

$$a^4 - 432a^2 + 20{,}736 = 0$$

$$a^2 = \frac{-(-432) \pm \sqrt{(-432)^2 - 4(1)(20{,}736)}}{2(1)} = 216 \pm 72\sqrt{5}$$

$$a = \pm\sqrt{216 \pm 72\sqrt{5}}$$

The possible values for a are ≈ 19.42, ≈ 7.42, ≈ -7.42, ≈ -19.42. Since the vertex of the mirror lies between 0 and 12, the vertex is $(\sqrt{216 - 72\sqrt{5}}, 0) \approx (7.42, 0)$.

43. $x^2 + y^2 - 6x + 4y + 9 = 0$

   $A = 1, \ C = 1$

   $A = C \Rightarrow$ Circle

45. $4x^2 - y^2 - 4x - 3 = 0$

   $A = 4, \ C = -1$

   $AC = 4(-1)$

   $\qquad = -4 < 0 \Rightarrow$ Hyperbola

47. $4x^2 + 3y^2 + 8x - 24y + 51 = 0$

   $A = 4, \ C = 3$

   $AC = 4(3) = 12 > 0 \Rightarrow$ Ellipse

49. $25x^2 - 10x - 200y - 119 = 0$

   $A = 25, \ C = 0$

   $AC = 25(0) = 0 \Rightarrow$ Parabola

Section 10.4   Rotation and Systems of Quadratic Equations

- You should be able to use the formula
$$\cot 2\theta = \frac{A - C}{B}$$
to rotate the general second degree equation
$$Ax^2 + Bxy + Cy^2 + Dx + Ey + F = 0$$
and eliminate the xy term.

- If θ is the angle that transforms the general second degree $Ax^2 + Bxy + Cy^2 + Dx + Ey + F = 0$ into the form $A'(x')^2 + C'(y')^2 + D'x' + E'y' + F' = 0$, then the following are rotation invariants.
  (a) $F = F'$
  (b) $A + C = A' + C'$
  (c) $B^2 - 4AC = (B')^2 - 4A'C'$

- You should be able to solve a system of quadratic equations analytically.

---

1. $xy + 1 = 0$

   $A = 0,\ B = 1,\ C = 0$

   $$\cot 2\theta = \frac{A - C}{B} = 0 \Rightarrow 2\theta = \frac{\pi}{2} \Rightarrow \theta = \frac{\pi}{4}$$

   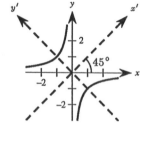

   $$x = x' \cos \frac{\pi}{4} - y' \sin \frac{\pi}{4} \qquad\qquad y = x' \sin \frac{\pi}{4} + y' \cos \frac{\pi}{4}$$

   $$= x' \left(\frac{\sqrt{2}}{2} \right) - y' \left(\frac{\sqrt{2}}{2} \right) \qquad\qquad = x' \left(\frac{\sqrt{2}}{2} \right) + y' \left(\frac{\sqrt{2}}{2} \right)$$

   $$= \frac{x' - y'}{\sqrt{2}} \qquad\qquad\qquad\qquad = \frac{x' + y'}{\sqrt{2}}$$

   $$xy + 1 = 0$$

   $$\left(\frac{x' - y'}{\sqrt{2}} \right) \left(\frac{x' + y'}{\sqrt{2}} \right) + 1 = 0$$

   $$\frac{(y')^2}{2} - \frac{(x')^2}{2} = 1$$

3. $x^2 - 10xy + y^2 + 1 = 0$

$A = 1, \ B = -10, \ C = 1$

$\cot 2\theta = \dfrac{A - C}{B} = 0 \Rightarrow 2\theta = \dfrac{\pi}{2} \Rightarrow \theta = \dfrac{\pi}{4}$

$x = x' \cos \dfrac{\pi}{4} - y' \sin \dfrac{\pi}{4}$ $\qquad\qquad$ $y = x' \sin \dfrac{\pi}{4} + y' \cos \dfrac{\pi}{4}$

$= x' \left(\dfrac{\sqrt{2}}{2} \right) - y' \left(\dfrac{\sqrt{2}}{2} \right)$ $\qquad\qquad$ $= x' \left(\dfrac{\sqrt{2}}{2} \right) + y' \left(\dfrac{\sqrt{2}}{2} \right)$

$= \dfrac{x' - y'}{\sqrt{2}}$ $\qquad\qquad\qquad\qquad$ $= \dfrac{x' + y'}{\sqrt{2}}$

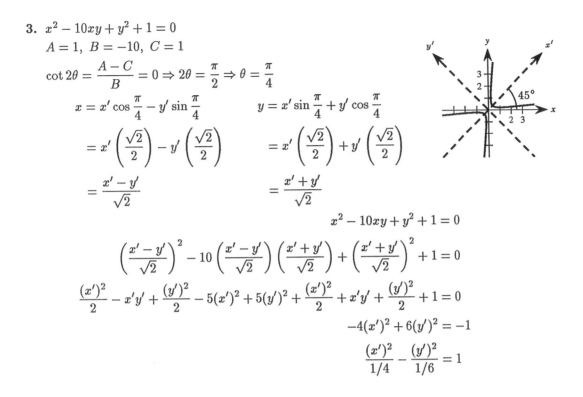

$x^2 - 10xy + y^2 + 1 = 0$

$\left(\dfrac{x' - y'}{\sqrt{2}} \right)^2 - 10 \left(\dfrac{x' - y'}{\sqrt{2}} \right) \left(\dfrac{x' + y'}{\sqrt{2}} \right) + \left(\dfrac{x' + y'}{\sqrt{2}} \right)^2 + 1 = 0$

$\dfrac{(x')^2}{2} - x'y' + \dfrac{(y')^2}{2} - 5(x')^2 + 5(y')^2 + \dfrac{(x')^2}{2} + x'y' + \dfrac{(y')^2}{2} + 1 = 0$

$-4(x')^2 + 6(y')^2 = -1$

$\dfrac{(x')^2}{1/4} - \dfrac{(y')^2}{1/6} = 1$

5. $xy - 2y - 4x = 0$

$A = 0, \ B = 1, \ C = 0$

$\cot 2\theta = \dfrac{A - C}{B} = 0 \Rightarrow 2\theta = \dfrac{\pi}{2} \Rightarrow \theta = \dfrac{\pi}{4}$

$x = x' \cos \dfrac{\pi}{4} - y' \sin \dfrac{\pi}{4}$
$\qquad\qquad\qquad\qquad$
$y = x' \sin \dfrac{\pi}{4} + y' \cos \dfrac{\pi}{4}$

$= x' \left(\dfrac{\sqrt{2}}{2} \right) - y' \left(\dfrac{\sqrt{2}}{2} \right)$
$\qquad\qquad\qquad$
$= x' \left(\dfrac{\sqrt{2}}{2} \right) + y' \left(\dfrac{\sqrt{2}}{2} \right)$

$= \dfrac{x' - y'}{\sqrt{2}}$
$\qquad\qquad\qquad\qquad\qquad$
$= \dfrac{x' + y'}{\sqrt{2}}$

$xy - 2y - 4x = 0$

$\left(\dfrac{x' - y'}{\sqrt{2}} \right) \left(\dfrac{x' + y'}{\sqrt{2}} \right) - 2 \left(\dfrac{x' + y'}{\sqrt{2}} \right) - 4 \left(\dfrac{x' - y'}{\sqrt{2}} \right) = 0$

$\dfrac{(x')^2}{2} - \dfrac{(y')^2}{2} - \sqrt{2}\,x' - \sqrt{2}\,y' - 2\sqrt{2}\,x' + 2\sqrt{2}\,y' = 0$

$\left[(x')^2 - 6\sqrt{2}\,x' + (3\sqrt{2})^2 \right] - \left[(y')^2 - 2\sqrt{2}\,y' + (\sqrt{2})^2 \right] = 0 + (3\sqrt{2})^2 - (\sqrt{2})^2$

$(x' - 3\sqrt{2})^2 - (y' - \sqrt{2})^2 = 16$

$\dfrac{(x' - 3\sqrt{2})^2}{16} - \dfrac{(y' - \sqrt{2})^2}{16} = 1$

7. $5x^2 - 2xy + 5y^2 - 12 = 0$

$A = 5,\ B = -2,\ C = 5$

$\cot 2\theta = \dfrac{A - C}{B} = 0 \Rightarrow 2\theta = \dfrac{\pi}{2} \Rightarrow \theta = \dfrac{\pi}{4}$

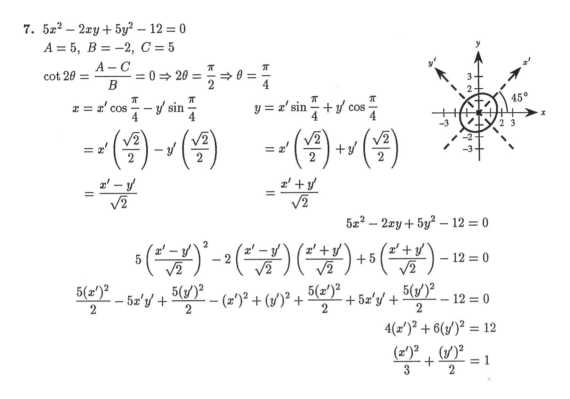

$x = x'\cos\dfrac{\pi}{4} - y'\sin\dfrac{\pi}{4}$

$\quad = x'\left(\dfrac{\sqrt{2}}{2}\right) - y'\left(\dfrac{\sqrt{2}}{2}\right)$

$\quad = \dfrac{x' - y'}{\sqrt{2}}$

$y = x'\sin\dfrac{\pi}{4} + y'\cos\dfrac{\pi}{4}$

$\quad = x'\left(\dfrac{\sqrt{2}}{2}\right) + y'\left(\dfrac{\sqrt{2}}{2}\right)$

$\quad = \dfrac{x' + y'}{\sqrt{2}}$

$$5x^2 - 2xy + 5y^2 - 12 = 0$$

$$5\left(\dfrac{x' - y'}{\sqrt{2}}\right)^2 - 2\left(\dfrac{x' - y'}{\sqrt{2}}\right)\left(\dfrac{x' + y'}{\sqrt{2}}\right) + 5\left(\dfrac{x' + y'}{\sqrt{2}}\right) - 12 = 0$$

$$\dfrac{5(x')^2}{2} - 5x'y' + \dfrac{5(y')^2}{2} - (x')^2 + (y')^2 + \dfrac{5(x')^2}{2} + 5x'y' + \dfrac{5(y')^2}{2} - 12 = 0$$

$$4(x')^2 + 6(y')^2 = 12$$

$$\dfrac{(x')^2}{3} + \dfrac{(y')^2}{2} = 1$$

9. $3x^2 - 2\sqrt{3}xy + y^2 + 2x + 2\sqrt{3}y = 0$

$A = 3,\ B = -2\sqrt{3},\ C = 1$

$\cot 2\theta = \dfrac{A - C}{B} = -\dfrac{1}{\sqrt{3}} \Rightarrow \theta = 60°$

$x = x' \cos 60° - y' \sin 60°$

$= x'\left(\dfrac{1}{2}\right) - y'\left(\dfrac{\sqrt{3}}{2}\right) = \dfrac{x' - \sqrt{3}y'}{2}$

$y = x' \sin 60° + y' \cos 60°$

$= x'\left(\dfrac{\sqrt{3}}{2}\right) + y'\left(\dfrac{1}{2}\right) = \dfrac{\sqrt{3}x' - y'}{2}$

$3x^2 - 2\sqrt{3}xy + y^2 + 2x + 2\sqrt{3}y = 0$

$3\left(\dfrac{x' - \sqrt{3}y'}{2}\right)^2 - 2\sqrt{3}\left(\dfrac{x' - \sqrt{3}y'}{2}\right)\left(\dfrac{\sqrt{3}x' + y'}{2}\right) + \left(\dfrac{\sqrt{3}x' + y'}{2}\right)^2 + 2\left(\dfrac{x' - \sqrt{3}y'}{2}\right)$

$+ 2\sqrt{3}\left(\dfrac{\sqrt{3}x' + y'}{2}\right) = 0$

$\dfrac{3(x')^2}{4} - \dfrac{6\sqrt{3}x'y'}{4} + \dfrac{9(y')^2}{4} - \dfrac{6(x')^2}{4} + \dfrac{4\sqrt{3}x'y'}{4} + \dfrac{6(y')^2}{4} + \dfrac{3(x')^2}{4} + \dfrac{2\sqrt{3}x'y'}{4} + \dfrac{(y')^2}{4}$

$+ x' - \sqrt{3}y' + 3x' + \sqrt{3}y' = 0$

$4(y')^2 + 4x' = 0$

$x' = -(y')^2$

11. $9x^2 + 24xy + 16y^2 + 90x - 130y = 0$

$A = 9, \; B = 24, \; C = 16$

$\cot 2\theta = \dfrac{A-C}{B} = -\dfrac{7}{24} \Rightarrow \theta \approx 53.13°$

$\cos 2\theta = -\dfrac{7}{25}$

$\sin \theta = \sqrt{\dfrac{1 - \cos 2\theta}{2}} = \sqrt{\dfrac{1 - (-7/25)}{2}} = \dfrac{4}{5}$

$\cos \theta = \sqrt{\dfrac{1 + \cos 2\theta}{2}} = \sqrt{\dfrac{1 + (-7/25)}{2}} = \dfrac{3}{5}$

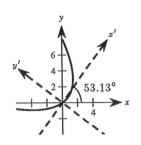

$x = x' \cos \theta - y' \sin \theta$

$\qquad = x'\left(\dfrac{3}{5}\right) - y'\left(\dfrac{4}{5}\right) = \dfrac{3x' - 4y'}{5}$

$y = x' \sin \theta + y' \cos \theta$

$\qquad = x'\left(\dfrac{4}{5}\right) + y'\left(\dfrac{3}{5}\right) = \dfrac{4x' + 3y'}{5}$

$$9x^2 + 24xy + 16y^2 + 90x - 130y = 0$$

$$9\left(\dfrac{3x'-4y'}{5}\right)^2 + 24\left(\dfrac{3x'-4y'}{5}\right)\left(\dfrac{4x'+3y'}{5}\right) + 16\left(\dfrac{4x'+3y'}{5}\right)^2 + 90\left(\dfrac{3x'-4y'}{5}\right)$$

$$- 130\left(\dfrac{4x'+3y'}{5}\right) = 0$$

$$\dfrac{81(x')^2}{25} - \dfrac{216x'y'}{25} + \dfrac{144(y')^2}{25} + \dfrac{288(x')^2}{25} - \dfrac{168x'y'}{25} - \dfrac{288(y')^2}{25} + \dfrac{256(x')^2}{25} + \dfrac{384x'y'}{25}$$

$$+ \dfrac{144(y')^2}{25} + 54x' - 72y' - 104x' - 78y' = 0$$

$$25(x')^2 - 50x' - 150y' = 0$$

$$(x')^2 - 2x' + 1 = 6y' + 1$$

$$(x' - 1)^2 = 4\left(\dfrac{3}{2}\right)\left(y' + \dfrac{1}{6}\right)$$

13. $x^2 + xy + y^2 = 10$

$$\cot 2\theta = \frac{A - C}{B} = 0 \Rightarrow \theta = \frac{\pi}{4}$$

$$x = x' \cos\theta - y' \sin\theta = x'\left(\frac{\sqrt{2}}{2}\right) - y'\left(\frac{\sqrt{2}}{2}\right) = \frac{x' - y'}{\sqrt{2}}$$

$$y = x' \sin\theta + y' \cos\theta = x'\left(\frac{\sqrt{2}}{2}\right) + y'\left(\frac{\sqrt{2}}{2}\right) = \frac{x' + y'}{\sqrt{2}}$$

Substituting into the original equation,

$$\left(\frac{x' - y'}{\sqrt{2}}\right)^2 + \left(\frac{x' - y'}{\sqrt{2}}\right)\left(\frac{x' + y'}{\sqrt{2}}\right) + \left(\frac{x' + y'}{\sqrt{2}}\right)^2 = 10$$

$$\frac{1}{2}\left[3(x')^2 + (y')^2\right] = 10$$

$$\frac{(x')^2}{20/3} + \frac{(y')^2}{20} = 1 \quad \text{ellipse}$$

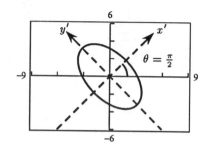

15. $17x^2 + 32xy - 7y^2 - 75 = 0$

$A = 17, \ B = 32, \ C = -7, \ D = 0, \ E = 0, \ F = -75$

$$\cot 2\theta = \frac{3}{4}, \ \cos 2\theta = \frac{3}{5}, \ \theta \approx 26.57°, \ \sin\theta = \frac{\sqrt{1 - (3/5)}}{\sqrt{2}} = \frac{\sqrt{2}}{\sqrt{10}}, \ \cos\theta = \frac{\sqrt{1 + (3/5)}}{\sqrt{2}} = 2\frac{\sqrt{2}}{\sqrt{10}}$$

$$A' = 17\left(\frac{8}{10}\right) + 32\left(\frac{2\sqrt{2}}{\sqrt{10}}\right)\left(\frac{\sqrt{2}}{\sqrt{10}}\right) - 7\left(\frac{2}{10}\right) = 25$$

$$C' = 17\left(\frac{2}{10}\right) - 32\left(\frac{2\sqrt{2}}{\sqrt{10}}\right)\left(\frac{\sqrt{2}}{\sqrt{10}}\right) - 7\left(\frac{8}{10}\right) = -15$$

$$D' = E' = 0$$

$$F' = -75$$

$$25(x')^2 - 15(y')^2 - 75 = 0 \quad \text{or} \quad \frac{(x')^2}{3} - \frac{(y')^2}{5} = 1$$

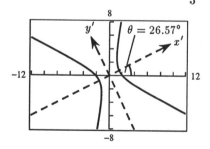

17. $32x^2 + 50xy + 7y^2 - 52 = 0$

$A = 32, \ B = 50, \ C = 7, \ D = 0, \ E = 0, \ F = -52$

$\cot 2\theta = \dfrac{1}{2}, \ \cos 2\theta = \dfrac{1}{\sqrt{5}}, \ \theta \approx 31.72°$

$\sin \theta = \dfrac{\sqrt{1 - (1/\sqrt{5})}}{\sqrt{2}} = \sqrt{\dfrac{\sqrt{5} - 1}{2\sqrt{5}}}$

$\cos \theta = \dfrac{\sqrt{1 + (1/\sqrt{5})}}{\sqrt{2}} = \sqrt{\dfrac{\sqrt{5} + 1}{2\sqrt{5}}}$

$A' = 32\left(\dfrac{\sqrt{5} + 1}{2\sqrt{5}}\right) + 50\sqrt{\dfrac{\sqrt{5} + 1}{2\sqrt{5}}}\left(\sqrt{\dfrac{\sqrt{5} - 1}{2\sqrt{5}}}\right) + 7\left(\dfrac{\sqrt{5} - 1}{2\sqrt{5}}\right) = \dfrac{39 + 25\sqrt{5}}{2} \approx 47.451$

$C' = 32\left(\dfrac{\sqrt{5} - 1}{2\sqrt{5}}\right) - 50\sqrt{\dfrac{\sqrt{5} - 1}{2\sqrt{5}}}\left(\sqrt{\dfrac{\sqrt{5} + 1}{2\sqrt{5}}}\right) + 7\left(\dfrac{\sqrt{5} + 1}{2\sqrt{5}}\right) = \dfrac{39 - 25\sqrt{5}}{2} \approx -8.451$

$D' = E' = 0$

$F' = -52$

$47.451(x')^2 - 8.451(y')^2 - 52 = 0 \ \text{ or } \ \dfrac{(x')^2}{1.096} - \dfrac{(y')^2}{6.153} = 1$

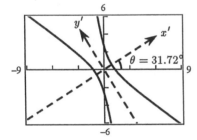

19. $B^2 - 4AC = (-24)^2 - 4(16)(9) = 0$

Parabola

21. $B^2 - 4AC = (-8)^2 - 4(13)(7) = -300$

Ellipse or circle

23. $B^2 - 4AC = (-6)^2 - 4(1)(-5) = 56$

Hyperbola

25. $B^2 - 4AC = (4)^2 - 4(1)(4) = 0$

Parabola

27. $-x^2 + y^2 + 4x - 6y + 4 = 0$

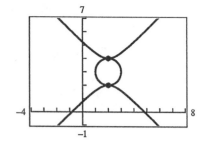

$x^2 + y^2 - 4x - 6y + 12 = 0$

Adding the two equations yields

$2y^2 - 12y + 16 = 0$

$y^2 - 6y + 8 = 0$

$(y - 4)(y - 2) = 0 \Rightarrow y = 2, \ 4$

When $y = 2$: $\quad x^2 + 4 - 4x - 12 + 12 = 0$

$x^2 - 4x + 4 = 0 \Rightarrow x = 2$

When $y = 4$: $\quad x^2 + 16 - 4x - 24 + 12 = 0$

$x^2 - 4x + 4 = 0 \Rightarrow x = 2$

Solutions: $(2, \ 2), \ (2, \ 4)$

29. $-4x^2 - y^2 - 32x + 24y - 64 = 0$

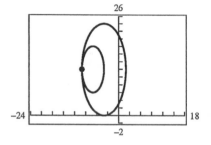

$4x^2 + y^2 + 56x - 24y + 304 = 0$

Adding the two equations yields

$24x + 240 = 0$

$x + 10 = 0 \Rightarrow x = -10$

$x = -10$: $\quad 4(100) + y^2 + 56(-10) - 24y + 304 = 0$

$y^2 - 24y + 144 = 0$

$(y - 12)^2 = 0 \Rightarrow y = 12$

Solution: $(-10, \ 12)$

31. $x^2 - y^2 - 12x + 12y - 36 = 0$

$x^2 + y^2 - 12x - 12y + 36 = 0$

Adding the two equations yields

$2x^2 - 24x = 0$

$x^2 - 12x = 0 \Rightarrow x = 0,\ 12$

When $x = 0$:

$y^2 - 12y + 36 = 0$

$(y - 6)^2 = 0 \Rightarrow y = 6$

When $x = 12$:

$144 + y^2 - 144 - 12y + 36 = 0$

$y^2 - 12y + 36 = 0$

$(y - 6)^2 = 0 \Rightarrow y = 6$

Solutions: $(0,\ 6),\ (12,\ 6)$

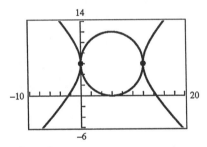

35. $x^2 + y^2 - 25 = 0$

$9x - 4y^2 = 0$

From the first equation, $y^2 = 25 - x^2$.

Substituting into the second equation,

$9x - 4(25 - x^2) = 0$

$4x^2 + 9x - 100 = 0$

$(4x + 25)(x - 4) = 0 \Rightarrow x = 4,\ \dfrac{-25}{4}$.

When $x = 4$, $y^2 = 25 - 4^2 = 9 \Rightarrow y = \pm 3$

When $x = \dfrac{-25}{4}$,

$y^2 = 25 - \left(\dfrac{-25}{4}\right)^2 = -14.0625$

no solution

Solutions: $(4,\ 3),\ (4,\ -3)$

33. $-16x^2 - y^2 + 24y - 80 = 0$

$16x^2 + 25y^2 - 400 = 0$

Adding the two equations yields

$24y^2 + 24y - 480 = 0$

$y^2 + y - 20 = 0$

$(y + 5)(y - 4) = 0 \Rightarrow y = 4,\ -5$

When $y = 4$:

$16x^2 + 25(4^2) - 400 = 0$

$16x^2 = 0 \Rightarrow x = 0$

When $y = -5$:

$16x^2 + 25(-5)^2 - 400 = 0$

$16x^2 + 225 = 0$

no solution

Solution: $(0,\ 4)$

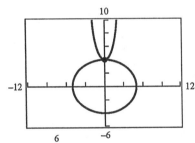

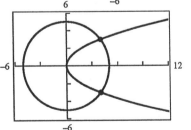

37. $x^2 + 2y^2 - 4x + 6y - 5 = 0$

$$x + y + 5 = 0$$

From the second equation, $y = -x - 5$. Substituting into the first equation,

$$x^2 + 2(-x - 5)^2 - 4x + 6(-x - 5) - 5 = 0$$

$$3x^2 + 10x + 15 = 0 \quad \text{no solution}$$

No solutions.

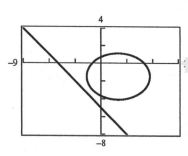

39. $xy + x - 2y + 3 = 0$

$$x^2 + 4y^2 - 9 = 0$$

From the first equation $xy - 2y = -x - 3$

$$y = \frac{x + 3}{2 - x}$$

Substituting into the second equation,

$$x^2 + 4\left(\frac{x + 3}{2 - x}\right)^2 - 9 = 0$$

$$x^2(2 - x)^2 + 4(x + 3)^2 - 9(2 - x)^2 = 0$$

$$x^4 - 4x^3 + 4x^2 + 4x^2 + 24x + 36 - 36 + 36x - 9x^2 = 0$$

$$x^4 - 4x^3 - x^2 + 60x = 0$$

$$x(x^3 - 4x^2 - x + 60) = 0$$

$$x(x + 3)(x^2 - 7x + 20) = 0 \Rightarrow x = 0, \ -3$$

When $x = 0, \quad y = \dfrac{3}{2}$

When $x = -3, \quad y = 0$

Solutions: $\left(0, \dfrac{3}{2}\right)$ and $(-3, \ 0)$

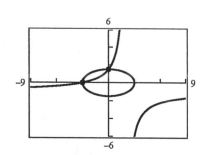

41. $(x')^2 + (y')^2 = (x \cos \theta + y \sin \theta)^2 + (y \cos \theta - x \sin \theta)^2$

$$= x^2 \cos^2 \theta + 2xy \cos \theta \sin \theta + y^2 \sin^2 \theta + y^2 \cos^2 \theta - 2xy \cos \theta \sin \theta + x^2 \sin^2 \theta$$

$$= x^2(\cos^2 \theta + \sin^2 \theta) + y^2(\sin^2 \theta + \cos^2 \theta) = x^2 + y^2 = r^2$$

Section 10.5   Plane Curves and Parametric Equations

■ If f and g are continuous functions of t on an interval I, then the set of ordered pairs $(f(t),\ g(t))$ is a *plane curve* C. The equations $x = f(t)$ and $y = g(t)$ are *parametric equations* for C and t is the *parameter*.

■ You should be able to graph plane curves with your graphing utility.

■ To eliminate the parameter:
   (a) Solve for t in one equation and substitute into the second equation.
   (b) Use trigonometric identities.

■ You should be able to find the parametric equations for a graph.

1. $x = t,\ y = -2t$

$y = -2x$

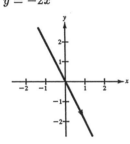

3. $x = 3t - 1,\ y = 2t + 1$

$y = 2\left(\dfrac{x+1}{3}\right) + 1$

$2x - 3y + 5 = 0$

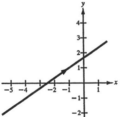

5. $x = \frac{1}{4}t,\ y = t^2$

$y = (4x)^2$

$y = 16x^2$

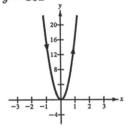

7. $x = t+1,\ y = t^2$
$y = (x-1)^2$

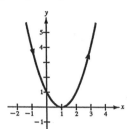

9. $x = t^3,\ y = \dfrac{t}{2}$

$y = \dfrac{1}{2}\sqrt[3]{x}$

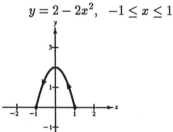

11. $x = 3\cos\theta \Rightarrow \left(\dfrac{x}{3}\right)^2 = \cos^2\theta$

$y = 3\sin\theta \Rightarrow \left(\dfrac{y}{3}\right)^2 = \sin^2\theta$

$\left(\dfrac{x}{3}\right)^2 + \left(\dfrac{y}{3}\right)^2 = 1$

$x^2 + y^2 = 9$

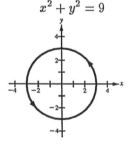

13. $x = \cos\theta \Rightarrow x^2 = \cos^2\theta$

$y = 2\sin^2\theta \Rightarrow \dfrac{y}{2} = \sin^2\theta$

$x^2 + \dfrac{y}{2} = 1$

$y = 2 - 2x^2,\quad -1 \le x \le 1$

15. $x = 4 + 2\cos\theta \Rightarrow \left(\dfrac{x-4}{2}\right)^2 = \cos^2\theta$

$y = -1 + 4\sin\theta \Rightarrow \left(\dfrac{y+1}{4}\right)^2 = \sin^2\theta$

$\left(\dfrac{x-4}{2}\right)^2 + \left(\dfrac{y+1}{4}\right)^2 = 1$

$\dfrac{(x-4)^2}{4} + \dfrac{(y+1)^2}{16} = 1$

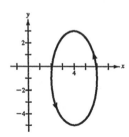

17. $x = e^{-t} \Rightarrow \dfrac{1}{x} = e^{t}$

$y = e^{3t} \Rightarrow y = (e^{t})^{3}$

$y = \left(\dfrac{1}{x}\right)^{3}$

$y = \dfrac{1}{x^{3}}, \quad x > 0, \; y > 0$

19. $x = t^{3} \Rightarrow x^{1/3} = t$

$y = 3 \ln t \Rightarrow y = \ln t^{3}$

$y = \ln(x^{1/3})^{3}$

$y = \ln x$

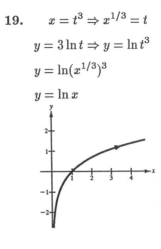

21. By eliminating the parameters in (a)–(d), we get $y = 2x + 1$. They differ from each other in restricted domain and in orientation.

(a) Domain: $-\infty < x < \infty$
    Orientation: up

(b) Domain: $-1 \le x \le 1$
    Orientation: Oscillates

(c) Domain: $0 < x < \infty$
    Orientation: Down

(d) Domain: $0 < x < \infty$
    Orientation: Up

23. $x = x_1 + t(x_2 - x_1)$

$y = y_1 + t(y_2 - y_1)$

$\dfrac{x - x_1}{x_2 - x_1} = t$

$y = y_1 + \left(\dfrac{x - x_1}{x_2 - x_1}\right)(y_2 - y_1)$

$y - y_1 = \dfrac{y_2 - y_1}{x_2 - x_1}(x - x_1)$

Notice that this is the point-slope form of the line.

25. $x = h + a \cos \theta$

$y = k + b \sin \theta$

$\dfrac{x - h}{a} = \cos \theta, \quad \dfrac{y - k}{b} = \sin \theta$

$\dfrac{(x - h)^{2}}{a^{2}} + \dfrac{(y - k)^{2}}{b^{2}} = 1$

27. From Exercise 23:

$x = 5t$

$y = -2t$

Solution not unique

29. From Exercise 24:

$x = 2 + 4\cos\theta$

$y = 1 + 4\sin\theta$

Solution not unique

31. From Exercise 25:

$a = 5$, $c = 4$, and hence, $b = 3$.

$x = 5\cos\theta$

$y = 3\sin\theta$

Center: $(0, 0)$

Solution not unique

33. From Exercise 26:

$a = 4$, $c = 5$, and hence, $b = 3$.

$x = 4\sec\theta$

$y = 3\tan\theta$

Center: $(0, 0)$

Solution not unique

35. $y = x^3$

Examples

$x = t, \quad y = t^3$

$x = \sqrt[3]{t}, \quad y = t$

$x = \tan t, \quad y = \tan^3 t$

37. $x = 2(\theta - \sin\theta)$

$y = 2(1 - \cos\theta)$

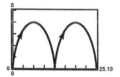

39. $x = \theta - \frac{3}{2}\sin\theta, \quad y = 1 - \frac{3}{2}\cos\theta$

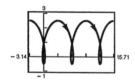

41. $x = 2\cot\theta, \quad y = 2\sin^2\theta$

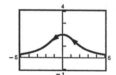

43. $x = 4\cos\theta, \quad y = 2\sin 2\theta$

θ	0	$\pi/2$	π	$3\pi/2$	2π
x	4	0	-4	0	4
y	0	0	0	0	0

Matches graph (b).

45. $x = \cos\theta + \theta\sin\theta, \quad y = \sin\theta - \theta\cos\theta$

θ	0	$\pi/2$	π	$3\pi/2$	2π
x	1	$\pi/2$	-1	$-3\pi/2$	1
y	0	1	π	-1	-2π

Matches graph (d).

47. When the circle has rolled θ radians, the center is at $(a\theta,\ a)$.

$$\sin\theta = \sin(180° - \theta)$$

$$= \frac{|AC|}{b} = \frac{|BD|}{b} \Rightarrow |BD| = b\sin\theta$$

$$\cos\theta = -\cos(180° - \theta)$$

$$= \frac{|AP|}{-b} \Rightarrow |AP| = -b\cos\theta$$

Therefore, $x = a\theta - b\sin\theta$ and $y = a - b\cos\theta$.

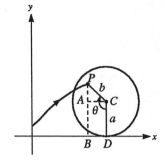

Section 10.6   Polar Coordinates

- ■ The polar coordinates (r, θ) of a point P in the plane are as follows:
  (a) r is the directed distance from the origin to P.
  (b) θ is the directed angle, counterclockwise from the x-axis to the segment joining the origin to P.

- ■ You should be able to plot points in the polar coordinate system.

- ■ The polar coordinates (r, θ) are related to the rectangular coordinates (x, y) as follows:
$$x = r \cos \theta \quad \text{and} \quad \tan \theta = \frac{x}{y}$$
$$y = r \sin \theta \quad \text{and} \quad r^2 = x^2 + Y^2$$

- ■ You should be able to convert from polar coordinates to rectangular coordinates, and vice-versa.

- ■ You should be able to convert polar equations to rectangular equations.

1. Polar coordinates: $\left(4, \dfrac{3\pi}{6}\right)$

$$x = 4 \cos \left(\frac{3\pi}{6}\right) = 0$$

$$y = 4 \sin \left(\frac{3\pi}{6}\right) = 4$$

Rectangular coordinates: $(0, 4)$

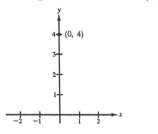

3. Polar coordinates: $\left(-1, \dfrac{5\pi}{4}\right)$

$$x = -1 \cos \left(\frac{5\pi}{4}\right) = \frac{\sqrt{2}}{2}$$

$$y = -1 \sin \left(\frac{5\pi}{4}\right) = \frac{\sqrt{2}}{2}$$

Rectangular coordinates: $\left(\dfrac{\sqrt{2}}{2}, \dfrac{\sqrt{2}}{2}\right)$

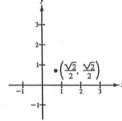

5. Polar coordinates: $\left(4, -\dfrac{\pi}{3}\right)$

$x = 4\cos\left(-\dfrac{\pi}{3}\right) = 2$

$y = 4\sin\left(-\dfrac{\pi}{3}\right) = -2\sqrt{3}$

Rectangular coordinates: $(2, -2\sqrt{3})$

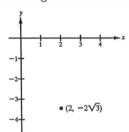

7. Polar coordinates: $\left(0, -\dfrac{7\pi}{6}\right)$

$x = 0\cos\left(-\dfrac{7\pi}{6}\right) = 0$

$y = 0\sin\left(-\dfrac{7\pi}{6}\right) = 0$

Rectangular coordinates: $(0, 0)$

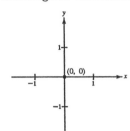

9. Polar coordinates: $(\sqrt{2}, 2.36)$

$x = \sqrt{2}\cos(2.36) \approx -1.004$

$y = \sqrt{2}\sin(2.36) \approx 0.996$

Rectangular coordinates: $(-1.004, 0.996)$

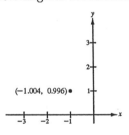

11. Rectangular coordinates: $(1, 1)$

$r = \sqrt{2}, \quad \tan\theta = 1, \quad \theta = \dfrac{\pi}{4}$

Polar coordinates:

$\left(\sqrt{2}, \dfrac{\pi}{4}\right), \left(-\sqrt{2}, \dfrac{5\pi}{4}\right)$

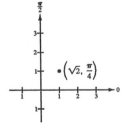

13. Rectangular coordinates: $(-6, 0)$

$r = 6, \ \tan \theta = 0, \ \theta = 0$

Polar coordinates: $(6, \pi), \ (-6, 0)$

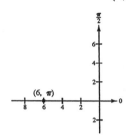

15. Rectangular coordinates: $(-3, 4)$

$r = \sqrt{9 + 16} = 5, \quad \tan \theta = -\frac{4}{3}, \quad \theta \approx 2.214$

Polar coordinates: $(5, 2.214), \ (-5, 5.356)$

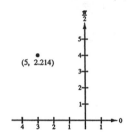

17. Rectangular coordinates: $(-\sqrt{3}, -\sqrt{3})$

$r = \sqrt{3 + 3} = \sqrt{6}, \quad \tan \theta = 1, \quad \theta = \dfrac{\pi}{4}$

Polar coordinates:

$\left(\sqrt{6}, \dfrac{5\pi}{4}\right), \ \left(-\sqrt{6}, \dfrac{\pi}{4}\right)$

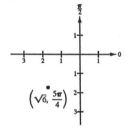

19. Rectangular coordinates: $(4, 6)$

$r = \sqrt{16 + 36} = 2\sqrt{13}$

$\tan \theta = \dfrac{3}{2}, \quad \theta \approx 0.983$

Polar coordinates:

$(2\sqrt{13}, 0.983), \ (-2\sqrt{13}, 4.124)$

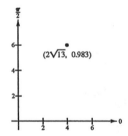

21. $x^2 + y^2 = 9$

$r = 3$

23. $x^2 + y^2 - 2ax = 0$

$r^2 - 2ar \cos \theta = 0$

$r(r - 2a \cos \theta) = 0$

$r = 2a \cos \theta$

25. $y = 4$

$r \sin \theta = 4$

$r = 4 \csc \theta$

27.

$$x = 10$$

$$r \cos \theta = 10$$

$$r = 10 \sec \theta$$

29.

$$3x - y + 2 = 0$$

$$3r \cos \theta - r \sin \theta + 2 = 0$$

$$r(3 \cos \theta - \sin \theta) = -2$$

$$r = \frac{-2}{3 \cos \theta - \sin \theta}$$

31.

$$xy = 4$$

$$(r \cos \theta)(r \sin \theta) = 4$$

$$r^2 = 4 \sec \theta \csc \theta = 8 \csc 2\theta$$

33.

$$(x^2 + y^2)^2 - 9(x^2 - y^2) = 0$$

$$(r^2)^2 - 9(r^2 \cos^2 \theta - r^2 \sin^2 \theta) = 0$$

$$r^2[r^2 - 9(\cos 2\theta)] = 0$$

$$r^2 = 9 \cos 2\theta$$

35.

$$r = 4 \sin \theta$$

$$r^2 = 4r \sin \theta$$

$$x^2 + y^2 = 4y$$

$$x^2 + y^2 - 4y = 0$$

37.

$$\theta = \frac{\pi}{6}$$

$$\tan \theta = \frac{\sqrt{3}}{3}$$

$$\frac{y}{x} = \frac{\sqrt{3}}{3}$$

$$y = \frac{\sqrt{3}}{3} x$$

$$\sqrt{3}\, x - 3y = 0$$

39.

$$r = 2 \csc \theta$$

$$r \sin \theta = 2$$

$$y = 2$$

41.

$$r = 2 \sin 3\theta$$

$$r = 2(3 \sin \theta - 4 \sin^3 \theta)$$

$$r^4 = 6r^3 \sin \theta - 8r^3 \sin^3 \theta$$

$$(x^2 + y^2)^2 = 6(x^2 + y^2)y - 8y^3$$

$$(x^2 + y^2)^2 = 6x^2 y - 2y^3$$

43.

$$r = \frac{6}{2 - 3 \sin \theta}$$

$$r(2 - 3 \sin \theta) = 6$$

$$2r = 6 + 3r \sin \theta$$

$$2(\pm\sqrt{x^2 + y^2}) = 6 + 3y$$

$$4(x^2 + y^2) = (6 + 3y)^2$$

$$4x^2 + 4y^2 = 36 + 36y + 9y^2$$

$$4x^2 - 5y^2 - 36y - 36 = 0$$

45. $r = 3$

$r^2 = 9$

$x^2 + y^2 = 9$

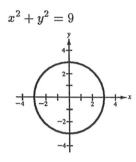

47. $\theta = \dfrac{\pi}{4}$

$\tan \theta = \tan \dfrac{\pi}{4}$

$\dfrac{y}{x} = 1$

$y = x$

$x - y = 0$

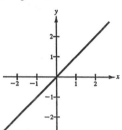

49. $r = 3 \sec \theta$

$r \cos \theta = 3$

$x = 3$

$x - 3 = 0$

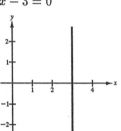

51. $(r_1,\ \theta_1) = (x_1,\ y_1)$ where $x_1 = r_1 \cos \theta_1$ and $y_1 = r_1 \sin \theta_1$.

$(r_2,\ \theta_2) = (x_2,\ y_2)$ where $x_2 = r_2 \cos \theta_2$ and $y_2 = r_2 \sin \theta_2$.

Then $x_1^2 + y_1^2 = r_1^2 \cos^2 \theta_1 + r_1^2 \sin^2 \theta_1 = r_1^2$ and $x_2^2 + y_2^2 = r_2^2$. Thus,

$$
\begin{aligned}
d &= \sqrt{(x_1 - x_2)^2 + (y_1 - y_2)^2} \\
&= \sqrt{x_1^2 - 2x_1 x_2 + x_2^2 + y_1^2 - 2y_1 y_2 + y_2^2} \\
&= \sqrt{(x_1^2 + y_1^2) + (x_2^2 + y_2^2) - 2(x_1 x_2 + y_1 y_2)} \\
&= \sqrt{r_1^2 + r_2^2 - 2(r_1 r_2 \cos \theta_1 \cos \theta_2 + r_1 r_2 \sin \theta_1 \sin \theta_2)} \\
&= \sqrt{r_1^2 + r_2^2 - 2 r_1 r_2 \cos(\theta_1 - \theta_2)}.
\end{aligned}
$$

53.

$$r = 2(h \cos \theta + k \sin \theta)$$

$$r = 2 \left(h \left(\frac{x}{r} \right) + k \left(\frac{y}{r} \right) \right)$$

$$r = \frac{2hx + 2ky}{r}$$

$$r^2 = 2hx + 2ky$$

$$x^2 + y^2 = 2hx + 2ky$$

$$x^2 - 2hx + y^2 - 2ky = 0$$

$$(x^2 - 2hx + h^2) + (y^2 - 2ky + k^2) = h^2 + k^2$$

$$(x - h)^2 + (y - k)^2 = h^2 + k^2$$

Center: $(h, \ k)$

Radius: $\sqrt{h^2 + k^2}$

Section 10.7   Graphs of Polar Equations

■ You should be able to graph a polar equation by point-plotting.

■ You should be able to graph a polar equation using a graphing utility. This might require expressing the polar equation $r = f(\theta)$ in the parametric form

$$x(t) = f(t) \cos t \qquad \text{and} \qquad y(t) = f(t) \sin t.$$

■ You should be able to test for symmetry in polar coordinates.
   (a) The line $\theta = \pi/2$: replace (r, θ) by $(r, \pi - \theta)$ or $(-r, \theta)$.
   (b) The polar axis: replace (r, θ) by $(r, -\theta)$ or $(-r, \pi - \theta)$.
   (c) The pole: replace (r, θ) by $(r, \pi + \theta)$ or $(-r, \theta)$.

■ You should be able to find the maximum r-values of a polar graph.

■ You should be familiar with the special polar graphs at the end of the section: Limacons, Rose curves, circles and lemniscates.

---

1. $r = 10 + 6 \cos \theta$

$\theta = \dfrac{\pi}{2}$: $-r = 10 + 6 \cos(-\theta)$

$\qquad\qquad -r = 10 + 6 \cos \theta$

$\qquad\qquad$ Not an equivalent equation

Polar axis: $r = 10 + 6 \cos(-\theta)$

$\qquad\qquad r = 10 + 6 \cos \theta$

$\qquad\qquad$ Equivalent equation

Pole: $-r = 10 + 6 \cos \theta$

$\qquad\qquad$ Not an equivalent equation

Answer: **Symmetric with respect to polar axis**

3. $r = \dfrac{2}{1 + \sin\theta}$

$\theta = \dfrac{\pi}{2}$: $r = \dfrac{2}{1 + \sin(\pi - \theta)}$

$r = \dfrac{2}{1 + \sin\pi\cos\theta - \cos\pi\sin\theta}$

$r = \dfrac{2}{1 + \sin\theta}$

Equivalent equation

Polar axis: $r = \dfrac{2}{1 + \sin(-\theta)}$

$r = \dfrac{2}{1 - \sin\theta}$

Not an equivalent equation

Pole: $-r = \dfrac{2}{1 + \sin\theta}$

Not an equivalent equation

Answer: Symmetric with respect to $\theta = \pi/2$.

7. $|r| = |5\cos 3\theta| = 5|\cos 3\theta| \le 5$

$|\cos 3\theta| = 1$

$\cos 3\theta = \pm 1$

$\theta = 0, \dfrac{\pi}{3}, \dfrac{2\pi}{3}$

Maximum: $|r| = 5$ when $\theta = 0, \dfrac{\pi}{3}, \dfrac{2\pi}{3}$.

5. $r = 4\sec\theta\csc\theta$

$\theta = \dfrac{\pi}{2}$: $-r = 4\sec(-\theta)\csc(-\theta)$

$-r = -4\sec\theta\csc\theta$

$r = 4\sec\theta\csc\theta$

Equivalent equation

Polar axis: $-r = 4\sec(\pi - \theta)\csc(\pi - \theta)$

$-r = 4(-\sec\theta)\csc\theta$

$r = 4\sec\theta\csc\theta$

Equivalent equation

Pole: $r = 4\sec(\pi + \theta)\csc(\pi + \theta)$

$r = 4(-\sec\theta)(-\csc\theta)$

$r = 4\sec\theta\csc\theta$

Equivalent equation

Answer: Symmetric with respect to $\theta = \pi/2$, polar axis, and pole

9. $|r| = |10(1 - \sin\theta)|$

$= 10|1 - \sin\theta| \le 10(2) = 20$

$|1 - \sin\theta| = 2$

$1 - \sin\theta = 2$ or $1 - \sin\theta = -2$

$\sin\theta = -1$ $\sin\theta = 3$

$\theta = \dfrac{3\pi}{2}$ Not possible

Maximum: $|r| = 20$ when $\theta = \dfrac{3\pi}{2}$.

11. Circle: $r = 5$

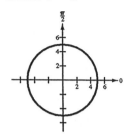

13.
$$\theta = \frac{\pi}{6}$$
$$\tan \theta = \tan \frac{\pi}{6}$$
$$\frac{y}{x} = \frac{1}{\sqrt{3}}$$
$$y = \frac{x}{\sqrt{3}} \Rightarrow \text{ Line}$$

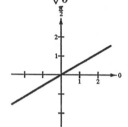

15. $r = 3 \sin \theta$

Symmetric with respect to $\theta = \pi/2$

Circle with a radius of $3/2$

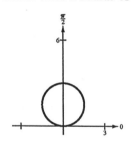

17. $r = 4 + 4 \sin \theta$

Symmetric with respect to $\theta = \frac{\pi}{2}$

$$\frac{a}{b} = \frac{4}{4} = 1 \Rightarrow \text{Cardioid}$$

$|r| = 8$ when $\theta = \frac{\pi}{2}$.

$r = 0$ when $\theta = \frac{3\pi}{2}$.

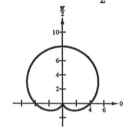

19. $r = 4 + 3\cos\theta$

Symmetric with respect to polar axis

$\dfrac{a}{b} = \dfrac{4}{3} > 1 \Rightarrow$ Dimpled limaçon

$|r| = 7$ when $\theta = 0$.

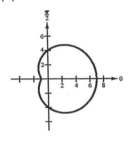

21. $r = 3 - 4\cos\theta$

Symmetric with respect to polar axis

$\dfrac{a}{b} = \dfrac{3}{4} < 1 \Rightarrow$ Limaçon with inner loop

$|r| = 7$ when $\theta = \pi$.

$r = 0$ when $\cos\theta = \dfrac{3}{4}$ or $\theta \approx 0.723,\ 5.560$.

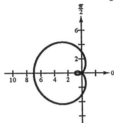

23. $r = 3\sin 2\theta$

Symmetric with respect to $\theta = \dfrac{\pi}{2}$,

polar axis, and pole

Rose curve $(n = 2)$ with 4 petals

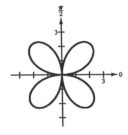

25.

$$r = \dfrac{3}{\sin\theta - 2\cos\theta}$$

$r(\sin\theta - 2\cos\theta) = 3$

$y - 2x = 3$

$y = 2x + 3 \Rightarrow$ Line

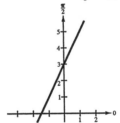

27. $r^2 = 4\cos 2\theta$

Symmetric with respect to polar axis

Lemniscate

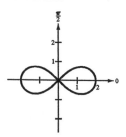

29. $r = \dfrac{\theta}{2}$

Symmetric with respect to $\theta = \dfrac{\pi}{2}$

and polar axis

Spiral

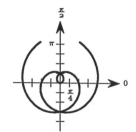

31.

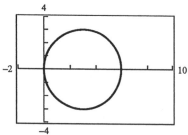

33.

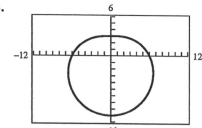

35.

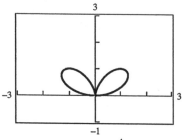

37.

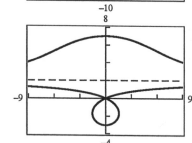

39.

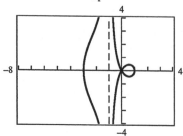

41.

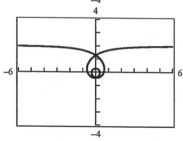

43.

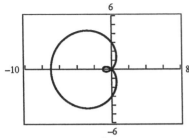

45.

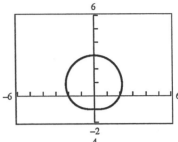

47.

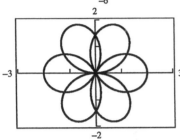

49.

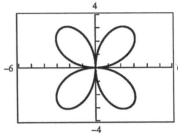

51.

$$r = 2 - \sec\theta = 2 - \frac{1}{\cos\theta}$$

$$r\cos\theta = 2\cos\theta - 1$$

$$r(r\cos\theta) = 2r\cos\theta - r$$

$$(\pm\sqrt{x^2 + y^2}\,)(x) = 2x - (\pm\sqrt{x^2 + y^2}\,)$$

$$(\pm\sqrt{x^2 + y^2}\,)(x + 1) = 2x$$

$$(\pm\sqrt{x^2 + y^2}\,) = \frac{2x}{x + 1}$$

$$x^2 + y^2 = \frac{4x^2}{(x + 1)^2}$$

$$y^2 = \frac{-x^2(x^2 + 2x - 3)}{(x + 1)^2}$$

$$y = \pm\sqrt{\frac{x^2(3 - 2x - x^2)}{(x + 1)^2}} = \pm\left|\frac{x}{x + 1}\right|\sqrt{3 - 2x - x^2}$$

The graph has an asymptote at $x = -1$.

53. The graph of $r = f(\theta)$ is rotated about the pole through an angle ϕ. Let $(r,\ \theta)$ be any point on the graph of $r = f(\theta)$. Then $(r,\ \theta + \phi)$ is rotated through the angle ϕ, and since

$$r = f((\theta + \phi) - \phi) = f(\theta),$$

it follows that $(r,\ \theta + \phi)$ is on the graph of $r = f(\theta - \phi)$.

55. (a) $r = 2 - \sin\left(\theta - \dfrac{\pi}{4}\right)$

$\qquad = 2 - \dfrac{\sqrt{2}}{2}(\sin\theta - \cos\theta)$

(c) $r = 2 - \sin\left(\theta - \pi\right)$

$\qquad = 2 + \sin\theta$

(b) $r = 2 - \sin\left(\theta - \dfrac{\pi}{2}\right)$

$\qquad = 2 + \cos\theta$

(d) $r = 2 - \sin\left(\theta - \dfrac{3\pi}{2}\right)$

$\qquad = 2 - \cos\theta$

57. (a) $r = 1 - \sin\theta$

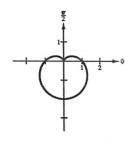

(b) $r = 1 - \sin\left(\theta - \dfrac{\pi}{4}\right)$

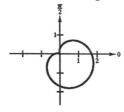

Section 10.8   Polar Equations of Conics

- The graph of a polar equation of the form

$$r = \frac{ep}{1 \pm e \cos \theta} \quad \text{or} \quad r = \frac{ep}{1 \pm e \sin \theta}$$

  is a conic, where $e > 0$ is the eccentricity and $|p|$ is the distance between the focus (pole) and the directrix.
  (a) If $e < 1$, the graph is an ellipse.
  (b) If $e = 1$, the graph is a parabola.
  (c) If $e > 1$, the graph is a hyperbola.

- Guidelines for finding polar equations of conics:

  (a) Horizontal directrix above the pole: $r = \dfrac{ep}{1 + e \sin \theta}$

  (b) Horizontal directrix below the pole: $r = \dfrac{ep}{1 - e \sin \theta}$

  (c) Vertical directrix to the right of the pole: $r = \dfrac{ep}{1 + e \cos \theta}$

  (d) Vertical directrix to the left of the pole: $r = \dfrac{ep}{1 - e \cos \theta}$

1. $r = \dfrac{6}{1 - \cos \theta} \Rightarrow e = 1$

Parabola with horizontal axis and vertex $(3, \pi)$

Matches graph (c)

3. $r = \dfrac{3}{1 - 2\sin \theta} \Rightarrow e = 2$

Hyperbola with vertical transverse axis

Vertices: $\left(-3, \dfrac{\pi}{2}\right), \left(1, \dfrac{3\pi}{2}\right)$

Matches graph (a)

5. $r = \dfrac{6}{2 - \sin\theta} \Rightarrow e = \dfrac{1}{2}$

Ellipse with vertical major axis

Vertices: $\left(6, \dfrac{\pi}{2}\right)$, $\left(2, \dfrac{3\pi}{2}\right)$

Matches graph (b)

7. $r = \dfrac{2}{1 - \cos\theta}$

$e = 1$ so the graph is a parabola.

Vertex: $(1, \pi)$

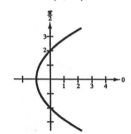

9. $r = \dfrac{5}{1 + \sin\theta}$

$e = 1$ so the graph is a parabola.

Vertex: $\left(\dfrac{5}{2}, \dfrac{\pi}{2}\right)$

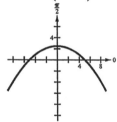

11. $r = \dfrac{2}{2 - \cos\theta} = \dfrac{1}{1 - (1/2)\cos\theta}$

$e = \dfrac{1}{2} < 1$, the graph is an ellipse.

Vertices: $(2, 0)$, $\left(\dfrac{2}{3}, \pi\right)$

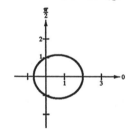

13. $r = \dfrac{4}{2 + \sin \theta} = \dfrac{2}{1 + (1/2) \sin \theta}$

$e = \frac{1}{2} < 1$, the graph is an ellipse.

Vertices: $\left(\dfrac{4}{3}, \dfrac{\pi}{2}\right)$, $\left(4, \dfrac{3\pi}{2}\right)$

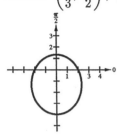

15. $r = \dfrac{3}{2 + 4 \sin \theta} = \dfrac{3/2}{1 + 2 \sin \theta}$

$e = 2 > 1$, the graph is a hyperbola.

Vertices: $\left(\dfrac{1}{2}, \dfrac{\pi}{2}\right)$, $\left(-\dfrac{3}{2}, \dfrac{3\pi}{2}\right)$

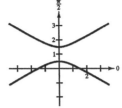

17. $r = \dfrac{3}{2 - 6 \cos \theta}$

$= \dfrac{3/2}{1 - 3 \cos \theta}$

$e = 3 > 1$, the graph is a hyperbola.

Vertices: $\left(-\frac{3}{4}, 0\right)$, $\left(\frac{3}{8}, \pi\right)$

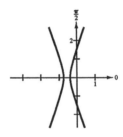

19. $e = 1$, $x = -1$, $p = 1$

Vertical directrix to the left of the pole

$r = \dfrac{1(1)}{1 - 1 \cos \theta} = \dfrac{1}{1 - \cos \theta}$

21. $e = \frac{1}{2}$, $y = 1$, $p = 1$

Horizontal directrix above the pole

$r = \dfrac{(1/2)(1)}{1 + (1/2) \sin \theta} = \dfrac{1}{2 + \sin \theta}$

23. $e = 2$, $x = 1$, $p = 1$

Vertical directrix to the right of the pole

$r = \dfrac{2(1)}{1 + 2 \cos \theta} = \dfrac{2}{1 + 2 \cos \theta}$

25. Vertex: $\left(1, -\dfrac{\pi}{2}\right) \Rightarrow e = 1$, $p = 2$

Horizontal directrix below the pole

$r = \dfrac{1(2)}{1 - 1 \sin \theta} = \dfrac{2}{1 - \sin \theta}$

27. Vertex: $(5, \pi) \Rightarrow e = 1$, $p = 10$

Vertical directrix to the left of the pole

$$r = \frac{1(10)}{1 - 1 \cos \theta} = \frac{10}{1 - \cos \theta}$$

29. Center: $(3, \pi)$; $c = 3$, $a = 5$, $e = \frac{3}{5}$

Vertical directrix to the right of the pole

$$r = \frac{(3/5)p}{1 + (3/5) \cos \theta} = \frac{3p}{5 + 3 \cos \theta}$$

$$2 = \frac{3p}{5 + 3 \cos 0}$$

$$p = \frac{16}{3}$$

$$r = \frac{3(16/3)}{5 + 3 \cos \theta} = \frac{16}{5 + 3 \cos \theta}$$

31. Center: $(8, 0)$; $c = 8$, $a = 12$, $e = \frac{2}{3}$

Vertical directrix to the left of the pole

$$r = \frac{(2/3)p}{1 - (2/3) \cos \theta} = \frac{2p}{3 - 2 \cos \theta}$$

$$20 = \frac{2p}{3 - 2 \cos 0}$$

$$p = 10$$

$$r = \frac{2(10)}{3 - 2 \cos \theta} = \frac{20}{3 - 2 \cos \theta}$$

33. Center: $\left(5, \frac{3\pi}{2}\right)$; $c = 5$, $a = 4$, $e = \frac{5}{4}$

Horizontal directrix below the pole

$$r = \frac{(5/4)p}{1 - (5/4) \sin \theta} = \frac{5p}{4 - 5 \sin \theta}$$

$$1 = \frac{5p}{4 - 5 \sin(3\pi/2)}$$

$$p = \frac{9}{5}$$

$$r = \frac{5(9/5)}{4 - 5 \sin \theta} = \frac{9}{4 - 5 \sin \theta}$$

35.

$$\frac{x^2}{a^2} + \frac{y^2}{b^2} = 1$$

$$\frac{r^2 \cos^2 \theta}{a^2} + \frac{r^2 \sin^2 \theta}{b^2} = 1$$

$$\frac{r^2 \cos^2 \theta}{a^2} + \frac{r^2(1 - \cos^2 \theta)}{b^2} = 1$$

$$r^2 b^2 \cos^2 \theta + r^2 a^2 - r^2 a^2 \cos^2 \theta = a^2 b^2$$

$$r^2(b^2 - a^2) \cos^2 \theta + r^2 a^2 = a^2 b^2$$

$$b^2 - a^2 = -c^2$$

$$-r^2 c^2 \cos^2 \theta + r^2 a^2 = a^2 b^2$$

$$-r^2 \left(\frac{c}{a}\right)^2 \cos^2 \theta + r^2 = b^2, \quad e = \frac{c}{a}$$

$$-r^2 e^2 \cos^2 \theta + r^2 = b^2$$

$$r^2(1 - e^2 \cos^2 \theta) = b^2$$

$$r^2 = \frac{b^2}{1 - e^2 \cos^2 \theta}$$

37. $\dfrac{x^2}{169} + \dfrac{y^2}{144} = 1$

$a = 13$, $b = 12$, $c = 5$, $e = \dfrac{5}{13}$

$$r^2 = \frac{144}{1 - (25/169) \cos^2 \theta}$$

$$= \frac{24{,}336}{169 - 25 \cos^2 \theta}$$

39. $\dfrac{x^2}{9} - \dfrac{y^2}{16} = 1$

$a = 3, \quad b = 4, \quad c = 5, \quad e = \dfrac{5}{3}$

$r^2 = \dfrac{-16}{1 - (25/9)\cos^2\theta} = \dfrac{144}{25\cos^2\theta - 9}$

41. Hyperbola

One focus: $(5, 0)$

Vertices: $(4, 0), \ (4, \pi)$

$a = 4, \ c = 5, \ b = 3, \ e = \dfrac{5}{4}$

$r^2 = \dfrac{-3^2}{1 - (5/4)^2\cos^2\theta}$

$= \dfrac{-144}{16 - 25\cos^2\theta} = \dfrac{144}{25\cos^2\theta - 16}$

43. $r = \dfrac{2}{1 - \cos[\theta - (\pi/4)]}$

45. When $\theta = 0, \quad r = c + a = ea + a = a(1+e)$.

Therefore,

$$a(1+e) = \dfrac{ep}{1 - e\cos 0}$$

$$a(1+e)(1-e) = ep$$

$$a(1 - e^2) = ep.$$

Thus, $r = \dfrac{ep}{1 - e\cos\theta} = \dfrac{(1 - e^2)a}{1 - e\cos\theta}$.

47. $r = \dfrac{[1 - (0.0167)^2](92.957 \times 10^6)}{1 - 0.0167\cos\theta}$

$\approx \dfrac{9.2931 \times 10^7}{1 - 0.0167\cos\theta}$

Perihelion distance:

$r = 92.957 \times 10^6(1 - 0.0167)$

$\approx 9.1405 \times 10^7$

Aphelion distance:

$r = 92.957 \times 10^6(1 + 0.0167)$

$\approx 9.4509 \times 10^7$

49. Directrix: $y = 8200, \ e = 1, \ p = 8200$

$$r = \dfrac{1(8200)}{1 + 1\sin\theta} = \dfrac{8200}{1 + \sin\theta}$$

Chapter 10   Review Exercises

1. $4x = y^2$
Parabola
Vertex: $(0, 0)$
Horizontal axis

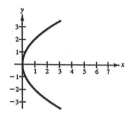

3. $x^2 - 6x + 2y + 9 = 0$
$$(x - 3)^2 = -2y$$
Parabola
Vertex: $(3, 0)$
Focus: $\left(3, -\frac{1}{2}\right)$

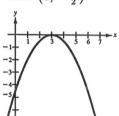

5.
$$x^2 + y^2 - 2x - 4y + 5 = 0$$
$$\left(x^2 - 2x + 1\right) + \left(y^2 - 4y + 4\right) = -5 + 1 + 4$$
$$(x - 1)^2 + (y - 2)^2 = 0$$
Point: $(1, 2)$
Note: This is a degenerate conic–a circle of radius zero.

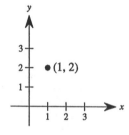

7. $4x^2 + y^2 = 16$

$$\frac{x^2}{4} + \frac{y^2}{16} = 1$$

Ellipse
Center: $(0, \ 0)$
Vertices: $(0, \ -4), \ (0, \ 4)$

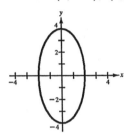

9. $x^2 + 9y^2 + 10x - 18y + 25 = 0$

$$(x + 5)^2 + 9(y - 1)^2 = 9$$

$$\frac{(x + 5)^2}{9} + (y - 1)^2 = 1$$

Ellipse
Center: $(-5, \ 1)$
Vertices: $(-8, \ 1), \ (-2, \ 1)$

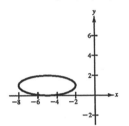

11. $5y^2 - 4x^2 = 20$

$$\frac{y^2}{4} - \frac{x^2}{5} = 1$$

Hyperbola
Vertical transverse axis
Center: $(0, \ 0)$
Vertices: $(0, \ \pm 2)$

Asymptotes: $y = \pm \dfrac{2\sqrt{5}}{5} x$

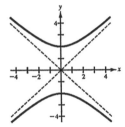

13. $\quad x^2 - 10xy + y^2 + 1 = 0$

$$y^2 - 10xy + (x^2 + 1) = 0$$

$$y = \frac{10x \pm \sqrt{100x^2 - 4(x^2 + 1)}}{2}$$

$$y = 5x + \sqrt{24x^2 - 1}$$

$$y = 5x - \sqrt{24x^2 - 1}$$

Hyperbola

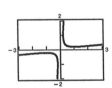

15. Vertical axis, $p = -2$

$(x - h)^2 = 4p(y - k)$

$(x - 4)^2 = 4(-2)(y - 2)$

$(x - 4)^2 = -8(y - 2)$

17. $(y - k)^2 = 4p(x - h)$

$(0 - 2)^2 = 4p(-1 - 0)$

$p = -1$

$(y - 2)^2 = 4(-1)(x - 0)$

$(y - 2)^2 = -4x$

19. Horizontal major axis
Center: $(2, 0)$
$a = 5, \ c = 2,$
$b = \sqrt{25 - 4} = \sqrt{21}$

$\dfrac{(x - h)^2}{a^2} + \dfrac{(y - k)^2}{b^2} = 1$

$\dfrac{(x - 2)^2}{25} + \dfrac{y^2}{21} = 1$

21. Vertical major axis
Center: $(0, 0)$
$a = 6$

$\dfrac{(x - h)^2}{b^2} + \dfrac{(y - k)^2}{a^2} = 1$

$\dfrac{(2 - 0)^2}{b^2} + \dfrac{(2 - 0)^2}{6^2} = 1$

$b^2 = \dfrac{9}{2}$

$\dfrac{2x^2}{9} + \dfrac{y^2}{36} = 1$

23. Vertical transverse axis
Center: $(0, 0)$
$a = 1, \ c = 3,$
$b = \sqrt{9 - 1} = \sqrt{8}$

$\dfrac{y^2}{1} - \dfrac{x^2}{8} = 1$

25. Horizontal transverse axis
Center: $(4, 0) \ \Rightarrow \ C = 4$

$\dfrac{b}{a} = 2 \ \Rightarrow \ b = 2a$

$a^2 + b^2 = c^2$

$a^2 + (2a)^2 = 4^2$

$a^2 = \dfrac{16}{5}$

$b^2 = \dfrac{64}{5}$

$\dfrac{(x - h)^2}{a^2} - \dfrac{(y - k)^2}{b^2} = 1$

$\dfrac{5(x - 4)^2}{16} - \dfrac{5y^2}{64} = 1$

27. $y = \dfrac{x^2}{200}, \quad 0 \le x \le 100$

Vertex: $(0, 0)$
$x^2 = 200y$
$4p = 200$
$p = 50$
Focus: $(0, 50)$

29. $x = 2t, \quad y = 4t$

$t = \dfrac{x}{2}$

$y = 4\left(\dfrac{x}{2}\right) = 2x$

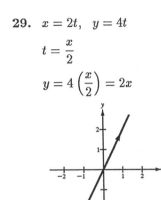

31. $x = 1 + 4t, \quad y = 2 - 3t$

$t = \dfrac{x - 1}{4}$

$y = 2 - 3\left(\dfrac{x - 1}{4}\right)$

$3x + 4y = 11$

33. $x = \dfrac{1}{t}, \quad y = t^2$

$t = \dfrac{1}{x}$

$y = \dfrac{1}{x^2}$

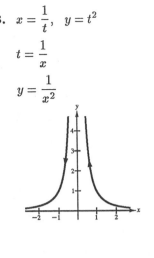

35. $x = 6\cos\theta, \quad y = 6\sin\theta$

$\cos\theta = \dfrac{x}{6}, \quad \sin\theta = \dfrac{y}{6}$

$\dfrac{x^2}{36} + \dfrac{y^2}{36} = 1$

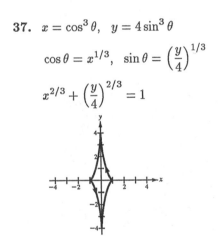

37. $x = \cos^3\theta, \quad y = 4\sin^3\theta$

$\cos\theta = x^{1/3}, \quad \sin\theta = \left(\dfrac{y}{4}\right)^{1/3}$

$x^{2/3} + \left(\dfrac{y}{4}\right)^{2/3} = 1$

39. $x = e^t, \quad y = e^{-t}$

   $t = \ln x$

   $y = e^{-\ln x}$

   $y = \dfrac{1}{e^{\ln x}} = \dfrac{1}{x}$

   $xy = 1, \quad x, \ y > 0$

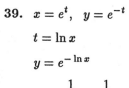

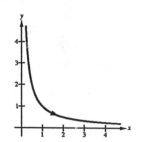

41. $r = 4$

   Circle of radius 4 centered at the pole

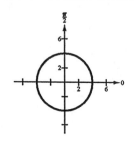

43. $r = 4 \sin 2\theta$

   Symmetric with respect to $\theta = \pi/2$,
   polar axis, and pole

   Rose curve $(n = 2)$ with 4 petals

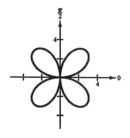

45. $r = -2 - 2 \cos \theta$

   Symmetric with respect to polar axis

   $\dfrac{a}{b} = \dfrac{2}{2} = 1 \Rightarrow$ Cardioid

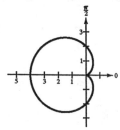

47. $r = 4 - 3 \cos \theta$

   Symmetric with respect to polar axis

   $\dfrac{a}{b} = \dfrac{4}{3} > 0 \Rightarrow$ Dimpled limaçon

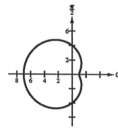

49. $r = -3\cos 3\theta$

Symmetric with respect to polar axis

Rose curve $(n = 3)$ with 3 petals

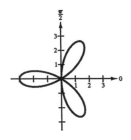

51. $r^2 = 4\sin 2\theta \Rightarrow r = \pm 2\sin 2\theta$

Symmetric with respect to pole

Lemniscate

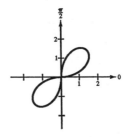

53.
$$r = \frac{3}{\cos(\theta - (\pi/4))}$$

$$r\cos\left(\theta - \frac{\pi}{4}\right) = 3$$

$$r\left[\frac{\sqrt{2}}{2}\cos\theta + \frac{\sqrt{2}}{2}\sin\theta\right] = 3$$

$$r\cos\theta + r\sin\theta = 3\sqrt{2}$$

$$x + y = 3\sqrt{2}$$

Line

55. $r = \dfrac{2}{1 - \sin\theta}$, $e = 1$

Parabola symmetric with
$\theta = \pi/2$ and the vertex at
$(1, 3\pi/2)$

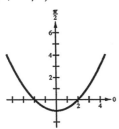

57.
$$r = 3\cos\theta$$
$$r^2 = 3r\cos\theta$$
$$x^2 + y^2 = 3x$$

59.
$$r = \frac{2}{1 + \sin\theta}$$
$$r + r\sin\theta = 2$$
$$r = 2 - r\sin\theta$$
$$r^2 = (2 - r\sin\theta)^2$$
$$x^2 + y^2 = (2 - y)^2$$
$$x^2 + y^2 = 4 - 4y + y^2$$
$$x^2 + 4y - 4 = 0$$

61.
$$r^2 = \cos 2\theta$$
$$r^2 = 1 - 2\sin^2\theta$$
$$r^4 = r^2 - 2r^2\sin^2\theta$$
$$(x^2 + y^2)^2 = x^2 + y^2 - 2y^2$$
$$(x^2 + y^2)^2 - x^2 + y^2 = 0$$

63. $(x^2 + y^2)^2 = ax^2 y$
$$(r^2)^2 = ar^2\cos^2\theta r\sin\theta$$
$$r = a\cos^2\theta\sin\theta$$

65. Circle symmetric to $\theta = \pi/2$
Center: $(5, \pi/2)$
Solution point:
  $(0, 0) \Rightarrow$ Radius $= 5 \Rightarrow a = 10$
$$r = a\sin\theta$$
$$r = 10\sin\theta$$

67. Parabola: $r = \dfrac{ep}{1 - e\cos\theta}$, $e = 1$
Vertex: $(2, \pi)$
Focus: $(0, 0) \Rightarrow p = 4$
$$r = \frac{4}{1 - \cos\theta}$$

69. Ellipse: $r = \dfrac{ep}{1 - e\cos\theta}$

Vertices: $(5, 0), (1, \pi) \Rightarrow a = 3$
One focus: $(0, 0) \Rightarrow c = 2$
$$e = \frac{c}{a} = \frac{2}{3}, \quad p = \frac{5}{2}$$
$$r = \frac{(2/3)(5/2)}{1 - (2/3)\cos\theta}$$
$$= \frac{5/3}{1 - (2/3)\cos\theta} = \frac{5}{3 - 2\cos\theta}$$

71. $\dfrac{(x+3)^2}{16} + \dfrac{(y-4)^2}{9} = 1$
$$x = -3 + 4\cos\theta$$
$$y = 4 + 3\sin\theta$$
This solution is not unique.

73. $x = a(\theta - \sin\theta)$, $\quad y = a(1 - \cos\theta)$
$$\cos\theta = 1 - \frac{y}{a}$$
$$\theta = \arccos\left(1 - \frac{y}{a}\right) = \arccos\left(\frac{a-y}{a}\right)$$
$$\sin\theta = \pm\sqrt{1 - \cos^2\theta} = \pm\sqrt{1 - \left(1 - \frac{y}{a}\right)^2}$$
$$= \pm\sqrt{\frac{2y}{a} - \frac{y^2}{a^2}} = \pm\frac{1}{a}\sqrt{2ay - y^2}$$
$$x = a\left[\arccos\left(\frac{a-y}{a}\right) \pm \frac{1}{a}\sqrt{2ay - y^2}\right]$$
$$x = a\arccos\left(\frac{a-y}{a}\right) \pm \sqrt{2ay - y^2}$$

75. $x = 2(\cos\theta + \theta\sin\theta)$
$y = 2(\sin\theta - \theta\cos\theta)$

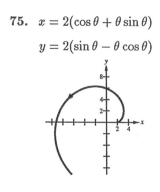

CHAPTER 11

Vectors in the Plane and in Space

Section 11.1   Vectors in the Plane

- A vector, $\mathbf{v}$, is the collection of all directed line segments that are equivalent to a given directed line segment $\overrightarrow{PQ}$.

- You should be able to *geometrically* perform the operations of vector addition and scalar multiplication.

- The component form of the vector with initial point $P = (p_1, \ p_2)$ and terminal point $Q = (q_1, \ q_2)$ is $\overrightarrow{PQ} = \langle q_1 - p_1, \ q_2 - p_2 \rangle = \langle v_1, \ v_2 \rangle = \mathbf{v}$.

- The magnitude of $\mathbf{v} = \langle v_1, \ v_2 \rangle$ is given by $\|\mathbf{v}\| = \sqrt{v_1{}^2 + v_2{}^2}$.

- You should be able to perform the operations of scalar multiplication and vector addition in component form.

- You should know the following properties of vector addition and scalar multiplication.
  (a) $\mathbf{u} + \mathbf{v} = \mathbf{v} + \mathbf{u}$ \qquad\qquad\qquad\qquad (b) $(\mathbf{u} + \mathbf{v}) + \mathbf{w} = \mathbf{u} + (\mathbf{v} + \mathbf{w})$
  (c) $\mathbf{u} + \mathbf{O} = \mathbf{u}$ \qquad\qquad\qquad\qquad\quad (d) $\mathbf{u} + (-\mathbf{u}) = \mathbf{O}$
  ($\mathbf{O}$ is the zero vector.)
  (e) $c(d\mathbf{u}) = (cd)\mathbf{u}$ \qquad\qquad\qquad\qquad (f) $(c + d)\mathbf{u} = c\mathbf{u} + d\mathbf{u}$
  (g) $c(\mathbf{u} + \mathbf{v}) = c\mathbf{u} + c\mathbf{v}$ \qquad\qquad\quad (h) $1(\mathbf{u}) = \mathbf{u}, \ 0\mathbf{u} = \mathbf{O}$
  (i) $\|c\mathbf{v}\| = |c| \, \|\mathbf{v}\|$

- A unit vector in the direction of $\mathbf{v}$ is given by $\mathbf{u} = \dfrac{\mathbf{v}}{\|\mathbf{v}\|}$.

- The standard unit vectors are $\mathbf{i} = \langle 1, \ 0 \rangle$ and $\mathbf{j} = \langle 0, \ 1 \rangle$. $\mathbf{v} = \langle v_1, \ v_2 \rangle$ can be written as $\mathbf{v} = v_1 \mathbf{i} + v_2 \mathbf{j}$.

- A vector, $\mathbf{v}$, with magnitude $\|\mathbf{v}\|$ and direction θ can be written as $\mathbf{v} = a\mathbf{i} + b\mathbf{j} = \|\mathbf{v}\|(\cos\theta)\mathbf{i} + \|\mathbf{v}\|(\sin\theta)\mathbf{j}$ where $\tan\theta = b/a$.

1. −u

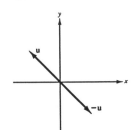

3. u + v

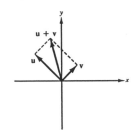

5. u − v

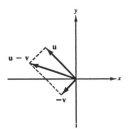

7. Initial point: $(0, 0)$
Terminal point: $(3, 4)$
$\mathbf{v} = \langle 3 - 0,\ 4 - 0 \rangle = \langle 3,\ 4 \rangle$
$\|\mathbf{v}\| = \sqrt{3^2 + 4^2} = 5$

9. Initial point: $(2, 1)$
Terminal point: $(-1, 3)$
$\mathbf{v} = \langle -1 - 2,\ 3 - 1 \rangle = \langle -3,\ 2 \rangle$
$\|\mathbf{v}\| = \sqrt{(-3)^2 + 2^2} = \sqrt{13}$

11. Initial point: $(2, -2)$
Terminal point: $(2, 3)$
$\mathbf{v} = \langle 2 - 2,\ 3 - (-2) \rangle = \langle 0,\ 5 \rangle$
$\|\mathbf{v}\| = \sqrt{0^2 + 5^2} = 5$

13. Initial point: $(-1, 5)$
Terminal point: $(15, 2)$
$\mathbf{v} = \langle 15 - (-1),\ 2 - 5 \rangle = \langle 16,\ -3 \rangle$
$\|\mathbf{v}\| = \sqrt{16^2 + (-3)^2} = \sqrt{265}$

15. Initial point: $(-3, -5)$
Terminal point: $(5, -1)$
$\mathbf{v} = \langle 5 - (-3),\ -1 - (-5) \rangle = \langle 8,\ 4 \rangle$
$\|\mathbf{v}\| = \sqrt{8^2 + 4^2} = 4\sqrt{5}$

17. $\mathbf{u} = \langle 1,\ 2 \rangle$, $\mathbf{v} = \langle 3,\ 1 \rangle$
(a) $\mathbf{u} + \mathbf{v} = \langle 4,\ 3 \rangle$
(b) $\mathbf{u} - \mathbf{v} = \langle -2,\ 1 \rangle$
(c) $2\mathbf{u} - 3\mathbf{v} = \langle -7,\ 1 \rangle$

19. $\mathbf{u} = \langle -2,\ 3 \rangle$, $\mathbf{v} = \langle -2,\ 1 \rangle$
(a) $\mathbf{u} + \mathbf{v} = \langle -4,\ 4 \rangle$
(b) $\mathbf{u} - \mathbf{v} = \langle 0,\ 2 \rangle$
(c) $2\mathbf{u} - 3\mathbf{v} = \langle 2,\ 3 \rangle$

21. $\mathbf{u} = \langle 4,\ -2 \rangle$, $\mathbf{v} = \langle 0,\ 0 \rangle$
(a) $\mathbf{u} + \mathbf{v} = \langle 4,\ -2 \rangle$
(b) $\mathbf{u} - \mathbf{v} = \langle 4,\ -2 \rangle$
(c) $2\mathbf{u} - 3\mathbf{v} = \langle 8,\ -4 \rangle$

23. $\mathbf{u} = \mathbf{i} + \mathbf{j}$, $\mathbf{v} = 2\mathbf{i} - 3\mathbf{j}$
(a) $\mathbf{u} + \mathbf{v} = 3\mathbf{i} - 2\mathbf{j}$
(b) $\mathbf{u} - \mathbf{v} = -\mathbf{i} + 4\mathbf{j}$
(c) $2\mathbf{u} - 3\mathbf{v} = -4\mathbf{i} + 11\mathbf{j}$

25. $\mathbf{u} = 2\mathbf{i}$, $\mathbf{v} = \mathbf{j}$
(a) $\mathbf{u} + \mathbf{v} = 2\mathbf{i} + \mathbf{j}$
(b) $\mathbf{u} - \mathbf{v} = 2\mathbf{i} - \mathbf{j}$
(c) $2\mathbf{u} - 3\mathbf{v} = 4\mathbf{i} - 3\mathbf{j}$

27. $\|\mathbf{v}\| = 5$, $\theta = 30°$

29. $\|\mathbf{v}\| = \sqrt{6^2 + (-6)^2} = \sqrt{72} = 6\sqrt{2}$

$$\tan \theta = \frac{-6}{6} = -1$$

Since $\mathbf{v}$ lies in Quadrant IV, $\theta = 315°$.

31. $\mathbf{v} = \langle 3\cos 0°, \ 3\sin 0° \rangle$

$= \langle 3, \ 0 \rangle$

33. $\mathbf{v} = \langle \cos 150°, \ \sin 150° \rangle$

$= \left\langle -\dfrac{\sqrt{3}}{2}, \ \dfrac{1}{2} \right\rangle$

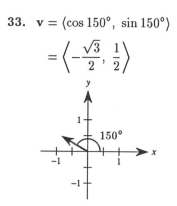

35. $\mathbf{v} = \langle 3\sqrt{2} \cos 150°, \ 3\sqrt{2} \sin 150° \rangle$

$= \left\langle -\dfrac{3\sqrt{6}}{2}, \ \dfrac{3\sqrt{2}}{2} \right\rangle$

37. $\mathbf{v} = 2 \left(\dfrac{1}{\sqrt{3^2 + 1^2}} \right) (\mathbf{i} + 3\mathbf{j})$

$= \dfrac{2}{\sqrt{10}} (\mathbf{i} + 3\mathbf{j})$

$= \dfrac{\sqrt{10}}{5} \mathbf{i} + \dfrac{3\sqrt{10}}{5} \mathbf{j}$

39. $\mathbf{v} = \frac{3}{2}\mathbf{u}$

$= \frac{3}{2}(2\mathbf{i} - \mathbf{j})$

$= 3\mathbf{i} - \frac{3}{2}\mathbf{j}$

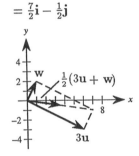

41. $\mathbf{v} = \mathbf{u} + 2\mathbf{w}$

$= (2\mathbf{i} - \mathbf{j}) + 2(\mathbf{i} + 2\mathbf{j})$

$= 4\mathbf{i} + 3\mathbf{j}$

43. $\mathbf{v} = \frac{1}{2}(3\mathbf{u} + \mathbf{w})$

$= \frac{1}{2}(6\mathbf{i} - 3\mathbf{j} + \mathbf{i} + 2\mathbf{j})$

$= \frac{7}{2}\mathbf{i} - \frac{1}{2}\mathbf{j}$

45. $\mathbf{u} = \langle 5\cos 0°,\ 5\sin 0°\rangle = \langle 5,\ 0\rangle$

$\mathbf{v} = \langle 5\cos 90°,\ 5\sin 90°\rangle = \langle 0,\ 5\rangle$

$\mathbf{u} + \mathbf{v} = \langle 5,\ 5\rangle$

47. $\mathbf{u} = \langle 20\cos 45°,\ 20\sin 45°\rangle$

$= \langle 10\sqrt{2},\ 10\sqrt{2}\rangle$

$\mathbf{v} = \langle 50\cos 180°,\ 50\sin 180°\rangle$

$= \langle -50,\ 0\rangle$

$\mathbf{u} + \mathbf{v} = \langle 10\sqrt{2} - 50,\ 10\sqrt{2}\rangle$

49. $\mathbf{u} = \dfrac{1}{\|\mathbf{v}\|}\mathbf{v}$

$= \dfrac{1}{\sqrt{16 + 9}}(4\mathbf{i} - 3\mathbf{j})$

$= \dfrac{1}{5}(4\mathbf{i} - 3\mathbf{j}) = \dfrac{4}{5}\mathbf{i} - \dfrac{3}{5}\mathbf{j}$

51. $\mathbf{u} = \dfrac{1}{\|\mathbf{v}\|}\mathbf{v} = \dfrac{1}{2}(2\mathbf{j}) = \mathbf{j}$

53. $\quad \mathbf{v} = \mathbf{i} + \mathbf{j}$

$\quad\quad \mathbf{w} = 2(\mathbf{i} - \mathbf{j})$

$\quad\quad \mathbf{u} = \mathbf{v} - \mathbf{w} = -\mathbf{i} + 3\mathbf{j}$

$\quad\quad \|\mathbf{v}\| = \sqrt{2}$

$\quad\quad \|\mathbf{w}\| = 2\sqrt{2}$

$\quad\quad \|\mathbf{v} - \mathbf{w}\| = \sqrt{10}$

$\quad\quad \cos\alpha = \dfrac{\|\mathbf{v}\|^2 + \|\mathbf{w}\|^2 - \|\mathbf{v} - \mathbf{w}\|^2}{2\|\mathbf{v}\|\,\|\mathbf{w}\|} = \dfrac{2 + 8 - 10}{2\sqrt{2} \cdot 2\sqrt{2}} = 0$

$\quad\quad \alpha = 90°$

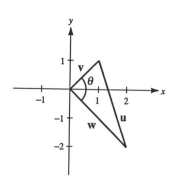

55. $\quad \mathbf{v} = \mathbf{i} + \mathbf{j}$

$\quad\quad \mathbf{w} = 3\mathbf{i} - \mathbf{j}$

$\quad\quad \mathbf{u} = \mathbf{v} - \mathbf{w} = -2\mathbf{i} + 2\mathbf{j}$

$\quad\quad \cos\theta = \dfrac{\|\mathbf{v}\|^2 + \|\mathbf{w}\|^2 - \|\mathbf{v} - \mathbf{w}\|^2}{2\|\mathbf{v}\|\,\|\mathbf{w}\|} = \dfrac{2 + 10 - 8}{2\sqrt{2}\sqrt{10}} \approx 0.4472$

$\quad\quad \theta \approx 63.4°$

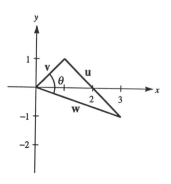

57. Force One: $\mathbf{u} = 45\mathbf{i}$

$\quad\quad$ Force Two: $\mathbf{v} = 60\cos\theta\,\mathbf{i} + 60\sin\theta\,\mathbf{j}$

$\quad\quad$ Resultant Force: $\mathbf{u} + \mathbf{v} = (45 + 60\cos\theta)\mathbf{i} + 60\sin\theta\,\mathbf{j}$

$\quad\quad \|\mathbf{u} + \mathbf{v}\| = \sqrt{(45 + 60\cos\theta)^2 + (60\sin\theta)^2} = 90$

$$2025 + 5400\cos\theta + 3600 = 8100$$

$$5400\cos\theta = 2475$$

$$\cos\theta = \frac{2475}{5400} \approx 0.4583$$

$$\theta \approx 62.7°$$

59. $\mathbf{u} = 50\mathbf{i}$

$$\mathbf{v} = 35\left(\frac{\sqrt{3}}{2}\mathbf{i} + \frac{1}{2}\mathbf{j}\right) = \frac{35\sqrt{3}}{2}\mathbf{i} + \frac{35}{2}\mathbf{j}$$

$$\mathbf{u} + \mathbf{v} = \left(50 + \frac{35\sqrt{3}}{2}\right)\mathbf{i} + \frac{35}{2}\mathbf{j}$$

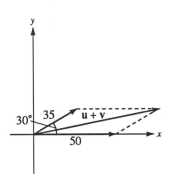

$$\|\mathbf{u} + \mathbf{v}\| = \sqrt{\left(50 + \frac{35\sqrt{3}}{2}\right)^2 + \left(\frac{35}{2}\right)^2} \approx 82.2 \text{ pounds}$$

$$\tan\theta = \frac{35/2}{(100 + 35\sqrt{3})/2} = \frac{35}{100 + 35\sqrt{3}}$$

$$\theta \approx 12.3°$$

61.
$$\mathbf{u} = (75\cos 30°)\mathbf{i} + (75\sin 30°)\mathbf{j} \approx 64.95\mathbf{i} + 37.5\mathbf{j}$$
$$\mathbf{v} = (100\cos 45°)\mathbf{i} + (100\sin 45°)\mathbf{j} \approx 70.71\mathbf{i} + 70.71\mathbf{j}$$
$$\mathbf{w} = (125\cos 120°)\mathbf{i} + (125\sin 120°)\mathbf{j} \approx -62.5\mathbf{i} + 108.3\mathbf{j}$$
$$\mathbf{u} + \mathbf{v} + \mathbf{w} \approx 73.16\mathbf{i} + 216.5\mathbf{j}$$
$$\|\mathbf{u} + \mathbf{v} + \mathbf{w}\| \approx 228.5 \text{ pounds}$$
$$\tan\theta \approx \frac{216.5}{73.16} \approx 2.9592$$
$$\theta \approx 71.3°$$

63. Horizontal component of velocity:
$$80\cos 50° \approx 51.42 \text{ ft/sec}$$
Vertical component of velocity:
$$80\sin 50° \approx 61.28 \text{ ft/sec}$$

65. Rope $\overrightarrow{AC}$: $\mathbf{u} = \|\mathbf{u}\|(\cos 50°\mathbf{i} - \sin 50°\mathbf{j})$
Rope $\overrightarrow{BC}$: $\mathbf{v} = \|\mathbf{v}\|(-\cos 30°\mathbf{i} - \sin 30°\mathbf{j})$
Resultant: $\mathbf{u} + \mathbf{v} = -1000\mathbf{j}$

$$\|\mathbf{u}\|\cos 50° - \|\mathbf{v}\|\cos 30° = 0$$
$$-\|\mathbf{u}\|\sin 50° - \|\mathbf{v}\|\sin 30° = -1000$$
Solving this system of equations yields:
$$T_{AC} = \|\mathbf{u}\| \approx 879.4 \text{ pounds}$$
$$T_{BC} = \|\mathbf{v}\| \approx 652.7 \text{ pounds}$$

67. Towline 1: $\mathbf{u} = \|\mathbf{u}\|(\cos 20°\mathbf{i} + \sin 20°\mathbf{j})$
Towline 2: $\mathbf{v} = \|\mathbf{u}\|(\cos 20°\mathbf{i} - \sin 20°\mathbf{j})$
Resultant: $\mathbf{u} + \mathbf{v} = 6000\mathbf{i}$

$$\|\mathbf{u}\|\cos 20° + \|\mathbf{u}\|\cos 20° = 6000$$

$$\|\mathbf{u}\| \approx 3192.5$$

Therefore, the tension on each towline is $\|\mathbf{u}\| \approx 3192.5$ pounds.

69. Airspeed: $\mathbf{u} = (540\cos 32°)\mathbf{i} - (540\sin 32°)\mathbf{j} \approx 457.9\mathbf{i} - 286.2\mathbf{j}$
Groundspeed: $\mathbf{v} = (500\cos 40°)\mathbf{i} - (500\sin 40°)\mathbf{j} \approx 383.0\mathbf{i} - 321.4\mathbf{j}$
Wind: $\mathbf{w} = \mathbf{v} - \mathbf{u} \approx -74.9\mathbf{i} - 35.2\mathbf{j}$
Wind speed: $\|\mathbf{w}\| \approx \sqrt{(-74.9)^2 + (-35.2)^2} \approx 82.8$ miles/hour
Wind direction: $\tan\theta \approx \dfrac{-35.2}{-74.9} \approx 0.4700$

$$\theta \approx 25.2°$$

$$\text{N } 25.2° \text{ E}$$

71. $W = FD = (85\cos 60°)(10) = 425$ ft-lb

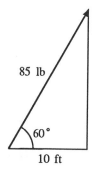

85 lb

60°

10 ft

73. The program draws the parallelogram determined by the origin, (A, B) and (C, D). It also draws the vector sum $(A + C, B + D)$ as a diagonal of this parallelogram.

Section 11.2   The Dot Product of Two Vectors

- The dot product of two vectors $\mathbf{u} = \langle u_1, u_2 \rangle$ and $\mathbf{v} = \langle v_1, v_2 \rangle$ is $\mathbf{u} \cdot \mathbf{v} = u_1 v_1 + u_2 v_2$.
- The dot product satisfies the following properties:
  - (a) $\mathbf{u} \cdot \mathbf{v} = \mathbf{v} \cdot \mathbf{u}$
  - (b) $\mathbf{0} \cdot \mathbf{v} = 0$
  - (c) $\mathbf{u} \cdot (\mathbf{v} + \mathbf{w}) = \mathbf{u} \cdot \mathbf{v} + \mathbf{u} \cdot \mathbf{w}$
  - (d) $\mathbf{v} \cdot \mathbf{v} = \|\mathbf{v}\|^2$
  - (e) $c(\mathbf{u} \cdot \mathbf{v}) = c\mathbf{v} \cdot \mathbf{u} = \mathbf{u} \cdot c\mathbf{v}$
- You should be able to find the angle between two vectors $\mathbf{u}$ and $\mathbf{v}$.
  $$\cos \theta = \frac{\mathbf{u} \cdot \mathbf{v}}{\|\mathbf{u}\| \, \|\mathbf{v}\|}$$
- Two vectors $\mathbf{u}$ and $\mathbf{v}$ are orthogonal if $\mathbf{u} \cdot \mathbf{v} = 0$.
- The projection of the vector $\mathbf{u}$ onto the vector $\mathbf{v}$ is
  $$\mathbf{w}_1 = \text{proj}_\mathbf{v} \mathbf{u} = \frac{\mathbf{u} \cdot \mathbf{v}}{\|\mathbf{v}\|^2} \mathbf{v}$$
  If $\mathbf{w}_2 = \mathbf{u} - \mathbf{w}_1$, then $\mathbf{w}_1$ and $\mathbf{w}_2$ are orthogonal.
- You should be able to decompose a vector into its components.
- The work W done by a constant force $\mathbf{F}$ along the vector $\overline{PQ}$ is given by either of the following.
  - (a) $W = \|\text{proj}_{\overline{PQ}} \mathbf{F}\| \, \|\overline{PQ}\|$
  - (b) $W = \mathbf{F} \cdot \overline{PQ}$

1. $\mathbf{u} \cdot \mathbf{v} = \langle 6, 2 \rangle \cdot \langle 2, -3 \rangle = 6(2) + 2(-3) = 12 - 6 = 6$

3. $\mathbf{u} \cdot \mathbf{v} = \langle 3, -3 \rangle \cdot \langle 0, 5 \rangle = 3(0) + (-3)5 = 0 - 15 = -15$

5. $\mathbf{u} \cdot \mathbf{v} = (4\mathbf{i} - 2\mathbf{j}) \cdot (\mathbf{i} + 3\mathbf{j}) = 4 - 6 = -2$

7. $\mathbf{u} \cdot \mathbf{u} = \langle 2, 2 \rangle \cdot \langle 2, 2 \rangle = 4 + 4 = 8$ scalar

9. $(\mathbf{u} \cdot \mathbf{v})\mathbf{v} = \left(\langle 2, 2 \rangle \cdot \langle -3, 4 \rangle \right) \mathbf{v} = (-6 + 8)\mathbf{v} = 2\langle -3, 4 \rangle = \langle -6, 8 \rangle$ vector

11. $\mathbf{u} \cdot \mathbf{v} = \|\mathbf{u}\| \; \|\mathbf{v}\| \cos \theta = (4)(10) \cos \dfrac{2\pi}{3} = 40 \left(-\dfrac{1}{2} \right) = -20$

13. $\mathbf{u} \cdot \mathbf{v} = \langle 1245, 2600 \rangle \cdot \langle 12.20, 8.50 \rangle$

$= 15189 + 22100 = \$37,289$

This represents the total revenue if all the units are sold at the given price.

15. $\cos \theta = \dfrac{\mathbf{u} \cdot \mathbf{v}}{\|\mathbf{u}\| \; \|\mathbf{v}\|} = \dfrac{\langle 1,0 \rangle \cdot \langle 0,-2 \rangle}{\|\langle 1,0 \rangle\| \; \|\langle 0,-2 \rangle\|} = 0 \Rightarrow \text{angle} = 90^\circ$

17. $\cos \theta = \dfrac{\mathbf{u} \cdot \mathbf{v}}{\|\mathbf{u}\| \; \|\mathbf{v}\|} = \dfrac{\langle 3,4 \rangle \cdot \langle 5,3 \rangle}{\|\langle 3,4 \rangle\| \; \|\langle 5,3 \rangle\|} = \dfrac{27}{5\sqrt{34}} \Rightarrow \theta \approx 22.17^\circ$

19. $\cos \theta = \dfrac{\mathbf{u} \cdot \mathbf{v}}{\|\mathbf{u}\| \; \|\mathbf{v}\|} = \dfrac{(2\mathbf{i} + 3\mathbf{j}) \cdot (-2\mathbf{i} + 2\mathbf{j})}{\sqrt{13} \; \sqrt{8}} = \dfrac{2}{\sqrt{13} \; 2\sqrt{2}} = \dfrac{1}{\sqrt{26}}$

21. $\cos \theta = \dfrac{\mathbf{u} \cdot \mathbf{v}}{\|\mathbf{u}\| \; \|\mathbf{v}\|} = \dfrac{\left(\frac{1}{2}\mathbf{i} + \frac{\sqrt{3}}{2}\mathbf{j} \right) \cdot \left(\frac{-\sqrt{2}}{2}\mathbf{i} + \frac{\sqrt{2}}{2}\mathbf{j} \right)}{(1)(1)}$

$= \dfrac{-\sqrt{2}}{4} + \dfrac{\sqrt{6}}{4} = \dfrac{\sqrt{6}-\sqrt{2}}{4} \Rightarrow \theta = 75^\circ$

Or, notice that the vector $\mathbf{v}$ is obtained from $\mathbf{u}$ by a rotation of $\frac{3\pi}{4} - \frac{\pi}{3} = \frac{5\pi}{12} = 75^\circ$.

23. $\theta \approx 91.33^\circ$ **25.** $\theta = 90^\circ$

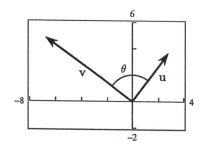   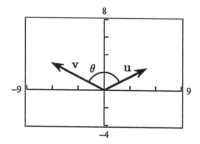

27. $\cos \theta = \dfrac{\mathbf{u} \cdot \mathbf{v}}{\|\mathbf{u}\| \; \|\mathbf{v}\|} = 0 \Rightarrow \text{orthogonal}$

29. $\cos \theta = \dfrac{\mathbf{u} \cdot \mathbf{v}}{\|\mathbf{u}\| \; \|\mathbf{v}\|} = \dfrac{-6 - 37.5}{\sqrt{1044} \; \sqrt{1.8125}} = \dfrac{-43.5}{43.5} = -1 \Rightarrow \text{parallel}$

31. $\cos\theta = \dfrac{\mathbf{u}\cdot\mathbf{v}}{\|\mathbf{u}\|\,\|\mathbf{v}\|} = \dfrac{\frac{-15}{4}-\frac{6}{4}}{\sqrt{\frac{5}{8}}\sqrt{61}} \approx \dfrac{\frac{-21}{4}}{6.17}$ neither

33. $\text{proj}_{\mathbf{v}}\mathbf{u} = \left(\dfrac{\mathbf{u}\cdot\mathbf{v}}{\|\mathbf{v}\|^2}\right)\mathbf{v} = \left(\dfrac{24+8}{68}\right)\langle 8,2\rangle = \left\langle \dfrac{64}{17},\dfrac{16}{17}\right\rangle$

$\mathbf{u}-\text{proj}_{\mathbf{v}}\mathbf{u} = \langle 3,4\rangle - \left\langle \dfrac{64}{17},\dfrac{16}{17}\right\rangle = \left\langle \dfrac{-13}{17},\dfrac{52}{17}\right\rangle$

35. $\text{proj}_{\mathbf{v}}\mathbf{u} = \left(\dfrac{\mathbf{u}\cdot\mathbf{v}}{\|\mathbf{v}\|^2}\right)\mathbf{v} = 0\mathbf{v} = \langle 0,0\rangle$

$\mathbf{u}-\text{proj}_{\mathbf{v}}\mathbf{u} = \mathbf{u} = \langle 4,2\rangle$

37. $\text{proj}_{\mathbf{v}}\mathbf{u} = \left(\dfrac{\mathbf{u}\cdot\mathbf{v}}{\|\mathbf{v}\|^2}\right)\mathbf{v} = \dfrac{8}{64}\langle 0,8\rangle = \langle 0,1\rangle$

$\mathbf{u}-\text{proj}_{\mathbf{v}}\mathbf{u} = \langle 2,1\rangle - \langle 0,1\rangle = \langle 2,0\rangle$

39. $\mathbf{F} = -26,000\mathbf{j}$

$\mathbf{v} = \cos 10°\mathbf{i} + \sin 10\mathbf{j}$

$\mathbf{w}_1 = \text{proj}_{\mathbf{v}}\mathbf{F} = \left(\dfrac{\mathbf{F}\cdot\mathbf{v}}{\|\mathbf{v}\|^2}\right)\mathbf{v} = \left(\dfrac{(-26000)(\sin 10)}{1}\right)\mathbf{v}$

$= (-4514.85)\langle 0.9848, 0.1736\rangle = \langle -4446.2, -784.0\rangle$

$\|\mathbf{w}_1\| = \sqrt{(-4446.2)^2 + (-784.0)^2} \approx 4514.8 \text{ lbs}$

$\mathbf{F} - \mathbf{w}_1 = \langle 0, -26000\rangle - \langle -4446.2, -784.0\rangle$

$= \langle 4446.2, -25216\rangle$

$\|\mathbf{F} - \mathbf{w}_1\| \approx 25605.0 \text{ lbs}$

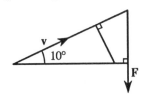

41. $W = \mathbf{F}\cdot\mathbf{PQ} = \langle 3600\cos 35°, 3600\sin 30°\rangle \cdot \langle 2500, 0\rangle$

$= 7.37 \times 10^6 \text{ ft lbs}$

43. $\mathbf{u} \cdot (\mathbf{u} + \mathbf{w}) = \langle u_1, u_2 \rangle \cdot (\langle v_1, v_2 \rangle + \langle w_1, w_2 \rangle)$

$= \langle u_1, u_2 \rangle \cdot \langle v_1 + w_1, v_2 + w_2 \rangle$

$= u_1(v_1 + w_1) + u_2(v_2 + w_2)$

$= u_1 v_1 + u_2 v_2 + u_1 w_1 + u_2 w_2$

$= \langle u_1, u_2 \rangle \cdot \langle v_1, v_2 \rangle + \langle u_1, u_2 \rangle \cdot w_1, w_2 \rangle$

$= \mathbf{u} \cdot \mathbf{v} + \mathbf{u} \cdot \mathbf{w}$

Section 11.3   The Three-Dimensional Coordinate System

- You should be able to plot points in the three-dimensional coordinate system.
- The distance between the points (x_1, y_1, z_1) and (x_2, y_2, z_2) is
  $$d = \sqrt{(x_2 - x_1)^2 + (y_2 - y_1)^2 + (z_2 - z_1)^2}$$
- The midpoint of the line segment joining the points (x_1, y_1, z_1) and (x_2, y_2, z_2) is
  $$\left(\frac{x_1 + x_2}{2}, \ \frac{y_1 + y_2}{x} + \frac{z_1 + z_2}{2} \right)$$
- The equation of the sphere with center (h, k, j) and radius r is
  $$(x - h)^2 + (y - k)^2 + (z - j)^2 = r^2$$
- You should be able to find the trace of a surface in space.

1.

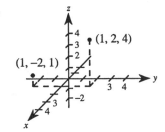

3.

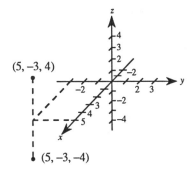

5. $AB = \sqrt{(3 - 0)^2 + (3 - 0)^2 + (2 - 0)^2} = \sqrt{9 + 9 + 4} = \sqrt{22}$

$BC = \sqrt{(3 - 3)^2 + (-6 - 3)^2 + (2 - 2)^2} = \sqrt{0 + 81 + 0} = 9$

$AC = \sqrt{(3 - 0)^2 + (-6 - 0)^2 + (2 - 0)^2} = \sqrt{9 + 36 + 4} = 7$

Neither

7. $AB = \sqrt{(6 - 2)^2 + (0 + 1)^2 + (3 - 0)^2} = \sqrt{16 + 1 + 9} = \sqrt{26}$

$BC = \sqrt{(0 - 6)^2 + (2 - 0)^2 + (3 - 3)^2} = \sqrt{36 + 4} = \sqrt{40}$

$AC = \sqrt{(0 - 2)^2 + (2 + 1)^2 + (3 - 0)^2} = 4 + 9 + 9 = \sqrt{22}$

Neither

9. midpoint $= \left(\dfrac{3-3}{2}, \dfrac{-6+2}{2}, \dfrac{10+2}{2}\right) = (0, -2, 6)$

11. midpoint $= \left(\dfrac{4-4}{2}, \dfrac{-2+2}{2}, \dfrac{5+8}{2}\right) = \left(0, 0, \dfrac{13}{2}\right)$

13. $(x-0)^2 + (y-4)^2 + (z-3)^2 = 4^2$

$\qquad x^2 + (y-4)^2 + (z-3)^2 = 16$

15. radius $=$ diameter$/2 = 5 : (x+3)^2 + (y-7)^2 + (z-5)^2 = 5^2 = 25$

17. center $= \left(\dfrac{3+0}{2}, \dfrac{0+0}{2}, \dfrac{0+6}{2}\right) = \left(\dfrac{3}{2}, 0, 3\right).$

$\qquad$ radius $= \sqrt{\left(3-\dfrac{3}{2}\right)^2 + (0-0)^2 + (0-3)^2} = \sqrt{\dfrac{9}{4}+9} = \sqrt{\dfrac{45}{4}}$

$\qquad$ sphere: $\left(x-\dfrac{3}{2}\right)^2 + (y-0)^2 + (z-3)^2 = \dfrac{45}{4}$

19. $(x^2 - 4x + 4) + (y^2 + 2y + 1) + (z^2 - 6z + 9) = -10 + 4 + 1 + 9$

$\qquad (x-2)^2 + (y+1)^2 + (z-3)^2 = 4 \qquad$ center: $(2, -1, 3)$

$\hspace{8cm}$ radius: 2

21. $(x^2 + 4x + 4) + y^2 + (z^2 - 8z + 16) = -19 + 4 + 16$

$\qquad (x+2)^2 + y^2 + (z-4)^2 = 1 \qquad$ center: $(-2, 0, 4)$

$\hspace{8cm}$ radius: 1

23. $x^2 + y^2 + z^2 - 2x - \dfrac{2}{3}y - 8z = \dfrac{-73}{9}$

$\qquad (x^2 - 2x + 1) + \left(y^2 - \dfrac{2}{3}y + \dfrac{1}{9}\right) + (z^2 - 8z + 16) = \dfrac{-73}{9} + 1 + \dfrac{1}{9} + 16$

$\qquad (x-1)^2 + \left(y - \dfrac{1}{3}\right)^2 + (z-4)^2 = 9 \qquad$ center: $\left(1, \dfrac{1}{3}, 4\right)$

$\hspace{8cm}$ radius: 3

25. a.

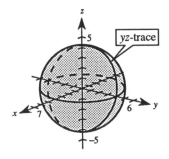

b.

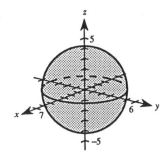

27. $z^2 = 16 - x^2 - y^2 \Rightarrow \begin{cases} z_1 = \sqrt{16 - x^2 - y^2} \\ z_2 = -\sqrt{16 - x^2 - y^2} \end{cases}$

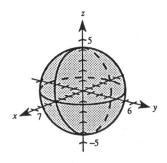

29. $(z - 5)^2 = 4 - (x - 3)^2 - (y - 4)^2 \Rightarrow \begin{cases} z_1 = 5 + \sqrt{4 - (x - 3)^2 - (y - 4)^2} \\ z_2 = 5 - \sqrt{4 - (x - 3)^2 - (y - 4)^2} \end{cases}$

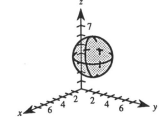

Section 11.4   Vectors in Space

> ■ Vectors in space $\mathbf{v} = \langle v_1,\ v_2,\ v_3 \rangle$ have many of the same properties as vectors in the plane.
>
> ■ The dot product of two vectors $\mathbf{u} = \langle u_1,\ u_2,\ u_3 \rangle$ and $\mathbf{v} = \langle v_1,\ v_2,\ v_3 \rangle$ in space is $\mathbf{u} \cdot \mathbf{v} = u_1v_1 + u_2v_2 + u_3v_3$.
>
> ■ Two vectors $\mathbf{u}$ and $\mathbf{v}$ are said to be parallel if there is some scalar c such that $\mathbf{u} - c\mathbf{v}$.
>
> ■ You should be able to use vectors to solve real life problems.

1. $\mathbf{v} = \langle 0 - 2,\ 3 - 0,\ 2 - 1 \rangle = \langle -2,\ 3,\ 1 \rangle$ **3.** $\mathbf{v} = \langle 4 - 0,\ 1 - (-3),\ 2 - 0 \rangle = \langle 4,\ 4,\ 2 \rangle$

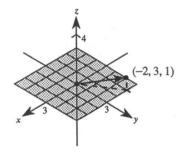

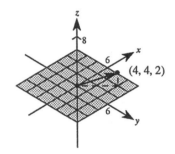

5. $\mathbf{v} = \langle 3 - (-1),\ 2 - (-2),\ 5 - 1 \rangle = \langle 4,\ 4,\ 4 \rangle$
any vector of form $c\langle 1,\ 1,\ 1 \rangle$, $c > 0$, is parallel to $\mathbf{v}$
any vector of form $c\langle 1,\ 1,\ 1 \rangle$, $c < 0$, is opposite direction

7. $\mathbf{z} = \mathbf{u} - 2\mathbf{v} = \langle -1,\ 3,\ 2 \rangle - 2\langle 1,\ -2,\ -2 \rangle = \langle -3,\ 7, 6 \rangle$

9. $\mathbf{z} = 2\mathbf{u} + 8\mathbf{v} - \mathbf{w} = 2\langle -1,\ 3,\ 2 \rangle + 8\langle 1,\ -2,\ -2 \rangle - \langle 5,\ 0,\ -5 \rangle = \langle 1,\ -10,\ -7 \rangle$

11. $2\mathbf{z} - 4\mathbf{u} = \mathbf{w} \Rightarrow \mathbf{z} = \frac{1}{2}(4\mathbf{u} + \mathbf{w}) = \frac{1}{2}\left(4\langle -1,\ 3,\ 2 \rangle + \langle 5,\ 0,\ -5 \rangle \right)$
$$= \langle \tfrac{1}{2},\ 6,\ \tfrac{3}{2} \rangle$$

13. $\|\mathbf{v}\| = \sqrt{4^2 + 1^2 + 4^2} = \sqrt{33}$

15. $\dfrac{\mathbf{u}}{\|\mathbf{u}\|} = \dfrac{\langle 8, \, 3, \, -1 \rangle}{\sqrt{74}} = \dfrac{1}{\sqrt{74}}(8\mathbf{i} + 3\mathbf{j} - \mathbf{k})$

17. $\mathbf{u} \cdot \mathbf{v} = 3(0) + (-3)(5) + 5(3) = 0$

19. $\mathbf{u} \cdot \mathbf{v} = 4(1) + (-2)(3) + (1)(-1) = -3$

21. $\cos \theta = \dfrac{\mathbf{u} \cdot \mathbf{v}}{\|\mathbf{u}\| \, \|\mathbf{v}\|} = \dfrac{-8}{\sqrt{8} \, \sqrt{25}} \Rightarrow \theta = 124.45°$

23. $\cos \theta = \dfrac{\mathbf{u} \cdot \mathbf{v}}{\|\mathbf{u}\| \, \|\mathbf{v}\|} = \dfrac{-120}{\sqrt{1700} \, \sqrt{73}} \Rightarrow \theta \approx 109.92$

25. $\cos \theta = \dfrac{\mathbf{u} \cdot \mathbf{v}}{\|\mathbf{u}\| \, \|\mathbf{v}\|} = \dfrac{-270}{\sqrt{405} \, \sqrt{180}} = -1 \Rightarrow$ parallel

27. Since $\mathbf{u} \cdot \mathbf{v} = 0$, the vectors are orthogonal.

29. $\mathbf{w}_1 = \text{proj}_{\mathbf{v}}\mathbf{u} = \left(\dfrac{\mathbf{u} \cdot \mathbf{v}}{\|\mathbf{v}\|^2} \right) \mathbf{v} = \dfrac{8}{73}\langle 0, \, 8, \, 3 \rangle = \left\langle 0, \, \dfrac{64}{73}, \, \dfrac{24}{73} \right\rangle$

$\mathbf{w}_2 = \mathbf{u} - \mathbf{w}_1 = \left\langle 2 - 0, \, 1 - \dfrac{64}{73}, \, 0 - \dfrac{24}{73} \right\rangle = \left\langle 2, \, \dfrac{9}{73}, \, \dfrac{-24}{73} \right\rangle$

31. $\mathbf{v} = \langle -1 - 1, \, 2 - 3, \, 5 - 2 \rangle = \langle -2, \, -1, \, 3 \rangle$

$\mathbf{u} = \langle 3 - (-1), \, 4 - 2, \, -1 - 5 \rangle = \langle 4, \, 2, \, -6 \rangle$

Since $\mathbf{u} = -2\mathbf{v}$, the points are collinear.

33. $\mathbf{v} = \langle 7 - 5, \, 3 - 4, \, -1 - 1 \rangle = \langle 2, \, -1, \, -2 \rangle$

$\mathbf{u} = \langle 4 - 7, \, 5 - 3, \, 3 - (-1) \rangle = \langle -3, \, 2, \, 4 \rangle$

Since $\mathbf{u}$ and $\mathbf{v}$ are not parallel, the points are not collinear.

35. $\mathbf{v} = \langle 2, \, -4, \, 7 \rangle = \langle q_1 - 1, \, q_2 - 5, \, q_3 - 0 \rangle \Rightarrow$

$\left. \begin{aligned} 2 &= q_1 - 1 \\ -4 &= q_2 - 5 \\ 7 &= q_3 \end{aligned} \right\} \Rightarrow \left. \begin{aligned} q_1 &= 3 \\ q_2 &= 1 \\ q_3 &- 7 \end{aligned} \right\} \Rightarrow$ Terminal point is $\langle 3, \, 1, \, 7 \rangle$

37. $\mathbf{v} = \langle q_1,\ q_2,\ q_3 \rangle$. Since $\mathbf{v}$ lies in the yz-plane, $q_1 = 0$. Since $\mathbf{v}$ makes an angle of $45°$, $q_2 = q_3$. Finally, $\|\mathbf{v}\| = 4$ implies that $q_2^2 + q_3^2 = 16$. Thus, $q_2 = q_3 = 2\sqrt{2}$ and $\mathbf{v} = \langle 0,\ 2\sqrt{2},\ 2\sqrt{2} \rangle$.

39. Sphere: $(x - x_1)^2 + (y - y_1)^2 + (z - z_1)^2 = 81$

41. $W = \mathbf{F} \cdot \mathbf{PQ} = \langle 3,\ 2,\ 7 \rangle \cdot \langle 10,\ 5,\ 4 \rangle = 68$ work units

Section 11.5   The Cross Product of Two Vectors

- ■ The cross product of two vectors $\mathbf{u} = u_1\mathbf{i} + u_2\mathbf{j} + u_3\mathbf{k}$ and $\mathbf{v} = v_1\mathbf{i} + v_2\mathbf{j} + v_3\mathbf{k}$ is given by

$$\mathbf{u} \times \mathbf{v} = (u_2v_3 - u_3v_2)\mathbf{i} - (u_1v_3 - u_3v_1)\mathbf{j} + (u_1v_2 - u_2v_1)\mathbf{k}$$

$$= \begin{vmatrix} \mathbf{i} & \mathbf{j} & \mathbf{k} \\ u_1 & u_2 & u_3 \\ v_1 & v_2 & v_3 \end{vmatrix}$$

- ■ The cross product satisfies the following algebraic properties.
  - (a) $\mathbf{u} \times \mathbf{v} = -(\mathbf{v} \times \mathbf{u})$
  - (b) $\mathbf{u} \times (\mathbf{v} + \mathbf{w}) = (\mathbf{u} \times \mathbf{v}) + (\mathbf{u} \times \mathbf{w})$
  - (c) $c(\mathbf{u} \times \mathbf{v}) = (c\mathbf{u}) \times \mathbf{v} = \mathbf{u} \times (c\mathbf{v})$
  - (d) $\mathbf{u} \times \mathbf{0} = \mathbf{0} \times \mathbf{u} = \mathbf{0}$
  - (e) $\mathbf{u} \times \mathbf{u} = \mathbf{0}$
  - (f) $\mathbf{u} \cdot (\mathbf{v} \times \mathbf{w}) = (\mathbf{u} \times \mathbf{v}) \cdot \mathbf{w}$

- ■ The following geometric properties of the cross product are valid, where θ is the angle between the vectors $\mathbf{u}$ and $\mathbf{v}$:
  - (a) $\mathbf{u} \times \mathbf{v}$ is orthogonal to both $\mathbf{u}$ and $\mathbf{v}$.
  - (b) $\|\mathbf{u} \times \mathbf{v}\| = \|\mathbf{u}\|\ \|\mathbf{v}\| \sin \theta$
  - (c) $\mathbf{u} \times \mathbf{v} = \mathbf{0}$ if and only if $\mathbf{u}$ and $\mathbf{v}$ are scalar multiples.
  - (d) $\|\mathbf{u} \times \mathbf{v}\|$ is the area of the parallelogram having $\mathbf{u}$ and $\mathbf{v}$ as sides.

- ■ The triple scalar product is the volume of the parallelepiped having $\mathbf{u}$, $\mathbf{v}$ and $\mathbf{w}$ as sides.

$$\mathbf{u} \cdot (\mathbf{v} \times \mathbf{w}) = \begin{vmatrix} u_1 & u_2 & u_3 \\ v_1 & v_2 & v_3 \\ w_1 & w_2 & w_3 \end{vmatrix}$$

1. $\mathbf{i} \times \mathbf{j} = \begin{vmatrix} \mathbf{i} & \mathbf{j} & \mathbf{k} \\ 1 & 0 & 0 \\ 0 & 1 & 0 \end{vmatrix} = \mathbf{k}$

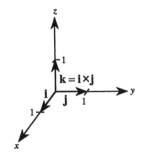

3. $\mathbf{i} \times \mathbf{k} = \begin{vmatrix} \mathbf{i} & \mathbf{j} & \mathbf{k} \\ 1 & 0 & 0 \\ 0 & 0 & 1 \end{vmatrix} = -\mathbf{j}$

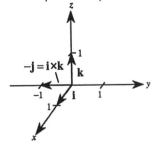

5. $\mathbf{u} \times \mathbf{v} = \begin{vmatrix} \mathbf{i} & \mathbf{j} & \mathbf{k} \\ 1 & -4 & 0 \\ 2 & 6 & 0 \end{vmatrix} = 14\mathbf{k} = \langle 0, 0, 14 \rangle$

7. $\mathbf{u} \times \mathbf{v} = \begin{vmatrix} \mathbf{i} & \mathbf{j} & \mathbf{k} \\ 7 & -5 & 2 \\ -1 & 4 & -1 \end{vmatrix} = \langle -3, 5, 23 \rangle$

9. $\mathbf{u} \times \mathbf{v} = \begin{vmatrix} \mathbf{i} & \mathbf{j} & \mathbf{k} \\ 2 & 4 & 3 \\ 0 & -2 & 1 \end{vmatrix} = \langle 10, -2, -4 \rangle$

11. $\mathbf{u} \times \mathbf{v} = \begin{vmatrix} \mathbf{i} & \mathbf{j} & \mathbf{k} \\ 6 & 2 & 1 \\ 1 & 3 & -2 \end{vmatrix} = \langle -7, 13, 16 \rangle = -7\mathbf{i} + 13\mathbf{j} + 16\mathbf{k}$

13. $\mathbf{u} \times \mathbf{v} = \begin{vmatrix} \mathbf{i} & \mathbf{j} & \mathbf{k} \\ 1 & \frac{3}{2} & \frac{-5}{2} \\ \frac{1}{2} & \frac{-3}{4} & \frac{1}{4} \end{vmatrix} = \langle \frac{-3}{2}, -\frac{3}{2}, -\frac{3}{2} \rangle = \frac{-3}{2}\mathbf{i} - \frac{3}{2}\mathbf{j} - \frac{3}{2}\mathbf{k}$

15. $\mathbf{u} \times \mathbf{v} = \begin{vmatrix} \mathbf{i} & \mathbf{j} & \mathbf{k} \\ 6 & -5 & 1 \\ \frac{1}{3} & -\frac{1}{3} & \frac{2}{3} \end{vmatrix} = \langle -3, -\frac{11}{3}, -\frac{1}{3} \rangle = -3\mathbf{i} - \frac{11}{3}\mathbf{j} - \frac{1}{3}\mathbf{k}$

17. $\mathbf{u} \times \mathbf{v} = \begin{vmatrix} \mathbf{i} & \mathbf{j} & \mathbf{k} \\ 3 & 1 & 0 \\ 0 & 1 & 1 \end{vmatrix} = \mathbf{i} - 3\mathbf{j} + 3\mathbf{k} \quad \|\mathbf{u} \times \mathbf{v}\| = \sqrt{19}$

$\text{unit vector} = \frac{\mathbf{u} \times \mathbf{v}}{\|\mathbf{u} \times \mathbf{v}\|} = \frac{1}{\sqrt{19}}(\mathbf{i} - 3\mathbf{j} + 3\mathbf{k})$

19. $\mathbf{u} \times \mathbf{v} = \begin{vmatrix} \mathbf{i} & \mathbf{j} & \mathbf{k} \\ -2 & 1 & 3 \\ 1 & 4 & 6 \end{vmatrix} = -6\mathbf{i} + 15\mathbf{j} - 9\mathbf{k}$

$\|\mathbf{u} \times \mathbf{v}\| = \sqrt{342}$

$\text{unit vector} = \frac{\mathbf{u} \times \mathbf{v}}{\|\mathbf{u} \times \mathbf{v}\|} = \frac{1}{\sqrt{342}}(-6\mathbf{i} + 15\mathbf{j} - 9\mathbf{k})$

21. $\mathbf{u} \times \mathbf{v} = \begin{vmatrix} \mathbf{i} & \mathbf{j} & \mathbf{k} \\ 1 & 1 & -1 \\ 1 & 1 & 1 \end{vmatrix} = 2\mathbf{i} - 2\mathbf{j} \quad \|\mathbf{u} \times \mathbf{v}\| = 2\sqrt{2}$

$\text{unit vector} = \frac{\mathbf{u} \times \mathbf{v}}{\|\mathbf{u} \times \mathbf{v}\|} = \frac{1}{2\sqrt{2}}(2\mathbf{i} - 2\mathbf{j}) = \frac{1}{\sqrt{2}}\mathbf{i} - \frac{1}{\sqrt{2}}\mathbf{j}$

23. $\mathbf{u} \times \mathbf{v} = \begin{vmatrix} \mathbf{i} & \mathbf{j} & \mathbf{k} \\ 0 & 0 & 1 \\ 1 & 0 & 1 \end{vmatrix} = \mathbf{j}.$

area $= \|\mathbf{u} \times \mathbf{v}\| = \|\mathbf{j}\| = 1$

25. $\mathbf{u} \times \mathbf{v} = \begin{vmatrix} \mathbf{i} & \mathbf{j} & \mathbf{k} \\ 3 & 4 & 6 \\ 2 & -1 & 5 \end{vmatrix} = 26\mathbf{i} + 3\mathbf{j} - 11\mathbf{k}$

area $= \|\mathbf{u} \times \mathbf{v}\| = \sqrt{26^2 + 3^2 + (-11)^2} = \sqrt{806}$

27. $\mathbf{u} \times \mathbf{v} = \begin{vmatrix} \mathbf{i} & \mathbf{j} & \mathbf{k} \\ 2 & 2 & -3 \\ 0 & 2 & 3 \end{vmatrix} = \langle 12, -6, 4 \rangle$

area $= \|\mathbf{u} \times \mathbf{v}\| = \sqrt{12^2 + (-6)^2 + 4^2} = 14$

29. $\overrightarrow{AB} = \langle 3 - 2, \ 1 - (-1), \ 2 - 4 \rangle = \langle 1, \ 2, \ -2 \rangle$ is parallel to

$\overrightarrow{DC} = \langle 0 - (-1), \ 5 - 3, \ 6 - 8 \rangle = \langle 1, \ 2, \ -2 \rangle$

$\overrightarrow{AD} = \langle -3, \ 4, \ 4 \rangle$ is parallel to $\overrightarrow{BC} = \langle -3, \ 4, \ 4 \rangle$

$\overrightarrow{AB} \times \overrightarrow{AD} = \begin{vmatrix} \mathbf{i} & \mathbf{j} & \mathbf{k} \\ 1 & 2 & -2 \\ -3 & 4 & 4 \end{vmatrix} = \langle 16, \ 2, \ 10 \rangle$

Area $= \|\overrightarrow{AB} \times \overrightarrow{AD}\| = \sqrt{16^2 + 2^2 + 10^2} = \sqrt{360} = 6\sqrt{10}$

31. $\mathbf{u} = \langle 4, \ -2, \ 6 \rangle, \quad \mathbf{v} = \langle -4, \ 0, \ 3 \rangle$

$\mathbf{u} \times \mathbf{v} = \begin{vmatrix} \mathbf{i} & \mathbf{j} & \mathbf{k} \\ 4 & -2 & 6 \\ -4 & 0 & 3 \end{vmatrix} = \langle -6, -36, -8 \rangle$

Area $+ \frac{1}{2}\|\mathbf{u} \times \mathbf{v}\| = \frac{1}{2}\sqrt{(-6)^2 + (-36)^2 + (-8)^2} = \frac{1}{2}\sqrt{1396} = \sqrt{349}$

33. $\mathbf{u} = \langle -2 - 2, \ -2 - 3, \ 0 - (-5) \rangle = \langle -4, \ -5, \ 5 \rangle$

$\mathbf{v} = \langle 3 - 2, \ 0 - 3, \ 6 - (-5) \rangle = \langle 1, \ -3, \ 11 \rangle$

$$\mathbf{u} \times \mathbf{v} = \begin{vmatrix} \mathbf{i} & \mathbf{j} & \mathbf{k} \\ -4 & -5 & 5 \\ 1 & -3 & 11 \end{vmatrix} = \langle -40, \ 49, \ 17 \rangle$$

$\text{area} = \frac{1}{2}\|\mathbf{u} \times \mathbf{v}\| = \frac{1}{2}\sqrt{(-40)^2 + 49^2 + 17^2} = \frac{1}{2}\sqrt{4290}$

35. $\mathbf{u} \cdot (\mathbf{v} \times \mathbf{w}) = \begin{vmatrix} 2 & 3 & 3 \\ 4 & 4 & 0 \\ 0 & 0 & 4 \end{vmatrix} = 2(16) - 3(16) + 3(0) = -16$

37. $\mathbf{u} \cdot (\mathbf{v} \times \mathbf{w}) = \begin{vmatrix} 2 & 0 & 0 \\ 0 & 2 & 0 \\ 2 & 2 & 1 \end{vmatrix} = 2(2) + 0 + 0 = 4$

$\text{volume} = |\mathbf{u} \cdot (\mathbf{v} \times \mathbf{w})| = 4 \text{ cubic units}$

39. $\mathbf{u} = \langle 4, \ 0, \ 0 \rangle, \quad \mathbf{v} = \langle 0, \ -2, \ 3 \rangle, \quad \mathbf{w} = \langle 0, \ 5, \ 3 \rangle$

$$\mathbf{u} \cdot (\mathbf{v} \times \mathbf{w}) = \begin{vmatrix} 4 & 0 & 0 \\ 0 & -2 & 3 \\ 0 & 5 & 3 \end{vmatrix} = 4(-21) = -84$$

$\text{volume} = |-84| = 84$

41. $\mathbf{u} \times \mathbf{u} = \begin{vmatrix} \mathbf{i} & \mathbf{j} & \mathbf{k} \\ u_1 & u_2 & u_3 \\ u_1 & u_2 & u_3 \end{vmatrix} = (u_2 u_3 - u_2 u_3)\mathbf{i} - (u_1 u_3 - u_1 u_3)\mathbf{j} + (u_1 u_2 - u_1 u_2)\mathbf{k}$

43. $\mathbf{u} \times \mathbf{v} = \begin{vmatrix} \mathbf{i} & \mathbf{j} & \mathbf{k} \\ \cos\beta & \sin\beta & 0 \\ \cos\alpha & \sin\alpha & 0 \end{vmatrix} = (\cos\beta \ \sin\alpha - \cos\alpha \ \sin\beta)\mathbf{k}$

The area of the triangle is $\frac{1}{2}bh = \frac{1}{2}(1)\sin(\alpha - \beta)$.

Moreover, the area is $\frac{1}{2}\|\mathbf{u} \times \mathbf{v}\| = \frac{1}{2}(\cos\beta \ \sin\alpha - \cos\alpha \sin\beta)$.

Hence, $\sin(\alpha - \beta) = \cos\beta \sin\alpha - \cos\alpha \sin\beta$.

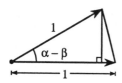

Section 11.6 Equations of Lines and Planes in Space

- The parametric equations of the line in space parallel to the vector $\langle a, b, c \rangle$ and passing through the point (x_1, y_1, z_1) are
$$x = x_1 + at, \quad y = y_1 + bt, \quad z = z_1 + ct.$$

- The standard equation of the plane in space containing the point (x_1, y_1, z_1) and having normal vector $\langle a, b, c \rangle$ is
$$a(x - x_1) + b(y - y_1) + c(z - z_1) = 0.$$

- You should be able to find the angle between two planes by calculating the angle between their normal vectors.

- You should be able to sketch a plane in space.

- The distance between a point Q and a plane having normal $\mathbf{n}$ is
$$D = \|\mathrm{proj}_{\mathbf{n}} \overline{PQ}\| = \frac{|\overline{PQ} \cdot \mathbf{n}|}{\|\mathbf{n}\|}$$
where P is a point in the plane.

---

1. $x = x_1 + at = 0 - 2t = -2t$

   $y = y_1 + bt = 0 + 4t = 4t$

   $z = z_1 + ct = 0 + t = t$

   (a) Parametric equations: $x = -2t, \ y = 4t, \ z = t$

   (b) Symmetric equations: $\dfrac{-x}{2} = \dfrac{y}{4} = z$

3. $x = x_1 + at = -4 + \frac{1}{2}t$

   $y = y_1 + bt = 1 + \frac{4}{3}t$

   $z = z_1 + ct = 0 - t$

   (a) Parametric equations: $\quad x = -4 + \frac{1}{2}t, \ y = 1 + \frac{4}{3}t, \ z = -t$

       equivalently: $\quad\quad\quad\quad x = -4 + 3t, \ y = 1 + 8t, \ z = -6t$

   (b) Symmetric equations: $\quad \dfrac{x+4}{3} = \dfrac{y-1}{8} = \dfrac{z}{-6}$

5. $x = x_1 + at = 2 + 2t$

$y = y_1 + bt = -3 - 3t$

$z = z_1 + ct = 5 + t$

(a) Parametric equations: $x = 2 + 2t,\ y = -3 - 3t,\ z = 5 + t$

(b) Symmetric equations: $\dfrac{x-2}{2} = \dfrac{y+3}{-3} = z - 5$

7. $\mathbf{v} = \left\langle 3 - \left(\frac{-3}{2}\right),\ -5 - \frac{3}{2},\ -4 - 2 \right\rangle = \left\langle \frac{9}{2},\ \frac{-13}{2},\ -6 \right\rangle$

Use $\langle 9,\ -13,\ -12 \rangle$:

(a) $x = 3 + 9t,\ y = -5 - 13t,\ z = -4 - 12t$ (Parametric)

(b) $\dfrac{x-3}{9} = \dfrac{y+5}{-13} = \dfrac{z+4}{-12}$ (Symmetric)

9. Use $\mathbf{v} = \mathbf{k}$. Then $x = -3,\ y = 8,\ z = 15 + t$

11. The line is $x = -4 + 3t,\ y = -1 - t,\ z = 7$, or $\dfrac{x+4}{3} = \dfrac{y+1}{-1},\ z = 7$.

Only (b) and (c) satisfy the equation.

13. Equating the two sets of parametric equations

$\left.\begin{array}{l} 6 + t = 7 + 5s \\ -5 - 2t = 5 + 2s \\ 1 + 3t = -8 + 3s \end{array}\right\} \Rightarrow \begin{array}{l} t - 5s = 1 \\ 2t - 2s = 10 \\ 3t - 3s = -9 \end{array}$

Solving for t and s, you obtain $t = -4$ and $s = -1$.

The point of intersection is $(x,\ y,\ z) = (2,\ 3,\ -11)$.

$\cos\theta = \dfrac{\langle 1,\ -2,\ 3\rangle \cdot \langle 5,\ 2,\ 3\rangle}{\|\langle 1,\ -2,\ 3\rangle\|\ \|\langle 5,\ 2,\ 3\rangle\|} = \dfrac{10}{\sqrt{14}\ \sqrt{38}} \Rightarrow \theta \approx 64.31°$

15.

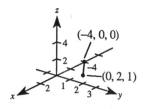

17. $a(x - x_1) + b(y - y_1) + c(z - z_1) = 0$

$\qquad 0(x - 3) + 1(y - 4) + 0(z + 2) = 0$

$\qquad\qquad\qquad y - 4 = 0$

19. $-2(x - 5) + 1(y - 6) - 2(z - 3) = 0$

$\qquad -2x + y - 2z + 10 = 0$

21. $\mathbf{n} = \langle -1, -2, 1 \rangle \quad -1(x - 2) - 2(y - 0) + 1(z - 0) = 0$

$\qquad\qquad\qquad\qquad\qquad -x - 2y + z + z = 0$

23. $\mathbf{u} = \langle 1, 1, 0 \rangle \qquad \mathbf{u} \times \mathbf{v} = \begin{vmatrix} \mathbf{i} & \mathbf{j} & \mathbf{k} \\ 1 & 1 & 0 \\ 0 & 3 & 3 \end{vmatrix} = \langle 3, -3, 3 \rangle$

$\quad\; \mathbf{v} = \langle 0, 3, 3 \rangle$

$\quad 3(x - 0) - 3(y - 0) + 3(z - 0) = 0$

$\qquad\qquad\qquad x - y + z = 0$

25. $\mathbf{u} = \langle 2 - 4, \; 5 - (-1), \; 1 - 3 \rangle = \langle -2, \; 6, \; -2 \rangle$

$\quad\; \mathbf{v} = \langle -1 - 4, \; 2 - (-1), \; 1 - 3 \rangle = \langle -5, \; 3, \; -2 \rangle$

$\quad \mathbf{u} \times \mathbf{v} = \begin{vmatrix} \mathbf{i} & \mathbf{j} & \mathbf{k} \\ -2 & 6 & -2 \\ -5 & 3 & -2 \end{vmatrix} = \langle -6, \; 6, \; 24 \rangle$

$\quad -6(x - 4) + 6(y + 1) + 24(z - 3) = 0$

$\qquad -(x - 4) + (y + 1) + 4(z - 3) = 0$

$\qquad\qquad\qquad -x + y + 4z - 7 = 0$

$\qquad\qquad\qquad\; x - y - 4z + 7 = 0$

27. $\mathbf{n} = \mathbf{j}: \quad 0(x - 2) + 1(y - 5) + 0(z - 3) = 0$

$\qquad\qquad\qquad\qquad y - 5 = 0$

29. $\mathbf{n} = \mathbf{j} - \mathbf{k}:$

$\quad$ point: $(0, 0, 0) \qquad 0(x - 0) + 1(y - 0) - 1(z - 0) = 0$

$\qquad\qquad\qquad\qquad\qquad y - z = 0$

31. $\mathbf{n}_1 = \langle 1,\ 0,\ 1 \rangle$

$\mathbf{n}_2 = \langle 1,\ -1,\ 0 \rangle$

$$\cos \theta = \frac{\mathbf{n}_1 \cdot \mathbf{n}_2}{\|\mathbf{n}_1\|\ \|\mathbf{n}_2\|} = \frac{1}{\sqrt{2}\ \sqrt{2}} = \frac{1}{2} \Rightarrow \theta = 60°$$

Solving the two equations simultaneously,

$x + z = 4 \Rightarrow z = 4 - x$

$x - y = 1 \Rightarrow y = x - 1$

Let $t = x$. Then $y = t - 1$ and $z = 4 - t$

Parametric equations: $x = t,\ y = -1 + t,\ z = 4 - t$.

33. $\mathbf{n}_1 = \langle 1,\ 1,\ 2 \rangle,\quad \mathbf{n}_2 = \langle 1,\ -2,\ 1 \rangle$

$$\cos \theta = \frac{\mathbf{n}_1 \cdot \mathbf{n}_2}{\|\mathbf{n}_1\|\ \|\mathbf{n}_2\|} = \frac{1}{\sqrt{6}\ \sqrt{6}} = \frac{1}{6} \Rightarrow \theta \approx 80.41°$$

$x + y + 2z = 4$

$x - 2y + z = 10$

Subtracting,

$3y + z = -6 \quad$ let $y = t$

$z = -6 - 3y = -6 - 3t$

$x = 10 - z + 2y = 10 - (-6 - 3t) + 2t = 16 + 5t$

Parametric equations: $x = 16 + 5t,\ y = t,\ z = -6 - 3t$

35.

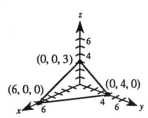

37.

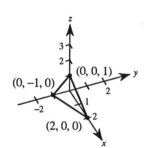

39.

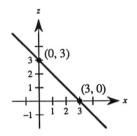

41.

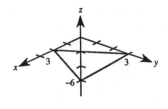

43.

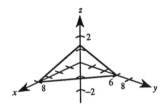

45. $D = \dfrac{|\mathbf{PQ} \cdot \mathbf{n}|}{\|\mathbf{n}\|}$ $P = (4,\ 0,\ 0)$ on plane, $Q = (0,\ 0,\ 0)$, $\mathbf{n} = \langle 3,\ 2,\ 1 \rangle$

$$D = \frac{|\langle -4, 0, 0 \rangle \cdot \langle 3, 2, 1 \rangle|}{\sqrt{14}} = \frac{12}{\sqrt{14}}$$

47. (a) Sphere: $(x - 4)^2 + (y + 1)^2 + (z - 1)^2 = 4$

(b) Two planes parallel to given plane.

Let $Q = (x, y, z)$ be a point on one of these planes, and pick $P = (0, 0, 10)$
on the given plane. By the distance formula,

$$\pm 2 = \frac{|\mathbf{PQ} \cdot \mathbf{n}|}{\|\mathbf{n}\|} = \frac{\langle x, y, z - 10 \rangle \cdot \langle 4, -3, 1 \rangle}{\sqrt{26}}$$

$$\pm 2\sqrt{26} = 4x - 3y + z - 10$$

$$4x - 3y + z = 10 \pm 2\sqrt{26}$$

49. Let the far bottom vertex represent the origin and find the 3 vectors beginning there:

$\mathbf{v}_1 = \langle 4,\ 0,\ 0 \rangle$

$\mathbf{v}_2 = \langle 0,\ 4,\ 0 \rangle$

$\mathbf{v}_3 = \langle -2,\ -2,\ 8 \rangle$

The normal vectors to the faces are:

$$\mathbf{n}_1 = \mathbf{v}_1 \times \mathbf{v}_3 = \begin{vmatrix} \mathbf{i} & \mathbf{j} & \mathbf{k} \\ 4 & 0 & 0 \\ -2 & -2 & 8 \end{vmatrix} = \langle 0,\ -32,\ -8 \rangle$$

$$\mathbf{n}_2 = \mathbf{v}_2 \times \mathbf{v}_3 = \begin{vmatrix} \mathbf{i} & \mathbf{j} & \mathbf{k} \\ 0 & 4 & 0 \\ -2 & -2 & 8 \end{vmatrix} = \langle 32,\ 0,\ 8 \rangle$$

$$\cos\theta = \frac{\mathbf{n}_1 \cdot \mathbf{n}_2}{\|\mathbf{n}_1\|\,\|\mathbf{n}_2\|} = \frac{-64}{\sqrt{1088}\,\sqrt{1088}} = \frac{-64}{1088} \Rightarrow \theta \approx 93.37°$$

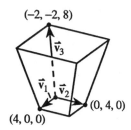

$(-2, -2, 8)$

$\vec{v}_3$

$\vec{v}_1$ $\vec{v}_2$

$(0, 4, 0)$

$(4, 0, 0)$

Chapter 11 Review Exercises

1. $\overrightarrow{AB} = \langle 5 - 2,\ 0 - 1 \rangle = \langle 3,\ -1 \rangle$

$\overrightarrow{AC} = \langle 2,\ 2 \rangle$

$\overrightarrow{AB} + \overrightarrow{AC} = \langle 3 + 2,\ -1 + 2 \rangle = \langle 5,\ 1 \rangle$

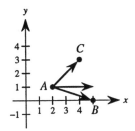

3. $\mathbf{v} = \langle 7 - 0,\ 3 - 10 \rangle = \langle 7,\ -7 \rangle$

5. $\mathbf{v} = \langle 8 \cos 120°,\ 8 \sin 120° \rangle = \langle -4,\ -4\sqrt{3} \rangle$

7. $\mathbf{v} = \langle 3 \cos 135°,\ 3 \sin 135° \rangle = \langle \frac{-3}{2}\sqrt{2},\ \frac{3}{2}\sqrt{2} \rangle$

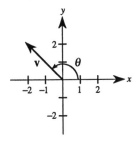

9. $\dfrac{1}{\|\mathbf{u}\|}\mathbf{u} = \dfrac{1}{\sqrt{61}}\langle 6,\,-5\rangle = \left\langle \dfrac{6}{\sqrt{61}},\,\dfrac{-5}{\sqrt{61}} \right\rangle$

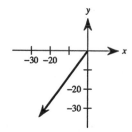

11. $4\mathbf{u} - 5\mathbf{v} = 4(6\mathbf{i} - 5\mathbf{j}) - 5(10\mathbf{i} + 3\mathbf{j}) = \langle -26,\,-35\rangle$

13. (a) $\mathbf{u} + \mathbf{v} = \left(\frac{7}{2}\mathbf{i} - \mathbf{j}\right) + (-\mathbf{i} + 2\mathbf{j}) = \frac{5}{2}\mathbf{i} + \mathbf{j}$

(b) $\mathbf{u} - \mathbf{v} = \left(\frac{7}{2}\mathbf{i} - \mathbf{j}\right) - (-\mathbf{i} + 2\mathbf{j}) = \frac{9}{2}\mathbf{i} - 3\mathbf{j}$

(c) $2\mathbf{u} - 3\mathbf{v} = 2\left(\frac{7}{2}\mathbf{i} - \mathbf{j}\right) - 3(-\mathbf{i} + 2\mathbf{j}) = 10\mathbf{i} - 8\mathbf{j}$

15. $\|\mathbf{v}\| = \sqrt{2^2 + (-2\sqrt{3})^2} = \sqrt{16} = 4$

$\tan\theta = \dfrac{-2\sqrt{3}}{2} = -\sqrt{3} \Rightarrow \theta = 300°$ (quadrant IV)

17. $\tan \alpha = \dfrac{12}{5} \Rightarrow \sin \alpha = \dfrac{12}{13}$ and $\cos \alpha = \dfrac{5}{13}$

$\tan \beta = \dfrac{3}{4} \Rightarrow \sin(180° - \beta) = \dfrac{3}{5}$ and $\cos(180° - \beta) = -\dfrac{4}{5}$

$\mathbf{u} = 300 \left(\dfrac{5}{13}\mathbf{i} + \dfrac{12}{13}\mathbf{j} \right)$

$\mathbf{v} = 150 \left(-\dfrac{4}{5}\mathbf{i} + \dfrac{3}{5}\mathbf{j} \right)$

$\mathbf{w} = 250(0\mathbf{i} - \mathbf{j})$

$\mathbf{r} = \mathbf{u} + \mathbf{v} + \mathbf{w} = \left(\dfrac{1500}{13} - 120 + 0 \right) \mathbf{i} + \left(\dfrac{3600}{13} + 90 - 250 \right) \mathbf{j} = -\dfrac{60}{13}\mathbf{i} + \dfrac{1520}{13}\mathbf{j}$

$\|\mathbf{r}\| = \sqrt{\left(-\dfrac{60}{13} \right)^2 + \left(\dfrac{1520}{13} \right)^2} \approx 117.0$ lb

$\theta = 180° - \arctan \dfrac{1520}{60} \approx 92.3°$

19. Rope One: $\mathbf{u} = \|\mathbf{u}\|(\cos 30°\mathbf{i} - \sin 30°\mathbf{j}) = \|\mathbf{u}\| \left(\dfrac{\sqrt{3}}{2}\mathbf{i} - \dfrac{1}{2}\mathbf{j} \right)$

Rope Two: $\mathbf{v} = \|\mathbf{u}\|(-\cos 30°\mathbf{i} - \sin 30°\mathbf{j}) = \|\mathbf{u}\| \left(-\dfrac{\sqrt{3}}{2}\mathbf{i} - \dfrac{1}{2}\mathbf{j} \right)$

Resultant: $\mathbf{u} + \mathbf{v} = \|\mathbf{u}\|\mathbf{j} = -100\mathbf{j}$

$\|\mathbf{u}\| = 100$

Therefore, the tension on each rope is $\|\mathbf{u}\| = 100$ lb.

21. Airspeed: $\mathbf{u} = 450 \cos 60°\mathbf{i} + 450 \sin 60°\mathbf{j} = 225\mathbf{i} + 225\sqrt{3}\mathbf{j}$

Wind: $\mathbf{w} = 20\mathbf{i}$

Groundspeed: $\mathbf{u} + \mathbf{w} = 245\mathbf{i} + 225\sqrt{3}\mathbf{j}$

$\|\mathbf{u} + \mathbf{w}\| = \sqrt{245^2 + (225\sqrt{3})^2} \approx 460.3$ miles/hour

$\tan\theta = \dfrac{225\sqrt{3}}{245} \approx 1.5907$

$\theta \approx 57.8°$

Bearing: N 32.2° E

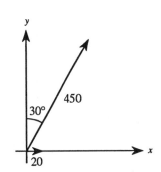

23. Midpoint = center = $\left(\dfrac{0+4}{2},\ \dfrac{0+6}{2},\ \dfrac{4+0}{2}\right) = (2,\ 3,\ 2)$

Radius = $\sqrt{(2-0)^2 + (3-0)^2 + (2-4)^2} = \sqrt{4+9+4} = \sqrt{17}$

Sphere = $(x-2)^2 + (y-3)^2 + (z-2)^2 = 17$

25. Unit vector = $\dfrac{\mathbf{PQ}}{\|\mathbf{PQ}\|} = \dfrac{\langle -10,\ 6,\ 7\rangle}{\|\langle -10,\ 6,\ 7\rangle\|} = \dfrac{1}{\sqrt{185}}\langle -10,\ 6,\ 7\rangle$

27. Since $\dfrac{-2}{3}\langle 39,\ -12,\ 21\rangle = \langle -26,\ 8,\ -14\rangle$, the vectors are parallel.

29. The angle is $\dfrac{7\pi}{4} - \dfrac{5\pi}{6} = \dfrac{11\pi}{12}$ or $165°$.

31. Since $\mathbf{u}\cdot\mathbf{v} = 0$, the angle is $90°$.

33. $\text{proj}_{\mathbf{v}}\mathbf{u} = \left(\dfrac{\mathbf{u}\cdot\mathbf{v}}{\|\mathbf{v}\|^2}\right)\mathbf{v} = \dfrac{32-6}{68}\langle -8,\ -2\rangle = \dfrac{26}{68}\langle -8,\ -2\rangle = \dfrac{-13}{17}\langle 4,\ 1\rangle$

35. $\text{proj}_{\mathbf{v}}\mathbf{u} = \left(\dfrac{\mathbf{u}\cdot\mathbf{v}}{\|\mathbf{v}\|^2}\right)\mathbf{v} = \dfrac{-5}{2}\langle 1,\ -1,\ 0\rangle = \left\langle \dfrac{-5}{2},\ \dfrac{5}{2},\ 0\right\rangle$

37. $\mathbf{u}\times\mathbf{v} = \begin{vmatrix} \mathbf{i} & \mathbf{j} & \mathbf{k} \\ -2 & 8 & 2 \\ 1 & 1 & -1 \end{vmatrix} = \langle -10,\ 0,\ -10\rangle$

39. $\mathbf{u}\cdot\mathbf{u} = \langle 1,\ -2,\ -1\rangle\cdot\langle 1,\ -2,\ -1\rangle = 1+4+1 = 6$

$\|\mathbf{u}\|^2 = 1^2 + (-2)^2 + (-1)^2 = 1+4+1 = 6$

41. $\mathbf{u}\times\mathbf{v} = \begin{vmatrix} \mathbf{i} & \mathbf{j} & \mathbf{k} \\ 1 & -2 & -1 \\ 2 & 4 & 0 \end{vmatrix} = \langle 4,\ -2,\ 8\rangle$

$\mathbf{v}\times\mathbf{u} = \begin{vmatrix} \mathbf{i} & \mathbf{j} & \mathbf{k} \\ 2 & 4 & 0 \\ 1 & -2 & -1 \end{vmatrix} = \langle -4,\ 2,\ -8\rangle$

Hence $\mathbf{u}\times\mathbf{v} = -(\mathbf{v}\times\mathbf{u})$

43. Volume = $\begin{vmatrix} 1 & -2 & -1 \\ 2 & 4 & 0 \\ 3 & 4 & 5 \end{vmatrix} = 1(20) + 2(10) - 1(-4) = 44$ cubic units

45. The angle between the adjacent edges is equal to the angle between the normal vectors of the adjacent sides. The vectors $\mathbf{v}_1 = 18\mathbf{j}$ and $\mathbf{v}_2 = -6\mathbf{i} + 24\mathbf{j} + 12\mathbf{k}$ determine the back side, and hence

$$\mathbf{n}_1 = \mathbf{v}_1 \times \mathbf{v}_2 = 216\mathbf{i} + 108\mathbf{k} = 108(2\mathbf{i} + \mathbf{k})$$

is normal to this side. Similarly, $\mathbf{w}_1 = 12\mathbf{i}$ and $\mathbf{w}_2 = 6\mathbf{i} + 6\mathbf{j} - 12\mathbf{k}$ determine the left side, and hence

$$\mathbf{n}_2 = \mathbf{w}_1 \times \mathbf{w}_2 = 144\mathbf{j} + 72\mathbf{k} = 72(2\mathbf{j} + \mathbf{k})$$

is normal to this side. Finally, the angle θ between n_1 and n_2 is given by

$$\cos\theta = \frac{\mathbf{n}_1 \cdot \mathbf{n}_2}{\|\mathbf{n}_1\|\,\|\mathbf{n}_2\|}$$

$$= \frac{1}{\sqrt{5}\,\sqrt{5}} = \frac{1}{5}$$

and $\theta \approx 78.46°$

47. $\mathbf{v} = \langle 4, \ 3, \ -6 \rangle$ $x = -1 + 4t, \ y = 3 + 3t, \ z = 5 - 6t$

49. $\mathbf{v} = \langle 1, \ 1, \ 1 \rangle$ $x = 3 + t, \ y = 1 + t, \ z = 2 + t$

51. $\mathbf{u} = \langle 5, \ 0, \ 2 \rangle, \quad \mathbf{v} = \langle 2, \ 3, \ 8 \rangle$

$$\mathbf{n} = \mathbf{u} \times \mathbf{v} = \begin{vmatrix} \mathbf{i} & \mathbf{j} & \mathbf{k} \\ 5 & 0 & 2 \\ 2 & 3 & 8 \end{vmatrix} = \langle -6, \ -36, \ 15 \rangle$$

Plane: $-6(x - 0) - 36(y - 0) + 15(z - 0) = 0$

$$-2x - 12y + 5z = 0$$

53. $\mathbf{n} = \langle 1, \ 1, \ 1 \rangle$ normal vector

Plane: $1(x - 3) + 1(y - 1) + 1(z - 2) = 0$

$$x + y + z - 6 = 0$$

55. $D = \dfrac{|\overrightarrow{PQ} \cdot \mathbf{n}|}{\|\mathbf{n}\|}$

$\mathbf{n} = \langle 2, \ -20, \ 6 \rangle$

$Q = (2, \ 3, \ 10)$

$P = (0, \ 0, 1)$ in plane

$$= \frac{|\langle 2, \ 3, \ 9 \rangle \cdot \langle 2, \ -20, \ 6 \rangle|}{\sqrt{4 + 400 + 36}}$$

$$= \frac{2}{\sqrt{440}} = \frac{1}{\sqrt{110}} \approx 0.0953$$

CHAPTER 12

Limits and an Introduction to Calculus

Section 12.1   Introduction to Limits

- If $f(x)$ becomes arbitrarily close to a unique number L as x approaches c from either side, then the limit of $f(x)$ as x approaches c is L:

    $$\lim_{x \to c} f(x) = L.$$

- You should be able to use a calculator to find a limit.

- You should be able to use a graph to find a limit.

- You should understand how limits can fail to exist:

    (a) $f(x)$ approaches a different number from the right of c than it approaches from the left of c.

    (b) $f(x)$ increases or decreases without bound as x approaches c.

    (c) $f(x)$ oscillates between two fixed values as x approaches c.

- You should know and be able to use the elementary propertries of limits.

---

1. $\lim\limits_{x \to 3} (3 - 2x) = -3$

x	2.9	2.99	2.999	3.0	3.001	3.01	3.1
$f(x)$	-2.8	-2.98	-2.998	-3	-3.002	-3.02	-3.2

3. $\lim\limits_{x \to 2} \dfrac{x - 2}{x^2 - 4} = \dfrac{1}{4}$

x	1.9	1.99	1.999	2.0	2.001	2.01	2.1
$f(x)$	0.2564	0.2506	0.2501	?	0.2499	0.2494	0.2439

5. $\lim\limits_{x \to 1} \dfrac{x - 1}{x^2 + 2x - 3} = \dfrac{1}{4}$

x	0.9	0.99	0.999	1.0	1.001	1.01	1.1
$f(x)$	0.2564	0.2506	0.2501	?	0.2499	0.2464	0.2439

7. $\lim\limits_{x \to -4} \dfrac{[x/(x+2)]-2}{x+4} = \dfrac{1}{2}$

x	-4.1	-4.01	-4.001	-4.0	-3.999	-3.99	-3.9
$f(x)$	0.4762	0.4975	0.4998	?	0.5003	0.5025	0.5263

9. Make sure your calculator is set in radian mode.

$\lim\limits_{x \to 0} \dfrac{\sin x}{x} = 1$

x	-0.1	-0.01	-0.001	0	0.001	0.01	0.1
$f(x)$	0.9983	0.99998	0.9999998	?	0.9999998	0.99998	0.9983

11. $\lim\limits_{x \to -1} \sin \dfrac{\pi x}{2} = -1$

13. The limit does not exist because $f(x)$ approaches different values from the left of $x = -2$ and the right of $x = -2$.

15. The limit does not exist because $f(x)$ oscillates between 2 and -2.

17. $\lim\limits_{x \to 2} (x^2 + 3x - 4) = 2^2 + 3(2) - 4 = 6$

19. $\lim\limits_{x \to 3} \dfrac{12}{x} = \dfrac{12}{3} = 4$

21. $\lim\limits_{x \to -1} \dfrac{x^2 - 1}{x} = \dfrac{(-1)^2 - 1}{-1} = 0$

23. $\lim\limits_{x \to 2} e^x = e^2 \approx 7.389$

25. $\lim\limits_{x \to \pi} \sin 2x = \sin 2\pi = 0$

27. $\lim\limits_{x \to 1/2} \arcsin x = \arcsin \dfrac{1}{2} = \dfrac{\pi}{6} \approx 0.5236$

29. The limit does not exist. As x approaches 2 from the left, $f(x)$ approaches 5. As x approaches 2 from the right, $f(x)$ approaches 6.

31. $\lim\limits_{x \to 2} f(x) = 2$. As x approaches 2 from both sides, $f(x)$ approaches 2.

33. (a) $\displaystyle\lim_{x\to c}\,[f(x)+g(x)]^2 = \lim_{x\to c}\,(f(x)^2 + 2f(x)\,g(x) + g(x)^2)$

$$= \left[\lim_{x\to c} f(x)\right]^2 + 2\left[\lim_{x\to c} f(x)\right]\left[\lim_{x\to c} g(x)\right] + \left[\lim_{x\to c} g(x)\right]^2$$

$$= \left(\frac{3}{2}\right)^2 + 2\left(\frac{3}{2}\right)\left(-\frac{1}{2}\right) + \left(\frac{-1}{2}\right)^2$$

$$= 1$$

(b) $\displaystyle\lim_{x\to c}\,[6f(x)\,g(x)] = 6\left[\lim_{x\to c} f(x)\right]\left[\lim_{x\to c} g(x)\right]$

$$= 6\left(\frac{3}{2}\right)\left(\frac{-1}{2}\right) = \frac{-9}{2}$$

(c) $\displaystyle\lim_{x\to c}\,\frac{5g(x)}{4f(x)} = \frac{5\lim\limits_{x\to c} g(x)}{4\lim\limits_{x\to c} f(x)} = \frac{5\left(\frac{-1}{2}\right)}{4\left(\frac{3}{2}\right)} = \frac{-5}{12}$

(d) $\displaystyle\lim_{x\to c}\,\frac{1}{\sqrt{f(x)}} = \frac{1}{\sqrt{\lim\limits_{x\to c} f(x)}} = \frac{1}{\sqrt{\frac{3}{2}}} = \sqrt{\frac{2}{3}}$

Section 12.2   Techniques for Evaluating Limits

- You can use direct substitution to find the limit of a polynomial function $p(x)$:
$$\lim_{x \to c} p(x) = p(c).$$

- You can use direct substitution to find the limit of a rational function $r(x) = \dfrac{p(x)}{q(x)}$, as long as $q(c) \neq 0$:
$$\lim_{x \to c} r(x) = r(c) = \frac{p(c)}{q(c)}, q(c) \neq 0.$$

- You should be able to use cancellation techniques to find a limit.

- You should know how to use rationalization techniques to find a limit.

- You should know how to use technology to find a limit.

- You should be able to calculate one-sided limits.

1. $g(x) = \dfrac{-2^2 + x}{x}$

   $g_2(x) = -2x + 1$

   (a) $\lim\limits_{x \to 0} g(x) = 1$ (b) $\lim\limits_{x \to -1} g(x) = 3$ (c) $\lim\limits_{x \to -2} g(x) = 5$

3. $g(x) = \dfrac{x^3 - x}{x - 1}$

   $g_2(x) = x^2 + x = x(x + 1)$

   (a) $\lim\limits_{x \to 1} g(x) = 2$ (b) $\lim\limits_{x \to -1} g(x) = 0$ (c) $\lim\limits_{x \to 0} g(x) = 0$

5. $\lim\limits_{x \to 5} 5(x^2 - 1) = 5(5^2 - 1) = 120$ 7. $\lim\limits_{x \to -3} \ln e^x = \ln e^{-3} = -3$

9. $\lim\limits_{\theta \to 1} \sin \dfrac{2\pi\theta}{3} = \sin \dfrac{\pi(1)}{3} = \dfrac{\sqrt{3}}{2} \approx 0.8660$

11. $\lim\limits_{x \to 7} \dfrac{x - 7}{x^2 - 49} = \lim\limits_{x \to 7} \dfrac{x - 7}{(x - 7)(x + 7)} = \lim\limits_{x \to 7} \dfrac{1}{x + 7} = \dfrac{1}{14}$

13. $\lim\limits_{x \to -1} \dfrac{1 - 2x - 3x^2}{1 + x} = \lim\limits_{x \to -1} \dfrac{(1 + x)(1 - 3x)}{1 + x} = \lim\limits_{x \to -1} (1 - 3x) = 4$

15. $\lim\limits_{y \to 0} \dfrac{\sqrt{3 + y} - \sqrt{3}}{y} = \lim\limits_{y \to 0} \dfrac{\sqrt{3 + y} - \sqrt{3}}{y} \cdot \dfrac{\sqrt{3 + y} + \sqrt{3}}{\sqrt{3 + y} + \sqrt{3}}$

$$= \lim\limits_{y \to 0} \dfrac{(3 + y) - 3}{y\left(\sqrt{3 + y} + \sqrt{3}\right)}$$

$$= \lim\limits_{y \to 0} \dfrac{1}{\sqrt{3 + y} + \sqrt{3}} = \dfrac{1}{2\sqrt{3}}$$

17. $\lim\limits_{x \to -3} \dfrac{\sqrt{x + 7} - 2}{x + 3} = \lim\limits_{x \to -3} \dfrac{\left(\sqrt{x + 7} - 2\right)}{x + 3} \cdot \dfrac{\sqrt{x + 7} + 2}{\sqrt{x + 7} + 2}$

$$= \lim\limits_{x \to -3} \dfrac{(x + 7) - 4}{(x + 3)\left(\sqrt{x + 7} + 2\right)}$$

$$= \lim\limits_{x \to -3} \dfrac{1}{\sqrt{x + 7} + 2} = \dfrac{1}{4}$$

19. $\lim\limits_{x \to 0} \dfrac{\frac{1}{1+x} - 1}{x} = \lim\limits_{x \to 0} \dfrac{1 - (1 + x)}{(1 + x)x} = \lim\limits_{x \to 0} \dfrac{-1}{1 + x} = -1$

21. $\lim\limits_{x \to 0} \dfrac{\sec x}{\tan x} = \lim\limits_{x \to 0} \dfrac{1}{\cos x} \cdot \dfrac{\cos x}{\sin x} = \lim\limits_{x \to 0} \dfrac{1}{\sin x}$, does not exist.

23. $\lim\limits_{x \to 3+} \dfrac{|x - 3|}{x - 3} = 1$

$\lim\limits_{x \to 3-} \dfrac{|x - 3|}{x - 3} = -1$

Limit does not exist.

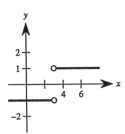

25. $\lim\limits_{x \to 1-} \dfrac{1}{x^2 + 1} = \lim\limits_{x \to 1+} \dfrac{1}{x^2 + 1} = \lim\limits_{x \to 1} \dfrac{1}{x^2 + 1} = \dfrac{1}{2}$

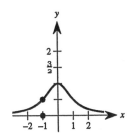

27. $\displaystyle\lim_{x\to 2^-} f(x) = 2-1 = 1$

$\displaystyle\lim_{x\to 2^+} f(x) = 2(2)-3 = 1$

$\displaystyle\lim_{x\to 2} f(x) = 1$

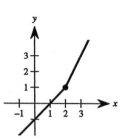

29. $\displaystyle\lim_{x\to 0} \frac{\sqrt{1-x}-1}{x} = \lim_{x\to 0} \frac{\sqrt{1-x}-1}{x} \cdot \frac{\sqrt{1-x}+1}{\sqrt{1-x}+1}$

$\displaystyle = \lim_{x\to 0} \frac{(1-x)-1}{x\left(\sqrt{1-x}+1\right)} = \lim_{x\to 0} \frac{-1}{\sqrt{1-x}+1} = \frac{-1}{2}$

31. $\displaystyle\lim_{x\to 0} \frac{\frac{1}{2x-5}+\frac{1}{5}}{x} = \lim_{x\to 0} \frac{5+(2x-5)}{(2x-5)5x} = \lim_{x\to 0} \frac{2}{(2x-5)5} = \frac{-2}{25}$

33. $\displaystyle\lim_{h\to 0} \frac{f(x+h)-f(x)}{h} = \lim_{h\to 0} \frac{\left((x+h)^2 - 3(x+h)\right) - (x^2-3x)}{h}$

$\displaystyle = \lim_{h\to 0} \frac{x^2 + 2xh + h^2 - 3x - 3h - x^2 + 3x}{h}$

$\displaystyle = \lim_{h\to 0} \frac{2xh + h^2 - 3h}{h} = \lim_{h\to 0} (2x + h - 3) = 2x - 3$

35. $\displaystyle\lim_{x\to 0^+} x\ln x = 0$

37. $\displaystyle\lim_{x\to 0} \frac{\sin 2x}{x} = 2$

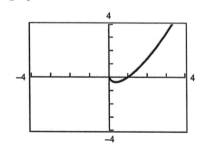

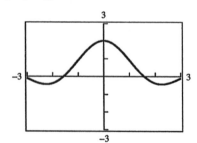

39. $\lim\limits_{x\to0}\dfrac{\tan x}{x}=1$

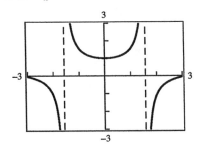

41. $\lim\limits_{x\to1}\dfrac{1-\sqrt[3]{x}}{1-x}=\dfrac{1}{3}\approx0.333$

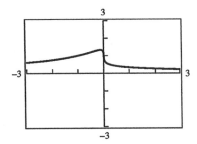

43. (a) can be evaluated by direct substitution:
$$\lim_{x\to0}x^2\sin x^2=0^2\sin0^2=0$$

(b) cannot be evaluated by direct substitution.
$$\lim_{x\to0}\frac{\sin x^2}{x^2}=1$$

45. (a) can be evaluated by direct substitution.
$$\lim_{x\to0}(1+x^2)^x=(1+0^2)^0=1$$

(b) cannot be evaluated by direct substitution.
$$\lim_{x\to0}(1+x^2)^{1/x}=1$$

47. $v=\lim\limits_{t\to2}\dfrac{s(2)-s(t)}{2-t}=\lim\limits_{t\to2}\dfrac{(-64+128)-(-16t^2+128)}{2-t}$

$=\lim\limits_{t\to2}\dfrac{16t^2-64}{2-t}=\lim\limits_{t\to2}\dfrac{16(t-2)(t+2)}{2-t}=\lim\limits_{t\to2}(-16(t+2))$

$=-64$ ft/sec

Section 12.3   The Tangent Line Problem

■ You should be able to visually approximate the slope of a graph.

■ The slope m of the graph of f at the point $(x, f(x))$ is given by

$$m = \lim_{h \to 0} \frac{f(x + h) - f(x)}{h}$$

provided this limit exists.

■ You should be able to use the limit definition to find the slope of a graph.

■ The derivative of f at x is given by

$$f'(x) = \lim_{h \to 0} \frac{f(x + h) - f(x)}{h}$$

provided this limit exists. Notice that this is the same limit as that for the tangent line slope.

■ You should be able to use the limit definition to find the derivative of a function.

1. Slope is 0 at (x, y)

3. Slope is $\frac{1}{2}$ at (x, y)

5.

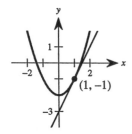

slope ≈ 2

7.

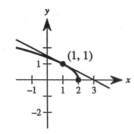

slope ≈ $-\frac{1}{2}$

9. The slope is approximately 500 when $t = 30$.

From 1979 to 1980, per capita debt increased by about \$500.

11. $m_{\text{sec}} = \dfrac{g(1 + h) - g(1)}{h} = \dfrac{4 - 3(1 + h) - 1}{h} = \dfrac{-3h}{h}$

$m = \lim_{h \to 0} \dfrac{-3h}{h} = -3$

13. $m_{\text{sec}} = \dfrac{f(2+h) - f(2)}{h} = \dfrac{(2+h)^2 - 3 - 1}{h} = \dfrac{h^2 + 4h}{h} = h + 4, \quad h \neq 0$

$m = \lim\limits_{h \to 0} (h + 4) = 4$

15. $m_{\text{sec}} = \dfrac{f(2+h) - f(2)}{h} = \dfrac{9 - (2+h)^2 - 5}{h} = \dfrac{-4h - h^2}{h} = -4 - h, \quad h \neq 0$

$m = \lim\limits_{h \to 0} (-4 - h) = -4$

17. $m_{\text{sec}} = \dfrac{g(2+h) - g(2)}{h} = \dfrac{\frac{4}{2+h} - 2}{h} = \dfrac{4 - 2(2+h)}{(2+h)h} = \dfrac{-2}{2+h}, \quad h \neq 0$

$m = \lim\limits_{h \to 0} \left(\dfrac{-2}{2+h} \right) = -1$

19. $m_{\text{sec}} = \dfrac{h(9+h) - h(9)}{h} = \dfrac{\sqrt{9+h} - 3}{h} \cdot \dfrac{\sqrt{9+h} + 3}{\sqrt{9+h} + 3}$

$= \dfrac{(9+h) - 9}{h \left[\sqrt{9+h} + 3 \right]} = \dfrac{1}{\sqrt{9+h} + 3}, \quad h \neq 0$

$m = \lim\limits_{h \to 0} \dfrac{1}{\sqrt{9+h} + 3} = \dfrac{1}{6}$

21. $m_{\text{sec}} = \dfrac{g(x+h) - g(x)}{h} = \dfrac{4 - (x+h)^2 - (4 - x^2)}{h}$

$= \dfrac{-2xh - h^2}{h} = -2x - h, \quad h \neq 0$

$m = \lim\limits_{h \to 0} (-2x - h) = -2x$

At $(0,\ 4), m = -2(0) = 0$

At $(-1,\ 3), m = -2(-1) = 2$

23. $m_{\text{sec}} = \dfrac{g(x+h) - g(x)}{h} = \dfrac{\frac{1}{x+h+4} - \frac{1}{x+4}}{h} = \dfrac{(x+4) - (x+4+h)}{(x+h+4)(x+4)(h)}$

$= \dfrac{-h}{(x+h+4)(x+4)h} = \dfrac{-1}{(x+h+4)(x+4)}, \quad h \neq 0$

$m = \lim\limits_{h \to 0} \dfrac{-1}{(x+h+4)(x+4)} = \dfrac{-1}{(x+4)^2}$

At $\left(0,\ \frac{1}{4}\right), m = \dfrac{-1}{(0+4)^2} = \dfrac{-1}{16}$

At $\left(-2,\ \frac{1}{2}\right), m = \dfrac{-1}{(-2+4)^2} = \dfrac{-1}{4}$

25. $f'(x) = \lim\limits_{h \to 0} \dfrac{f(x+h) - f(x)}{h} = \lim\limits_{h \to 0} \dfrac{5-5}{h} = 0$

27. $g'(x) = \lim\limits_{h \to 0} \dfrac{g(x+h) - g(x)}{h} = \lim\limits_{h \to 0} \dfrac{\left(6 - \frac{2}{3}(x+h)\right) - \left(6 - \frac{2}{3}x\right)}{h}$

$\qquad = \lim\limits_{h \to 0} \dfrac{-\frac{2}{3}h}{h} = \dfrac{-2}{3}$

29. $f'(x) = \lim\limits_{h \to 0} \dfrac{f(x+h) - f(x)}{h} = \lim\limits_{h \to 0} \dfrac{\frac{1}{(x+h)^2} - \frac{1}{x^2}}{h}$

$\qquad = \lim\limits_{h \to 0} \dfrac{x^2 - (x^2 + 2xh + h^2)}{(x+h)^2 x^2 h} = \lim\limits_{h \to 0} \dfrac{-2x - h}{(x+h)^2 x^2}$

$\qquad = \dfrac{-2x}{x^4} = \dfrac{-2}{x^3}$

31. $m_{\text{sec}} = \dfrac{f(2+h) - f(2)}{h} = \dfrac{(2+h)^2 - 1 - 3}{h} = \dfrac{4h + h^2}{h} = 4 + h, \;\; h \neq 0$

$\qquad m = \lim\limits_{h \to 0} (4 + h) = 4.$

Tangent line: $\quad y - 3 = 4(x - 2)$

$\qquad\qquad\qquad\quad y = 4x - 5$

33. $m_{\text{sec}} = \dfrac{f(3+h) - f(3)}{h} = \dfrac{\sqrt{3+h+1} - 2}{h} \cdot \dfrac{\sqrt{4+h} + 2}{\sqrt{4+h} + 2}$

$\qquad = \dfrac{(4+h) - 4}{h\left[\sqrt{4+h} + 2\right]} = \dfrac{1}{\sqrt{4+h} + 2}$

$\qquad m = \lim\limits_{h \to 0} \dfrac{1}{\sqrt{4+h} + 2} = \dfrac{1}{4}$

Tangent line: $\quad y - 2 = \frac{1}{4}(x_3)$

$\qquad\qquad\qquad\quad 4y = x + 5$

35.

x	-2	-1.5	-1	-0.5	0	0.5	1	1.5	2
$f(x)$	2	1.125	0.5	0.125	0	0.125	0.5	0.125	2
$f'(x)$	-2	-1.5	-1	-0.5	0	0.5	1	1.5	2

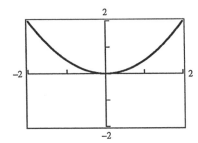

$$f(x) = \tfrac{1}{2}x^2$$

$$f'(x) = x$$

37.

x	-2	-1.5	-1	-0.5	0	0.5	1	1.5	2
$f(x)$	-2	$-.844$	$-.25$	$-.031$	0	.031	0.25	.844	2
$f'(x)$	3	1.688	.75	.188	0	.188	.75	1.688	3

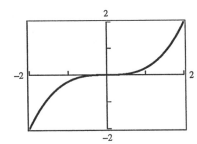

$$f(x) = \tfrac{1}{4}x^3$$

$$f'(x) = \tfrac{3}{4}x^2$$

39. $f'(x) = \lim\limits_{h \to o} \dfrac{f(x+h) - f(x)}{h} = \lim\limits_{h \to 0} \dfrac{9 - (x+h)^2 - (9 - x^2)}{h}$

$\qquad = \lim\limits_{h \to 0} \dfrac{-2xh - h^2}{h} = -2x$

$f'(x) = 0 = -2x \Rightarrow x = 0$

f has a horizontal tangent at $(0,\ 9)$

41. $f'(x) = \lim\limits_{h \to 0} \dfrac{f(x+h) - f(x)}{h} = \lim\limits_{h \to 0} \dfrac{(x+h)^3 + 3 - (x^3 + 3)}{h}$

$\qquad = \lim\limits_{h \to 0} \dfrac{3x^2 h + 3xh^2 + h^3}{h} = 3x^2$

$f'(x) = 0 = 3x^2 \Rightarrow x = 0$

f has a horizontal tangent at $(0,\ 3)$

43. $f'(x) = \lim\limits_{h \to 0} \dfrac{f(x+h) - f(x)}{h} = \lim\limits_{h \to 0} \dfrac{3(x+h)^3 - 9(x+h) - (3x^3 - 9x)}{h}$

$\qquad = \lim\limits_{h \to 0} \dfrac{9x^2h + 9xh^2 + 3h^3 - 9h}{h} = 9x^2 - 9$

$\quad f'(x) = 0 = 9x^2 - 9 \;\Rightarrow\; x = \pm 1$

$\quad f$ has horizontal tangents at $(1, -6)$ and $(-1, 6)$

45. Matches (c)   (function has constant slope)

47. Matches (b)   (derivative is always positive, and defined for $x > 0$)

Section 12.4   Limits at Infinity and Limits of Sequences

■ The limit at infinity
$$\lim_{x \to \infty} f(x) = L$$
means that $f(x)$ gets arbitrarily close to L as x increases without bound.

■ Similarly, the limit at infinity
$$\lim_{x \to -\infty} f(x) = L$$
means that $F(x)$ gets arbitrarily close to L as x decreases without bound.

■ You should be able to calculate limits at infinity, especially those arising from rational functions.

■ Limits of functions can be used to evaluate limits of sequences. If f is a function such that $\lim_{x \to \infty} f(x) = L$ and if a_n is a sequence such that $f(n) = a_n$, then $\lim_{x \to \infty} a_n = L$.

1. $\displaystyle\lim_{x \to \infty} \frac{2}{x^2} = 0$

3. $\displaystyle\lim_{x \to \infty} \frac{2+x}{2-x} = -1$

5. $\displaystyle\lim_{x \to -\infty} \frac{4x-3}{2x+1} = 2$

7. $\displaystyle\lim_{t \to \infty} \frac{t^2}{t+2}$ Does not exist

9. $\displaystyle\lim_{x \to -\infty} \left(-2 + \frac{2}{x}\right) = -2 + 0 = -2$

11. $\displaystyle\lim_{x \to -\infty} \frac{x}{(x+1)^2} = \lim_{x \to -\infty} \frac{x}{x^2+2x+1} = 0$

13. $\displaystyle\lim_{t \to \infty} \left(\frac{1}{3t^2} - \frac{5t}{t+2}\right) = 0 - 5 = -5$

15. $\displaystyle\lim_{n \to \infty} \frac{1}{n} = 0$

17. $\displaystyle\lim_{n \to \infty} \frac{5n}{n-5} = 5$

19. Matches (c)

21. Matches (d)

23.

x	10^0	10^1	10^2	10^3	10^4	10^5	10^6
$f(x)$	$-.7321$	-0.0995	-0.00999	$-.001$	-1×10^{-4}	-1×10^{-5}	-1×10^{-6}

$$\lim_{x \to \infty} \left(x - \sqrt{x^2 + 2} \right) = 0$$

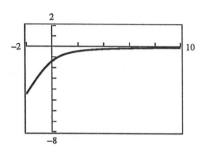

25.

x	10^0	10^1	10^2	10^3	10^4	10^5	10^6
$f(x)$	$-.7082$	$-.7454$	$-.7495$	$-.74995$	$-.749995$	$-.75$	$-.75$

$$\lim_{x \to \infty} 3 \left(2x - \sqrt{4x^2 + x} \right) = -\frac{3}{4}$$

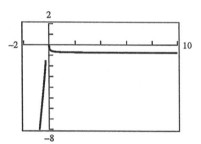

27. (a) Average cost $= \dfrac{c}{x} = \dfrac{1.35x + 4570}{x}$

when $x = 100$, average cost $= \$47.05$

when $x = 1000$, average cost $= \$5.92$

(b) $\displaystyle\lim_{x \to \infty} \frac{c}{x} = \lim_{x \to \infty} \frac{1.35x + 4570}{x} = \$1.35$

29. $3, \dfrac{4}{3}, 1, \dfrac{6}{7}, \dfrac{7}{9} \cdot \displaystyle\lim_{n \to \infty} \dfrac{n + 2}{2n - 1} = \dfrac{1}{2}$ **31.** $1, \dfrac{3}{5}, \dfrac{2}{5}, \dfrac{5}{17}, \dfrac{3}{13} \cdot \displaystyle\lim_{n \to \infty} \dfrac{n + 1}{n^2 + 1} = 0$

33. $\dfrac{1}{7}, \dfrac{1}{3}, \dfrac{9}{17}, \dfrac{8}{11}, \dfrac{25}{27} \cdot \displaystyle\lim_{n \to \infty} \dfrac{n^2}{5n + 2}$ does not exist

35. $2, 3, 4, 5, 6, \cdot \displaystyle\lim_{n \to \infty} \dfrac{(n + 1)!}{n!} = \lim_{n \to \infty} (n + 1)$ does not exist

37. $10, 2, 26, 64, 138 \cdot \displaystyle\lim_{n \to \infty} 2 \left[5 + (n - 1)^3 \right]$ does not exist

39. $\dfrac{1}{3}, \dfrac{-2}{5}, \dfrac{3}{7}, \dfrac{-4}{9}, \dfrac{5}{11}$ • $\displaystyle\lim_{n\to\infty} (-1)^{n-1}\dfrac{n}{2n+1}$ does not exist

41. $\displaystyle\lim_{n\to\infty} a_n = \dfrac{3}{2}$

n	10^0	10^1	10^2	10^3	10^4	10^5	10^6
a_n	2	1.55	1.505	1.5005	1.50005	1.500005	1.5000005

43. $\displaystyle\lim_{n\to\infty} a_n = 4$

n	10^0	10^1	10^2	10^3	10^4	10^5	10^6
a_n	2	3.8	3.98	3.998	3.9998	3.99998	3.999998

45. $\displaystyle\lim_{n\to\infty} a_n = \dfrac{16}{3}$

n	10^0	10^1	10^2	10^3	10^4	10^5	10^6
a_n	16	6.16	5.4136	5.341336	5.3341	5.33341	5.333341

47. Converges to 0

49. Diverges

51. Converges if $|r| < 1$. In this case,

$r^n \to 0$ as $n \to \infty$ and $1 - r^n \to 1$.

Thus, $\displaystyle\lim_{n\to\infty} \dfrac{a(1 - r^n)}{1 - r} = \dfrac{a}{1 - r}$

Section 12.5   The Area Problem

■ You should know the following summation formulas and properties.

(a) $\displaystyle\sum_{i=1}^{n} c = cn$

(b) $\displaystyle\sum_{i=1}^{n} i = \frac{n(n+1)}{2}$

(c) $\displaystyle\sum_{i=1}^{n} i^2 = \frac{n(n+1)(2n+1)}{6}$

(d) $\displaystyle\sum_{i=1}^{n} i^3 = \frac{n^2(n+1)^2}{4}$

(e) $\displaystyle\sum_{i=1}^{n} (a_i \pm b_i) = \sum_{i=1}^{n} a_i \pm \sum_{i=1}^{n} b_i$

(f) $\displaystyle\sum_{i=1}^{n} k a_i = k \sum_{i=1}^{n} a_i$

■ You should be able to evaluate a limit of a summation, $\displaystyle\lim_{n\to\infty} S(n)$.

■ You should be able to approximate the area of a region using rectangles. By increasing the number of rectangles, the approximation improves.

■ The area of a plane region bounded by f between $x = a$ and $x = b$ is the limit of the sum of the approximating rectangles:

$$A = \lim_{n\to\infty} \sum_{i=1}^{n} f\left(a + \frac{(b-a)i}{n}\right)\left(\frac{b-a}{n}\right)$$

■ You should be able to use the limit definition of area to find the area bounded by simple functions in the plane.

---

1. $\displaystyle\sum_{i=1}^{60} i = \frac{n(n+1)}{2} = \frac{60(61)}{2} = 1830$

3. $\displaystyle\sum_{k=1}^{20} k^3 = \frac{n^2(n+1)^2}{4} = \frac{20^2(21)^2}{4} = 44,100$

5. $\displaystyle\sum_{j=1}^{25} (j^2 + j) = \frac{25(26)(51)}{6} + \frac{25(26)}{2} = 5850$

7. $S(n) = \sum\limits_{i=1}^{n} \dfrac{4i^2}{n^3} = \dfrac{4}{n^3}(n(n+1)(2n+1)/6) = \dfrac{4n^3 + 6n^2 + 2n}{3n^3}$

n	10^0	10^1	10^2	10^3
$S(n)$	4	1.54	1.353	1.335

$\lim\limits_{n\to\infty} S(n) = \dfrac{4}{3}$

9. $S(n) = \sum\limits_{i=1}^{n} \dfrac{3}{n^3}(1+i^2) = \dfrac{3}{n^3}\left[n + \dfrac{n(n+1)(2n+1)}{6}\right] = \dfrac{3}{n^2} + \dfrac{6n^2 + 9n + 3}{6n^2}$

n	10^0	10^1	10^2	10^3
$S(n)$	6	1.185	1.0154	1.0015

$\lim\limits_{n\to\infty} S(n) = 1$

11. $S(n) = \sum\limits_{i=1}^{n} \dfrac{2i+3}{n^2} = \dfrac{1}{n^2}\left(2\left(\dfrac{n(n+1)}{2}\right) + 3n\right) = \dfrac{n+1}{N} + \dfrac{3}{n}$

n	10^0	10^1	10^2	10^3
$S(n)$	5	1.4	1.04	1.004

$\lim\limits_{n\to\infty} S(n) = 1$

13. $S(n) = \sum\limits_{i=1}^{n} \left(\dfrac{i^2}{n^3} + \dfrac{2}{n}\right)\left(\dfrac{1}{n}\right) = \dfrac{1}{n}\left[\dfrac{n(n+1)(2n+1)}{6n^3} + \dfrac{2n}{n}\right] = \dfrac{1}{6n^3}(2n^2 + 3n + 1) + \dfrac{2}{n}$

n	10^0	10^1	10^2	10^3
$S(n)$	3	0.2385	0.02338	0.00233

$\lim\limits_{n\to\infty} S(n) = 0$

15. $S(n) = \sum\limits_{i=1}^{n} \left[1 - \left(\dfrac{i}{n}\right)^2\right]\left(\dfrac{1}{n}\right) = \dfrac{1}{n}\left[n - \dfrac{1}{n^2}\left(\dfrac{n(n+1)(2n+1)}{6}\right)\right] = 1 - \dfrac{2n^2 + 3n + 1}{6n^2}$

n	10^0	10^1	10^2	10^3
$S(n)$	0	0.615	0.66165	0.66617

$\lim\limits_{n\to\infty} S(n) = \dfrac{2}{3}$

17. $S(n) = \sum\limits_{i=1}^{n} \left(\dfrac{4i^2}{n^2} - \dfrac{i}{n}\right)\dfrac{1}{n} = \dfrac{1}{n}\left[\dfrac{4}{n^2}\dfrac{n(n+1)(2n+1)}{6} - \dfrac{1}{n}\dfrac{n(n+1)}{2}\right] = \dfrac{4n^2 + 6n + 2}{3n^2} - \dfrac{n+1}{2n}$

n	10^0	10^1	10^2	10^3
$S(n)$	3	0.99	0.8484	0.8348

$\lim\limits_{n\to\infty} S(n) = \dfrac{5}{6}$

19. Width of each rectangle is $\frac{1}{2}$. The height is obtained by evaluating f at the right hand endpoint of each interval.

$$A \approx \sum_{i=1}^{4} f\left(\frac{i}{2}\right)\left(\frac{1}{2}\right) = \sum_{i=1}^{4} \left(\frac{i}{2}+1\right)\frac{1}{2} = 9\left(\frac{1}{2}\right) = 4.5$$

21. The width of each rectangle is $\frac{1}{4}$. The height is obtained by evaluating f at the right hand endpoint of each interval.

$$A \approx \sum_{i=1}^{4} f\left(\frac{i}{4}\right)\left(\frac{1}{4}\right) = \sum_{i=1}^{4} \left(4-\left(\frac{i}{4}\right)^2\right)\frac{1}{4} = 14.125\left(\frac{1}{4}\right) = 3.53125$$

23. The width of each rectangle is $\frac{1}{4}$. The height is obtained by evaluating f at the right hand endpoint of each interval.

$$A \approx \sum_{i=1}^{8} f\left(\frac{i}{4}\right)\left(\frac{1}{4}\right) = \sum_{i=1}^{8} \frac{1}{4}\left(\frac{i}{4}\right)^3\left(\frac{1}{4}\right) = 1.265625$$

25. The width of each rectangle is $\frac{8}{n}$. The height is $f\left(\frac{8i}{n}\right) = -\frac{1}{2}\left(\frac{8i}{n}\right)+4$.

$$A \approx \sum_{i=1}^{n} \left[-\frac{1}{2}\left(\frac{8i}{n}\right)+4\right]\left(\frac{8}{n}\right).$$

(note: exact area is 16)

n	4	8	20	50
Approximate area	12	14	15.2	15.68

27. The width of each rectangle is $\frac{4-1}{3} = \frac{3}{n}$. The height is $f\left(1+\frac{3i}{n}\right) = \frac{1}{4}\left(1+\frac{3i}{n}\right)^2$.

$$A \approx \sum_{i=1}^{n} \frac{1}{4}\left(1+\frac{3i}{n}\right)^2\left(\frac{3}{n}\right)$$

(note: exact area is 5.25)

n	4	8	20	50
Approximate area	6.727	5.971	5.534	5.363

29. The width of each rectangle is $\dfrac{2}{n}$. The height is $f\left(1+\dfrac{2i}{n}\right) = \dfrac{1}{9}\left(1+\dfrac{2i}{n}\right)^3$

$$\text{Area} \approx \sum_{i=1}^{n} \frac{1}{9}\left(1+\frac{2i}{n}\right)^3 \left(\frac{2}{n}\right)$$

(note: exact area is $\dfrac{20}{9}$)

n	4	8	20	50
Approximate area	3	2.597	2.369	2.280

31. $A = \displaystyle\sum_{i=1}^{n} f\left(\frac{2i}{n}\right)\left(\frac{2}{n}\right)$

$= \displaystyle\sum_{i=1}^{n} 3\left(\frac{2i}{n}\right)\left(\frac{2}{n}\right)$

$= \dfrac{12}{n^2}\displaystyle\sum_{i=1}^{n} i$

$= \dfrac{12}{n^2}\dfrac{n(n+1)}{2}$

$= \dfrac{12n^2+12n}{2n^2}$

$A = \displaystyle\lim_{n\to\infty}\left(\frac{12n^2+12n}{2n^2}\right) = 6$

33. $A \approx \displaystyle\sum_{i=1}^{n} f\left(2+\frac{6i}{n}\right)\left(\frac{6}{n}\right)$

$= \displaystyle\sum_{i=1}^{n}\left[4-\frac{1}{2}\left(2+\frac{6i}{n}\right)\right]\frac{6}{n}$

$= \dfrac{18}{n}\displaystyle\sum_{i=1}^{n} 1 - \dfrac{18}{n^2}\displaystyle\sum_{i=1}^{n} i$

$= \dfrac{18}{n}(n) - \dfrac{18}{n^2}\dfrac{n(n+1)}{2} = 18 - 9\dfrac{n^2+n}{n^2}$

$A = \displaystyle\lim_{n\to\infty}\left(18 - 9\frac{n^2+n}{n^2}\right) = 18 - 9 = 9$

35. $A \approx \displaystyle\sum_{i=1}^{n} f\left(-1+\frac{2i}{n}\right)\left(\frac{2}{n}\right)$

$= \displaystyle\sum_{i=1}^{n}\left[3-\left(-1+\frac{2i}{n}\right)^2\right]\frac{2}{n}$

$= \displaystyle\sum_{i=1}^{n}\left[3-1+\frac{4i}{n}-\frac{4i^2}{n^2}\right]\left(\frac{2}{n}\right)$

$= \dfrac{4}{n}\displaystyle\sum_{i=1}^{n} 1 + \dfrac{8}{n^2}\displaystyle\sum_{i=1}^{n} i - \dfrac{8}{n^3}\displaystyle\sum_{i=1}^{n} i^2$

$= \dfrac{4}{n}(n) + \dfrac{8}{n^2}\dfrac{n(n+1)}{2} - \dfrac{8}{n^3}\dfrac{n(n+1)(2n+1)}{6}$

$A = \displaystyle\lim_{n\to\infty}\left[4+4\frac{n(n+1)}{n^2} - \frac{4}{3}\frac{n(n+1)(2n+1)}{n^3}\right] = 4+4-\frac{8}{3} = \frac{16}{3}$

37. $A \approx \sum_{i=1}^{n} g\left(1+\frac{i}{n}\right)\left(\frac{1}{n}\right)$

$$= \sum_{i=1}^{n} \left[8 - \left(1+\frac{i}{n}\right)^3\right]\left(\frac{1}{n}\right)$$

$$= \sum_{i=1}^{n} \left[7 - \frac{3i}{n} + \frac{3i^2}{n^2} + \frac{i^3}{n^3}\right]\frac{1}{n}$$

$$= \frac{7}{n}\sum_{i=1}^{n} 1 - \frac{3}{n^2}\sum_{i=1}^{n} i - \frac{3}{n^3}\sum_{i=1}^{n} i^2 - \frac{1}{n^4}\sum_{i=1}^{n} i^3$$

$$= \frac{7}{n}(n) - \frac{3}{n^2}\frac{n(n+1)}{2} - \frac{3}{n^3}\frac{n(n+1)(2n+1)}{6} - \frac{1}{n^4}\frac{n^2(n+1)^2}{4}$$

$$A = \lim_{n\to\infty} \left[7 - \frac{3}{2}\frac{n(n+1)}{n^2} - \frac{1}{2n^3}n(n+1)(2n+1) - \frac{1}{n^4}\frac{n^2(n+1)^2}{4}\right]$$

$$= 7 - \frac{3}{2} - 1 - \frac{1}{4} = \frac{17}{4}$$

39. $A \approx \sum_{i=1}^{n} f\left(1+\frac{3i}{n}\right)\left(\frac{3}{n}\right)$

$$= \sum_{i=1}^{n} \left[\frac{1}{4}\left(1+\frac{3i}{n}\right)^2 + \left(1+\frac{3i}{n}\right)\right]\left(\frac{3}{n}\right)$$

$$= \sum_{i=1}^{4} \left(\frac{1}{4} + \frac{3}{2}\frac{i}{n} + \frac{9}{4}\frac{i^2}{n^2} + 1 + \frac{3i}{n}\right)\left(\frac{3}{n}\right)$$

$$= \frac{15}{4n}\sum_{i=1}^{n} 1 + \frac{27}{2n^2}\sum_{i=1}^{n} i + \frac{27}{4n^3}\sum_{i=1}^{n} i^2$$

$$= \frac{15}{4n}(n) + \frac{27}{2n^2}\left(\frac{n(n+1)}{2}\right) + \frac{27}{4n^3}\frac{n(n+1)(2n+1)}{6}$$

$$A = \lim_{n\to\infty} \left[\frac{15}{4} + \frac{27}{4}\frac{n(n+1)}{n^2} + \frac{9}{8n^3}n(n+1)(2n+1)\right]$$

$$= \frac{15}{4} + \frac{27}{4} + \frac{9}{4} = \frac{51}{4}$$

Chapter 12 Review Exercises

1. $\lim\limits_{x \to 2} \dfrac{x - 2}{3x^2 - 4x - 4} = \dfrac{1}{8}$

x	1.9	1.99	1.999	2	2.001	2.01	2.1
$f(x)$	.1299	.1255	.1250	?	.1250	.1245	.1205

3. $\lim\limits_{x \to 3} (5x - 4) = 5(3) - 4 = 11$

5. $\lim\limits_{x \to 5} \dfrac{x - 5}{x^2 + 5x - 50} = \lim\limits_{x \to 5} \dfrac{x - 5}{(x - 5)(x + 10)} = \lim\limits_{x \to 5} \dfrac{1}{x + 10} = \dfrac{1}{15}$

7. $\lim\limits_{u \to 0} \dfrac{\sqrt{4 + u} - 2}{u} = \lim\limits_{u \to 0} \dfrac{\sqrt{4 + u} - 2}{u} \cdot \dfrac{\sqrt{4 + u} + 2}{\sqrt{4 + u} + 2}$

$$= \lim\limits_{u \to 0} \dfrac{(4 + u) - 4}{u\left(\sqrt{4 + u} + 2\right)} = \lim\limits_{u \to 0} \dfrac{1}{\sqrt{4 + u} + 2} = \dfrac{1}{4}$$

9. $\lim\limits_{x \to -1} \dfrac{\frac{1}{x + 2} - 1}{x + 1} = \lim\limits_{x \to -1} \dfrac{1 - (x - 2)}{(x + 2)(x + 1)} = \lim\limits_{x \to -1} \dfrac{-(x + 1)}{(x + 2)(x + 1)}$

$$= \lim\limits_{x \to -1} \dfrac{-1}{(x + 2)} = -1$$

11. $\lim\limits_{h \to 0} \dfrac{f(x + h) - f(x)}{h} = \lim\limits_{h \to 0} \dfrac{3(x + h) - (x + h)^2 - (3x - x^2)}{h}$

$$= \lim\limits_{h \to 0} \dfrac{3x + 3h - x^2 - 2xh - h^2 - 3x + x^2}{h} = \lim\limits_{h \to 0} \dfrac{3h - 2xh - h^2}{h}$$

$$= \lim\limits_{h \to 0} (3 - 2x - h) = 3 - 2x$$

13. $m = \lim\limits_{h \to 0} \dfrac{g(x + h) - g(x)}{h} = \lim\limits_{h \to 0} \dfrac{(x + h)^2 - 4(x + h) - (x^2 - 4x)}{h}$

$$= \lim\limits_{h \to 0} \dfrac{x^2 + 2xh + h^2 - 4x - 4h - x^2 + 4x}{h}$$

$$= \lim\limits_{h \to 0} \dfrac{2xh + h^2 - 4h}{h} = \lim\limits_{h \to 0} (2x + h - 4) = 2x - 4$$

(a) At $(0, 0), m = 2(0) - 4 = -4$

(b) At $(5, 5), m = 2(5) - 4 = 6$

15. $m = \lim\limits_{h \to 0} \dfrac{f(x+h) - f(x)}{h} = \lim\limits_{h \to 0} \dfrac{\frac{4}{x+h-6} - \frac{4}{x-6}}{h}$

$= \lim\limits_{h \to 0} \dfrac{4(x-6) - 4(x+h-6)}{(x+h-6)(x-6)h} = \lim\limits_{h \to 0} \dfrac{-4h}{(x+h-6)(x-6)h}$

$= \lim\limits_{h \to 0} \dfrac{-4}{(x+h-6)(x-6)} = \dfrac{-4}{(x-6)^2}$

(a) At $(7, 4), m = \dfrac{-4}{(7-6)^2} = -4$

(b) At $(8, 2), m = \dfrac{-4}{(8-6)^2} = -1$

17. $g'(x) = \lim\limits_{h \to 0} \dfrac{g(x+h) - g(x)}{h} = \lim\limits_{h \to 0} \dfrac{-4 - (-4)}{h} = 0$

19. $h'(x) = \lim\limits_{h \to 0} \dfrac{h(x+h) - h(x)}{h} = \lim\limits_{h \to 0} \dfrac{\left[5 - \frac{1}{2}(x+h)\right] - \left[5 - \frac{1}{2}x\right]}{h}$

$= \lim\limits_{h \to 0} \dfrac{-\frac{1}{2}h}{h} = -\dfrac{1}{2}$

21. $f'(t) = \lim\limits_{h \to 0} \dfrac{f(t+h) - f(t)}{h} = \lim\limits_{h \to 0} \dfrac{\sqrt{t+h+5} - \sqrt{t+5}}{h} \cdot \dfrac{\sqrt{t+h+5} + \sqrt{t+5}}{\sqrt{t+h+5} + \sqrt{t+5}}$

$= \lim\limits_{h \to 0} \dfrac{(t+h+5) - (t-5)}{h\left(\sqrt{t+h+5} + \sqrt{t+5}\right)} = \lim\limits_{h \to 0} \dfrac{1}{\sqrt{t+h+5} + \sqrt{t+5}}$

$= \dfrac{1}{2\sqrt{t+5}}$

23. $\lim\limits_{x \to \infty} \dfrac{4x}{2x-3} = \dfrac{4}{2} = 2$

25. $\lim\limits_{x \to \infty} \dfrac{x^2 + 5x}{x^2 - 25} = \dfrac{1}{1} = 1$

27. $\lim\limits_{x \to \infty} \left(4 - \dfrac{7}{x^3}\right) = 4 - 0 = 4$

29. $\lim\limits_{n \to \infty} \dfrac{1}{2n^2}[3 - 2n(n+1)] = \lim\limits_{n \to \infty} \left[\dfrac{3}{2n^2} - \dfrac{2(n+1)}{2n}\right] = -1$

31. $A \approx \displaystyle\sum_{i=1}^{5} (10 - (2i))(2) = 40$ approximate area

$$A = \lim_{n \to \infty} \sum_{i=1}^{n} \left(10 - \frac{10i}{n}\right)\left(\frac{10}{n}\right)$$

$$= \lim_{n \to \infty} \left[\frac{100}{n} \sum_{i=1}^{n} 1 - \frac{100}{n^2} \sum_{i=1}^{n} i\right]$$

$$= \lim_{n \to \infty} \left[\frac{100}{n}(n) - \frac{100}{n^2}\left(\frac{n(n+1)}{2}\right)\right]$$

$$= \lim_{n \to \infty} \left[100 - 50\frac{n(n+1)}{n^2}\right] = 100 - 50 = 50 \quad \text{exact area}$$

33. $A \approx \displaystyle\sum_{i=1}^{6} \left[\left(-1 + \frac{i}{2}\right)^2 + 4\right]\left(\frac{1}{2}\right)$

$$= \sum_{i=1}^{6} \left[5 - i + \frac{i^2}{4}\right]\frac{1}{2}$$

$$= \frac{5}{2}\sum_{i=1}^{6} 1 = \frac{1}{2}\sum_{i=1}^{6} i + \frac{1}{8}\sum_{i=1}^{6} i^2$$

$$= \frac{5}{2}(6) - \frac{1}{2}(21) + \frac{1}{8} \, 91 = \frac{127}{8} = 15.875 \quad \text{approximate area}$$

$$A = \lim_{n \to \infty} \sum_{i=1}^{n} \left[\left(-1 + \frac{3i}{n}\right)^2 + 4\right]\left(\frac{3}{n}\right) = \lim_{n \to \infty} \sum_{i=1}^{n} \left[5 - \frac{6i}{n} + \frac{9i^2}{n^2}\right]\frac{3}{n}$$

$$= \lim_{n \to \infty} \left[\frac{15}{n}\sum_{i=1}^{n} 1 - \frac{18}{n^2}\sum_{i=1}^{n} i + \frac{27}{n^3}\sum_{i=1}^{n} i^2\right]$$

$$= \lim_{n \to \infty} \left[\frac{15}{n}(n) - \frac{18}{n^2}\frac{n(n+1)}{2} + \frac{27}{n^3}\frac{n(n+1)(2n+1)}{6}\right]$$

$$= 15 - 9 + 9 = 15 \quad \text{exact area}$$

35. $A \approx \sum\limits_{i=1}^{4} 2\left[\left(-1+\dfrac{i}{2}\right)^2 - \left(-1+\dfrac{i}{3}\right)^3\right]\left(\dfrac{1}{2}\right) = \sum\limits_{i=1}^{4}\left[\left(-1+\dfrac{i}{2}\right)^2 - \left(-1+\dfrac{i}{3}\right)^3\right] = \dfrac{1}{2}$

approximate area

$A = \lim\limits_{n\to\infty}\sum\limits_{i=1}^{n} 2\left[\left(-1+\dfrac{2i}{n}\right)^2 - \left(-1+\dfrac{2i}{n}\right)^3\right]\left(\dfrac{2}{n}\right)$

$= \lim\limits_{n\to\infty}\sum\limits_{i=1}^{n}\dfrac{4}{n}\left(1-\dfrac{4i}{n}+\dfrac{4i^2}{n^2} - \left(-1+\dfrac{6i}{n}-\dfrac{12i^2}{n^2}+\dfrac{8i^3}{n^3}\right)\right)$

$= \lim\limits_{n\to\infty}\sum\limits_{i=1}^{n}\dfrac{4}{n}\left(2-\dfrac{10i}{n}+\dfrac{16i^2}{n^2}-\dfrac{8i^3}{n^3}\right)$

$= \lim\limits_{n\to\infty}\left[\dfrac{8}{n}\sum\limits_{i=1}^{n}1-\dfrac{40}{n^2}\sum\limits_{i=1}^{n}i+\dfrac{64}{n^3}\sum\limits_{i=1}^{n}i^2-\dfrac{32}{n^4}\sum\limits_{i=1}^{n}i^3\right]$

$= \lim\limits_{n\to\infty}\left[\dfrac{8}{n}(n)-\dfrac{40}{n^2}\dfrac{n(n+1)}{2}+\dfrac{64}{n^3}\dfrac{n(n+1)(2n+1)}{6}-\dfrac{32}{n^4}\dfrac{n^2(n+1)^2}{4}\right]$

$= 8-20+\dfrac{64}{3}-8 = \dfrac{4}{3}$ exact area